investigating the
earth

COVER

On the cover of *Investigating the Earth* are 14 color photographs taken by astronauts orbiting the earth at approximately 250 kilometers above its surface. The photographs are keyed to the above illustration and identified by number as follows: 1 West coast of Spanish Sahara and Morocco (Gemini 9). 2 Desert in northern Afghanistan (Gemini 5). 3 Coast of Somali Republic (Gemini 9). 4 Northeast of Malagasy Republic in the distance (Gemini 6). 5 Mouth of Yangtze River, left, and Hang Chow Wan River, right, China (Gemini 5). 6 Edward White in "space walk" over Gulf of Mexico (Gemini 4). 7 Kyushu and Honshu Islands, Japan (Gemini 5). 8 Hawaiian Islands beneath heavy cloud (Gemini 5). 9 Baja California jutting into Pacific (Gemini 5). 10 Andes Mountains and the coast of Peru, with Amazon Basin beyond (Gemini 9). 11 View to southeast over Florida peninsula (Gemini 5). 12 Moon over western Pacific (Gemini 7). 13 and 14 Cloud patterns over the Pacific.

investigating the
earth

EARTH SCIENCE CURRICULUM PROJECT

Sponsored by the American Geological Institute

Supported by the National Science Foundation

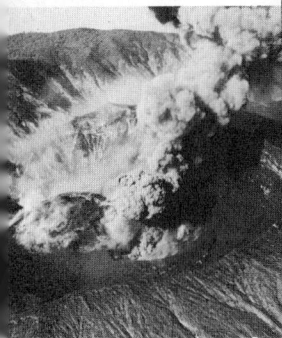

escp

HOUGHTON MIFFLIN COMPANY · BOSTON

New York · Atlanta · Geneva, Ill. · Dallas · Palo Alto

CONTRIBUTORS

ESCP ADMINISTRATIVE STAFF

Project Director: *Ramon E. Bisque* (1965–67), Colorado School of Mines; *Robert L. Heller* (1963–65), University of Minnesota, Duluth.

Associate Director: *Merrill K. Ridd* (1965-67), University of Utah; *Daniel J. Jones* (1963-65), University of Utah.

Administrative Assistants: *James H. Shea,* University of Tennessee; *Virginia R. Soderling,* Watertown, Mass. Evaluation Program: *John F. Thompson* (Coordinator), Maple Heights, Ohio; *Rufus F. Morton* (Assistant Coordinator), Lakewood, Colo. Director of Teacher Preparation: *John W. Shrum,* The Ohio State University. Director Laboratory Development: *Robert E. Samples,* Evergreen, Colo. Director of Publications Program: *Ted Dutton,* Boulder, Colo.; *Daniel S. Turner,* Eastern Michigan University. Administrative Officer: *Kenneth A. Butts,* Boulder, Colo. Administrative Secretary: *Patricia A. Stoneburner,* Boulder, Colo. Art Director: *Eleanor A. Dye,* New York, N.Y. Photo Research: *Mary G. Pitchford,* Boulder, Colo. Staff Consultants: Consulting Art Director, *William B. Nelson,* Los Angeles, Calif.; Design Consultant, *George T. Gates,* Condit Corporation, Denver, Colo. Illustrator, *Robert A. Clayton,* Condit Corporation, Denver, Colo. Staff Assistants: *William W. Clark,* Boulder, Colo.; *John M. Cys,* Boulder, Colo.; *David Laing,* Boulder, Colo.; *Horace A. MacMahan, Jr.,* Boulder, Colo.; *Edward C. Maruna,* Maple Heights, Ohio; *Elwyn R. Owen,* Denver, Colo.; *Richard D. Shepard,* Monroe, Ohio; *Joanne Stolte,* Jamesville, New York; *LeRoy E. Warren,* Duluth, Minn. Staff Editorial Assistants: *Paula J. Erdwinn, Gwendolyn Eurich, Bonnie B. Offerle, Saundra K. Smith.* Artists: *Harry L. Blodgett, Eugene J. Diodato, Grant A. Duncan, Robert G. Haynes, Britton R. Holmbeck, Gerald G. Hunt, Jr., Richard D. Nass.*

ESCP WRITERS

Norman R. Anderson (geology), University of Puget Sound; *Robert S. Arthur* (oceanography), Scripps Institute of Oceanography; *Rolland B. Bartholomew* (science teacher) Palo Alto, Calif.; *Frank R. Bellaire* (meteorology), The University of Michigan; *Ramon E. Bisque* (geochemistry), Colorado School of Mines; *Delbert A. Bowman* (science teacher), New York, N.Y.; *Douglas B. Carter* (geography), Southern Illinois University; *Joe S. Creager* (oceanography), University of Washing-

ton; *Whitman Cross II* (science teacher), Philadelphia, Penn.; *Christopher Crowe* (geophysics), Texas Instruments, Inc.; *Louis W. Currier* (geology), University of Maryland; *Robert B. Daley* (science teacher), DeWitt, N.Y.; *William A. Dexter* (science teacher), Dallas, Texas; *Robert W. Durrenberger* (geography), San Fernando Valley State College; *James L. Dyson* (geology), Lafayette College; *William H. Easton* (geology), University of Southern California; *Henry D. Foth* (soil science), Michigan State University; *Marjorie H. Gardner* (science education), University of Maryland; *H. Richard Gerfin* (science teacher), Great Barrington, Mass.; *Richard P. Hamilton* (science teacher), Williamstown, Mass.; *Donald V. Hansen* (oceanography), ESSA Institute for Oceanography; *Miles F. Harris* (meteorology), ESSA Scientific Information; *H. Bowman Hawkes* (geography), University of Utah; *O. T. Hayward* (geology), Baylor University; *Robert L. Heller* (geology), University of Minnesota, Duluth; *Donald M. Henderson* (geology), University of Illinois; *Dale T. Hesser* (science teacher), Mattydale, N.Y.; *Charles M. Huffer* (astronomy), San Diego State College; *J. Allen Hynek* (astronomy), Northwestern University; *Hyde S. Jacobs* (soil science), Kansas State University; *Kenneth H. Jehn* (meteorology), The University of Texas; *Daniel J. Jones* (geology), University of Utah; *David L. Jones* (meteorology), Southern Illinois University; *David L. Kendall* (science teacher), West Hartford, Conn.; *Carl Kisslinger* (geophysics), St. Louis University; *Owen Kluksdahl* (science teacher), Sheridan, Wyo.; *Donald E. Kocher* (science teacher), Horsham, Penn.; *Philip Kutner* (science teacher), Fairlawn, N.J.; *Henry Lepp* (geology), Macalester College; *Richard S. Lewis* (science writer), Chicago Sun-Times; *Myron G. H. Ligda* (meteorology), Stanford Research Institute; *Paul D. Lowman, Jr.* (geology), NASA Goddard Space Flight Center; *John A. Maccini* (science teacher), Sudbury, Mass.; *Edward C. Maruna* (science teacher), Maple Heights, Ohio; *William H. Matthews III* (geology), Lamar State College of Technology; *Margaret A. McBrien* (science teacher), Lynn, Mass.; *John H. Merrill* (science teacher), West Hartford, Conn.; *William M. Merrill* (geology), University of Kansas; *David H. Miller* (geography), University of Wisconsin, Milwaukee; *Rufus F. Morton* (science teacher), Lakewood, Colo.; *Vance E. Moyer* (meteorology), Texas A & M University; *Robert A. Muller* (geography), Rutgers, The State University; *Gordon B.*

Oakeshott (geology), California State Division of Mines and Geology; *Lou W. Page* (geology), Connecticut Geological and Natural History Survey; *Thornton L. Page* (astronomy), Wesleyan University; *June G. Pattulo* (oceanography), Oregon State University; *James A. Peoples* (geophysics), University of Kansas; *George L. Pickard* (oceanography), The University of British Columbia; *Howard J. Pincus* (geology), The Ohio State University; *Merrill K. Ridd* (geography), University of Utah; *William D. Romey* (science education and geology), Syracuse University; *Robert E. Samples* (science teacher), Evergreen, Colo.; *John S. Shelton* (geology), Claremont, Calif.; *James W. Skehan, S. J.* (geology), Boston College; *Arne E. Slettebak* (astronomy), The Ohio State University; *Richard A. Smith* (science education), San Jose State College; *Robert E. Stevenson* (oceanography), Bureau of Commercial Fisheries, Galveston, Tex.; *John F. Thompson* (science teacher), Maple Heights, Ohio.

ESCP STEERING COMMITTEE MEMBERS

Chalmer J. Roy, Chairman (geology), Iowa State University of Science and Technology; *Rolland B. Bartholomew* (science teacher), Palo Alto, Calif.; *Armand J. Eardley* (geology), University of Utah; *Samuel P. Ellison, Jr.* (geology), The University of Texas (1963–1964); *Richard H. Fleming* (oceanography), University of Washington; *Robert L. Heller* (geology), University of Minnesota, Duluth; *Ben F. Howell, Jr.* (geophysics), The Pennsylvania State University; *Dale F. Leipper* (oceanography), Texas A & M University; *Ralph W. Marsden* (geology), U. S. Steel Corporation; *Ralph J. McCracken* (soil science), North Carolina State, UNC at Raleigh; *Dean B. McLaughlin* (astronomy), University of Michigan, (deceased); *William M. Merrill* (geology), University of Kansas; *Chester W. Newton* (meteorology), National Center for Atmospheric Research; *Theodore H. Schmudde* (geography), Southern Illinois University; *Arne E. Slettebak* (astronomy), The Ohio State University; *Robert C. Stephenson* (geology), The Ohio State University Research Foundation. *Ex Officio* Members: *Ramon E. Bisque, Linn Hoover* and *John L. Snyder.*

ESCP ADVISORY BOARD MEMBERS

Chalmer J. Roy, Chairman (geology), Iowa State University of Science and Technology; *Rachel L. Carson* (science writer), Silver Spring, Md. (deceased); *Donald G. Decker* (science education), Colorado State College; *Edward B. Espenshade, Jr.* (geography), Northwestern University; *Hollis D. Hedberg* (geology), Princeton University; *Mason L. Hill* (geology), Richfield Oil Cor-

poration; *Richard H. Jahns* (geology), Stanford University; *Thomas F. Malone* (meteorology), Travelers Insurance Company (1963–1964); *Ruth Moore* (science writer), Chicago Sun-Times; *Thornton L. Page* (astronomy), Wesleyan University; *Louis C. Pakiser, Jr.* (geophysics), USGS Branch of Crustal Studies; *Kenneth C. Spengler* (meteorology), American Meteorological Society; *Rear Admiral E. C. Stephan* (oceanography), Oceans Systems, Incorporated; *Hugh B. Templeton* (science education), New York State Education Department; *Fletcher G. Watson* (science education), Harvard University (1963–1964); *J. Tuzo Wilson* (geophysics), University of Toronto (1963–1965). *Ex Officio* Members: *Ramon E. Bisque, Robert L. Heller, Linn Hoover,* and *John L. Snyder.*

1963 PLANNING CONFERENCE PARTICIPANTS

Henry Albers (astronomy), Vassar College; *Norman R. Anderson* (geology), University of Puget Sound; *Harry P. Bailey* (geography), University of California; *Joseph W. Berg* (geophysics), Oregon State University; *Clarence H. Boeck* (science education), University of Minnesota; *Robert E. Boyer* (geology), The University of Texas; *Earl W. Brakken, Jr.* (science education), Florida State University; *Whitman Cross II* (science teacher), Philadelphia, Penn.; *Christopher Crowe* (geophysics), Texas Instruments, Incorporated; *Francis J. Heyden, S. J.* (astronomy), Georgetown University; *Richard H. Fleming* (oceanography), University of Washington; *Donn S. Gorsline* (oceanography), University of Southern California; *Francis D. Hole* (soil science), University of Wisconsin; *Walter D. Keller* (geology), University of Missouri; *Willard L. Leeds* (meteorology), University of Wisconsin, Milwaukee; *William Lignos* (science teacher), Baton Rouge, La.; *David Ludlum* (science editor), Princeton, N.J.; *John H. Moss* (geology), Franklin and Marshall College; *Chalmer J. Roy* (geology), Iowa State University of Science and Technology; *John W. Shrum* (science education), The Ohio State University.

AGI PRESIDENTS

B. Warren Beebe, 1967; *John C. Frye*, 1966; *Armand J. Eardley*, 1965; *Konrad B. Krauskopf*, 1964; *Hollis D. Hedberg*, 1963.

AGI ADMINISTRATIVE STAFF:

Executive Director: *Linn Hoover*, 1963–   ; *Robert C. Stephenson*, 1963. Director of Education: *John L. Snyder*. Business Manager: *W. Lawrence Tew.*

PREFACE

We would like to tell you how this book came about. Hundreds of people worked more than three years to prepare it. Why were so many people involved? Why did the work take so long?

The scientists and educators who planned *Investigating the Earth* wanted many different persons to be involved. They sought the help of scientists in many fields to make sure that the basic principles in all these fields formed an integrated and up-to-date story of planet earth and its environment in space. They wanted advice from teachers using the book about how young people could best investigate and learn. Finally, they wanted the reactions and opinions of students like yourself — what was exciting for them and what helped them to learn.

At the beginning of this project, a planning group prepared an outline for a science book that would encompass the story of the planet earth. They then invited 40 scientists and teachers to meet and write a first version of the book. Astronomers, geologists, geographers, geophysicists, meteorologists, oceanographers, soil scientists, science educators and teachers came to Boulder, Colorado to prepare manuscript for the book.

The first version of *Investigating the Earth* was sent to 77 teachers in schools across the country. During that first year it was used by 7,500 students. Each week the teachers sent their comments and the comments of their students back to the ESCP staff. The following summer another group of writers assembled in Boulder to write a second version of the Text. Changes in that Text were based on the reactions of the teachers and students who had used the book. The second version was also evaluated in many schools and involved thousands of students. The comments of teachers and students were gathered each week, studied, and used to prepare the third and final version of the book during the spring and summer of 1966. This is the book you are now reading. The many people involved in its preparation hope that their efforts have produced a stimulating book, one that will make your investigation of the earth more interesting.

The contents of this book may raise many new questions in your mind. You will answer some of these questions yourself by observing and performing investigations. Some will be answered in the Text and others by your teacher. Many will remain unanswered. When you read newspapers and magazines you find that you are not alone in wondering about these unanswered questions. Thousands of people such as scientists, philosophers, and teachers are constantly inquiring into the unknown.

Although basic principles are modified slowly, many of the ideas presented in this book are changing rapidly as man expands his knowledge. You will find it interesting to understand and keep pace with these advances. The people who worked on *Investigating the Earth* have attempted to give you some of the exciting developments in earth science by letting you find answers for yourself. They hope that in this way you may better appreciate future discoveries and perhaps participate in them yourself.

Ramon E. Bisque   *Robert L. Heller*

TABLE OF CONTENTS

UNIT I *The Dynamic Earth*

UNIT **II** *Earth Cycles*

14 Mountains From the Sea 310

15 Rocks Within Mountains 330

16 Interior of the Earth 348

UNIT III *Earth's Biography*

17 Time and Its Measurement 372

UNIT IV Earth's Environment in Space

The earth photographed by the United
States' Lunar Orbiter 1 from a height
of 1200 kilometers (745 miles) above
the moon's surface (foreground).
What features of the earth and the
moon can you identify? Why does
the earth appear as a crescent?

Investigating the Earth

How did the earth begin, how has it changed, and what will it become? Born deep in space and time, and moving through the universe for billions of years, the earth presents countless challenging questions.

Imagine that you are speeding from deep in the darkness of space toward the star called the sun. Many things arouse your curiosity as you flash through the universe. Where did all the galaxies with their billions of stars come from? What makes the stars shine? Will they always remain so bright? With all of these stars shining, why is space so dark?

As you approach the solar system, the sun's brilliance becomes almost blinding. Looking away from the sun, you notice the planets glinting in the sunlight. Many of the planets have moons around them. What are these moons and planets like? The third planet from the sun catches your attention. Through its atmosphere, a surface can be seen that is a patchwork of light and dark. You decide to take a closer look at this unusual body—the planet earth.

As you begin to slow down for a landing, more and more details of the earth become clear, although it is partly hidden by masses of clouds. Openings in the clouds give you a view of large areas of land and water. You notice that seas cover more than half of the earth's surface. Why, then, is this planet not called the "Planet Sea"? You notice that some land masses look as if they would fit together like pieces in a jigsaw puzzle. Could they have been one land area in the past? On the land, there are deserts, forests, and ice caps. Belts of mountains rim some of the land areas.

Finally you touch down on the solid surface of the earth and begin to explore the land. Soil, rocks, and grass—great rivers and small streams—clouds, sun, and sky are all around you. You are amazed at the great variety of things and impressed by their beauty. The earth, it seems, is much more complicated than it appeared from space. Life is everywhere —in the air, in the waters, and on the land. As the sun rises in the sky, you sense its importance in supporting the life of plants and animals on the earth. Looking up, you notice that clouds are gathering overhead. The air begins to stir as the sky grows dark and threatening. Rain falls. Tiny streams of muddy water gather where the land was dry a few minutes before and you realize that the streams are carrying away part of the land. Where does it go?

Figure 1 *The world's largest telescope (left), the 200-inch giant on Palomar Mountain in California; an undersea craft (above) designed to explore the ocean deeps; the heart of an electronic computer (right), which can process millions of bits of information in seconds.*

Downstream you notice that the mud is dumped into a small lake. You have found the answer to one question, but new ones take its place: What will happen when the lake fills with mud? If rain continues to wash away the land, how long will it last? By the time the storm is over and the sun reappears, you realize this is the way investigating the earth is—solving one problem often raises new questions. You investigate, discover, and go on to new problems.

Investigation of the earth is far from complete. How old is the earth? What is the earth made of? How lasting is the soil? Is the earth like any other planet in the universe? What would happen to the earth if the sun stopped shining? Man's endless curiosity drives him into the unknown. You may become so fascinated by the things that you learn and investigate in studying this book that you will discover something new in yourself—the urge to inquire!

Observing and Interpreting

What is the most effective means to explore the world in which we live? Is it the great 200-inch telescope shown in Figure 1? Could it be the sturdy undersea craft with which man explores the ocean? Or is it an electronic computer that organizes and stores millions of bits of information?

All of these are powerful tools, but none is as valuable as a single asset each of you possesses—your own mind. Even if you had these instruments and other tools, they would all be useless without your mind to direct them. In fact these instruments are invented by the mind to assist it in gathering and organizing information.

Figure 2 *A series of time exposure photographs of the moon (right) and the planet Venus.*

How does your mind help you to investigate the earth? To begin with, it records the observations made by your five senses. **Observations** are first-hand experiences of things or events. Sometimes, however, your senses need assistance. Man has invented instruments to enable him to extend his senses and to make accurate observations. The mind must then take the information sent to it by the senses and interpret its meaning. **Interpretations** are judgments about observations of things or events, or explanations of them.

You have often observed, for example, that the moon moves across the sky like the sun. Look at the series of exposures of the moon in Figure 2. How can you interpret this motion of the moon? Does the earth move around the moon? Or does the moon move around the earth? Or do they move around each other? Whichever answer you choose will be your interpretation of these observations. Both in observing and interpreting, your mind will help you investigate.

3

What Is Your Power of Observation? (P-1)

In this investigation, you make your own observations as the students are in Figure 3, and then interpret them. See if you can tell when you use only your senses, when and why you use instruments, and when you use judgment as well.

Procedure

Your teacher will give you information about the general procedures to follow in this investigation. You will also find some specific instructions at the stations where the boxes are located. Read the instructions at each station carefully before you begin your observations.

What Is Investigating?

Now that you have completed an investigation, you are better prepared to answer the question, What is investigating? In your investigation, you attempted to judge or interpret the nature of the objects in the boxes. Because you were sometimes permitted to use only one of your five senses, your powers of observation were limited, and you had to work with only a little evidence in making interpretations of the contents of each box. In spite of this, you may have been quite accurate in describing the objects in the boxes.

Suppose that you wished to solve a more complex problem than the one in the investigation. How would you begin? Perhaps the best way to start would be to decide exactly what the problem is or what question you wish to answer. You might want to test an interpretation of a situation or a guess about why something happens as it does. Such a guess is called an **hypothesis.** An hypothesis is always based on observation and it usually raises new questions. The new questions need to be tested and the additional information interpreted to determine whether or not the hypothesis is correct. You will use this approach in doing many of the investigations in this book.

When you begin to test an idea, you may find that you need information that your senses cannot provide, such as accurate measurements. **Measurement** is a method of describing the characteristics of objects in numbers. It requires the use of instruments. For example, instruments like thermometers and meter sticks enable you to express temperature and length in exact numbers. They provide a system for measuring *how* hot or cold, *how* short or long, things are in **units of measurement,** such as degrees of temperature or centimeters of length.

Scientists have designed many instruments so that they can measure such properties as hardness, brightness, loud-

Figure 3 What senses are the students using?

ness, and many others. (See Figure 4.) One function of instruments is to increase the accuracy of measurement in an investigation. Another is to help man observe things his unaided senses cannot detect. The telescope extends the sense of sight. Man looks much farther out in space with telescopes than he can with the unaided eye. Similarly, the microscope opens up the world of very small things. An instrument called a seismograph detects vibrations in the earth that are far too slight to feel. Another instrument called a gravity meter makes possible the measurement of extremely small differences in the attraction of gravity.

The magnetic dip needle, compass, and magnetometer are instruments that measure the magnetic properties of the earth. Man can neither hear, see, smell, taste, nor touch the magnetic forces around and in the earth. Without instruments we would be unable to measure these forces. The Geiger counter detects and measures atomic radiations that would not otherwise be noticed.

All of these complex instruments may make you feel that observation based purely on the senses is not useful. This is not so. The kind of observation you make depends on the nature of the problem being investigated. Suppose you wanted to find out if the soils near the equator are different from those in the middle of the Great Plains in the United States. You might discover the answer to this question and other questions by visual observation alone.

Figure 4 *Scientists design instruments to measure many things: (below, top) US Navy weather station, (below, bottom) a bottle to collect samples of ocean water at depth, (center) a platinum thermometer to measure temperatures electrically, (right) this IMP satellite will gather information from space about the earth.*

Your next investigation gives you the opportunity to try almost all of the things done in scientific investigations. You use a number of instruments in your observations. You will make measurements, and then you will make calculations with the numbers, following a mathematical formula. Finally, you will interpret your results and reach your own conclusions. Try to notice which of these steps you are doing, one after the other, as you carry out the investigation.

Investigating Mass, Volume, and Density (P-2)

Figure 5 *Why does a piece of granite sink to the bottom of the beaker on the left and another piece float on the liquid in the beaker on the right?*

Observe the two beakers in Figure 5. Each beaker contains a liquid and a solid. In the beaker on the left, the liquid is water and the solid is a piece of granite. The beaker on the right also contains a piece of granite but the liquid is mercury. What is the difference between the mercury and the water that accounts for what you observe?

You can answer this question after you learn about a property common to all matter, density. The **density** of a substance is its mass divided by its volume. The **mass** of a substance is the quantity of matter in it. The **volume** of a substance is the amount of space it occupies. Density is commonly expressed in terms of grams (mass) per cubic centimeter (volume). If you let the letter D stand for density, the letter M for mass, and the letter V for volume, density can be expressed by the formula

Figure 6 *A student uses a balance to measure the mass of an object and (bottom) a metric ruler to measure an object. What can cause errors in such measurements?*

$$D = \frac{M}{V}.$$

This means that you can obtain the density (D) by dividing the mass (M) by the volume (V), as follows:

$$V \overline{)\,M}^{\,D}$$

Suppose that an object has a mass (M) of 100 grams and a volume (V) of 20 cubic centimeters, what is its density (D) in grams per cubic centimeter?

Procedure

Part A · Determining Some Densities.

Calculate the density (D) of each of the objects given to your group. In order to do this, you must know both the mass (M) and the volume (V) of the objects. Use a balance to determine the mass, as shown in Figure 6. Volume can be determined in many ways. One way is shown in Figure 6. Can you think of another? After a class discussion, decide what method or methods you will use. Determine and record the mass and volume of each object. Make a table to help you record and organize your data. Use the formula $D = \dfrac{M}{V}$ to calculate the densities of the objects.

(1) What effect does the difference in the shape of the metal samples have on their density? Explain your answer.

(2) What effect does the difference in the amount of the sample have on the density of the modeling clay? Explain your answer.

(3) Arrange your materials in order of decreasing density.

(4) What is your calculated value for the density of water?

Part B · Determining the Density of an Ice Cube.

Now that you are familiar with density, you are ready for another problem. Observe the demonstration by your teacher. Using the materials at your station, determine the approximate density of an ice cube. (See Figure 7.)

(1) What is the approximate density of your ice cube?

(2) Explain how you obtained this value.

Figure 7

Reporting Investigations

Ever since man has carried out investigations, he has felt the need to keep records or reports of them. Why is this practice useful? What should a report include?

The pages from reports shown in Figure 8 will give you an idea of ways in which some early scientists recorded their investigations. There is no single best way to record and report an investigation. Generally, a good report should include three main parts of an investigation: (1) Why you did the investigation, (2) what you did, and (3) what you found out. Another way of expressing this would be (1) purpose, (2) procedure, and (3) results. In some of the investigations in this book the purpose and procedure will be stated in the investigation. In this case, briefly write each of these in your report so that the investigation can be reviewed later. When you yourself design the procedure, it is particularly important that you describe exactly what you did. Then someone else reading the report could repeat your investigation in order to test your results.

When a scientist performs an investigation, he writes a report similar to the ones you will write for your investigations. If his report is published, his work becomes useful to other scientists. His results can be tested by others and used to discover more about whatever problem he is working on. Similarly, writing reports will help you to organize your information and allow you to share it with your classmates.

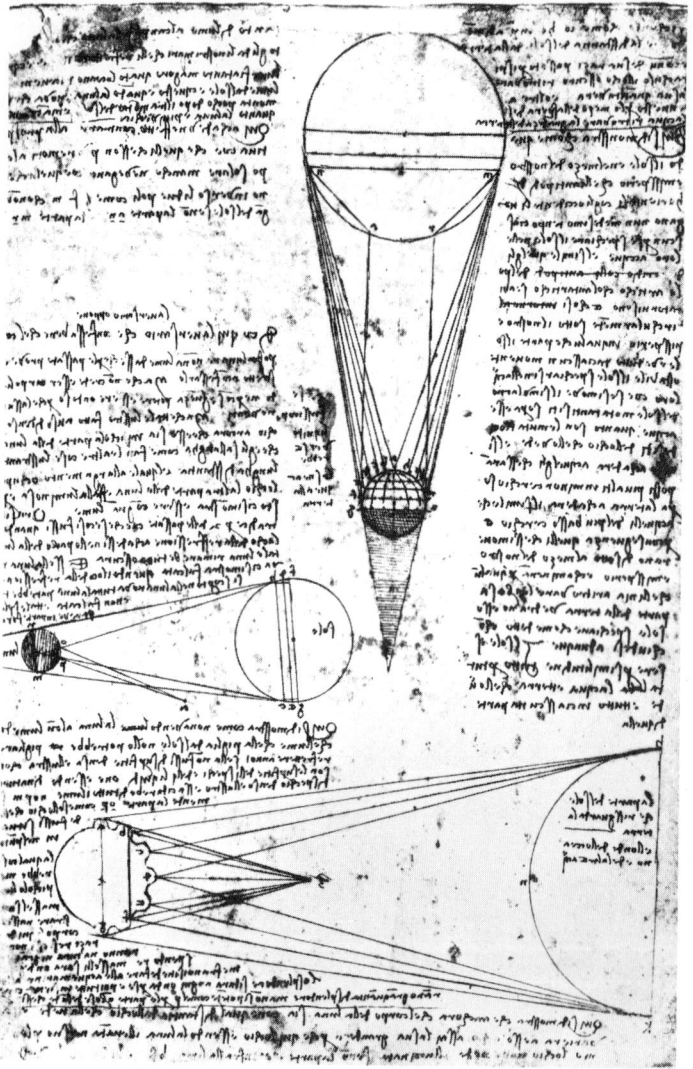

Figure 8 *Leonardo da Vinci (1452–1519) recorded his studies of the sun-earth distance in notes like those shown (above). The page (right) is one of over 25,000 pages printed from the data gathered during the voyage of the H.M.S. Challenger from 1872 to 1876.*

Variation of Thunderstorms. — The following table shows the distribution through the hours of the day of the cases of occurrence during the cruise—(1) of thunderstorms or thunder with lightning, and (2) of lightning alone :—

	THUNDERSTORMS			LIGHTNING ONLY.		THUNDERSTORMS			LIGHTNING ONLY.
	Open Sea.	Near Land.	Total.			Open Sea.	Near Land.	Total.	
Midnight to 2 A.M.	4	2	6	42	2 P.M. to 4 P.M.	2	2	4	2
2 A.M. „ 4 „	7	2	9	36	4 „ „ 6 „	0	1	1	7
4 „ „ 6 „	5	0	5	11	6 „ „ 8 „	0	2	2	25
6 „ „ 8 „	3	2	5	0	8 „ „ 10 „	1	2	3	46
8 „ „ 10 „	1	2	3	0	10 „ „ midnight .	3	3	6	89
10 „ „ noon .	0	0	0	0					
Noon „ 2 P.M.	0	1	1	1	Total	26	19	45	209

Of the 45 thunderstorms recorded, 26 occurred over the open sea, and 19 near land. Of those recorded over the open sea 22 occurred during the ten hours from 10 P.M. to 8 A.M., whereas during the other fourteen hours of the day only 4 occurred (Plate II. fig. 25). Hence the important conclusion that over the open sea thunderstorms are essentially phenomena of the night, and occur chiefly during the morning minimum of pressure. On the other hand, as regards the thunderstorms which occurred near land, they are pretty evenly distributed during the twenty-four hours.

Looking Ahead

As you do more investigations, you will see that there is no set route for an investigation to follow. Observing and gathering information lead to questions and possible interpretations or hypotheses. These hypotheses suggest further observations, measurements, calculations, and testing.

Even with the many new instruments and equipment available today (see Figure 9), methods of observation in the sciences are still limited. There are still places to which man cannot go. He cannot yet visit a star or another planet or go very far down into the earth. Instruments are still imperfect too. However, instruments are constantly extending man's powers of observation. The investigations he performs are becoming more complicated and the amount of information they provide is increasing from day to day. New information always leads to new questions. The more man investigates, the more he finds to investigate.

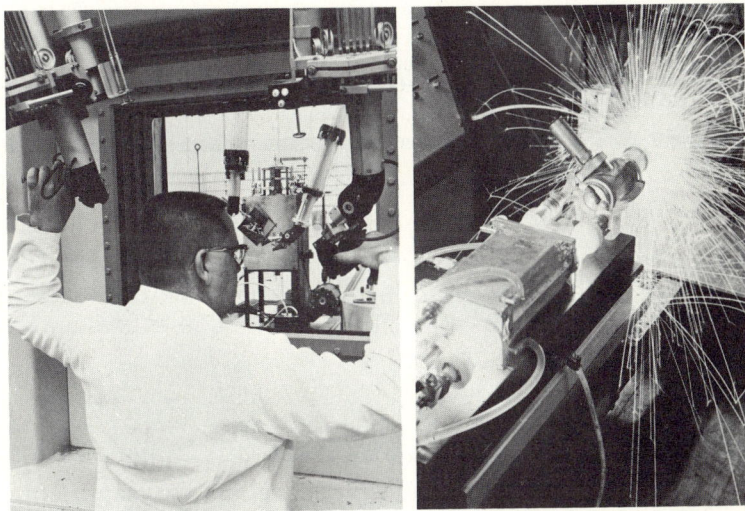

Figure 9 *A scientist works with radioactive material (right) by means of remotely controlled manipulators. The intense light beam of a laser (far right) can cut through hard metals like molybdenum and tungsten. Many other applications have been found for the laser in research and industry.*

UNIT **I** *The Dynamic Earth*

Storms, earthquakes, and other natural events have always captured man's imagination. Lacking the knowledge to explain these events in terms of nature, man at first interpreted them in terms of human experience. As he came to understand the natural causes of events, he replaced the mythical interpretations with more scientifically accurate explanations.

As you read the ancient myths introducing the units of this book, you may feel that they sound very unscientific. In our time we have the benefit of centuries of investigation. You will gain from this knowledge as you read this book, but you will also become aware that much is still unknown. Explanations for many earth processes are still stated

in terms of theories to be tested. Will our "modern" explanations of natural events and theories of the unknown sound primitive to future generations of investigators?

Myths about the awesome ball of light that rises and moves across the sky each day are common in early civilizations. In ancient Egypt, Ra was the god of the sun and creator of the universe. He was typically pictured as a man-like creature with a hawk's head. During the twelve hours of daylight Ra rode his boat from east to west across his kingdom. He was born each morning, grew until midday, and died an old man at night. In his trip across the sky he was careful to avoid attack by his eternal enemy Apep, the serpent of the celestial Nile. Sometimes Apep succeeded in swallowing the solar barque, and an eclipse would result. Yet Ra was always victorious, finally casting Apep back into the Nile. At night Ra passed through caverns, bringing light to creatures of the underworld. They fell into darkness again as Ra departed.

Ra, chief god and ruler of the world, was especially revered by the Pharaohs, who called themselves the "sons of Ra." As you learn more about the sun's vital role in earth processes in Unit I, you will understand why ancient peoples so worshipped it.

Chapter 1. The Changing Earth

A spectacular earth change — the volcanic island Surtsey, off the southern coast of Iceland, photographed a few hours after it emerged from beneath the sea.

In the early evening of November 26, 1883, the people of London were amazed at the magnificence of the sunset. Although they were used to an occasional spectacular sunset, this one was particularly impressive because of its intense color. Another unusual aspect was that the brilliant color appeared each evening for many days. Some people called this the "season of sunsets." At first no one could explain what caused them.

At the same time the sunsets were occurring in London, the people on the island of Java were still repairing damage that had been done four months earlier. A crushing wall of water had swept over the coast and devastated many villages. Strangely enough the great waves that destroyed the villages and the change in the atmosphere that produced the brilliant sunsets were caused by the same event.

This was the violently explosive eruption of the volcanic island of Krakatoa in the South Pacific. The force of the eruption ripped the island from the sea and sent shattered fragments of rock and ash and clouds of smoke nearly twenty kilometers into the air. This eruption triggered a series of changes that were noticed all over the world. The explosion and the ocean wave were the changes noticed first. But changes in the atmosphere were not evident until weeks after the explosion. Some of the changes caused by the eruption of Krakatoa are still going on. Today particles of ash from the explosion are still filtering downward in the oceans of the world. The changes involved in the destruction of Krakatoa were not confined to a single point on the earth's surface. Their effects spread over the entire earth.

Not all earth changes are as spectacular as the eruption of Krakatoa, nor are their effects so far-reaching. Many changes are so common that you hardly notice them. When you start thinking about change, it is difficult to find anything on the earth that does not undergo change.

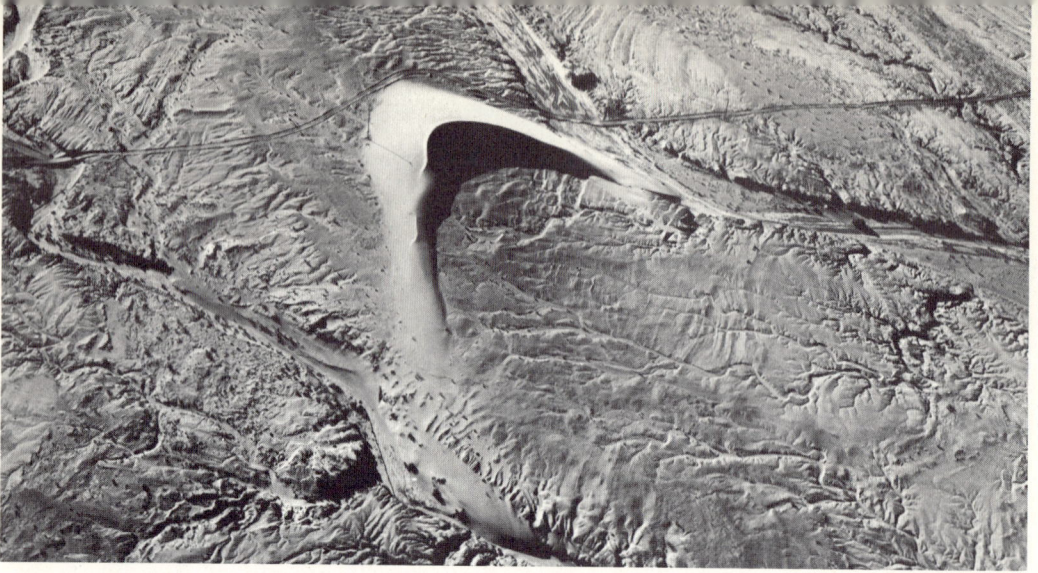

Evidence of Change

1–1 Change is everywhere.

Changes are all around you. What does the word "change" mean? If you try to give a definition of change, you will see how difficult it is to state a meaning that is acceptable to everyone.

Consider this definition. **Change** has taken place when anything that is observed is different from what it was when last observed. Is this definition accurate? Can you think of changes not described by this statement?

Look at Figure 1–1 and answer the questions about each before and after pair of drawings. Describe the evidence for change that you observe in the before and after pictures in Part A. What kinds of events could cause the changes you observe? In Part B you see the material only *after* the change has occurred. Try to guess what the material was like *before* it changed. What could have caused the changes to take place?

After you answer these questions, look again at the definition of change. Do you think the definition given is a good one? Are there changes that you cannot see taking place in nature? Continue testing the definition throughout your reading of Chapter 1. Try to find out for

yourself what conditions must be observed to provide an accurate description of change. Does answering the questions about Figure 1–2 give you a clearer idea of ways to describe change?

Can you think of anything that is *not* changing? Have you changed since yes-

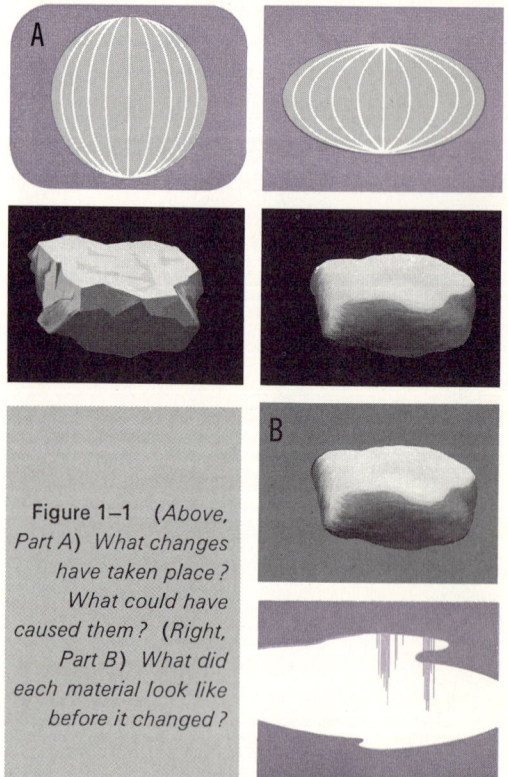

Figure 1–1 (*Above, Part A*) *What changes have taken place? What could have caused them?* (*Right, Part B*) *What did each material look like before it changed?*

14

Figure 1–2 *Two photos of a sand dune taken seven years apart. What evidence allows you to prove which photo was taken earlier?*

terday? Are you exactly the same weight as you were twenty-four hours ago? Are you in exactly the same place? In answering such questions it should be obvious that you *have* changed in many ways. Thousands of events have taken place within your body in the span of a single day. Are you digesting the same food? Have your hair and fingernails changed? In what other ways have you changed since yesterday? And your surroundings? Are they exactly the same as they were two days ago or two weeks ago, or have they changed?

Your surroundings do change constantly, but you are seldom aware of any difference from one minute, or even one hour, to the next. Although a tree near your window may change with the seasons, the tree itself remains in place from one season and from one year to the next. If you were to glance out the window some morning and find that the tree had vanished, you would probably be surprised, perhaps even alarmed. Suppose you looked over into your neighbor's yard and saw a tree grow up to full size in two minutes time. It's very unlikely that this would happen. But suppose you heard that an island had ap-

peared in one day where there had been no island before.

One November day in 1963 in the North Atlantic Ocean near Iceland, a volcanic island suddenly emerged from beneath the surface of the ocean. The island, now called Surtsey, is shown in Figure 1–3. (See map, page 453.) This spectacular volcanic eruption caused changes in the atmosphere that produced lightning and clouds.

Dramatic and sudden as the event was to the people who watched it, it did not completely surprise the scientists who study the internal behavior of the earth. For this new volcanic island appeared in line with a chain of mountains that extend from the Arctic Ocean near the North Pole southward to the continent of Antarctica. You may never see most of these mountains because they are beneath the surface of the Atlantic Ocean. A few islands, like Surtsey and Ascension Island off the coast of Africa, have peaks that tower above the ocean floor, above the ocean surface, and into the atmosphere. (See map, page 296.)

Both Krakatoa and Surtsey are examples of volcanic eruption. In the first instance volcanic processes destroyed an

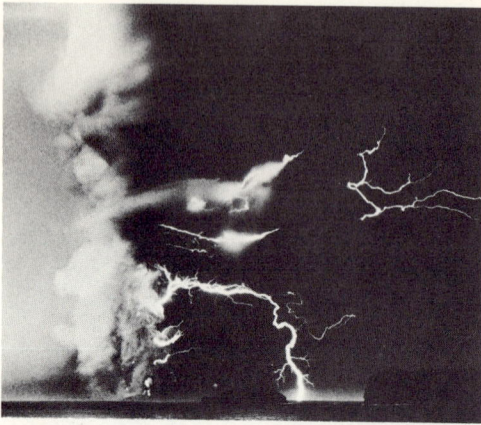

Figure 1–3 *The birth of a new volcanic island (above) is an earth change that attracts attention. The geologists are going ashore to study the new island.*

information about the way volcanoes change. Scientists may be able to explain why volcanoes change as they do. Someday they may even be able to explain the causes of volcanic activity.

No matter where you look on this earth or what you look at, you will find evidence of change. Volcanic eruptions are obvious evidences of change. Other signs of change are not so noticeable. Whether or not change is evident, it is taking place in all material, from the particles within atoms to the far reaches of the universe.

Sometimes things change without appearing to have changed at all. For example, a pebble lying on a beach is heated by the sun's rays. At night the pebble cools down. To anyone who did not touch the pebble at both times it would not seem to have changed. However, to an insect walking across the pebble during the day and again at night, the pebble would seem to have changed a great deal. So to some extent, recognizing change depends on point of view. What does this suggest about the definition of change given earlier?

Other times the changes are so obvious that you can reconstruct what happened without actually having seen the changes take place. Can you think of examples of such changes?

In the next section you will observe changes in an earth material. Some of the changes will be obvious, and others may be difficult to detect.

island, and in the second, an island was born. If an observer had seen and described only the explosion of Krakatoa, he might have reached the conclusion that volcanic action destroys islands. Another observer viewing only Surtsey might conclude that islands are formed from volcanic action. What is wrong with each of these interpretations?

Earth scientists investigate the earth by observing the way things are at a particular time and describing *how* they change. They also attempt to interpret their observations and to explain *why* things change. For example, a program of study has been developed to gather

The dark line in this high-altitude aerial photograph is a stream. What evidence of change can you see?

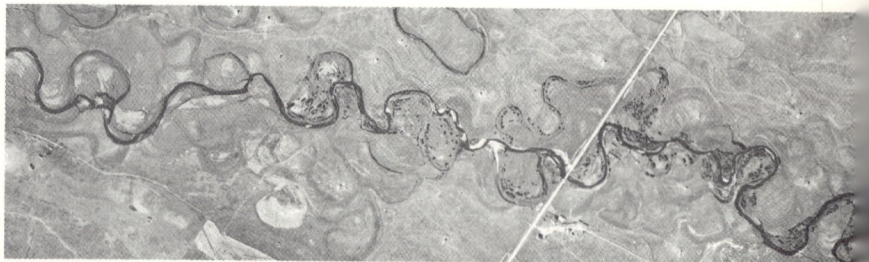

1–2 Investigating change.

You have an interesting role in this investigation. Each of you will change the same earth material in any ways you can think of. Then you will examine the materials of the others *after* they have been changed and try to determine exactly what changes were produced and how.

Procedure

Your teacher will supply you with a sample of an earth material. Take it home with you and change it in as many ways as you can.

Examine the material to see exactly what it looks like before you change it. Keep a record of the changes you cause, how you caused them, and what the material is like after you have changed it. Record any other ways in which you think it might have been changed.

After discussing in class the ways this material can be changed, suggest some other earth materials in which you can observe similar changes. Think about the causes of the changes you produced. Can you identify natural processes that would have caused the same changes?

1–3 Changes occur across interfaces.

Many changes occur at the place where two materials come together. In observing changes, scientists refer to the boundary between materials as an **interface**. Interfaces occur at all scales, large and small, and are the place where different materials or different forms of the same material meet. In Investigation 1–2 perhaps some members of your class placed the earth material in water. Where was the boundary or interface between the earth material and water? Did a change take place at this boundary? Look at Figure 1–4 and answer the question in the caption.

Some interfaces are abrupt and some are gradual, depending on your point of view. For example, there is an interface between this book and the air surrounding it. There is another interface between the book and the desk on which it lies. These are distinct interfaces. Many interfaces studied in earth science are just as distinct. How would you describe the interface between a wet sponge and water?

Consider the interface between a sand grain and the surrounding water in the sea, or the interface between the stony surface of an onrushing meteor and the space through which it speeds.

Figure 1–4 *Compare the interfaces in the two drawings (right). Relate these to interfaces in the photograph (far right).*

(Above) Where would you separate the birds from the fish in this interface?

Figure 1–5 (Below) A great spiral galaxy in space. What interfaces can be seen in the views of the earth from space, the ocean bottom, and a dust storm?

Both illustrate abrupt differences in materials across interfaces.

Look at the galaxy in Figure 1–5. It is a system of billions of stars a great distance from us. Can you see the gradual transition zone between the galaxy and the darkness of space around it? Examine one of the bright foreground stars in our galaxy, the Milky Way. Is it easier to determine the interface between a star and space or the interface between a galaxy and space?

In trying to describe an interface or an earth change, your description will depend on your point of view and your method of observation. If you were trying to establish the interface between a lake and its bottom, it would make a great deal of difference whether you dropped a stone to the bottom or tried to determine exactly where the water stops and the mud begins. Why?

Think of all the interfaces at the earth's surface, on which you live. Here you find the interfaces between the earth with its variety of solid materials, the atmosphere with its many gases, and the water in the oceans, lakes, and rivers as well as the water vapor in the atmosphere. Many of the earth changes that you will observe, measure, and study in this course occur at these interfaces. In this way, you will learn more about the changes that affect us all and shape the environment in which we live.

All the way down the scale of size from an enormous galaxy to a tiny atom, every material has an interface with its surroundings. *Interfaces are the places where change occurs.* You live in an ever-changing series of interfaces between the ground, the air, and water at the surface of the dynamic earth. As you observe change taking place in the world around you, look for interfaces and describe the change.

Figure 1–6 *Canyon of the Little Colorado River, with the Grand Canyon in the background to the left.*

1–4 Investigating change in rocks.

In Investigation 1–2 you became aware of the many different kinds of changes that could occur in a single substance. In performing this next investigation you will again cause changes to take place. This time you will work with fragments of rock. Instead of being concerned with the many kinds of changes that can take place, you will focus on only one—the wearing away of rock fragments.

Procedure

List as many factors as you can that will affect the rate at which rocks wear away. Using some rock fragments, a container, and water, investigate these factors. **Rate** means how fast the change takes place. The factors that affect the change are called **variables.**

(1)How could you investigate one variable at a time? Choose one of the variables that you wish to investigate and determine how it affects the rate at which the fragments wear away. (2)What interfaces are involved in the changes you observed in this investigation?

Look at Figure 1–6. (3)What variables do you think were important in the rate of formation of the canyon?

Figure 1–7

Thought and Discussion . . .

Answer the following questions about the photograph Figure 1–7.
1. Where is the interface between the air and water?
2. How are the changes in investigations 1–2 and 1–4 illustrated in Figure 1–7?

A photographer took these 13 separate exposures of the moon during a partial lunar eclipse on July 15, 1954. In which direction was the moon moving? Explain your answer.

Prediction and Patterns of Change

1–5 Are changes predictable?

Suppose you wanted to predict how warm it will be on your next birthday. Suppose you also wanted to predict how high the sun would be at noon on the same day. Which prediction would be easier to make? Your experience tells you that there are daily differences in temperature. You may have also noticed that the path of the summer sun across the sky is quite different from the path of the winter sun. Which of these values, the temperature or the height of the sun, is more easily predicted and why?

If you examined the records of your local weather bureau for each of your past birthdays, you might find ten different values for the temperature. If at the same time you checked on the elevation of the noontime sun, you would find the same figure for all of your past birthdays. Do you think as many variables affect the height of the noonday sun as affect daily temperature?

The predictability of change depends in part on the number of variables in-

volved. The more variables that affect a change, the less predictable that change can be. If there are very few factors that affect a change, the change is usually more predictable. But what does "more predictable" mean? It means you can state more about a future event, not only that it will happen but *when* and *where* it will happen.

Predictions about changes involving a great many variables are easy to make if they state only that the change *will* occur. For example, if you wanted to predict the time required for a mountain to wear down, you would have to take many variables into consideration. Among these variables are the kind of rock in the mountain, the speed and size of the streams, the climate of the area, the presence or absence of vegetation, and the types of vegetation.

Not only are there a large number of variables that affect the wearing down of the mountain, but the variables themselves change as time passes. Consequently, although scientists can predict

ACTIVITY *How does an earth scientist recognize that a pattern of change exists? One method used is to construct a graph that relates a change to time. Use the information in Table 1–1 to make a graph showing the change in the number of sunspots from year to year. Use your graph to make the predictions necessary to answer the questions listed on the right.*

What is the average time between the high points (periods of maximum sunspot activity) on your graph? How many sunspots will there be in the year that you graduate from high school? What years will be best for the next International Quiet Sun Year, when there will be a minimum of sunspots? In what year will the next maximum sunspot activity take place?

TABLE 1–1   ANNUAL SUNSPOT NUMBERS, 1906–1965

YEAR	SUNSPOT NUMBER	YEAR	SUNSPOT NUMBER	YEAR	SUNSPOT NUMBER
1906	53.8	1926	63.9	1946	92.6
1907	62.0	1927	69.0	1947	151.5
1908	48.5	1928	77.8	1948	136.2
1909	43.9	1929	65.0	1949	134.7
1910	18.6	1930	35.7	1950	83.9
1911	5.7	1931	21.2	1951	69.3
1912	3.6	1932	11.1	1952	31.5
1913	1.4	1933	5.7	1953	13.9
1914	9.6	1934	8.7	1954	4.4
1915	47.4	1935	36.1	1955	38.0
1916	57.1	1936	79.7	1956	141.7
1917	103.9	1937	114.4	1957	189.9
1918	80.6	1938	109.6	1958	184.6
1919	63.6	1939	88.8	1959	158.8
1920	37.6	1940	67.8	1960	112.3
1921	26.1	1941	47.5	1961	53.9
1922	14.2	1942	30.6	1962	37.6
1923	5.8	1943	16.3	1963	27.9
1924	16.7	1944	11.0	1964	10.2
1925	44.3	1945	33.2	1965	15.1

that a mountain will eventually be worn down, they can only roughly estimate the time required for this to happen.

The predictability of change is also related to the laws of probability. You may have heard your local weather forecaster predict a 4 out of 10 or 40 percent probability of rain. The chance or probability of a coin landing heads up is one out of two or 50 percent. If you reached blindfolded into a bag containing ten balls of equal size, nine red and one white, the probability or chance of picking a red ball is 9 out of 10 or 90 percent.

Even though some changes are not completely understood, they are still partly predictable by applying the laws of probability. Predicting the high temperature on your next birthday is somewhat similar to the problem of predicting the height of the first person to walk out of your school at noon. If you measured the height of everyone in the school and found that the heights ranged from five feet to six feet, what could you predict? You would be reasonably safe in saying that the first person out of the doors would be taller than five feet and shorter than six feet. You might still be wrong. Suppose a seven-foot basketball player who was visiting your school was the first one out of the doors. You could say that he set a "record"!

Interpretations and predictions based on the laws of probability are most accurate when a great many observations have been made. Often after many thousands of observations have been made of a particular earth change, a pattern can be defined. When such patterns are recognized, prediction is much easier. Are there patterns that have been discovered about volcanic eruptions that make their prediction easier? Which is easier to predict, where they will appear or when they will occur? Why?

1–6 Change takes place in time and space.

Almost every one has heard a bubble break, but have you ever heard a rose bloom? If a rose bloomed as fast as a bubble breaks, you would hear it! The reason you cannot hear a rose bloom is that its petals do not open as suddenly as a bubble breaks. We are so used to observing changes continually taking place around us that we sometimes do not notice the amount of time required for the changes to take place.

It takes a relatively long time for a rose to bloom or a cloud to drift across the sky. On the other hand, it seems to take "no time at all" for a bubble to break or for a lightning bolt to streak between clouds and earth. But is it possible for something to happen in no time at all? Is it possible that some changes will never be finished? You have gathered evidence to prove that it takes time to wear a rock down, but do you have any notion of how long it takes to form a mountain range like the Alps?

Iguaçu Falls in Brazil. How might this scene change overnight? in a hundred years?

If changes involve too much or too little time for your senses to detect, you sometimes think of them as taking "forever" or occurring "instantly." However, the words "forever" and "instantly" are not very useful in the earth sciences because they are not exact descriptions of time. Even extremely rapid or extremely slow rates of change can be measured on some scale of time. For example, a flash of lightning is measured in kilometers per second. On the other hand, the uplift of a mountain is measured in centimeters per century.

The lightning bolts shown in Figure 1-8 streak a distance of about two kilometers between a cloud and the earth. You may have noticed that it is possible to detect the direction the lightning travels as it links the clouds and earth. If it is possible to detect whether the lightning goes from earth to cloud or from cloud to earth, then it must be possible to measure the time of the flash.

Careful measurements show that lightning like that shown in the illustration takes about $\frac{1}{50,000}$ of a second to span the two-kilometer distance between these clouds and the earth. At that rate the lightning could go around the earth about three times in one second. A speed of this sort might at first seem to be extremely high for an earth process. However, this speed is barely one third the speed of light. Light, as you may know, could go around the earth over seven times in a single second.

In contrast to the rate of a lightning flash is the rate at which mountains are uplifted. Some areas of the Sierra Nevada Mountains in California have been measured carefully over a period of years. In these areas the land is rising at the rate of a few centimeters per century. At this rate of uplift, mountains that are 4300 meters high would take 9 million years to form. And yet these same mountains contain rocks that are 350 million years old. Do these figures contradict each other?

Is time the only factor to consider in describing change? Time is really only half the framework used to describe change. The other half is space. Lightning bolts streak through the space

Figure 1-8 *Lightning passes between clouds and earth. The bench mark (below) indicated by the arrow in the Cajon Pass, California (below, left) rose 17 cm in 37 years.*

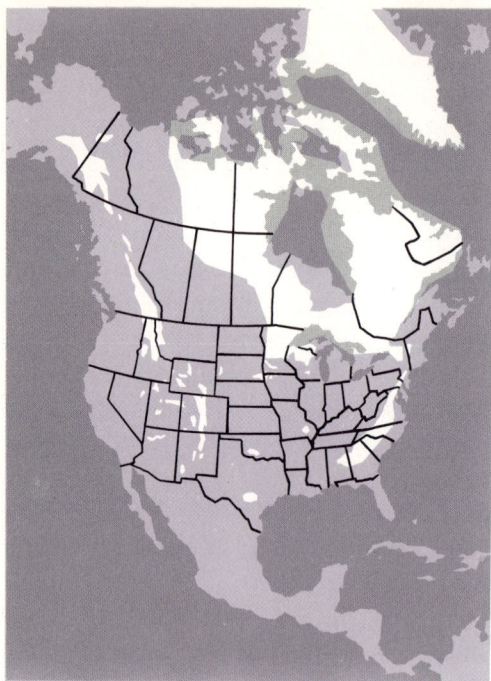

Figure 1–9 *The colored areas on the continent show where rocks exist that have formed in the sea.*

between clouds and earth. The mountain ranges move slowly upward, changing their position in space as they rise centimeter by centimeter.

The map in Figure 1–9 illustrates the relation between change and space. It shows areas in North America presently covered by rocks formed in the sea. There may be no spot in North America where the ocean has never been. Even the place where you are sitting now was once covered by an ocean. How do we know this? Evidence for the past presence of oceans on what are now land areas is found in rocks nearly everywhere in North America. Some of the evidence is in the form of the preserved remains of ancient sea life. Other evidence is found in sandstone layers that contain features similar to modern shorelines. The shorelines and their position on a map provide us with the present location of the boundary between land and sea. Compare the sea's position in the past with that of today. Is there significant evidence for change? Could you have answered this question without having the evidence for change shown in terms of space?

When did the sea cover the place where you are? You have evidence in Figure 1–9 of *where* the seas have been, but this last question asks *when*. *When* and *where* are words that represent the way we ask questions about time and space. The relationship between time and space in describing change is especially important in science.

Time and space together make up the framework in which you describe change. Both are needed for a complete description of what kind of change takes place and how much change has occurred. Time and space are not the only factors in describing change. You will find in later chapters that an understanding of earth materials, forces, and energy is needed to study change further. Does what you have learned here about time

This ship (left) was wrecked on Sable Island south of Nova Scotia. The maps (right) show how this sand island has moved in 200 years.

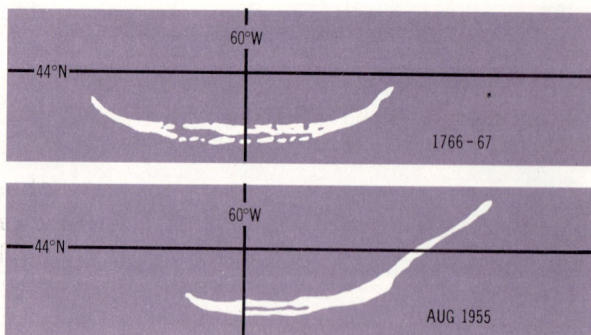

and space affect the definition of change given in Section 1-1?

In the investigations that follow you will be observing changes that take place inside the earth, in the air, and in the sky. These investigations are called the Earthquake Watch, the Weather Watch, and the Sky Watch. Many observations are required in each investigation. During the weeks ahead, try to organize the information you gather so that you can look for patterns of change. If you discover patterns, determine whether they exist in time or space or both. Try to discover whether or not the changes are predictable. If the changes do not seem to be predictable, try to determine what information might be needed to predict them. How could the needed information be gathered?

1-7 Investigating patterns of change—Earthquake Watch.

Late one afternoon in March, 1964, a smooth level city street in Anchorage, Alaska, suddenly became a jumble of broken buildings and shattered pavement. A violent earthquake had occurred. In a matter of seconds parts of the street had dropped down three to four meters (10 to 13 feet) relative to other parts. The energy that caused this destruction was so great that it caused abnormal ocean waves in the Gulf of Mexico along the coast of Louisiana. If an attempt were made to equal the energy with man-made explosives, it would require about 200 billion tons of TNT. With this amount of energy released during earthquakes, it is little wonder that rigid steel rails can be bent like pieces of soft wire. (See Figure 1-10.)

Where do earthquakes occur? How often do they occur? Only long-term observations will give you the answers to these questions. You will begin such observations here in the Earthquake Watch.

Scientists estimate that as many as 1000 to 5000 earthquakes take place around the world every day. Is it possible to predict the magnitude of earthquakes and predict exactly *when* and *where* on the earth's surface they will occur?

Figure 1-10 *Rails in Anchorage, Alaska, after the 1964 earthquake.*

Procedure

You will use the data from sensitive detecting instruments called **seismographs.** Seismographs detect the almost continuous trembling of the earth at many different points on the globe. Analysis of the data from three or more seismographs can pinpoint the time of occurrence and location of earthquakes on the earth's surface. It also indicates their depth and magnitude. Perhaps you can discover patterns in earthquake locations and frequency. The information needed for this investigation comes from the U.S. Environmental Science Services Administration, Coast and Geodetic Survey. This information will include the surface location, time of occurrence, depth, and intensity of earthquakes.

(Top) A farm house in Japan collapses during a severe earthquake. (Left) The Saada Hotel in Morocco, before and after an earthquake. (Right) Zákinthos, an island community of Greece, was destroyed by a series of earthquakes in 1953.

Figure 1–11
Locating earthquake epicenters on a world map.

The geographic location on the earth's surface is not the exact location of the earthquake. The actual location of the earthquake, called the **focus**, is at some depth *beneath* the surface. The geographic point *on* the earth's surface directly above the focus is called the **epicenter.** Epicenter locations are given in latitude and longitude. The focus is given as shallow, intermediate, or deep.

Use map pins to plot the position of the epicenter as shown in Figure 1–11. Pins of different colors should be used for shallow-, intermediate-, and deep-focus earthquakes. The location of the pin will show the epicenter, and the color of the pin will indicate the depth of the focus.

1–8 Investigating patterns of change—Weather Watch.

Weather can be defined as the condition of the atmosphere at any one time and place. If you were to ask, "Is there a pattern to the weather?," it should be obvious that you could not go outside, describe the weather, and answer the question. Again, as in Investigation 1–7, the information needed to discover what kind of weather patterns exist in your region takes a long time to collect.

Procedure

In order to gather information for this investigation, observations and measurements will be made over the next two and one-half months. During that period you will keep track of changes in the atmosphere from one day to the next. Use a wall chart to record these changes. See if you can discover patterns in the changes.

Discuss with your teacher how the chart can be constructed so that your observations and measurements will contribute most to the discovery of patterns. By the time you are studying Chapter 8, you may be ready to make some of your own predictions about weather changes. Your observations and record will involve time patterns (in the form of a graph) and space patterns (in the form of a map). See Appendix B for the factors to measure and record.

1–9 Investigating patterns of change—Sky Watch.

Changes occur in the sky as well as on the earth. The position of the sun in the sky changes from hour to hour, and also from day to day. Many of the changes of position in the sky are called *apparent* changes. This is because the change we *see* is not the change that is actually taking place. An example of this is the apparent rising and setting of the sun. Actually these changes are caused by the turning of the earth. We know that the sun does not really rise and set, but only appears to do so.

Other changes in the sky are real, and not just apparent. The night-to-night motion of the moon eastward among the stars is a good example. Apparent or real, these changes are nevertheless observable.

To investigate the change in the sun's path in the sky, you must plot the sun's daily path several times during the year. In order to discuss Sky Watch in Chapter 4, you must start collecting the necessary data now.

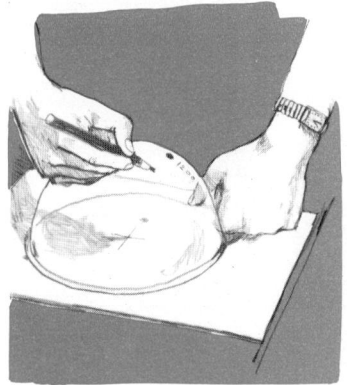

Figure 1–12
Plotting the sun's position.

Figure 1–13 *Coastal town of the Azores Islands in the North Atlantic Ocean.*

Procedure

Using the plastic hemisphere and globe as shown in Figure 1–12, plot the position of the sun on the sky several times during the day. Start as early in the school day as possible, when the sun is far in the east. Make your last observation late in the afternoon when the sun is in the western part of the sky. When you connect all the points you have plotted, you will have a record of the path the sun made on the sky that day. *Keep this record for future use.* You will compare the sun's path in the sky now with its path at other times of the year. Plot the sun's path again on or near the following seven dates: October 20, November 20, December 22, January 20, February 20, March 20, and April 20.

Thought and Discussion . . .

1. What evidence do you have from Figure 1–13 that the people living in the village are alert to earth change?
2. Can you think of any better ways to adjust to these earth changes?
3. What kinds of patterned earth changes do you think affect the lives of the people living here?
4. Can you predict any earth changes that will occur in this area in the future?

Figure 1–14 (*Top left*) *The small trees were planted by man. Could they have been replaced as quickly by natural seeding?* (*Top right*) *Selected tree cutting.*
Figure 1–15 (*Bottom left*) *A farmer plows contour furrows on a sloping field.* (*Bottom right*) *Aerial view of contour plowing.*
Figure 1–16 (*Right-hand page*) *Can you pick out the results of man's interfering with natural change?*

Earth Changes and Man

1–10 Man and his environment.

Among all of the creatures on earth, man is most able to adapt to a wide range of conditions. For example, he can live in the tropics or near the poles. How do these environments differ? How does man adjust to them? Will he be able to adjust to the environment of the moon?

A natural environment is determined by the interaction between the earth processes and earth materials at any given place. Man's ability to adapt to natural environments comes from his success in creating artificial environments. In order to do this effectively man has had to learn much about the conditions that exist in natural environments, including earth changes.

In adjusting to different sets of conditions, man must use many earth materials in many different ways. The metals in his tools and buildings, the fabrics in his clothing, and the food that he con-

sumes for energy are all derived from the earth. Man uses earth materials to modify or change his environment for comfort and convenience. Can you think of an example where man's use of natural materials has led to results that are not entirely beneficial?

Steel, copper, aluminum, and other metals necessary for man's activities are taken from the earth. In time, huge pits or caverns are dug and many tons of waste material are disposed of. Large mills and manufacturing centers where these metals are processed and formed into useful items also produce waste materials. If these materials are dumped into streams and rivers for many years, changes in the water become significant. Huge smokestacks constantly pour smoke and gases into the atmosphere. Where do these wastes go? What effects do they have on other activities of man? These unfavorable changes have not

gone unnoticed. Many individuals and groups are presently attempting to do something about them.

ACTIVITY *Using newspapers and recent magazines, prepare a brief report on some of the problems caused by waste disposal and the solutions to these problems that have been used or suggested.*

In some instances man attempts to change the rate of natural processes for his benefit. Painting of a house or a boat is an example. What natural process is slowed down by a coating of paint? Can you think of an example where man acts to increase the rate of a natural process for his benefit? As one example, the small trees in the area shown in the photograph in Figure 1–14 were planted by men. How much longer do you think it would have taken for natural processes to reestablish this forest?

The farmer pictured in Figure 1–15, being fully aware of the tendency of water to wash away the topsoil of his field, cuts each furrow so that it acts as a long curving dam to hold back runoff water. This type of plowing is called contour plowing. At the same time the farmer can put fertilizers back into the soil. The chemical fertilizers he uses replace those originally found in the soil that were used up by the crops.

In modifying the conditions in his environment by contour plowing and fertilization, the farmer has altered the rate of two earth processes. You could argue that the rich topsoil would never have been in danger of being lost if the farmer had not removed the natural cover of vegetation to plant his field. Therefore the precautions he must take to prevent the soil from washing away are necessary because he disturbed a natural situation.

Often man's activities affect natural processes and interrupt the patterns of natural change. Four examples are shown in Figure 1–16. Examine each photograph in the figure and decide which natural changes have been affected by man's actions.

Deep gullies can be cut into a bull-dozed hillside in a period of a few months. Changes such as these can be detected fairly quickly and steps may be taken to remedy them. However, it is becoming clear that not all of the changes that man causes are so obvious.

The same tractor that plowed the contoured rows in Figure 1–15 was pouring contaminating gases into the atmosphere. Although no one standing near the breeze-swept field where the farmer plowed could detect it, the exhaust fumes were changing the air surrounding the earth. The tractor is but one of millions of sources of contaminating gases that have produced dramatic results in certain areas. (See Figure 1–17.)

The experience man has gained by living in and studying the dynamic environment has provided a significant amount of understanding about the earth. In applying this understanding to processes of change man will be better able to adjust to changes he causes and to natural changes that affect him.

1–11 Environment and prediction.

It is valuable to study earth processes and change for two major reasons. The first is to gain knowledge of earth processes and the way they affect our lives. The second reason is to gain an under-standing of how men might predict and possibly alter natural events.

To better understand natural change, earth scientists have created networks of observation and communication that aid in gathering new information about earth processes. Agencies have been created by governments to study the land, sea, and sky. Investigators in many countries of the world probe the inner depths of our planet with seismographs to seek more information about earth-quakes and the energy they release.

Weather conditions around the world are constantly surveyed by satellites and thousands of ground observing stations. Ocean-going research vessels chart the sea floor and gather information about the sea. These and other investigations of earth changes are evidence of man's curiosity about the earth and his desire to adjust to his environment favorably.

Which of the headlines in Figure 1–18 are related to prediction and control of change? What kinds of change do you think man might be able to control? Why do you think it is important to be able to control certain changes?

Until we know how a stream behaves, we cannot hope to control it wisely. Until we know how natural processes affect the behavior of the atmosphere, we cannot hope to understand how man's ac-

Figure 1–17 *The air can become contaminated with waste gases. (Far left) Before and after smoke control measures. (Left) Smog in a large city.*
Figure 1–18 *(Right) Earth changes make the headlines around the world.*

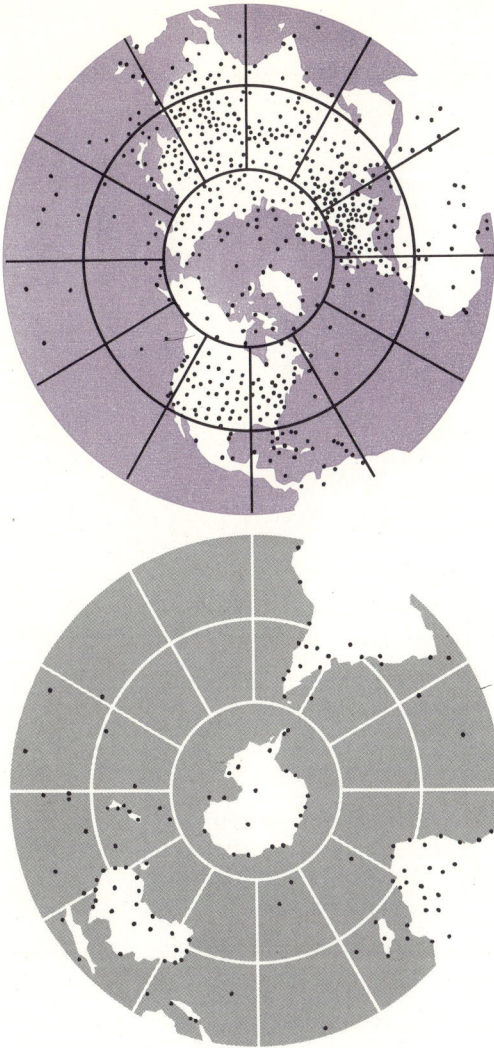

Locations of weather stations in the Northern Hemisphere (*top*) and Southern Hemisphere (*above*). In which hemisphere would you expect weather predictions to be most reliable?

tivities may alter atmospheric processes.

If the time comes when man completely understands the conditions of a particular environment, then he may be able to control it. Control is related to the idea of design. We usually think of design in terms of some structure such as a house or a bridge. However, have you ever been in an environment that was designed? How about a heated swimming pool or an air-conditioned building? Man had to understand certain processes and conditions rather completely before such designing could take place. Many scientists and engineers think that certain conditions could be designed into parts of our environment. If this is true, then we will have to know much more about the processes of change in the world around us.

As you study the dynamic earth, look for patterns of change. Try to understand these patterns so that you can see how they affect the thin zone in which we live on the surface of the earth.

Thought and Discussion . . .

1. Why is it difficult to study the way earth changes affect man?
2. What evidence do you have that man has made favorable and unfavorable adjustments to his environment?

A COMPUTER STUDY OF CLIMATE ASKED

Simulation of Changes Is Suggested by Scientist

By HAROLD M. SCHMECK Jr.

The prospect of using a computer to simulate vast changes in weather and climate has been raised by a leading specialist in research on earth's atmosphere.

By these means, man could play at changing the climate in any imaginable way, but would not have to play for keeps. Costly projects of great potential benefit to mankind could be evaluated and even more costly mistakes avoided, according to Dr. Walter Orr Roberts, director of the National Center for Atmospheric Research at Boulder, Col.

"For example," he said, "a

Volcan sous-marin en éruption au large de l'Islande

Reykjavik. 14 novembre. — Vapeurs jaillissantes à la surface de la mer hivernale, mêlées de fumées multicolores et de masses incandescentes, tel est l'étrange et fantastique spectacle observé hier à quelques milles au sud de l'Islande.

Il s'agit d'un volcan sous-marin qui est entré en éruption. Les navires ont été avisés de se tenir à l'écart, en raison du risque de raz de marée.

'Mountain' Still Grows in Atlantic

REYKJAVIK, Iceland (AP)— Iceland's new volcanic "mountain," near the Vestmannaeyjar Islands in the Atlantic, tripled in size Friday night and is now some 130 feet (39 meters) high and more than a quarter of a mile (400 m.) long.

The underwater eruption still continues violently, scientists reported. Gigantic explosions are throwing glowing lava ashes

---

SUN IS MERCILESS IN MATABELELAND

Light Rain Does No Good as Drought Topples Cattle

By LAWRENCE FELLOWS
Special to The New York Times

GWANDA, Rhodesia, Jan. 8 —In the sun-scorched heart of Matabeleland a few drops of rain fell this morning. If the rain did anything, it helped to settle the

It did n
which hav
hundreds
starvation
ling vultu
ence of d
southweste
sia.

The earl
no longer
the newly
soil is dry
mopani tr
the thorn
and gray.

SDAY, JULY 5

AIR FROM CANADA ENDS HEAT WAVE AFTER 3D-DAY 98°

Mercury Falls 11 Degrees in Two Hours as Weekend

Landslides Set Off by Down

Many Shanties Swept Away as 9-Inch Rain Floods City

By JUAN de ONIS
Special to The New York Times

RIO DE JANEIRO, Jan. 11—Landslides let loose by the heaviest recorded rainstorm in Rio's history thundered through

How permanent are the changes which man has made on our planet? What changes are made at the time when a city is established?

CHAPTER REVIEW

Summary

Change is everywhere. Evidence for change can be found on every scale of time and space. Many of the changes we view seem to occur in patterns. Although the patterns can be recognized and certain predictions can be made about them, very few are completely understood.

Change takes place at an interface. Usually an interface is the place where two materials meet, or a transition zone between two materials. Interfaces, like changes, occur on all scales. Some interfaces, such as the boundary between the sea and the atmosphere, are familiar to us. Other interfaces, like the interface between the atmosphere and space, require very precise and specialized methods of detection. Certain aspects of change involve man. Although man is unable to affect the earth as a whole, he is able to and does effect changes near the earth's surface. Only through experience and careful study of earth changes will man be able to make useful predictions about his environment.

Questions and Problems

A

1. What is an interface? List several examples.
2. What is a variable?
3. Why is it important to understand variables in scientific investigations?

4. What variables affect the rate at which rocks wear?
5. Why is it difficult to predict some changes?
6. In this chapter, change is described in what framework?

B

1. How can you change water so its density does not equal 1.00 gm/cm³?
2. List some changes that you think are patterned. Defend your choices.
3. Imagine that you observe a particular event every day at 10:30 A.M. for ten days. Explain how you can prove that this event is part of a pattern.
4. How accurate is the statement, "An earthquake will occur sometime in the next ten minutes"?
5. Discuss the statement, "If a pattern of change is recognized and the change is predictable, then the change and its causes are completely understood."

C

1. In Investigation 1–4, how did probability relate to the rate at which the rock fragments wear?
2. Why is it difficult to predict the exact time when you might see a meteor streak through the atmosphere tonight?
3. Give examples of natural change that have a pattern in space but not in time.
4. Explain what is meant by the statement,

"The only really constant condition is change"?

5. Discuss the meaning of the phrase, "balance of nature."

Suggested Readings

BOOKS

Alterman, Hyman. *Numbers at Work*. Harcourt, Brace & World, Inc., New York, 1966. Pages 53–153, probability.

Dubos, Réne J. and Maya Pines. *Health and Disease*. Time, Inc. (Life Science Library), New York, 1965. Pages 84–116, air pollution.

Dyson, James L. *The World of Ice*. Alfred A. Knopf, Inc., New York, 1963. Chapter 17, future ice ages.

Fisher, Robert M. *How About the Weather*. Harper & Row, Publishers, New York, 1958. Pages 47–50, lightning.

Furnos, C. C. and Joe McCarthy. *The Engineer*. Time, Inc. (Life Science Library), New York, 1966. Pages 172–175, engineer's view of pollution problems and solution.

Harris, Miles F. *Man against Storm: The Challenge of Weather*. Coward-McCann, Inc., New York, 1962.

Hillcourt, William. *Field Book of Nature Activities and Conservation*. G. P. Putnam's Sons, New York, 1961. Problems of air and water pollution.

Inglis, Stuart J. *Planets, Stars and Galaxies*. John Wiley & Sons, Inc., New York, 1962. Pages 210–215, sunspots.

Leopold, Luna B. and Kenneth B. Davis. *Water*. Time, Inc. (Life Science Library), New York, 1966. Pages 171–190, water pollution problems.

Milne, Lorus J. and Margery Milne. *The Mountains*. Time, Inc. (Life Nature Library), New York, 1962. Page 55 and pages 68–69, Krakatoa.

Wolfe, C. Wroe, *et al. Earth and Space Science*. D. C. Heath & Company, Boston, 1966. Pages 56–57, Krakatoa.

PERIODICALS

Grantaz, A., G. Plafker, and R. Kachadoorian. *Alaska's Good Friday Earthquake, March 27, 1964*. Circular No. 491, U.S. Geological Survey, Washington, D.C.

Lear, J. "Surtsey—Child of an Expanding Earth?" *Saturday Review*, July 3, 1965.

Sky and Telescope. Sky Publishing Company, Cambridge, Massachusetts.

Thorarinsson, Sigurdur. "Surtsey: Island Born of Fire." *National Geographic*, May, 1965.

Weatherwise. American Meteorological Society, Boston, Massachusetts.

The gullied land in the photograph on the left was replanted. The results are shown after 20 years in the photograph on the right.

Chapter 2 Earth Materials

If you flew over the northern regions of Canada, you would pass over vast stretches of wilderness without seeing a town or even a cabin. No human being seems to live in this cold, flat, treeless land within the Arctic Circle. You could travel for hundreds of kilometers through mountainous Alaska or along the rocky coast of Labrador without finding a human settlement. Yet, if you looked closely, you could find evidence of man even in those isolated areas. Here you might see a pit blasted in a hillside, and there a pile of broken rock. Old campsites and rusted tools testify that man once worked there. Occasionally you might discover men at work in the wilderness, drilling for oil on the Arctic islands or panning gold beside a Yukon river.

Men have searched the earth for precious metals and gems since the Stone Age. History has been shaped by the men who sought gold and other rare materials. Alexander the Great was aided in his conquests by riches from the gold mines of his native Macedonia, which equipped and supplied his powerful army. The Roman Empire depended on gold and silver from the mines of conquered countries. The Western Hemisphere was discovered and explored largely because men were lured by tales of riches to be found across the sea.

Prospectors played an important role in the early settling of the Americas. With the discovery of gold in the West, thousands of hopeful miners flocked to Colorado and California. Other men followed the miners. They looked for fertile soils, for building materials and water. Later the miners left in large numbers for newer strikes in Canada and Alaska. The men who followed the miners founded settlements that later became cities.

Today the search for valuable materials continues. Instead of a pickax and luck, modern prospectors use complex instruments to help detect deposits of metals. They travel in helicopters rather than with burros. The future of mankind depends partly on the success of scientists in locating new sources of fuel, metals, and water supplies.

You will discover the answers to many questions about earth materials in your work with this chapter: Of what are earth materials made? How do they change? How can you use them to uncover the history of the earth's changing surface? How are they distributed?

Earth materials may be in the solid, liquid, or gaseous state. Can you identify an example of earth materials in each state in this Pacific Ocean scene in the Hawaiian Islands?

From Planet to Atom

2-1 What is the earth made of?

You took an imaginary look at the earth from space in the Prologue. What could you tell about earth materials from such a distance? You could see the fascinating patterns of clouds swirled by the winds across the surface of the earth. Here and there openings in the cloud cover revealed dark patches of ocean and brighter spots of land. Clouds, land, ocean—how do they differ from each other? How can you use their differences to begin your study of the makeup or composition of the earth?

The solid outer shell of the earth, the crust, is called the **lithosphere.** This word comes from the Greek word *lithos*, meaning stone. The water in the vast oceans, flowing in rivers and streams, or locked in ice, is the **hydrosphere.** The air surrounding the earth and moving in currents around it forms the **atmosphere.** With these three terms you have begun to **classify,** or group, the regions of the earth. **Classification** consists of grouping together those things which have common characteristics or properties.

What do you see when you examine the materials of the earth in greater detail? As you look at the earth in Figure 2-1, you can see different characteristics in each scale of observation. Closer inspection of the land in Figure 2-1B reveals surface features that were not visible from a great distance. As you examine the surface of the earth in even more detail, you see that it is composed of a variety of materials. The building units of the crust shown in Figures 2-1C and D are called **rocks.** There are many kinds of rocks: Some are layered and some are not, some are white and others are black, some contain coarse grains and others show no grains. The more you look around, the greater the variety you see. You will need to classify this astonishing variety of rocks into smaller groups to find out more about them.

Classification is an important scientific tool because it enables you to sort a number of different objects into a few groups or classes of similar objects for easier study. This may sound easy, but can be quite difficult. You must use judgment in deciding which properties or characteristics should be used as a basis for classification. For instance, the first people who were curious about rocks may have grouped them on the basis of their color. This is a **descriptive classification** because it is based on an easily observed and described property. Did you ever start a rock collection? If you did, you can probably remember wondering how to group your rocks. As earth scientists examined and grouped rocks, it became clear that the color of rocks is not the most important property to use in classifying them.

The early study of rocks brought up a number of questions. Why are there so many kinds of rocks? How do rocks form? These questions led to further observations. Earth scientists observed that certain rocks occurred in layers and had many of the characteristics of the layers of sand and mud that are found in lakes and along the margins of oceans. Other rocks were seen to show the properties observed in the liquid rock matter that flows from volcanoes. Investigations of the ways in which rocks seem to be forming now eventually led to a genetic classification of rocks. A **genetic classification** is based on the genesis of a material or the way it was formed. Many properties are used to determine the probable manner of formation of a given rock. Genetic classifications require greater knowledge of the objects being grouped than descriptive classifications do. If you know how rocks form

Figure 2–1 *Focusing on earth materials at different scales: (A) earth from space, (B) Superstition Mountains, a large surface feature seen from an aircraft, (C) ground view of the Superstition Mountains from near Phoenix, Arizona, (D) rock specimen from Superstition Mountains, (E) photomicrograph of a thin section of the rock, (F) model of the internal structure of a mineral from the rock, and (G) model of an atom.*

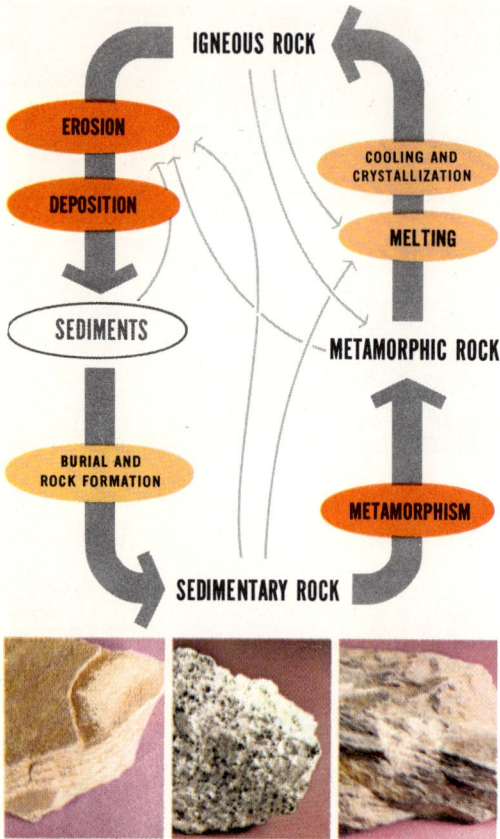

IGNEOUS ROCK

EROSION

DEPOSITION

COOLING AND
CRYSTALLIZATION

MELTING

SEDIMENTS

METAMORPHIC ROCK

BURIAL AND
ROCK FORMATION

METAMORPHISM

SEDIMENTARY ROCK

Figure 2–2 *The rock cycle represents the relationships between igneous, sedimentary, and metamorphic rocks. Can you tell which of the rocks pictured above is igneous? metamorphic? sedimentary? How did you decide?*

you can also discover what conditions existed on the earth at the time and place that a given rock was formed.

Figure 2–2 shows the relationship between the three principal genetic classes of rocks: igneous, sedimentary, and metamorphic rocks. This relationship is known as the **rock cycle. Igneous** rocks

form by the cooling and hardening of melted materials. (See Figure 2–3.) The word *"igneous"* comes from the Latin word for fire. Igneous rocks and other kinds of rocks exposed at the surface of the earth are subject to weathering. **Weathering** involves both the chemical and physical breakdown of rock exposed to the atmosphere and hydrosphere at the earth's surface.

The weathered rock that collects on the earth's surface is continually moved by water, wind, and ice. This process of moving materials is known as **erosion.** Erosion eventually carries much of the broken-down rock material to the oceans where it is spread in layers of sediments as shown in Figure 2–4.

The sands and other sediments that make up our beaches extend out along the bottom of the sea. In time they are covered by other sediments and may become pressed together to form rock. Such rocks are called **sedimentary rocks.** Sedimentary rocks can form from any type of rock that happens to be exposed at the earth's surface. (See Figure 2–2.)

Metamorphic rocks are formed from rocks that are heated or pressed together under high pressure for long periods of time. They form deep beneath the surface of the earth. Bricks are made by pressing and heating blocks of soft clay. In somewhat the same way metamorphic rocks form from sedimentary rocks. They may also form from igneous rocks. The type of metamorphic rock formed depends on the amount of heat and pressure and on the composition of the rock being changed. *Metamorphic* comes from Greek words for change and form.

Figure 2–3 *Hot lava from this volcanic eruption will form igneous rock as it cools. The island that you see rose above the surface of the Atlantic Ocean near Iceland in 1963.*

Figure 2–4
Weathered rock material from the continents is deposited in layers on the ocean floor.

2–2 Investigating rocks and minerals.

In your ordinary experience, you have seen many different kinds of rocks. Probably you can list at least a dozen rock types. Have you examined many kinds of rocks carefully however? Exactly how do they differ from each other?

Procedure

Part A · Rocks. To find out how rocks are different, take the rocks that are provided for you by your teacher and describe them as clearly as you can. (See Figure 2–5.) Use any word that seems to describe a particular characteristic best. Make a list of your descriptive words.

When each student's list is complete you will have a class discussion to make up a master list of descriptive terms. After the master list is finished, see if you can relate your rock specimens to the terms. Are some terms better than others for identifying rocks?

Figure 2–5 *A hand lens gives you a closer look at rock fragments.*

Part B · Rock Particles. In Part A of this investigation you examined several different kinds of rocks. In describing the rocks you probably noticed that they were made up of small grains of many different materials. In Part B of the investigation you will examine only one rock and some crushed material from that same rock. Separate the crushed material into piles of similar particles. (1)How many piles of material did you get? Look carefully at the materials in each pile and describe them in your own words. List the descriptive terms and compare them with the terms that you listed in Part A. (2)What is the difference between the two lists? The materials that you have separated from the crushed rock are minerals. (3)Which are easier to separate and describe, rocks or minerals? Why do you think this is true?

2–3 Can minerals be broken down into smaller parts?

You have examined some of the properties of minerals in Section 2–2, but probably you still do not know exactly what minerals are. Are they the smallest building units of the earth's crust or are they, like rocks, made up of combinations of smaller particles? Even microscopes fail to reveal any smaller parts in a mineral. On the basis of what you see, you might think that minerals are indeed

STAUROLITE

CHALCOPYRITE

FELDSPAR

QUARTZ

PYROXENE

GARNET

the smallest building units of the earth's crust and that they cannot be broken down into other substances. However, you have already learned that direct observation often does not provide a scientist with all the information he needs.

Examine the larger specimens of minerals again. You will notice that some of them appear in the form of crystals. **Crystals** are solids with naturally formed regular geometric shapes and smooth flat surfaces called **crystal faces.** These crystal faces show a definite pattern. If you measure the angles between matching faces of many crystals of a given mineral, you will find that they are always the same. (See Figure 2–6.) Each mineral has a typical crystal shape. The photographs above show crystals of some of the common minerals. However, minerals often form under crowded conditions in the earth's crust, and are hemmed in by other growing crystals so that the resulting minerals do not show flat faces. (See Figure 2–1E.)

What causes minerals to form in regular geometric shapes? Could there be smaller particles within the minerals, whose regular arrangement gives crystals their shape? You may guess that the pattern shown by the faces of a crys-

tal results from something inside the mineral. If this is so, then minerals must be made up of smaller parts, even though you cannot see them. How could you test this idea? One way is to heat the red mineral cinnabar in a test tube. (CAUTION: HEAT ONLY IN WELL-VENTILATED AREAS.) You will find that cinnabar gives off a yellow smoke that smells like sulfur and leaves shiny droplets of mercury in the test tube. The red mineral seems to be made up of at least two other substances as shown in Figure 2–7. Because cinnabar can be separated into other substances, it is known as a **compound.** The mercury and sulfur, on the other hand, cannot be broken down by ordinary chemical means. They are known as **elements.** Most minerals are compounds of two or more elements, but some like gold, silver, and diamond contain only one element. Whether they are compounds or elements, they are called minerals because they occur naturally.

The term *element* has a long history. Over 2000 years ago the Greek philosopher Aristotle taught that matter consists of the four "elements"—earth, air, fire, and water. (See Figure 2–8.) He believed that the properties of different

Figure 2–6 (*left*) *Although crystals of a substance may look different, the angles between their equivalent faces are always the same.*

Figure 2–7 *The red mineral, cinnabar (right), breaks down into mercury and fumes containing sulfur when heated.*

materials resulted from the different ways that these four elements were mixed together. Long before the time of Aristotle, men had discovered that if they heated a certain soft red rock with charcoal, it would change into a much harder gray material called iron. This change was thought of as a re-arrangement of the elements fire, water, earth, and air in the red rock. Why then, reasoned some Egyptian experimenters, couldn't the gray metal be changed into shiny yellow gold? Thus was born the "science" of **alchemy,** the search for a way to change common earth materials into valuable gold.

Alchemy was practiced over a span of many centuries. Although the alchemists never succeeded in making gold, they did make many valuable scientific dis-coveries. They finally realized that cer-tain substances like iron, mercury, gold, and sulfur could not be broken down, or changed into other materials. The al-chemists concluded that iron which they were able to extract from certain red rocks must have been present in the rock as metallic iron.

How many elements can you name? You are probably aware of many from your own experience. The soft black

lead in your pencil called graphite is a form of the element carbon. The bright yellow element, gold, gleams in rings and watches. Shiny liquid mercury rises in thermometers. There are both oxygen and nitrogen in the air around you. These are only a few of the chemical elements found in nature. A few of the elements are pictured in Figure 2–9 and you will find a complete list of all the elements in Appendix C.

Figure 2–8 *The world composed of the four elements of matter according to Aristotle's theory, as pictured by an artist. The elements of earth and water in the center were surrounded by the element of air within a ring of elemental fire.*

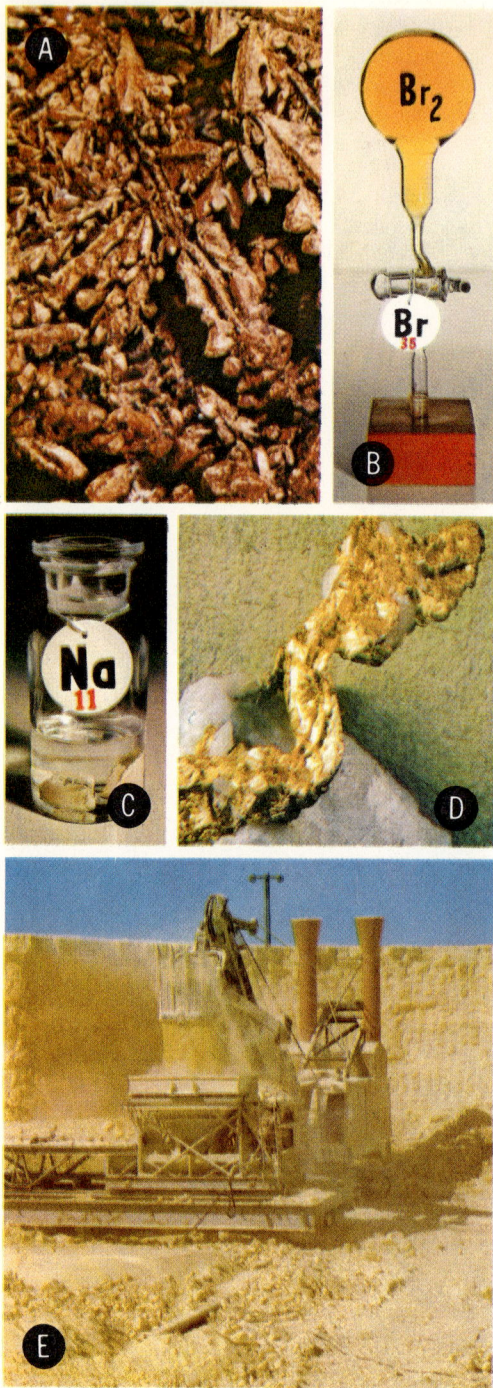

Figure 2–9 *These elements are but a few of the 90 chemical elements found in nature. (A) Native copper from northern Michigan. (B) Bromine, a gas at room temperature. (C) Sodium, an active metal, must be stored in oil. (D) Native gold found in California. (E) Sulfur being transferred to a conveyor belt at Port Sulphur, Louisiana.*

ACTIVITY *Make a list of all the elements with which you are familiar. At room temperature, how many of these elements occur as solids? as liquids? as gases?*

You have found that **minerals** are naturally occurring solids, composed of one or more elements. Are elements then the smallest parts into which matter can be broken? If so, what makes the elements different from each other? Do elements account for the tendency of minerals to form crystals? Questions such as these led scientists to a theory explaining even smaller parts of minerals and elements—atoms.

2–4 Atoms and their parts are earth building units.

The theory that earth materials have an internal structure of small indivisible particles is not a new one. It was first proposed more than two thousand years ago by a Greek, Democritus, who suggested that all matter is made up of tiny particles called atoms. Democritus's idea was not generally accepted in his own time, and for many centuries it was regarded as an oddity. The atomic theory of matter was not established until the seventeenth century.

The English scientist John Dalton laid the foundation for the modern atomic theory in 1808. He proposed the following ideas to explain the differences between elements and to account for the ways in which gases and other materials behaved. (1) All substances are composed of small, solid, indestructible particles called **atoms.** (2) The atoms of a given substance have the same size shape, and volume. (3) The atom is the smallest particle of an element that enters into a chemical change. (4) Combinations of the atoms of two or more elements form a compound. Scientists later discovered that the differences between atoms of different elements resulted from the arrangement of even smaller particles within the atom. Thus John Dalton's indestructible atoms were broken down and today a large number of subatomic particles are known.

The main building units of the atom are electrons, protons, and neutrons. The electron was the first particle to be recognized as a basic part of all atoms, largely as a result of the discovery that electricity consists of a stream of electrons. Each **electron** has a negative (−) electrical charge. Since atoms themselves do not have negative electrical charges, scientists reasoned that there must be another particle in the atom with a positive (+) charge to balance the electron's negative charge. The proton was soon discovered. **Protons** have more than 1800 times as much mass as electrons and carry a positive charge. In 1932, particles with about the same mass as protons but with no electrical charge were discovered and named **neutrons.**

Once the main parts of an atom were known, scientists began to form a mental picture or mental model of it. In studying matter, scientists found that atoms

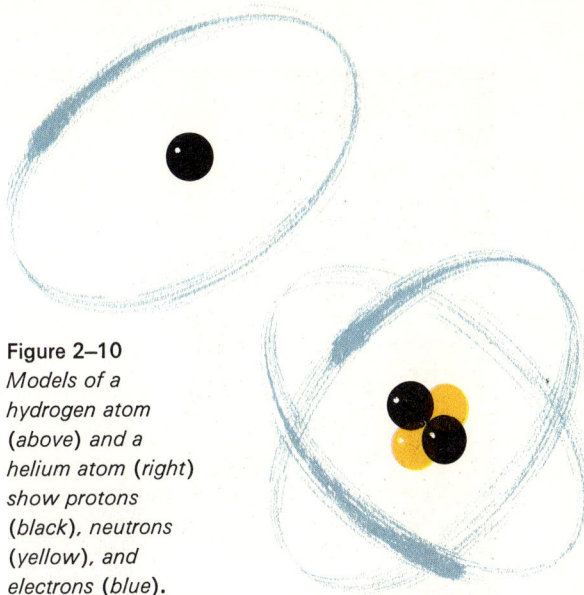

Figure 2–10
Models of a hydrogen atom (above) and a helium atom (right) show protons (black), neutrons (yellow), and electrons (blue).

behave as if they were tiny spheres with a **nucleus,** or center, composed of protons and neutrons, surrounded by clouds of electrons. Each atom has the same number of protons as electrons. Thus, the positive and negative charges balance each other, and the atom behaves as a stable unit. A model of the simplest atom, the hydrogen atom, is shown in Figure 2–10. This hydrogen atom has no neutron, and only one proton and

Equipment that shoots atomic particles into a target. The smashing of atoms in the target yields information about their parts.

What Is a Model?

The way the word *model* is used here may be new to you. Obviously it means something different from model trains or model airplanes. Models of trains and airplanes, globes, and the like, are **physical models** that you can see and touch. Some models, however, exist only in the mind. They are a kind of mental picture of something, such as what may be inside the earth or what an atom is made of. These are called **mental models.** Is it possible to make a physical model from a mental model?

one electron. The slightly more complex helium atom, (See Figure 2–10.) has all three particles. Since protons and neutrons are 1800 times heavier than electrons, most of the mass of an atom is concentrated in its nucleus.

This model of the atom helps you to understand why different elements have different properties. The subatomic particles are the same in all atoms, but they vary in number and arrangement. The properties of atoms of different elements are determined by the number of protons in the nucleus. An **element** is a substance in which all the atoms have the same positive charge in the nucleus. Why is this a better definition of an element than the first definition you learned? (An **element** is a substance that cannot be broken down into other substances by ordinary chemical means.) Both definitions are true. However, one is more specific than the other.

The fact that elements cannot be further broken down by ordinary chemical means was discovered experimentally. After the atomic theory had been formed, and the subatomic particles had been discovered, scientists knew *why* elements behave the way they do. They found that an element could be broken down into another element if its atoms were split. Splitting an atom changes the positive charge in the nucleus. This new definition of an element is based on a theory of its inner structure and is therefore much more useful. Definitions improve as knowledge increases and theories are tested.

Many attempts have been made to visualize or make a model of the way electrons are arranged around the nucleus of an atom. The earliest model resembled a solar system, with the nucleus surrounded by electrons circling it in definite paths like planets around the sun. Advances in physics have shown this model to be inaccurate, though it is still sometimes used for simplicity. The motions of electrons cannot be pictured accurately in a diagram. Such diagrams, as those in Figure 2–10, are commonly used to suggest the motion of electrons.

You have already learned that most minerals are compounds. In other words, most minerals are composed of several elements. How do the atoms of elements combine to form compounds? The answer lies in the forces within the atom. The forces that hold atoms together are largely electrical in nature. The farther an electron is from the nucleus, the more readily it can take part in chemical reactions. These outer electrons may be transferred from one atom to another or shared between atoms in compounds. When an atom loses an electron, it has fewer electrons than protons and its electrical charges no longer balance. Therefore, it has a positive charge. If an atom gains an electron, it has more electrons than protons, which gives it a negative charge. Such atoms are no longer stable, balanced units, and they are called **ions**. Because ions are electrically unbalanced they are apt to combine with ions of opposite charge to reach a balanced state.

All atoms of one element are not necessarily alike. Atoms of one element have the same number of electrons and protons, but the number of neutrons can vary. The presence or absence of a neutron does not change the charge of the atom. For instance, if a neutron were added to the hydrogen atom, the new atom, deuterium, shown in Figure 2–11, would still behave like ordinary hydrogen chemically, but it would have almost twice as much mass. Atoms of an element that differ in mass because they have different numbers of neutrons are

Figure 2–11
*Compare this model
of the deuterium
atom, an isotope,
with the hydrogen
atom model that
appears in
Figure 2–10.*

called **isotopes.** Scientists have discovered that isotopes of many elements occur in nature. Some of the isotopes are unstable; they decay or break down to other isotopes by giving off nuclear particles and energy. These are known as **radioactive isotopes.**

Because the names of some elements are too long to use easily, a system of chemical symbols is used to identify them. The symbols are a kind of shorthand for the names of the elements, like H for hydrogen, O for oxygen, and Ca for calcium. To avoid using the same symbol for elements starting with the same letter, scientists sometimes use the first letters of the Greek or Latin word

for the element. For instance, the symbol for sodium, Na, comes from the Latin word *natrium* (NAY-tree-uhm). In a chemical formula, numbers added to a symbol indicate the ratios of elements in a compound. The chemical formula for lime is CaO, since it contains one atom of calcium for each atom of oxygen. Lime is made by heating a kind of rock called limestone. The chemical formula for calcite, the most common mineral in limestone, is $CaCO_3$. What is the ratio of the elements in calcite?

Thought and Discussion . . .

1. Why do scientists classify things?
2. How does a descriptive classification differ from a genetic classification?
3. What is the difference between a rock and a mineral?
4. How are the atoms of one element different from the atoms of another?
5. The alchemists never succeeded in making precious metals out of common material. Was their work useful? Do you think that they were scientists?

Atoms and Molecules in Earth Materials

2–5 Gases and liquids contain groups of atoms called molecules.

Air is known to consist chiefly of the elements nitrogen and oxygen. These elements exist in air as **molecules.** The oxygen molecule, for example, consists of two oxygen atoms (O_2), as shown in

Figure 2–12 *Molecular oxygen. Two linked oxygen atoms make up the oxygen molecule.*

Figure 2–12. These are joined together by sharing electrons. In a gas such as air these and other molecules move about rapidly, colliding with each other.

Almost everyone recognizes H_2O, the formula for the water molecule. This molecule consists of one oxygen atom and two hydrogen atoms held together by forces that are electrical in nature. In a liquid such as water the individual molecules move about, but they are, of course, much more crowded than the molecules of a gas. Even though they are closely packed together, the molecules of a liquid do not show an orderly arrangement or pattern.

Figure 2–13 *The shape of the sodium chloride crystal (above) expresses its internal atomic pattern shown in the model (above, right).*

Figure 2–14 *Both pieces of quartz have the same internal atomic arrangement. Which is a crystal? Which is crystalline?*

A sodium chloride crystal (table salt) and a model of its atomic structure are shown in Figure 2–13. Sodium chloride is a crystalline solid, and when it occurs naturally as a mineral, it is given the name **halite.** Notice how the orderly arrangement of ions in the model accounts for the shape of the mineral and for the shapes of the broken fragments. The formula for sodium chloride is NaCl. However, scientists never speak of one

Water in its liquid state (left, below) and solid state (center). Water may change from its vapor state into either liquid raindrops or solid ice crystals in clouds (right). Can you think of other ways in which water exists in any of its three states?

NaCl molecule. With one sodium ion and one chloride ion, the six-sided pattern shown by the NaCl crystal could not be built. The atoms of crystalline solids are arranged in regular patterns. The basic units of these patterns cannot be built with only a few atoms. The term molecule, therefore, is not useful in describing a mineral.

The regular internal pattern of atoms determines the external shapes of mineral crystals. All minerals have this orderly internal atomic arrangement and are thus said to be **crystalline.** Only a few of the mineral specimens that you see will have crystal faces because most minerals grew under crowded conditions or they were broken. The contrast, between a crystal and a crystalline substance that is not a crystal is shown by the photograph of a quartz crystal and quartz fragment in Figure 2–14.

Have you ever stopped to think that water commonly occurs in its three forms in your immediate surroundings? The ice cubes in cold drinks, the raindrops on a window, and the invisible vapor above water boiling in a pot are examples of the solid, liquid, and gaseous forms of water. These forms are known as **states of matter.** Can you think of any other material on the earth's surface that normally occurs in all three states?

Knowing that the water molecule is composed of two parts hydrogen and

one part oxygen gives no clue to its unusual properties. It is the special way the hydrogen and oxygen ions are joined together that accounts for the properties and behavior of water. Figure 2–15 shows a model of the way scientists believe that atoms are arranged in the water molecule. Because the hydrogens carry a positive charge and are both on one side of the molecule, that side becomes more positively charged than the side with the negative oxygen. The water molecule thus has two ends or poles, one of which is negatively charged and the other positively, so it is said to be a **dipolar** molecule.

The positive and negative charged ends of the water molecule cause it to attract other water molecules. The negative ends of some molecules are attracted to the positive ends of others. Even though the water molecules are fairly free to move about, their attraction for each other holds them together more tightly than if they were not dipolar. For example, scientists have calculated that water would boil below 0° Celsius rather than at 100° Celsius if the molecules were not attracted to one another. The Celsius temperature scale is described and compared with the Fahrenheit scale in Appendix B. Celsius is usually abbreviated as C.

The dipolar attraction of water molecules is responsible for another property of water that you have all observed— the property of surface tension. Have you ever filled a glass to the top and then added a little more water so that the water surface was actually higher than the top of the glass? Surface tension, resulting from the strong attraction of the molecules, acts as a thin skin across the top of the water surface.

ACTIVITY *Carefully place a clean needle or a razor blade on top of a quiet water surface. What happens? Why?*

One of water's most important properties is its ability to dissolve many substances. Can you think of any reason why the dipolar nature of the water molecule might help it to dissolve other materials? How does water dissolve the salt, sodium chloride? **Salts** are combinations of positive and negative ions held together by electrical charges. Ordinary salt, NaCl, is made up of positive sodium ions and negative chloride ions. When salt dissolves in water, the salt's constituent ions must be loosened from their fixed positions. The ions from the salt are surrounded by a cluster of water molecules, with their positive ends

Figure 2–15 *Water molecule models (left, below).*
Figure 2–16 *Clusters of water molecules around a sodium ion and a chloride ion (center, below). Is the sodium ion on the left or right?*
Figure 2–17 *Water molecules in ice (right, below).*

toward negative chloride ions (Cl—) and their negative ends toward positive sodium ions (Na+). If enough water molecules do this, their force of attraction becomes great enough to break the ions free, as shown in Figure 2–16. How do you think the properties of water might change after you add salt? Do you know why salt is spread on icy roads? Why doesn't ocean water freeze as readily as fresh water?

When water freezes to ice, the molecules arrange themselves in a pattern. A diagram of this pattern is shown in Figure 2–17. Do you think that ice is a mineral? There is more space between the water molecules in solid ice than in liquid water. Water expands as it freezes. Therefore ice is less dense than water and will float. How do you think the world would change if ice suddenly became more dense than water?

2–6 Many minerals form only under special conditions.

In investigating rock and mineral properties, you learned it is possible to identify and classify minerals on the basis of these properties. These properties express the arrangement of the atoms in the minerals. Scientists cannot see this internal atomic structure, but they can now determine it by X-ray studies.

Many elements and compounds exist in more than one mineral form. Differences in the arrangement of carbon atoms produce the two minerals, diamond and graphite. You can see this difference in arrangement in Figure 2–18. Both these minerals are composed only of carbon, yet diamond is the hardest natural substance known and graphite is so flaky and soft that it is used as a lubricant. What caused the carbon atoms to combine into the diamond pat-

Figure 2–18 *The arrangement of carbon atoms (above) in diamond (left) and graphite (right) determines their physical properties.*

Figure 2–19 *The same chemical compound iron sulfide (FeS₂) occurs in two mineral forms, pyrite (left, below) and marcasite (right, below).*

tern in one instance and into the graphite pattern in another? Why does the FeS_2 shown in Figure 2–19 occur in different forms? Scientists have tried to answer some of these questions by making minerals in the laboratory. In 1955, after many years of trying, they succeeded in producing artificial diamonds. Before then all efforts to make carbon crystallize into the diamond form resulted in the formation of graphite. Success in forming diamonds was achieved by using extremely high pressures.

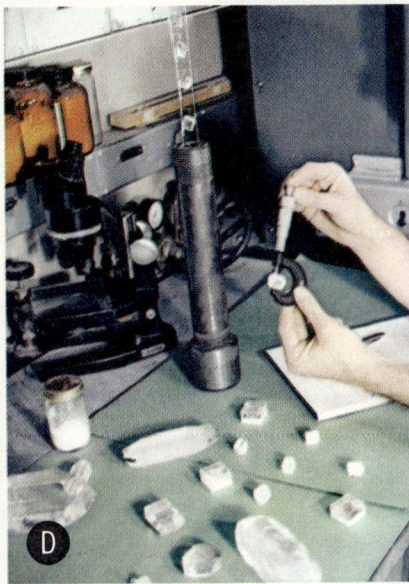

Copper ore is mined in an open-pit copper mine (A), in Bingham Canyon, Utah, (B) gold ore was once mined in this abandoned mine in Colorado, and (C) molten iron is poured into an open-hearth furnace. Quartz crystals are grown in the laboratory (D), phosphate rock is mined in Florida (E), and synthetic diamonds are formed under high temperatures and pressures (F).

Knowing this, what can you conclude about past conditions in the part of the crust where a diamond crystal is found?

The diamond-graphite example illustrates the importance of the internal structure of solids. The mineral form, determined by the internal structure, reflects the conditions under which the substance grew. Some minerals form only at high temperatures. If the atoms of which they are composed combine at low temperatures, a different structure or mineral will form. Other minerals, such as diamond, form only under high pressure. Still others are the product of certain chemical conditions. The two forms of FeS_2 shown in Figure 2–19, represent the combination of iron and sulfur under different chemical conditions.

Minerals that form only under special conditions are of great importance to the geologist in his job of working out the history of the earth. The geologist can learn from laboratory studies that a certain mineral forms only at a temperature above 300°C. When he finds this mineral in a rock, he can infer that the temperature must have been at least 300°C at the time and place the rock was formed. Groups of minerals are even more useful clues to past conditions on earth because some minerals can form together under one set of conditions, but not under another. Minerals are like words in the story of the earth, and groups of minerals or rocks are like sentences. The earth scientist can use them to read the story of the earth's past.

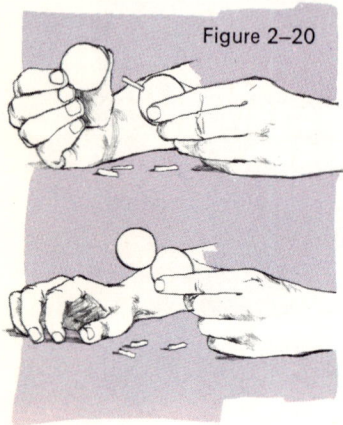

Figure 2–20

2–7 Investigating the 'Big O'.

You have learned that oxygen is an important element in air and water. It may surprise you to learn that oxygen is also the major element in minerals. How does the oxygen atom combine with atoms of other elements to form the various materials at the earth's surface?

In this investigation you will construct physical models of the way in which oxygen atoms combine with atoms of other elements. The models which you make will then be physical models representing mental models.

Procedure

Begin by joining two of the large spheres with pipe cleaners. (See Figure 2–20.) This is a model of an oxygen molecule (O_2), and it shows the main way in which oxygen exists in the atmosphere. Next, connect two small spheres to another of the large spheres so that the centers of the small spheres are about 105 degrees apart. (1)Why is a water molecule said to be dipolar like a magnet? (2)How would you arrange two water molecules close together in such a way that they will attract each other? (3)What difference would it make in the way water behaves if the molecule were constructed as shown in Figure 2–21?

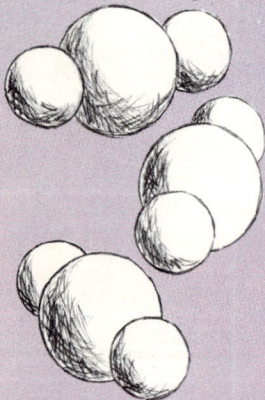

Figure 2–21

Next take four of the large spheres (oxygen atoms) and one of the small spheres (silicon atom) and put them together as compactly as possible. All of the oxygen atoms should be at an equal distance from the silicon atom. This is a model of a silicon-oxygen tetrahedron—the basic pattern of oxygen and silicon in the silicate minerals of the crust. The ratio of silicon to oxygen in this tetrahedron is one to four, so its formula is SiO_4. Build a second tetrahedron in the same way as the first. Now join the two tetrahedrons in such a way that they share one oxygen atom, as shown in Figure 2–22. Try to build a chain of tetrahedrons. (4)What would be the silicon-oxygen ratio in this chain?

Figure 2–22

(5)From what you have learned in this investigation and the information in Section 2–8, what element do you think makes up the greatest percentage of the earth's crust? (6)How is the internal arrangement of the atoms in a mineral indicated by what you can see when you examine it?

2–8 Mineral properties are related to atomic structure.

Silicon combines with oxygen and other common elements to form the **silicate minerals.** These minerals are by far the most abundant type of material in the earth's crust. They may be used to illustrate the relation between internal atomic arrangement and physical characteristics of minerals. Remember that the same ideas apply to all minerals.

In all of the silicate minerals, silicon and oxygen are joined in a tetrahedral (four-sided) arrangement so that four oxygen atoms surround each silicon atom. The chemical formula is SiO_4. These silicon-oxygen tetrahedrons may occur singly in the crystal structure or they may join together by sharing oxygen atoms as illustrated in Figure 2–23. The different internal arrangements determine the properties of the four common rock-forming silicate minerals pictured in Figure 2–23 as follows:

Figure 2–23 *Silica tetrahedrons share oxygen atoms in different patterns as shown by the models below. The pattern of sharing determines the physical properties of silicate minerals.*

1. The mineral **olivine** is an iron magnesium silicate. The silicon-oxygen tetrahedrons occur singly in the structure and they are bonded together by the iron and magnesium atoms. Olivine breaks in an irregular fashion.

2. The mineral **hornblende** is also an iron magnesium silicate, but in this mineral the silicon-oxygen tetrahedrons form chains by sharing alternately two and then three oxygen atoms. Hornblende breaks into long narrow pieces.

3. The **micas** are a group of silicates in which the silicon-oxygen tetrahedrons share three oxygen atoms to form continuous sheets. This structure is reflected in the flaky way micas break.

4. The mineral **quartz** is composed only of silicon and oxygen. Each tetrahedron shares four oxygen atoms with neighboring tetrahedrons to form a continuous framework. Quartz is hard and breaks irregularly, which suggests that there are no special weaknesses in any direction in the mineral.

Feldspars, which are the most common silicate minerals in the earth's crust, are structurally related to quartz. The tetra-

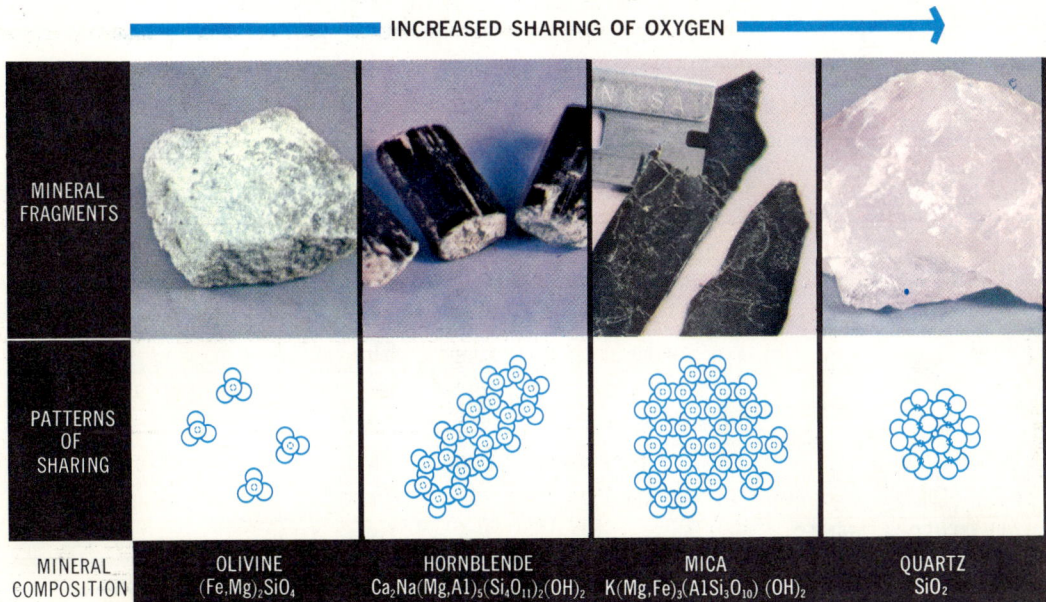

INCREASED SHARING OF OXYGEN

MINERAL FRAGMENTS

PATTERNS OF SHARING

| MINERAL COMPOSITION | OLIVINE $(Fe,Mg)_2SiO_4$ | HORNBLENDE $Ca_2Na(Mg,Al)_5(Si_4O_{11})_2(OH)_2$ | MICA $K(Mg,Fe)_3(AlSi_3O_{10})(OH)_2$ | QUARTZ SiO_2 |

hedrons are shared in a three-dimensional pattern but aluminum atoms take the place of some of the silicon atoms, and other elements (potassium, sodium, and calcium) occur. The presence of these atoms causes feldspars to break along regular planes unlike quartz.

The relation between the internal atomic arrangement of minerals and their physical properties is not always as clear as the examples in Figure 2–23 may indicate. Other factors such as the elements in a mineral and how its atoms are bonded also affect its properties.

Thought and Discussion . . .

1. Why is the term molecule not useful in describing a crystalline solid like sodium chloride?
2. How are minerals useful in reconstructing past earth conditions?
3. Air, water, and minerals all contain atoms. Why, then, are these materials so different?
4. Why is it useful to study the formation of minerals in the laboratory?
5. Are the properties of minerals mainly the result of their chemical composition or are other factors more important?

Abundance of the Elements

2–9 What is the chemical composition of the earth's crust?

Have you ever eaten oxygen? Did you ever drink oxygen? Have you ever been hit on the head with some oxygen? You already know that you must breathe oxygen to live and that water is mostly oxygen. However, you may not have realized that the rock you studied in the investigation in Section 2–2 is almost all oxygen.

It may come as a surprise to you to learn that oxygen, which you think of as a gas, is the major element of the solid crust. Oxygen is *not* the most abundant element in the atmosphere. Surprising is the fact that oxygen makes up almost 94 percent of the crust by volume. This is because the oxygen atom is so large compared to the atoms of other common elements like silicon or aluminum. You can think of the earth's crust as a framework of oxygen atoms with the smaller atoms of other elements fitting into spaces between the oxygen atoms.

TABLE 2–1   THE AVERAGE CHEMICAL COMPOSITION OF THE EARTH'S CRUST

ELEMENT	SYMBOL	PERCENTAGE	
		BY WEIGHT IN CRUST	BY VOLUME IN CRUST
OXYGEN	O	46.6	93.8
SILICON	Si	27.7	0.9
ALUMINUM	Al	8.1	0.5
IRON	Fe	5.0	0.4
CALCIUM	Ca	3.6	1.0
SODIUM	Na	2.8	1.3
POTASSIUM	K	2.6	1.8
MAGNESIUM	Mg	2.1	0.3
ALL OTHER ELEMENTS	—	1.5	—
TOTAL		100.0	100.0

How abundant are such seemingly common elements as copper, lead, iron or zinc in the materials of the earth's crust? To answer this question, you must realize that the crust of the earth makes up over 95 percent of the combined mass of the crust, hydrosphere, and atmosphere. The average composition of the earth's crust is shown in Table 2–1. The values given here are based on averages of chemical analyses of rocks from all over the world.

Seemingly common elements like carbon, copper, nickel, lead, and sulfur do not appear in Table 2–1 because they each make up less than one percent of the crust. Eight elements listed in the table together account for 98.5 percent of the crust. All of the 80 or so other elements together make up only 1.5 percent of the crust. Copper, for example, makes up only 0.0045 percent, lead only 0.0015, and gold only 0.0000007 percent of the average crust. Small wonder that the prospectors mentioned at the beginning of the chapter have to search hard for these metals.

Where are such important elements as copper and lead found if they are so rare? The earth's crust is in a constant state of change. The various processes that produce change often act to increase the concentration of some elements in certain localities. As a result, the earth's crust has a highly variable composition. Fortunately there are small, local areas where copper, for example, may make up as much as 2 to 20 percent of the rock. A quartz vein, a source of gold, and concentrated sources for other earth materials are shown in Figure 2–24.

How are the chemical elements listed in Table 2–1 combined in the crust? Your investigation in Section 2–7 showed you that many of these elements occur as silicates, as compounds of silicon and

Antoine Lavoisier

Antoine Lavoisier, the son of a wealthy lawyer, was born in Paris in 1743. Although his father wished him to study law, Lavoisier soon decided that his interest lay in science. He began to study geology and at 21 studied the composition of the mineral gypsum. Lavoisier's interest soon turned to chemistry. In 1768, at only 25, he was invited to join the French Academy of Sciences.

Lavoisier began to experiment with air in 1772. He and some other chemists placed a diamond in a closed vessel and focused sunlight on it with a magnifying glass. The diamond disappeared and carbon dioxide gas filled the vessel. When Lavoisier tried the experiment without air in the vessel, the diamond would not disappear. This convinced Lavoisier that diamonds were made of carbon.

From such experiments Lavoisier concluded that burning takes place when a material combines with oxygen. This discovery of the true nature of burning gave chemistry its modern basis. Lavoisier was the first to announce that air consisted of several gases, one of which supported burning. In 1789 he published a classic textbook, Elementary Treatise on Chemistry. It was the first modern chemical textbook and contained a list of all the elements then known.

oxygen together with other atoms. The feldspars are the most abundant silicates in the crust. In fact, they account for about 60 percent of all minerals.

2–10 What elements are most common in the atmosphere and hydrosphere?

Water consists of 88.9 percent oxygen and 11.1 percent hydrogen by weight. Again the oxygen atom is by far the most abundant component of the hydrosphere. Does the hydrosphere contain any other elements? You must guess that it does if you have ever tasted seawater or the water of salty lakes. Almost every element found in the crust is present in seawater in very small amounts. Chemical analyses of samples of seawater show that it contains 3.5 percent dissolved materials. The principal ions in solution are the sodium ion and the chloride ion, the elements in ordinary table salt. You will learn why these ions are in the sea when you study the water cycle.

Does air, like water, have a uniform composition? This question was answered only some 200 years ago by Antoine Lavoisier (La-vwah-ZYAY) now known as the father of modern chemistry. In the 1770's Lavoisier performed a brilliant series of experiments with air.

In one experiment he heated mercury in a bottle exposed to a fixed amount of air in a large bell jar. For 12 days he heated the mercury at just under its boiling point. He noticed that at first red particles formed on the mercury. The particles stopped forming before the 12 days were up. Lavoisier made corrections for changes in air pressure and temperature and calculated that the original 800 cubic centimeters of air in the bell jar had been reduced to between 685 and 670 cubic centimeters.

Lavoisier reasoned or hypothesized that the 115 to 130 cubic centimeters of air had somehow been taken up by the mercury to form the red particles. He found that the gas remaining in the bell jar was less dense than ordinary air. It put out the flame of a candle and quickly suffocated a mouse. Lavoisier called this gas "azote." You know it as nitrogen. He then collected the red mercuric particles and heated them to a high temperature to test his hypothesis. They gave off between 115 and 130 cubic centimeters of gas, the amount previ-

Figure 2–24 (*Left to right*) *A drilling rig is used to search for oil in the waters off southern Texas. Granite blocks are cut from the solid rock in a deep quarry at Barre, Vermont. The white vein of quartz in the photo is a source of gold. The geologist's hammer shows the scale. Evaporation of the water of a salt lake in Australia yields many salts.*

TABLE 2–2 COMPOSITION OF THE ATMO-
SPHERE AT SEA LEVEL—EXCLUDING WATER

NAME	CHEMICAL COMPOSITION	PERCENTAGE BY VOLUME
NITROGEN	N_2	78.1
OXYGEN	O_2	20.9
ARGON	Ar	0.9
CARBON DIOXIDE	CO_2	0.03
OTHER MATERIALS		0.07
TOTAL		100.00

ously removed from the air. This gas made candles flame more brightly and did not suffocate a mouse. He called it "air eminently respirable, pure or vital." It was later named oxygen. The red particles were mercuric oxide.

Many advances have been made since Lavoisier conducted his famous experiment. We now know from many chemical analyses that air has a uniform composition compared to the lithosphere. Two gases, oxygen and nitrogen, account for 99 percent of the gases in the lower atmosphere. (See Table 2–2.) Carbon dioxide is a very small but important part of air. Carbon dioxide absorbs much of the heat that is radiated toward space from the earth's surface.

The earth's atmosphere is never quite dry. Water may make up as much as 3 percent of the atmosphere in very moist conditions. Because of this wide variation from almost 0 percent to about 3 percent, water is not entered in Table 2–2. You see some of this water as clouds, but most of it you cannot see for it is in vapor form. The importance of this small amount of water in the atmosphere will become evident in future chapters.

In this chapter we have identified three basic spheres of earth material. It should be kept in mind that the interfaces between them are not sharp. We find that the atmosphere contains both water and solid earth materials; the lithosphere contains both water and air; and the hydrosphere contains both air and solid earth materials. You will see in the next chapter that the earth's atmosphere, hydrosphere, and crust make up only a small part of the entire earth. To determine the relative sizes of the various parts of the earth, you must measure the planet. How would you measure the circumference of the earth? Some of the ways in which scientists have made this measurement are discussed in the next chapter.

Thought and Discussion . . .

1. The atmosphere and the hydrosphere have remarkably uniform composition when compared to the lithosphere of the earth. Why is this so?
2. If the crust contains such small amounts of elements like copper and lead, how can man obtain these useful materials?
3. What, if anything, is the significance of the fact that oxygen is a major constituent of the atmosphere, the hydrosphere, and the lithosphere?
4. Look up the composition of the sun in an encyclopedia. How does the earth differ from the sun in composition?

Unsolved Problems Although the average composition of the atmosphere, hydrosphere, and lithosphere is reasonably well known today, scientists are uncertain how these spheres have changed in composition with time. Were the seas as deep and extensive a billion years ago as they are today? Did they contain the same quantity of dissolved materials then? Was the atmosphere composed of the same gases in the geologic past? If not, when did the present composition of the atmosphere develop?

Much remains to be learned about the environments or conditions under which minerals form. Scientists use minerals as guides to past conditions on earth and in order to do this they must determine experimentally the conditions necessary for their formation in the laboratory. This work is complicated by the fact that many variables are involved. A given mineral may form only at high temperatures under one set of conditions, but in the presence of certain other minerals or solutions it may form under completely different conditions. In order to use minerals to interpret past conditions, scientists must recognize all of the variables that can affect mineral formation.

CHAPTER REVIEW

Summary

In this chapter you have looked at earth materials from several vantage points—far out in space, close up with the unaided eye, and even closer with a magnifier in the laboratory. You have learned how scientists discovered the invisible basic parts of all matter, the atoms. You have seen that most of the different earth materials are made up of only a few elements. The way in which atoms of these elements are combined determines the characteristics of a substance. Oxygen is the most abundant element in the earth's crust and in its waters, as well as being an important part of air.

Early scientists, in an effort to bring order to their studies, classified the various earth materials. You have seen how their initial observations led them to investigate the origin of rocks. As these questions were answered, scientists were able to move from descriptive to genetic classifications.

You have learned that the silicate minerals are the most common minerals in the crust and that the feldspars are the most abundant silicates. Finally, you discovered that the characteristics of water and the composition of the hydrosphere result from the nature of the water molecule.

Questions and Problems

A

1. How do the three main types of rocks form?
2. What is the definition of a mineral?
3. What is the difference between an element and a compound?
4. How can the shape of its crystal faces help to identify a mineral?
5. What is an ion?
6. What subatomic particles form the nucleus of an atom?
7. Is ice more dense than water or less dense?
8. How does the abundance of metals in the earth's crust compare with the abundance of oxygen?
9. What did Lavoisier learn about air?

B

1. What is the difference between an atom and an ion?
2. What keeps atoms together in a compound?
3. How was the practice of alchemy important to the development of modern science?
4. Why do minerals appear in the form of crystals?

5. Sketch the arrangement of protons, neutrons, and electrons in helium.
6. If water is composed of two parts of hydrogen and only one part of oxygen, why does oxygen make up most of the mass of the hydrosphere?

C

1. John Dalton proposed that all substances are composed of small, solid, indestructible particles called atoms. Are atoms still considered to be small, solid, and indestructible? Explain.
2. How does salt (NaCl) dissolve in water?
3. What difference in structure accounts for the fact that mica flakes whereas quartz breaks irregularly?
4. Look at Table 2–1. Which atom has the larger volume, the Fe atom or the Na atom?

Suggested Readings

BOOKS

Davis, Kenneth S. and John Arthur Day. *Water: The Mirror of Science.* Doubleday & Company, Inc., Garden City, N.Y., 1961.

Day, F. H. *The Chemical Elements in Nature.* Reinhold Publishing Corp., New York, 1963.

Dennen, William H. *Principles of Mineralogy,* rev. ed. The Ronald Press Company, New York, 1960.

Gilluly, James, A. C. Waters, and A. O. Woodford. *Principles of Geology.* W. H. Freeman & Co., Publishers, 1959.

Grunwald, Ernest and Russell H. Johnson. *Atoms, Molecules and Chemical Change,* 2nd ed. Prentice-Hall, Inc., Englewood Cliffs, N.J., 1965.

Harland, W. B. *The Earth: Rocks, Minerals, and Fossils.* Franklin Watts, Inc., New York, 1960.

Longwell, C. R. and R. F. Flint. *Introduction to Physical Geology,* 2nd ed. John Wiley & Sons, Inc., New York, 1962.

McKie, Douglas. *Antoine Lavoisier, Scientist, Economist, Social Reformer.* Abelard-Schuman Limited, New York, 1952.

Pearl, Richard M. *How to Know the Minerals and Rocks.* McGraw-Hill Book Company, New York, 1955.

Pough, Frederick H. *A Field Guide to Rocks and Minerals.* Houghton Mifflin Company, Boston, 1960.

Spar, Jerome. *Earth, Sea, and Air: A Survey of the Geophysical Sciences.* Addison-Wesley Publishing Co., Inc., Reading, Mass., 1962.

Strahler, Arthur N. *The Earth Sciences.* Harper & Row, Publishers, New York, 1963. Chapter 19, Rocks and Minerals.

PERIODICALS

Germer, Lester H. "The Structure of Crystal Surfaces." *Scientific American,* March, 1965.

Potter, P. E. "Sedimentary Origins of Rock Layering." *Natural History,* December, 1965.

Geologists exploring for mineral deposits in remote areas find helicopters useful.

Chapter 3 Earth Measurement

Almost from the day you were born, you have been exploring. Your natural curiosity leads you constantly to extend the limits of your experience. From the beginning men have been exploring as you have, pushing back the limits of their known world. Thousands of years have gone by and millions of people have lived and died without knowing a fraction of what you know right now. How is this possible?

One of the things unknown to men of old is something you learned in elementary school or before — that the earth is round. You learned this many years ago, but could you present convincing evidence for it? Could you prove to someone who questioned that the earth is round?

The picture above was taken during the flight of the Gemini 10 spacecraft. From this altitude of 330 kilometers above the Atlantic Ocean, can you identify the Strait of Gibraltar and the Mediterranean Sea beyond the Strait? What else does the photograph show about the earth?

To find out about the size and shape of this planet, you will have to use methods of investigation very different from those you used to study the

Compare the Gemini photograph (left) and the ancient map (right) with a modern map of the Mediterranean area. How do photographs from space increase our knowledge of the earth?

materials of the earth. Think back for a moment to Chapter 2 on Earth Materials. Earth scientists have learned about the materials of the earth from studies involving small specimens. These specimens were first examined with the unaided eye, then under microscopes. Finally, the world of atoms was discovered indirectly when scientists conducted chemical and physical experiments on small quantities of earth materials.

Now enlarge your view and consider the whole earth. The photograph taken from space shows a part of the earth's edge about a thousand kilometers long. If the curved edge of the earth appearing in this picture were extended into a full circle, how large would the diameter of the circle be? Can you think of any way in which the size of the earth itself can be measured? How did men first try to determine the size of the earth?

In this chapter you investigate our planet as a whole. The earth is the biggest solid thing you can touch. Did you realize the earth is the largest of the rocky planets in the solar system? You will see how the size and shape of the earth have been determined and how scientists learn about the interior of our planet even though the deepest drill holes scarcely penetrate its surface.

The historic voyage of Ferdinand Magellan around the earth from 1519 to 1522 provided evidence that the earth is round.

Determining the Shape of the Earth

3–1 How can you discover the shape of the earth?

When you take a long trip or explore a strange city, you know how easy it is to get lost without a map. A map helps you determine where you are and what direction to take to get to your destination. On maps representing a small area such as a city or county, the earth can be treated as if it were flat. If you want to make an accurate map of a large region such as a continent, however, you must allow for the earth's shape.

From your own experience, what clues relating to the curvature of the earth can you think of? If you live near the ocean or a large lake, perhaps you have noticed how ships sailing away from shore seem to sink slowly below the horizon. The lower part of the ship disappears first, as shown in Figure 3–1, and finally the high mast fades from view. Such evidence indicates that the ocean's surface is gently curved. The same effect can sometimes be seen on a very smooth, large land surface such as the Bonneville Salt Flats in Utah pictured in Figure 3–2.

When the moon enters the earth's shadow, a lunar eclipse results. During a lunar eclipse, people on earth can see the curved edge of the earth's shadow passing across the face of the moon as

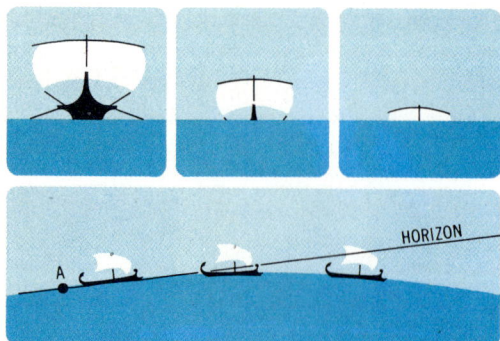

shown in Figure 3–3. Is this proof that the earth is round, or that the moon is round, or both? Could an egg-shaped earth cast a curved shadow on the moon?

ACTIVITY *Using a variety of differently shaped objects and a light source, find out how many differently shaped objects will cast a curved shadow on a sphere.*

What is the difference between evidence and proof? You recall from your investigation on Powers of Observation that there is a difference between observation and interpretation. **Evidence** is an observation that tends to support a conclusion. A **conclusion** is an interpretation or judgment based on the evidence. When there is little evidence for it, a conclusion is only probable. The conclusion becomes proved when there is sufficient evidence to support it. For example, are the views shown in Figure 3–1 *proof* that the earth is shaped like a ball, or only that it is not flat? Do these views contain *evidence* that the earth is spherical in shape?

For centuries men have looked to the stars for answers to questions about their earth home. The sky may seem like a strange place to look for the answer to questions about the earth, but as you read this book you will begin to see how much information the sky has given us. For example, an ancient method that

Figure 3–4 *The observer at A* (below) *is measuring the altitude of a star above his horizon. On the training ship,* Eagle, *a U.S. Coast Guard cadet* (above) *uses a sextant to sight the sun and determine his location.*

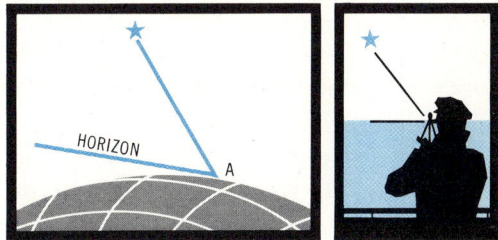

is still used for locating positions on the earth may also be used to determine the earth's shape. This method is based on identifying the position of stars as seen by an observer at some point on earth. (See Figure 3–4.) Using this method, the observer first notes the direction (to the north, to the southeast, for example) in which he is facing as he looks at a star. Then the observer measures the vertical angle between his line of sight to the star and the line from his eye to the horizon in the direction he is facing. Note in Figure 3–4 that for an observer at A, the angle of the star above his horizon is 50 degrees. This angle is the **altitude** of the star. The man in Figure 3–4 is preparing to use an instrument called a sextant to measure the star's altitude.

The altitude of a star on the horizon is 0 degrees, and the altitude of a star directly overhead is 90 degrees. The point directly above the observer in the sky is called his **zenith.** The horizon is in

Figures 3–1, 3–2, 3–3
Three illustrations of the earth's curvature. Left, a ship vanishes over the horizon. Center, the slightly curved surface of the Bonneville Salt Flats. Right, earth's shadow on the moon.

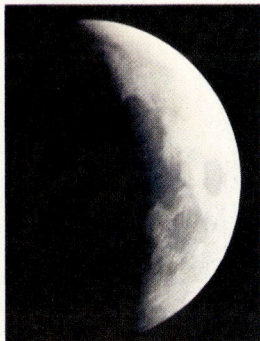

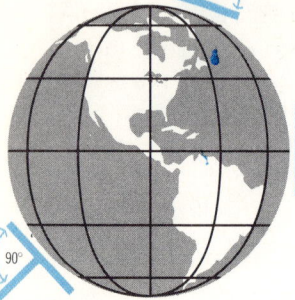

Figure 3–5
Wherever an observer is on earth, his zenith is directly overhead. The

directions of "up" and "down" are relative to the observer's position on the earth.

every situation perpendicular to the zenith, as shown in Figure 3–5.

How can measuring the altitude of a star help to determine the earth's shape? Before you can answer this question you must understand an idea outside your ordinary experience. Stars are so far away compared to the size of the earth that even two people looking at the same star from different locations on earth, are still looking in the same direction in space. The lines of sight of two people to a star are essentially parallel. This would be true no matter how far apart the people are on the earth.

The distances separating the observers on earth are very small compared to the

trillions of kilometers to the stars. The nearest star, excluding the sun, is one in a group called Alpha Centauri. It is almost 41 trillion kilometers away. Light, traveling at a speed of 300,000 kilometers per second, takes 4.3 years to travel this great distance. The light from the stars shown in Figure 3–6 takes about 2300 years to reach us. The light that we see from some distant galaxies has traveled for millions or even billions of years before it reaches us on the earth.

Suppose you put this new idea of parallel lines of sight to work. If the earth were flat, two observers at two different positions on the earth looking at the same star at the same time would find that the stars had the same altitude, as shown in Figure 3–7 (top). If the earth's surface were curved, the two observers would have different horizons and would obtain different angles of altitude for the

Figure 3–6 *(left, below) Most of the stars of the Veil Nebula are thousands of light-years away.*
Figure 3–7 *(below) The altitude of a star as it would be measured from a flat earth (A and B) and as it is measured from a curved earth (C and D).*

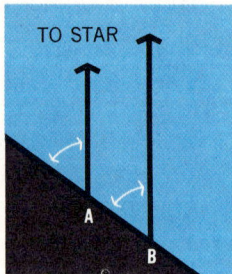

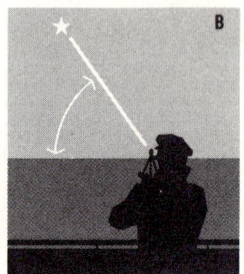

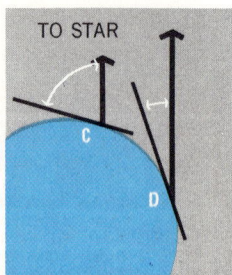

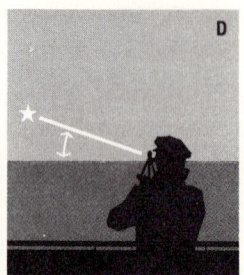

same star at the same time. (See Figure 3–7, bottom.) Such measurements, along with observations like those in Figure 3–1, *prove* that the earth's surface is curved. Similar observations can be made farther around on the earth to show that the curve continues. If many such observations are combined, they indicate without question that the earth is spherical in shape.

3–2 Investigating positions on a sphere.

How are positions on the earth located? It is easy to direct a person to a house in an area where there are roads or streets. The problem of locating a point becomes more difficult on a surface where there are no reference lines such as roads. It is still more difficult to try to locate a point on a sphere.

Procedure

See if you can work out for yourself a system for locating points on an unmarked ball. Is the method that navigators use to locate positions on the earth the only possible method? Can you find another way?

(1) If a friend wanted to visit you but did not know where you lived, what directions would you give him? (2) Would you need any information from your friend? If so, what?

Suppose that instead of living where you do, you were working on an oceanic research project and were living on a ship in the middle of a large ocean. (3) How could you tell your friend where you are? How would your directions for reaching the ship differ from the directions you would give your friend to your home?

Using the sphere provided by your teacher, establish a system for locating any point on the sphere.

Now that you have investigated reference systems on the surface of a sphere, can you see a way in which lines drawn on a sphere could be used to prove that the earth is spherical? Remember that two lines drawn perpendicular to a third line are parallel, as shown in Figure 3–8. Parallel lines never meet no matter how far you extend them. (4) Using a flexible ruler and a protractor, apply this notion (Figure 3–8) to the sphere and see if you can show that it is round.

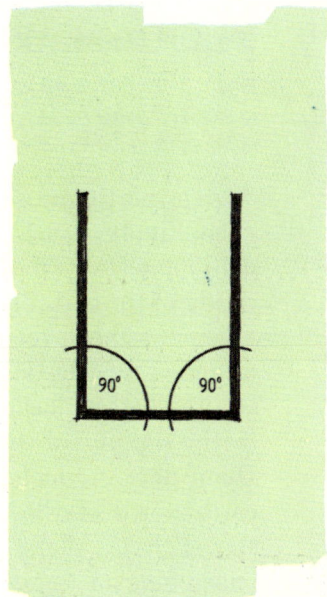

Figure 3–8 *The two vertical lines are parallel.*

3–3 How do we locate places on the earth?

In order to make careful measurements on the earth and to find its shape more precisely, you need a frame of reference. In a town you can locate a certain place by saying that it is so many blocks north and so many blocks west of a given location. Locations on a sphere are best described in terms of angles measured in degrees of arc rather than described and measured in blocks or kilometers.

The earth's rotation establishes an imaginary axis whose intersection with the surface of the earth identifies the two poles. Halfway between the poles lies the **equator,** an imaginary line around the earth. **Latitude** is measured in

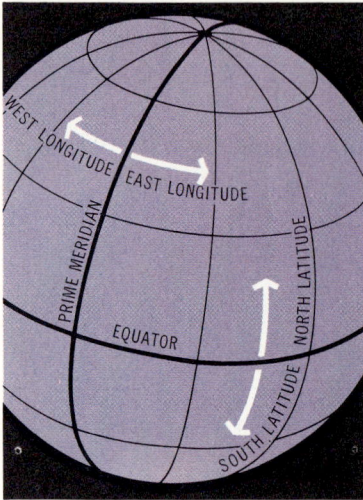

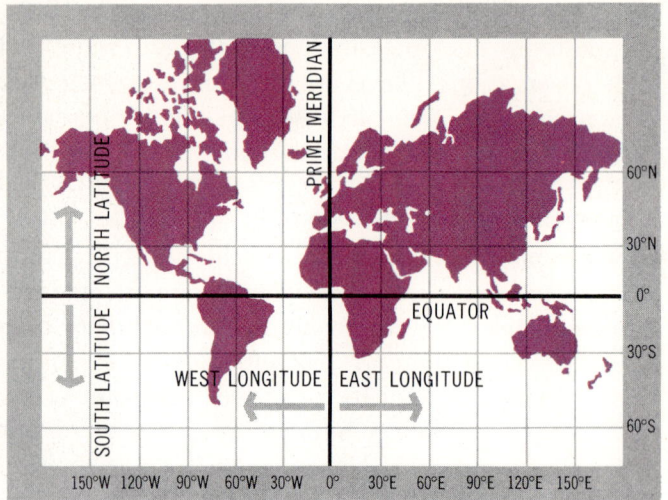

Figure 3–9 *Points are located on the earth by means of latitude north and south of the equator and longitude east and west of the Prime Meridian.*

degrees north and south of the equator. (See Figure 3–9.) How is this angle determined—by measuring it from the center of the earth? Obviously not, since no one has been there. The angle is determined by **celestial observation,** which is a method of locating points on earth by the sighting of stars. In the **Northern Hemisphere,** which is the half of the earth north of the equator, the North star, Polaris, offers a convenient reference point for the determination of latitude. In the Southern Hemisphere, the star Sigma Octantis might serve as a reference point. However, it is very faint compared to Polaris. Because of this, it cannot be depended on as a reference for navigation.

Polaris is almost directly over the earth's North Pole. For any observer in the Northern Hemisphere the altitude of Polaris is very nearly the same as the observer's latitude. An observer at the North Pole, latitude 90 degrees north, would see Polaris at an altitude of 90 degrees above his horizon, as shown in Figure 3–10. To an observer at the equator, which is at zero degrees latitude,

Polaris would appear on the horizon. What do you think the altitude of Polaris would be for an observer at point B in Figure 3–10, halfway between the equator and the pole? What would the observer's latitude be?

Figure 3–10 *The altitude of Polaris will vary for observers at different latitudes in the Northern Hemisphere. On a clear night, identify Polaris and do the Activity on the next page.*

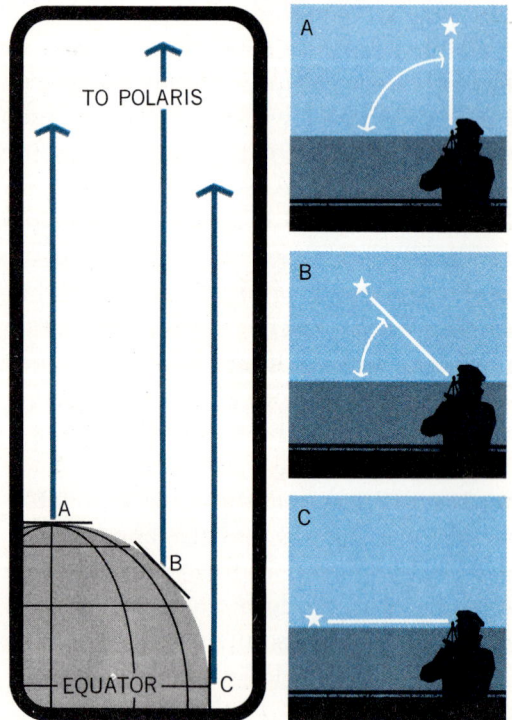

ANGLE OF ELEVATION

ACTIVITY *Determine your own latitude by observing the altitude of Polaris above your northern horizon, using the simple equipment shown.*

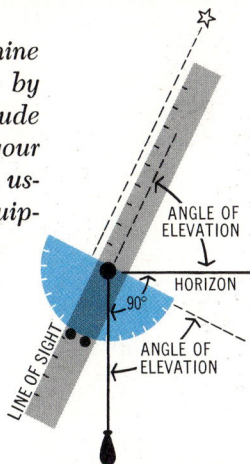

ANGLE OF ELEVATION

HORIZON

90°

LINE OF SIGHT

ANGLE OF ELEVATION

Figure 3–11 *Longitude zero degrees at the old Royal Observatory at Greenwich, England. The Prime Meridian runs between the white stripes.*

Latitude refers to location north or south of the equator, whereas **longitude** refers to location east or west on the earth. Both are measured in degrees. A full circle is divided into 360 degrees.

Where do you begin to measure longitude? You measured latitude from the equator, but is there any logical geographic starting point for longitude? By international agreement, in 1884 the point was set at the Royal Astronomical Observatory in Greenwich, near London, England. An imaginary line running from a point on the equator directly to the North and South poles forms a half circle known as a **meridian.** The starting meridian, called the **Prime Meridian,** runs directly through the point agreed on at Greenwich. (See Figure 3–11.) Running north and south through the middle of North America is the meridian at 90 degrees west longitude. Any point between the North Pole and the South Pole on that meridian is said to be located at 90 degrees west longitude.

Longitude is much more difficult to determine than latitude. It involves measurement of local time at a place and comparing it with local time at Greenwich at the same instant. The earth rotates 360 degrees in 24 hours, or 15 degrees per hour. Therefore, 15 degrees of longitude equals one hour of time difference. The time referred to here is not the zone time shown on watches, but rather, local sun time. When the sun is at its highest in the sky, it is **local apparent noon.** Suppose you were watching the sun, and when it reached its highest point you radioed to Greenwich, England, and found that the sun time there was 5:00 P.M. The time difference between your location and Greenwich would thus be five hours. Your longitude then would be $5 \times 15 = 75$ degrees. Would this longitude be east or west of Greenwich?

Great advances in locating positions on earth and in making maps have been made since the time, over 2000 years ago, when a Greek geographer, Eratosthenes, drew a map of the world as it was then known. He marked his map with lines of latitude and longitude as shown in Figure 3–12. However, instead of drawing these lines in the regular pattern we use today, he simply drew them through places he considered important. It was thus logical for him to

Eratosthenes, a Greek geographer (about 276 to 194 B.C.), made a surprisingly accurate estimate of the earth's circumference. In the great library in Alexandria he read that a deep vertical well near Syene, in southern Egypt, was entirely lit up by the sun at noon once a year. Eratosthenes reasoned that at this time the sun must be directly overhead, with its rays shining directly into the well. In Alexandria, almost due north of Syene, he knew that the sun was not directly overhead at noon on that same day because a vertical object cast a shadow. Eratosthenes could now measure the circumference of the earth by making two assumptions—that the earth is round and that the sun's rays are essentially parallel. He set up a vertical post at Alexandria and measured the angle of its shadow when the well at Syene was completely sunlit. Eratosthenes knew from geometry that the size of the measured angle equaled the size of the angle at the earth's center between Syene and Alexandria. Knowing also that the arc of an angle this size was $\frac{1}{50}$ of a circle, and that the distance between Syene and Alexandria was 5000 stadia, he multiplied 5000 by 50 to find the earth's circumference. His result, 250,000 stadia (about 46,250 km) is quite close to modern measurements.

draw his reference lines through places familiar to him, such as Syene and Alexandria in Egypt. It was left to another Greek, Hipparchus, who lived a century later, to apply the idea of dividing the earth into 360 degrees. In this way Hipparchus began the system of latitude and longitude that is still in use.

ACTIVITY *On a globe, a world map, or maps in an atlas, find as accurately as you can the latitude and longitude of the place at which you live. Compare this with the latitude and longitude of some large cities in the United States and with familiar places in South America, Europe, Africa, and Asia. Is Australia generally as far south of the equator as the United States is north of it? Is Reno, Nevada, east or west of Los Angeles, California? Does the Panama Canal run east-west or north-south?*

3–4 How round is the earth?

All points on the surface of a sphere are equally distant from the center, just as all points on the circumference of a circle are equally distant from the center. The relationships between the parts of circles and spheres are shown in Figure 3–13. Now you know a way to describe the position of a point on the earth. Can you see how the method of sighting the stars you learned in Section 3–1 can be used to determine just how round the earth really is?

Imagine yourself on a ship at sea exactly at the equator. After sighting the North Star, Polaris, directly north of you on the horizon, you sail the ship toward this star until it is just one degree above the horizon. You have traveled northward one degree of latitude. Therefore, the latitude of your new position is one degree north. Suppose that you have carefully measured the distance traveled

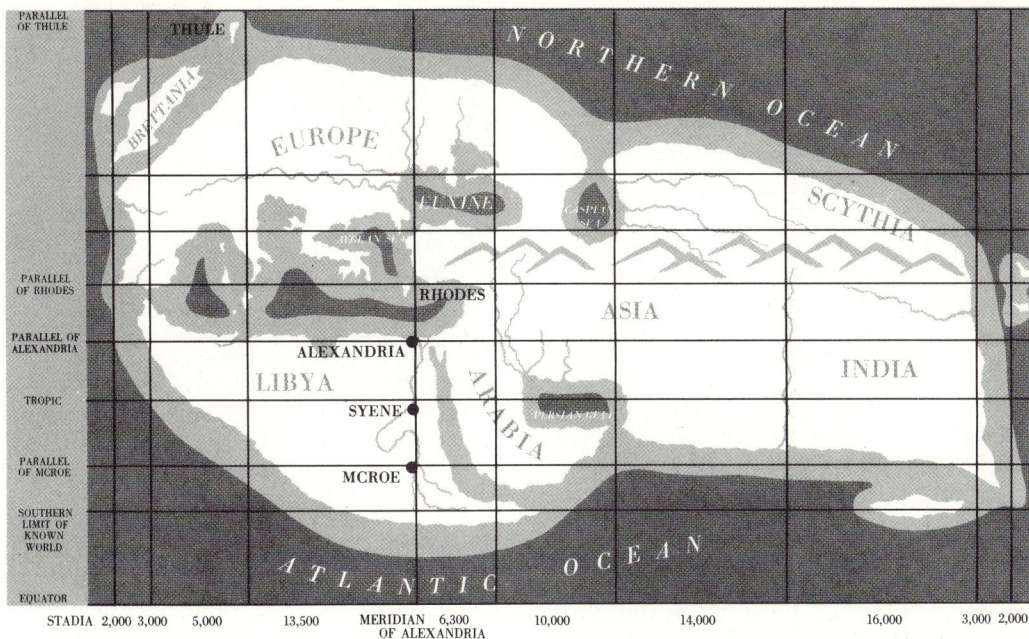

STADIA 2,000 3,000   5,000   13,500   MERIDIAN 6,300   10,000   14,000   16,000   3,000 2,000
OF ALEXANDRIA

Figure 3-12 *At the time Eratosthenes drew his map, little was known of the world beyond the shores of the Mediterranean Sea. He assumed that the unknown areas consisted of oceans.*

from your starting point. You find that you have sailed just 110.57 kilometers, or 68.55 miles.

Continuing to sail northward, you find it becomes necessary to go a little farther each time to change the altitude of Polaris one degree. By the time you are halfway to the North Pole, it takes 111.14 kilometers of travel to make the one-de-

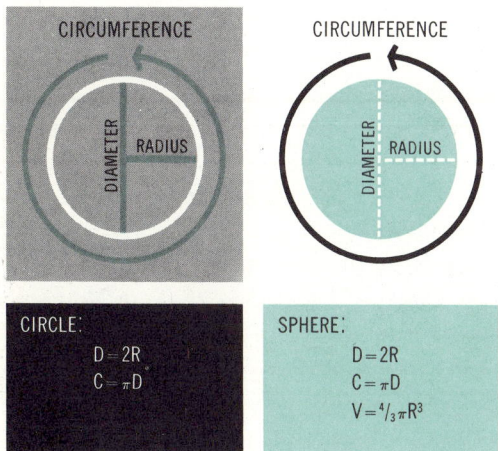

Figure 3-13

gree change in the star's altitude. Traveling farther northward, you note that the distance of travel for each degree continues to increase. You finally measure a distance of 111.70 kilometers between 89 and 90 degrees north latitude, as you reach the Pole.

Using the data from these observations, what can you infer about the shape of the earth? From equator to Pole, the distance for each degree was almost, but not quite, the same—about 111 kilometers. Does this mean that the curve followed in your journey was almost, but not quite, a circle? Can the curvature of a circle be different from one part of the circle to another? Look at Figure 3-13 and answer this question.

You can conclude that the earth flattens gradually from the equator to the North Pole. Measurements show that the earth flattens in the same way toward the South Pole. Would this flattening of the earth have been discovered if your measurements had been rounded off to the nearest five kilometers? to the nearest tenth of a kilometer? What does this tell you about the need for accurate measurements?

Another way of describing the shape of the earth is to say that the equatorial region bulges outward. What could cause this bulging around the middle of the earth? The planets Jupiter and Saturn both have a large amount of polar flattening—large enough to be easily detected. (See Figure 3–14). Both of these planets spin very rapidly and are made of materials that are less rigid than those on earth.

Because of the earth's flattening in its polar regions, the meridians are actually ellipses and not perfect circles. An ellipse is a flattened circle similar to the shape obtained by pushing on the opposite sides of a hoop. Earth scientists describe the earth's shape as an oblate spheroid. Since oblate simply means flattened, they are describing the earth as a flattened kind of sphere, like a ball that has been pressed down. You may be wondering how great the earth's polar flattening is. Could an astronaut notice it while orbiting the earth? The amount of flattening will be easier for you to determine once you have learned to find the earth's circumference.

Figure 3–14 *Can you see the planet Jupiter's equatorial bulge? Does measurement of this view of the planet prove that it has a bulge?*

Thought and Discussion . . .

1. How is the location of the earth's equator determined?
2. In what directions could you travel and find that the length of a degree does not change?
3. If the earth were a true sphere, would the length of a degree vary anywhere on its surface?
4. Why do the stars and even the moon seem to move with you when you drive along at night?
5. What evidence for roundness would be the same for a spherical earth and an egg-shaped earth?

Measuring the Earth

3–5 You can measure the earth.

How big is the earth? What is its circumference? Man started asking these questions long ago. How much bigger is the earth, they wished to learn, than those small regions of it that they had seen?

Can you think of any way to measure the circumference of the earth without taking a trip all the way around it? Even if you could travel around the earth and measure the distance you traveled, might there not be an easier and more accurate method? Is there a way to find the circumference of the earth by measuring much smaller distances? or angles? or parts of the earth's circumference? Two thousand years ago, when a few hundred kilometers was a long journey, Eratosthenes used some very simple ideas of geometry to estimate the size of the earth. Read about this experiment of Eratosthenes on page 66. His estimate was surprisingly close to the value accepted today, and he did it without even leaving home. In this investigation you will use the same basic idea developed by Eratosthenes to determine the earth's circumference yourself.

Procedure

(1)What is the angle *a* of the shadow cast in your schoolyard at midday by a stick placed in the ground in a vertical position? (See Figure 3–15.)

(2)Copy Figure 3–16 in your report and indicate on the diagram where you would place a vertical stick that would cast no shadow.

You could calculate the circumference of the earth if you knew (1) the distance between the stick that you placed in a vertical position (See Figure 3–16.) and the stick S that is already there, and (2) the angle *a* that the shadow of stick S casts. Using the globe and the suction cups, set up the globe so that it is similar to Figure 3–17. Measure the distance between the two sticks, using the millimeter ruler provided with the globe, and also measure the shadow angle *a*. (3)Use the following formula and calculate the circumference of the globe. How close is your answer to the true value?

$$\frac{\text{Distance around globe}}{\text{distance between sticks}} = \frac{\text{Angle of full circle } A}{\text{angle } a}$$

$$\text{or } \frac{D}{d} = \frac{A}{a}$$

This proportion can be stated in the following words: The entire distance (D) is to part of the distance (d) as the entire angle (A) is to part of the angle (a).

In your report, label Figure 3–16, using the values for the formula above. (4)What relationship does your shadow angle *a* have to angle *a* in Figure 3–17? (5)How does your calculated value for the circumference of the globe compare with the measured circumference of the earth as shown in Table 3–1? (6)Use the formula and work backward to calculate the latitude on the earth's surface where the sun would have been directly overhead when you measured the shadow angle in answering Question 1.

If you know the difference in latitude between your position and the latitude calculated in Question 6, you can use Eratosthenes' method for calculating the circumference of the earth. (7) What is your answer?

Figure 3–15

Figure 3–16

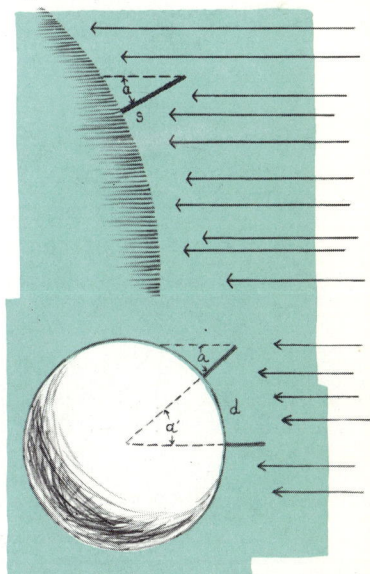

Figure 3–17

TABLE 3–1   DIMENSIONS OF THE EARTH

DIMENSIONS	APPROXIMATE VALUE KILOMETERS	MILES	ACCEPTED VALUE KILOMETERS	MILES
EQUATORIAL RADIUS	6,400	4,000	6,378	3,963
POLAR RADIUS	6,400	4,000	6,357	3,950
EQUATORIAL CIRCUMFERENCE	40,000	25,000	40,076	24,902
POLAR CIRCUMFERENCE	40,000	25,000	40,008	24,860
LENGTH OF A DEGREE OF A GREAT CIRCLE	111	69	111.32	69.17

3–6 Other dimensions of the earth.

Another way to determine the earth's circumference is by using the length of a degree of arc of the earth's surface as given in Section 3–4. For simplicity, round off the figures and assume an average of 111 kilometers for one degree of latitude. What, then, will be the length of the 90-degree arc from equator to pole? If this 90-degree arc is a quarter of the way around the earth, what is the full distance around? Check your answer in Table 3–1.

Having found the approximate circumference of the earth, you can easily determine its diameter from the geometry of a circle shown in Figure 3–13. The circumference (C) of a circle is equal to π (the Greek letter, pi) times its diameter (D). This can be represented by the formula $C = \pi D$. When this formula is expressed with D on the left as the unknown, the diameter D equals the circumference C divided by π. This can be represented by the formula $D = \dfrac{C}{\pi}$. Using your approximate value of 40,000 kilometers for the circumference and 3.14 for π, calculate the diameter of the earth. Your answer should be 12,739 kilometers.

The values for the earth's circumference and diameter that you calculated are only approximate, because you rounded off the length of a degree to 111 kilometers. There is another reason why they are approximate. Can you think of it? You found in Section 3–4 that the earth is not exactly spherical. Scientists have made precise measurements of the earth's size using the same techniques that you used in Section 3–5. Their results are shown in Table 3–1.

3–7 Measurement gives you perspective.

You learned in Section 3–4 that the earth is described by scientists as an

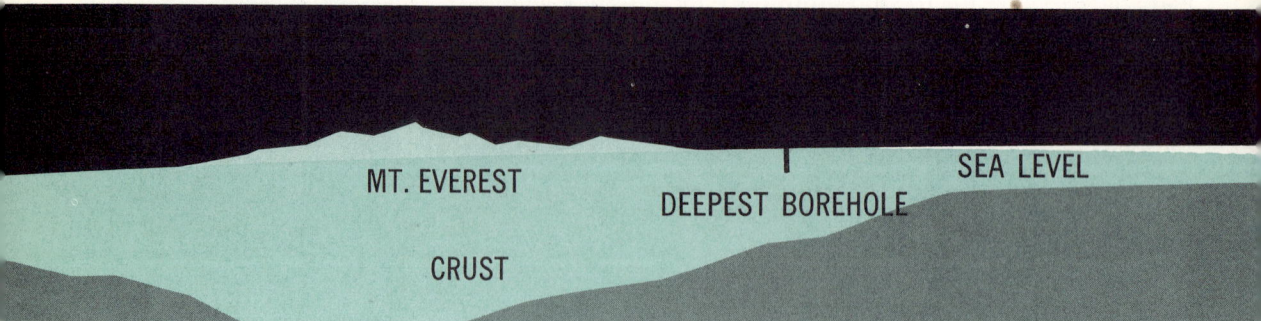

MT. EVEREST   DEEPEST BOREHOLE   SEA LEVEL

CRUST

Figure 3–18 *Climbing to high elevations on mountains like Everest (far left) in the Himalyas (top) requires special equipment. (Left) Sir Edmund Hillary and Tenzing Norkay complete the historic first ascent.*

oblate spheroid, a somewhat flattened sphere. Table 3–1 shows that the amount of flattening is not very great. The radius at the equator is larger than the radius at the poles by a mere 21 kilometers (13 miles).

You can now work out the extent of flattening of the earth referred to at the end of Section 3–4. Twenty-one kilometers seems like a tremendous amount of flattening. When you compare this with the great size of the earth, however, it turns out to be only $\frac{21}{6378} \times 100 = 0.33$ percent, or one-third of one percent of the earth's equatorial radius. Measure the polar and equatorial diameters of Jupiter shown in Figure 3–14. How does its ratio of flattening compare with that of the earth?

Are mountains as high as they look? Your answer to this question depends on your point of view. The surface of our planet seems very irregular to a traveler trudging up and down hills. Mighty Mount Everest in Asia, the highest point of land on the earth, rises some 8.8 kilometers above the sea. (See Figure 3–18.) Although men in many expeditions attempted to climb Mount Everest, its summit was not finally conquered until 1953. Is it any wonder that the surface of the earth seems most irregular to an earthbound observer? For comparison, the height of Mount Everest, the depth of the deepest part of the oceans off the Mariana Islands in the Pacific Ocean Basin, and the deepest drill hole in the world are drawn to scale in Figure 3–19.

How do these irregularities appear when you compare them to the size of the entire earth? The earth has a radius

Figure 3–19 *If the earth were only 6 meters in diameter, its curvature and its highest and lowest points would appear as shown here. The ocean is represented by the narrow white band.*

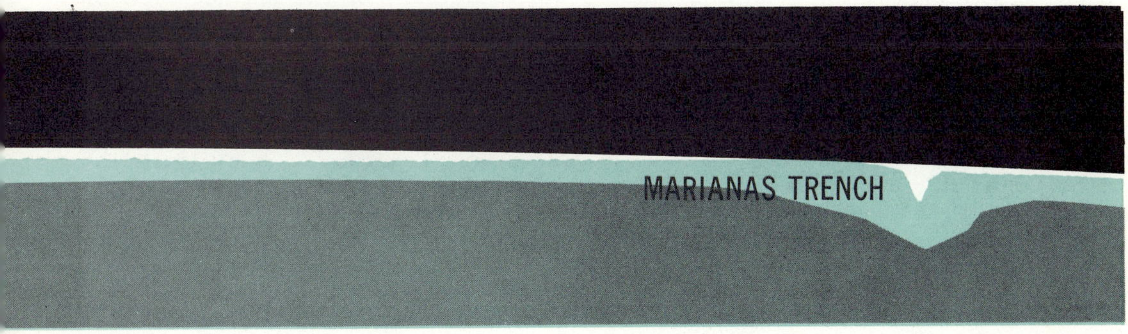

MARIANAS TRENCH

CORE

6371	KILOMETERS	5000		4000		3000
4000	MILES		3000		2000	

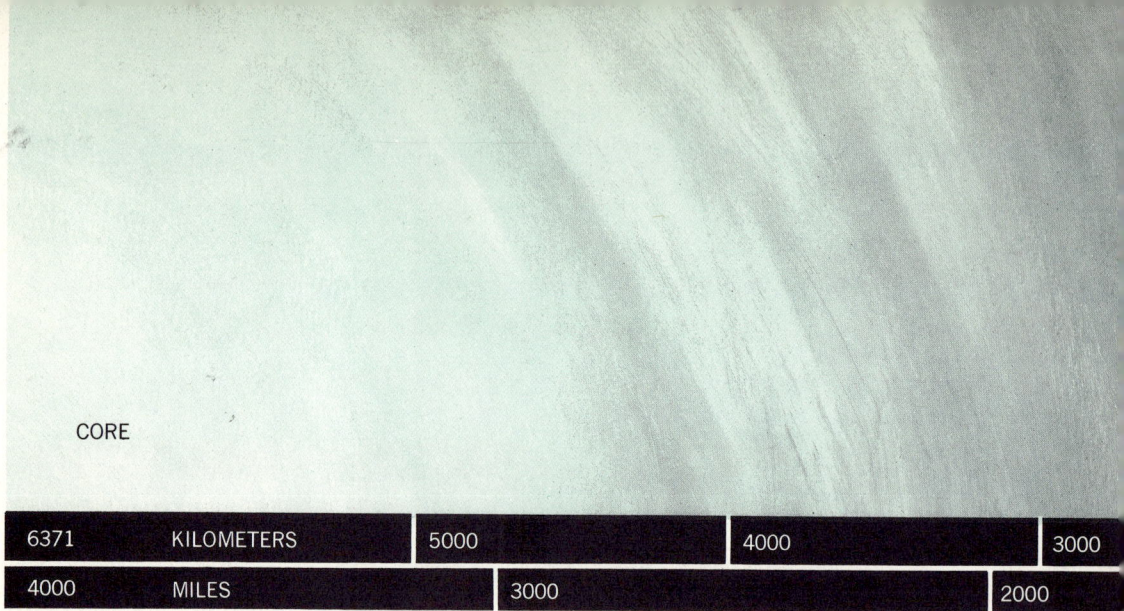

Figure 3–20 *Cross section of the earth from its center to the surface and on out to space. The black box at the earth's surface represents the portion of the earth and its atmosphere shown in Figure 3–22.*

of nearly 6400 kilometers. The vertical distance from the top of Mount Everest to the deepest part of the oceans is about 19 kilometers. This seems like an enormous vertical distance, yet it is only about $\frac{1}{337}$, or 0.3 percent of the earth's radius. The greatest irregularity, from mountain top to ocean bottom, amounts to less than the earth's small polar flattening. The highest mountain and the deepest part of the ocean lose their immensity when drawn to scale with the earth and its atmosphere. This has been done in Figure 3–20.

In fact, most things that you think of as being perfectly round, such as a ball or a marble, probably have greater ir-

regularities in proportion to their size than the equatorial bulge of the earth in proportion to its size. (See Figure 3–21.)

The early explorers who spent months and even years crossing the earth's great oceans must have been impressed with the tremendous amount of water on the earth's surface. What has measurement revealed about the proportion of water to air and to solid earth? In figures 3–19 and 3–20 you can see that the oceans and crust of the earth make up only a small fraction of the entire earth. Even the atmosphere is only a thin shell as you can see in looking at the line marking 99 percent of the air in Figure 3–22. These parts of the earth are very important to us, for they interact in all of the surface processes, yet they make up only a very thin skin when viewed in relation to the whole earth.

Measurement of the surface area of the earth has shown that about 71 per-

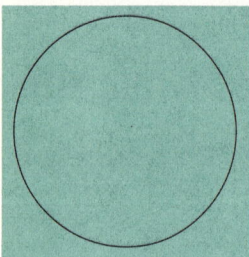

Figure 3–21 *All surface irregularities are contained in this line (left). If enlarged to earth size, this ball bearing (right) would have 8000-meter irregularities.*

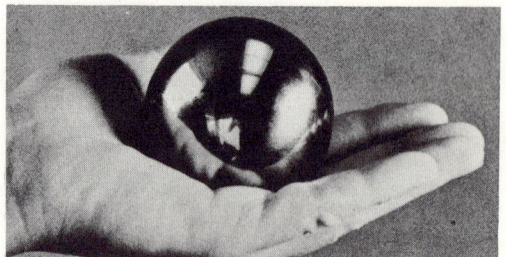

MANNED
SPACE
FLIGHT

TIROS

CRUST ————————

| 2000 | | 1000 | | 0 | | 1000 |

| | 1000 | | 0 | | 500 |

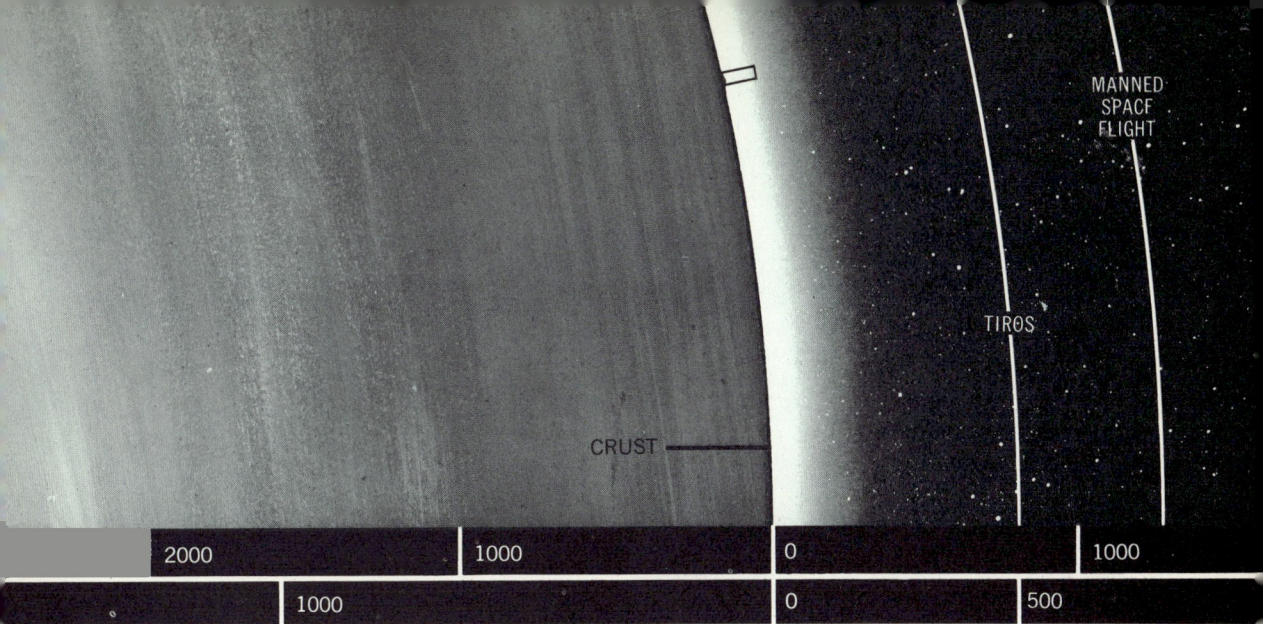

cent of the surface is covered by water and 29 percent by land. The atmosphere blankets the entire globe. However, with increasing altitude the air becomes thinner and thinner and gradually blends into space. Measurement has shown that 99 percent of the molecules of the air are within 32 kilometers of sea level. In fact, if you stood on a mountain 5500 meters (18,000 feet) high, half of the nitrogen and oxygen molecules that make up air would be below you.

In our age everyone has seen the thin vapor trails of high-flying jet aircraft. Look at Figure 3–22 and notice the height of the commercial jet in relation to the high clouds and the manned balloon. Now look back at Figure 3–20. The black box there represents the portion of the earth's atmosphere shown in Figure 3–22. How high would the commercial jet appear above the earth in Figure 3–20? the atmosphere?

What do you see when you hold up a globe and look at it in the region of the South Pacific?

ACTIVITY   *Try your hand at drawing some earth features to the same scale. Find a large piece of wrapping paper and draw a circle representing the earth and show the following things to scale:*

Polar earth radius—6357 kilometers
Equatorial earth radius—6378 kilometers
Orbit of Gemini spacecraft—245 kilometers
Greatest ocean depth—11 kilometers
Deepest well—8 kilometers
Mount Everest—8.8 kilometers

3–8 What's inside the earth?

You have learned that the size of the earth was first measured over 2000 years ago by Eratosthenes. With more refined measuring methods, modern scientists have measured the earth's surface area, its circumference, and the areas of oceans and land. You can form a good mental picture of the dimensions of our globe, but what is the earth made of? Are the materials on the inside similar to the rocks and soil on the surface? Are there great caverns of water or air inside the earth? How can you find out, when the deepest hole that man has drilled so far is a mere pinprick in the earth's surface? Since there is no way to examine directly the materials in the interior of

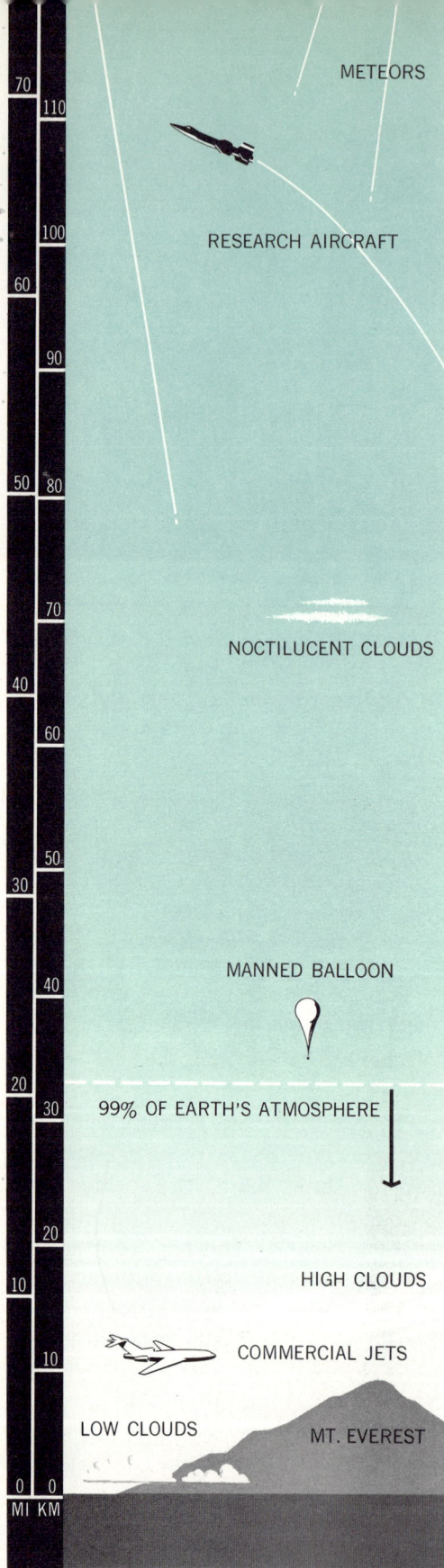

The figure shows an altitude scale in miles (MI) and kilometers (KM):

70 — 110 — METEORS

100 — RESEARCH AIRCRAFT

60 — 90

50 — 80

70 — NOCTILUCENT CLOUDS

40 — 60

50 — MANNED BALLOON

20 — 30 — 99% OF EARTH'S ATMOSPHERE

20 — HIGH CLOUDS

10 — 10 — COMMERCIAL JETS

LOW CLOUDS — MT. EVEREST

0 — 0

MI KM

the earth, the evidence of measurements made from the surface of the earth must be used to infer the nature of the earth's interior.

What information is available from surface measurements? You have learned how scientists determine the radius of the earth, in fact you have calculated this yourself. Once you know the radius, it is simple to calculate the volume of the earth. The geometry of a sphere is such that its volume (V) is equal to $\frac{4}{3}$ times π times the cube of the radius (R). (The cube of a number is the number multiplied by itself twice. For instance, 2 cubed, which is also written as 2^3, is $2 \times 2 \times 2 = 8$.) Expressed in a formula, the relation between the volume and radius of a sphere is $V = \frac{4}{3}\pi R^3$. The values of π (3.14) and R (6370 kilometers, as the average radius) are known. With these values, the volume of the earth can be calculated to be 1.08×10^{12} cubic kilometers. This may be written 1.08×10^{12} km³. When you convert this to cubic centimeters, it is 1.08×10^{27} cm³. What does 10^{27} mean?

Your knowledge of the volume of the earth does not give you any clues about the nature of the material inside, however. Can you ever identify things without seeing them? If you were asked to close your eyes and then were handed two blocks of equal size, one composed of lead and the other of wood, could you tell the difference between them? How? The lead block is much heavier, of course. It is heavier because it has a higher density than wood. You measured the densities of some things in the sec-

Figure 3–22 *Commercial jet airliners cruise at about 10 kilometers, manned balloons have reached above 30 kilometers, and certain research aircraft have reached heights greater than 65 kilometers.*

ond investigation in the Prologue. Is it possible to determine the density of material inside the earth without actually obtaining a sample of it?

Nearly three centuries ago, from a study of moving bodies and the motions of the planets, the great British scientist Sir Isaac Newton developed certain laws or relations that make it possible to determine the mass of the planet earth. You will learn more about Newton's law of gravitation, which is used to compute the mass of the whole earth. For the moment, let us accept the result of calculations of the earth's mass based on Newton's law. We find that the mass of the earth is 5.98×10^{27} grams.

Since you now know the volume and mass of the earth, it is easy to compute its density by using the same formula that you used in Investigation P-2 in the Prologue, $D = \dfrac{M}{V}$. Density (D) equals mass (M) divided by volume (V). Substituting the values for the mass and vol-

ume of the earth, you obtain its density:

$$D = \frac{5.98 \times 10^{27} \text{ grams}}{1.08 \times 10^{27} \text{ cubic centimeters}}.$$

The equation above contains 10^{27} above and below the line. What does any number divided by itself equal? That part of the above equation that contains $\dfrac{10^{27}}{10^{27}}$ is equal to 1. This leaves the number 5.98 to be divided by 1.08. Carrying out this division you should obtain 5.5 grams per cubic centimeter as the density of the earth.

Suppose you imagined that the earth were filled with water. How does this model fit the observed facts? Since the earth has a density of 5.5 grams per cubic centimeter, this model is obviously very poor because water has a density of only about 1 gram per cubic centimeter. Suppose your mental model called for an interior made of rock similar to that found on the surface. You may recall that the density of the rocks you worked with in Investigation P-2 was less than 3 grams per cubic centimeter (gm/cm^3). If the density of the earth as a whole is 5.5 gm/cm^3 and the density of surface rocks is less than 3 gm/cm^3, what can you

(A) Balloon to carry instruments high into the atmosphere. (B) A meteor streaks across the sky. (C) How did the cloud form? (D) High flying jets carry oxygen. (E) NASA research aircraft.

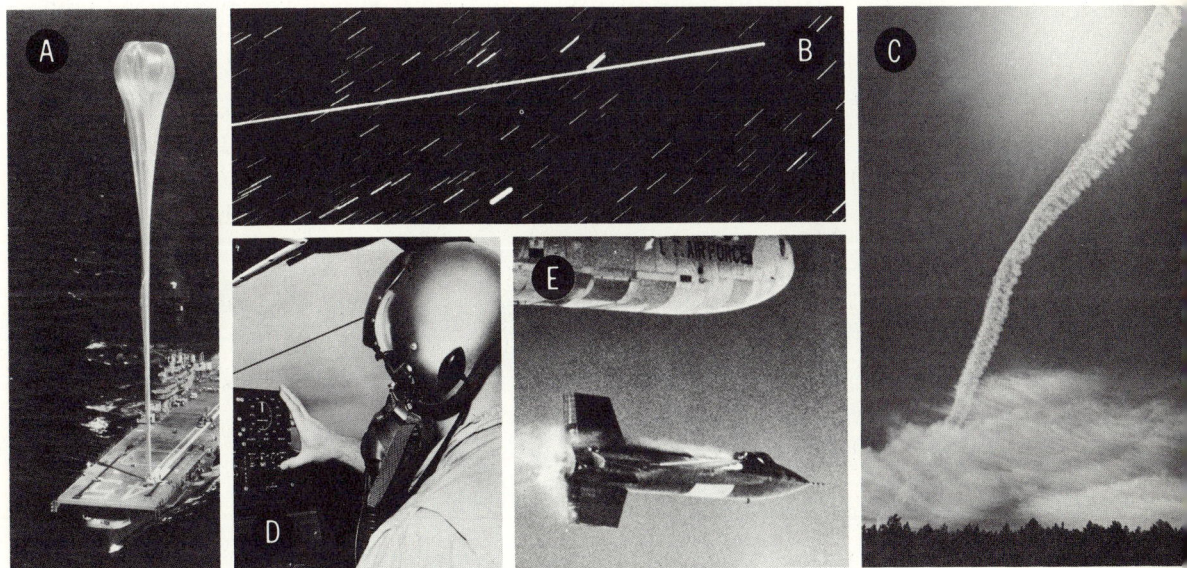

infer about the density of materials inside the earth? Obviously it must be much denser than surface rock. Would it have to be denser than 5.5 gm/cm^3? By now you are beginning to get a mental picture of the nature of the interior. You need more information to determine whether the interior of the earth shows a gradual increase in density as you go deeper or whether it consists of layers of different materials. You will find in Chapter 16 that geophysicists have been able to make inferences about the materials deep within the earth from measurements of earthquake waves. They have calculated the kind of a model that could account for the recorded measurements.

Perhaps you have heard of Project Mohole. In this project scientists hope to accomplish something entirely new— to drill through the earth's crust and take a sample of the material beneath. They

have planned to drill the Mohole through the floor of the ocean rather than through a continent. Can you see why in Figure 3–19? To obtain a sample of the sub-crustal material beneath a continent might require a 50-kilometer (30-mile) hole. A tentative drilling site has been selected in the Pacific Ocean northeast of Hawaii. It is believed that the lower limit of the crust may be reached there at a depth of only about 11 kilometers (7 miles) below sea level. Only 6 of the total 11 kilometers would have to be drilled, because the sea is 5 kilometers deep at that point.

Why would anyone want to drill such a deep hole? The answer is simple—to satisfy our curiosity about a mysterious part of the earth. By obtaining a sample of the sub-crustal material, we hope to determine whether or not our model of this part of the earth's interior is correct.

3–9 Investigating maps as models.

In sections 2–4 and 2–7 you have been introduced to the way models are used in science. In this investigation you will examine several kinds of models. You learned that models can be grouped into two major types, mental and physical. As you proceed through this investigation keep referring back to these two types and see if you can recognize the kind of model you are working with.

If you were standing in a field near the town of Morrison, Colorado, looking north toward Red Rocks Park, you would see a view like that shown in Figure 3–23. This represents the point of view you most commonly have of the world in which you live. That view is from near the earth's surface.

Figure 3–23   (*left*)
Figure 3–24   (*right*)
Figure 3–25   (*page 77*)

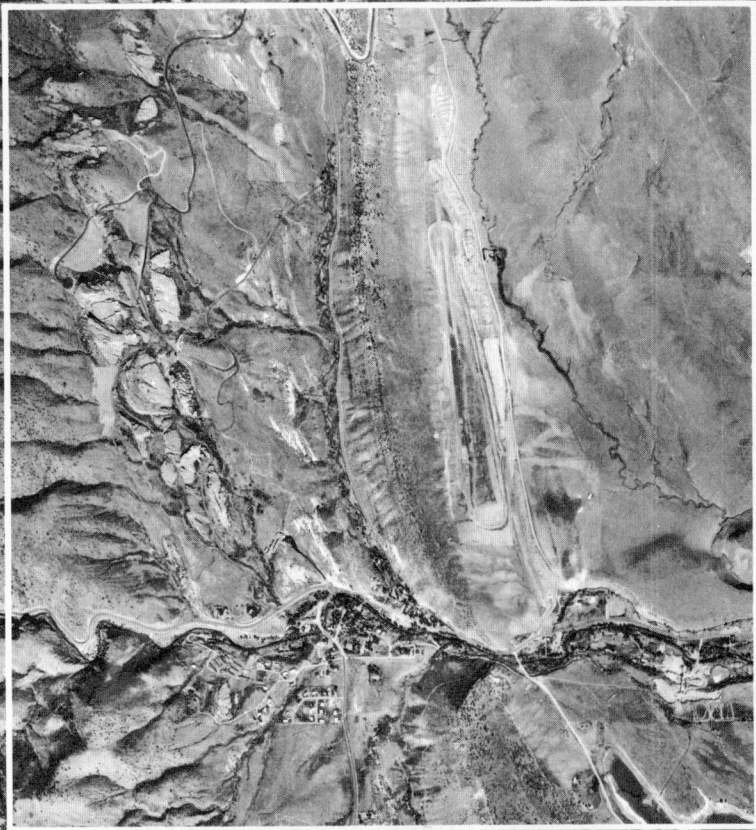

0-5-64

2-4-5

(1)If you were asked to make a model of the earth's surface as you see it in this picture, how would you do it? (2)What other kinds of information would you need to complete your model? (3)How does what you see in Figure 3–24 provide you with more information?

Look at Figure 3–24. Where do you think the photographer was when he photographed the view shown in Figure 3–23? Now imagine that you are flying directly above the area and looking straight down as shown in Figure 3–25. (4)What kinds of additional information does this aerial view provide? Using the stereoscope examine Figure 3–25. Identify as many features as you can. Use a sheet of clear plastic and a marker and make a map of the area with the white line around it. Compare your map with the map of the same area in Figure 3–26. Also compare figures 3–23 and 3–24 with your map.

Examine the U.S.G.S. topographic map in Figure 3–26. (5)How does a topographic map represent the hills and valleys you viewed with the stereoscope in Figure 3–25?

To better understand the way topographic maps show hills and valleys you will need a transparent box, a model of a mountain, and a grease pencil. Use the equipment as

Figure 3–26

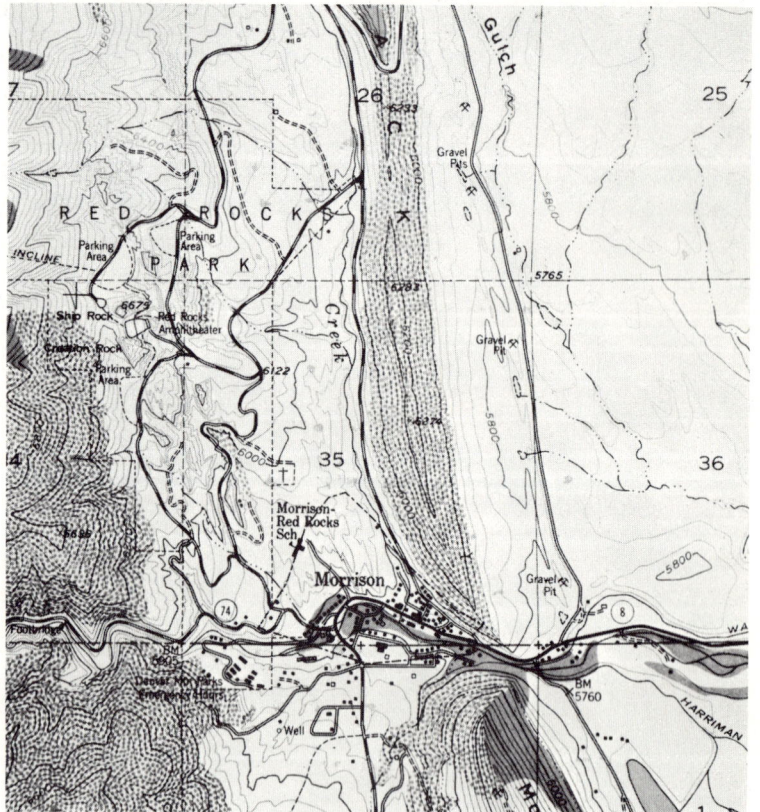

Figure 3–27

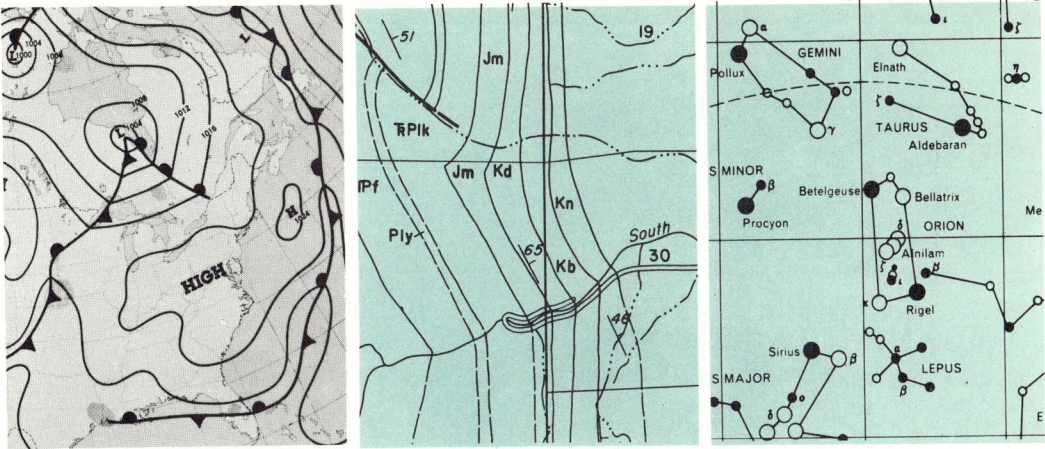

Figure 3–28

shown in Figure 3–27 and follow the directions given by your teacher. (6)How does the way your map of the model mountain shows hills and valleys compare with the method used on the U.S.G.S. topographic map? (7)Discuss the statement "A map is a paper model of the real world."

(8)How do each of the "maps" shown in Figure 3–28 represent the world in which we live? (9)How are they useful?

Thought and Discussion . . .

1. When you use Eratosthenes' method to measure the earth, what assumptions do you have to make?
2. Would you notice the earth's polar flattening if you looked at the earth from the moon?
3. How do you know that the inside of the earth is not composed of the same material as the surface? What evidence can you give to support your answer?
4. Look up the origin of the word *geometry* in a dictionary. Do you think it likely that the early students of geometry were thinking of determining the circumference of the earth when they developed the relationships between the radius, circumference, area, and volume of a sphere?

Unsolved Problems You may be surprised to learn that even today we cannot make accurate measurements of the distances between continents separated by oceans. The distance between points on a single continent can be determined with satisfactory accuracy by methods that have been in use for a long time. Such measurements are accurate to 1 part in 300,000 or better. This means that a distance of 3 kilometers (300,000 centimeters) is known to an accuracy of 1 centimeter. The problem of reaching similar accuracy between points on different continents is still unsolved. The distances between even carefully established points in Europe and America, points that have been determined astronomically, are in error by about 100 meters. For example, we do not really know the exact distance between New York and Paris or between Paris and Bombay, India. New navigational satellites will be very valuable in solving this problem. If the accuracy of measurement between such points can be increased, we may someday discover whether the continents are moving.

CHAPTER REVIEW

Summary

The earth is a very large body when compared to most things we know. It is so large that, from what they could see of its surface, men were convinced for a long time that the earth was flat. Only when men began making measurements of the earth did they learn that it is spherical. Measurements of the altitude of stars, combined with a knowledge of the geometry of a sphere, can be used to determine the size of the earth.

By assuming that the earth is a sphere, its radius, volume, surface area, and density can be calculated. Such calculations show that all of the surface irregularities of the earth amount to a very small departure from true spherical shape. In fact, its polar flattening can only be discovered by very precise measurements.

Measurements made on the earth's surface are used to gain information about the earth's interior. The earth is the densest planet in the solar system. It has an average density of 5.5 grams per cubic centimeter. This means that the interior must be composed of materials much more dense than surface rocks.

You have measured this giant sphere, the third planet from the sun, and have begun to get an idea of its many dimensions. This huge planet moves very rapidly through space. The next chapter describes how the earth spins unsupported and its pattern of movement as it speeds swiftly through the solar system.

Questions and Problems

A

1. List as many kinds of evidence as you can that suggest that the earth is curved. See if you can list some evidence not mentioned in the text.
2. Why can the lines of sight to a star from different places on earth be treated as parallel?
3. If the altitude of a star is 35 degrees for an observer, how many degrees is this star from the observer's zenith?
4. If a globe representing the earth has an equatorial radius of 45 centimeters, what is its scale compared to the earth?
5. How many kilometers is it from Philadelphia to the North Pole? Philadelphia is located at about 40 degrees north latitude.
6. Translate the following numbers into powers of 10: circumference of the earth, 40,000 kilometers; radius of the earth, 6400 kilometers; $\frac{1}{1000}$ of a kilometer; 1000 kilometers; depth of crust under a mountain, 35 kilometers; average distance from earth to sun, 150,000,000 kilometers. (Consult Appendix A on Powers of Ten if necesary.)
7. Translate the following powers of 10 into regular numbers: average length of one degree of latitude in kilometers, 1.11×10^2; π, 3.14×10^0; altitude of Mount Everest in feet, 2.9028×10^4; estimated age of the earth in years, 4.5×10^9; average distance to the moon in kilometers, 3.84×10^5; radius of the sun in centimeters, 6.96×10^{10}. (If you find that it is necessary, consult Appendix A on Powers of Ten.)

B

1. How does evidence differ from proof? Use examples of the difference from your study of the shape of the earth.
2. What features of the earth do you think an astronaut might notice 160 kilometers above it, by day? by night?
3. Why did Eratosthenes have to measure the sun's shadow in Alexandria on a certain day in the year?
4. The equatorial *radius* of the planet Mars is about 3360 kilometers. Com-

pare the length of one degree at the equator of Mars with one equatorial degree on Earth.

5. How many degrees of longitude, and in what direction, do you have to travel for the sun to come up an hour earlier? two hours later?

6. The moon's equatorial *radius* is roughly 1738 kilometers. What would be the radius of a globe of the moon on the same scale as that of the globe you used in Section 3–5?

7. How many kilometers is it from Chicago to the South Pole? Chicago is at about 42 degrees north latitude.

C

1. When your horizon is a water surface, like the ocean or a large lake, why doesn't the surface appear to curve toward the horizon?

2. How does the rotation of the earth affect its shape?

3. What is the mathematical formula that will enable you to calculate the length of a degree (L_d) on any sphere. Use the equatorial radius (R), π, and the number of degrees in a circle ($360°$).

4. The equatorial *radius* of the moon is about 1738 kilometers. How far will astronauts have to travel along the moon's equator to cover one degree? How many times farther do we have to travel on the earth to cover one equatorial degree?

5. Mars' equatorial *radius* is about 3360 kilometers. What would be the diameter of a globe modeling Mars on the same scale as that of the globe you used representing the earth?

Suggested Readings

BOOKS

Beiser, A. *The Earth.* Time, Inc., New York, 1962.

Editors of *Life* and Lincoln Barnett. *The World We Live In.* Time, Inc., New York, 1955.

Greenhood, David. *Mapping.* rev. ed. University of Chicago, Chicago, Illinois, 1963.

Raisz, Erwin. *Mapping the World: Mother Earth's Portrait.* Abelard-Schuman Limited, New York, 1956.

Raisz, Erwin. *Principles of Cartography.* McGraw-Hill Book Company, New York, 1962.

Strahler, Arthur N. *The Earth Sciences.* Harper & Row, Publishers, New York, 1963. Chapter 7.

Van Riper, Joseph E. *Man's Physical World.* McGraw-Hill Book Company, New York, 1962. Chapter 2.

PERIODICALS

"Apple Into Pear." *Senior Scholastic,* February 20, 1959.

Ashbrook, Joseph. "Earth's Shape." *Sky and Telescope,* August, 1965.

Gould, Rupert T. *John Harrison and His Timekeepers.* National Maritime Museum, Greenwich, England, 1958. Pamphlet.

Rothbrock, G. A. "Early Mapping of the Land and Sea." *Natural History,* February, 1966.

Takahashi, T. and W. A. Bassett. "Composition of the Earth's Interior." *Scientific American,* June, 1965.

White, G. F. "Rediscovering the Earth." *American Education,* February, 1965.

Publishers Newspaper Syndicate 1966

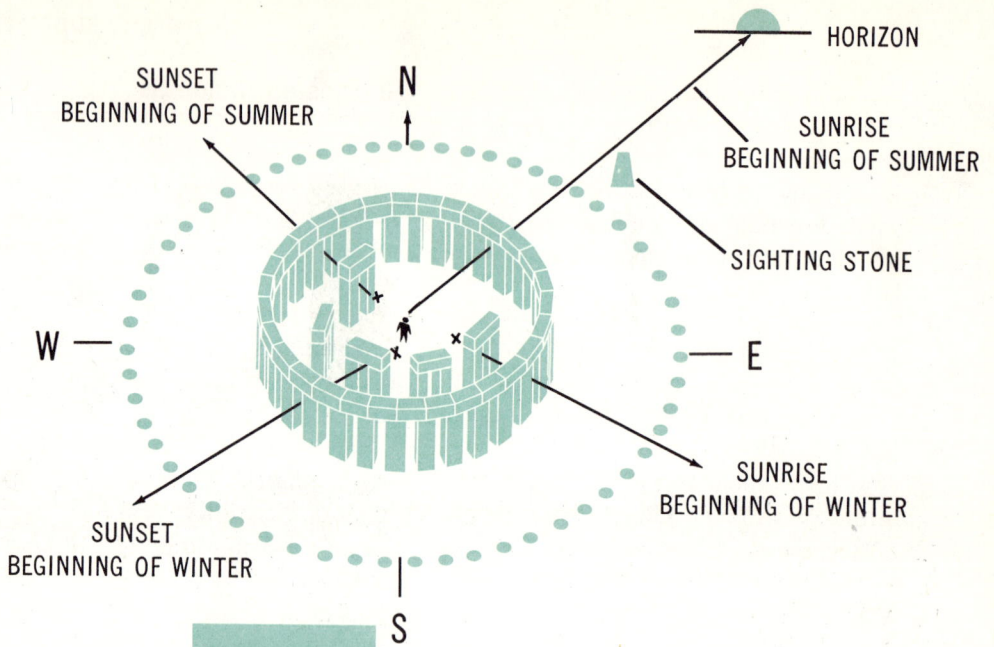

SUNSET BEGINNING OF SUMMER

SUNRISE BEGINNING OF SUMMER

HORIZON

N

W

E

SIGHTING STONE

S

SUNSET BEGINNING OF WINTER

SUNRISE BEGINNING OF WINTER

Chapter 4 Earth Motions

Man has been on the earth for many hundreds of thousands of years. For all but a small fraction of that time he firmly believed that his home, the earth, was the solid, massive, stationary center of the universe. The people who built Stonehenge, a great stone observatory in southern England, believed this.

Stonehenge, pictured here, was completed about 1650 B.C., yet only recently have we discovered a probable explanation for its construction. We believe now that the prehistoric men who built this ring of rocks used it as a highly accurate instrument for keeping track of the motions in the sky of the sun, moon, and stars. An electronic computer has shown that this stone observatory could have enabled the users to keep account of the passage of time, to follow the seasons, and probably even to predict the exact day of eclipses of the sun and moon.

Even though the early scientists at Stonehenge may have made all of these observations, it probably never occurred to them that the earth was moving, as well as the sun, moon, and stars. They believed that when the sun rose it really *was* coming up around the rim of the earth. They thought that the sun would make its journey through the skies, set in the west, and mysteriously find its way back to rise again the next day. On about the same day in early summer each year, the sun came up exactly over the pointed rock called the sighting stone, placed beyond the ring of rocks. From that day on until a half

year later, the sun would rise each day a little more to the south. Yet these ancient people would not have believed that it was the motion of the earth that caused the sun to rise in a slightly different place each morning. Indeed, the gigantic rocks of Stonehenge seem to symbolize a permanent, immovable place from which man watched the stately processions of the heavenly bodies.

Just a few hundred years ago men discovered what is really going on. The earth moves like the merry-go-rounds you see at fairs and circuses. Of course, the earth is spherical like a ball and thousands of times larger than a merry-go-round but its motion is the same. From the moment you are born, you have an automatic free ride, good for a lifetime.

Today we all know the earth is moving and take for granted that it is not the center of the universe. But men had to struggle to gain that knowledge and the exciting struggle for more knowledge still goes on. Even now we do not know everything about the motions of the earth. Past experience tells us that what we believe is true today may be proved false tomorrow.

In the investigation that follows you will make observations similar to those made at Stonehenge more than 2500 years ago. But you will not have to sight the sun and stars between giant rocks. Instead, you will use simpler tools which were unknown in those early times.

The Many Motions of the Earth

4–1 Investigating motions in the sky – Sky Watch.

When you are outdoors on a clear night and look up at the stars, your first reaction may be that they are beautiful, gleaming brightly in the darkness. But the stars have many things to tell you. For one thing, you know that the stars will have moved if you look up at them again in an hour or two. In what directions do the stars move and how fast? How can you obtain accurate answers to these questions? The men who built Stonehenge found one way to keep track of these motions. Aren't there easier ways than this?

In Sky Watch, which you started several weeks ago, you have learned how to plot the path of the sun. This is much the same thing the observers at Stonehenge did more than three thousand years ago. How can you do exactly the same thing for the stars that you did for the sun?

Procedure

Using the materials shown in Figure 4–1, find the North Star, as indicated in Figure 4–2, and plot its position. Then plot the positions of three other stars, one in the east, one in the south, and one in the west. The brighter the stars you pick, the easier they will be to plot.

An hour later, repeat the procedure, plotting the positions of the same four stars. Try not to move the hemisphere and baseboard between observations. If the baseboard must be moved, make a marker line along one edge of the baseboard and replace it exactly on the marker line for your second set of observations. If possible, plot the positions of these stars a third, and even a fourth time. Then take to class the transparent hemisphere with the positions plotted on it and answer the followng questions.

(1) In which direction did the stars move? (2) Did any of the positions of the stars shift in relation to each other? Explain. (3) How many degrees above the horizon was the North Star?

Place the transparent hemisphere on which you recorded your observations of the star positions on top of the globe and answer the following questions.

(4) Where should you locate the position of the North Star marked on the transparent hemisphere in relation to the globe? (5) What is the relationship of the paths of the stars to latitude lines on the globe?

Figure 4–1

Figure 4–2 *An imaginary arrow through the same two stars of the Big Dipper always points toward the North Star, Polaris.*

ACTIVITY *About one month after your first observations, repeat your observations of the same stars at the same time of night. See if you can determine how many degrees they have moved during the whole period and how many degrees they move each day.*

4–2 The stars provide a frame of reference for earth motions.

We live on the surface of our spherical merry-go-round, the earth, and so we can look out into space. What is out there to see? If you should say, jokingly, "Other merry-go-rounds," oddly enough, you'd be right! All bodies in the universe, planets and stars alike, spin (rotate) on their axis. At the same time, in addition to spinning, they move through space. The planet earth and the other planets move (revolve) around the sun, and the sun and many other stars travel around the center of our large galaxy.

It is the rotation of the earth that successively turns us toward and away from the sun. This is why the sun appears to rise and set. When the country you live

Figure 4–3 *Stars do move relative to one another over a period of many years. The noticeable motion of Barnard's star (arrow) in 22 years' time is unusually great. Upper photograph 1894, lower 1916.*

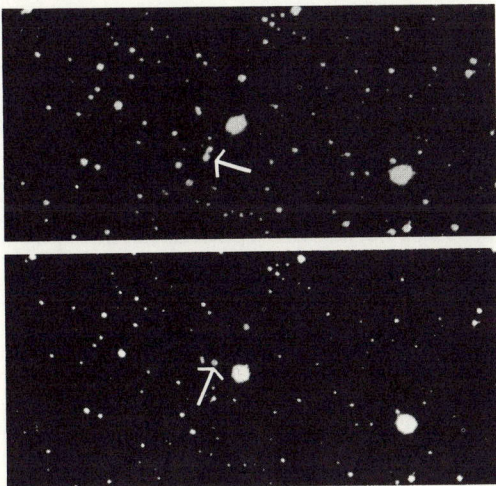

in is turned toward the sun, its light prevents your seeing the stars. Sunlight has all the colors of the rainbow in it. Air itself is colorless, but air particles can scatter the blue portion of sunlight in all directions. That is why the sky is like a blue dome high above your heads. You seem to be in the center of a huge inverted bowl. Astronomers speak of this dome as the **celestial sphere** and use the stars on this sphere as a frame of reference for earth motions. A **frame of reference** consists of objects forming a background against which motions can be observed and measured.

ACTIVITY *Some clear night, find a high place where you have an uninterrupted view and take a good, general look at the night sky. Can you see why it is referred to as the celestial sphere? What part of the celestial sphere are you seeing?*

The stars are extremely far away—so far that even though each star is speeding through space at many miles a second, it takes thousands of years before any change in the **constellations**, the patterns that groups of stars make in the sky, can be easily noticed. Many of the constellations are shown in the sky maps in Appendix E. The noticeable differences in the position of the star called Barnard's Star over a period of 22 years are shown in Figure 4–3.

You can think of stars as bright markers on the sky. When the earth has made exactly one turn on its axis, you see the same set of stars in the sky as you saw the night before. When a merry-go-round has made exactly one turn, you see the same gate and ticket stand as you saw in the previous turn. As the earth turns, the stars appear to move slowly in circles around a point in the sky very close to the North Star. A photograph of these circles appears in Figure 4–4. That point around which the stars turn is called the **North Celestial Pole** of the celestial sphere. If you lived at the North Pole, where would the Celestial Pole be in relation to you the year around?

If turning on its axis were the only motion the earth had, then at exactly the same time every night, the same stars would always be in exactly the same places on the sky. Our merry-go-round earth would have turned around exactly once. But you have probably observed that this is not so. The stars of the winter sky are quite different from those you see on summer evenings. The reason is that the earth has another motion in addition to spinning. The earth revolves around the sun.

As the earth moves around the sun, you see the sun from a slightly different angle every day. Of course, in the daytime, when the blue sky blots out all the other stars you cannot notice this. If you look out at midnight, however, when you are facing opposite to the direction of the sun, you can see the effects of the earth's revolution around the sun. A star that is on the **celestial meridian**, the north-south line directly over your head, at midnight tonight will be a little to the west of the meridian tomorrow night at the same time and so on, night after night. A month's difference in star positions is illustrated in Figure 4–5.

Slowly the stars of the summer night are replaced by the stars of autumn, starting in the east and gradually moving toward the west, as night follows night. As winter comes on, the brilliant stars of Orion and other winter constellations gradually take the stage, replacing the stars of earlier seasons. (See Figure 4–6.) After a year has passed, you and the earth have traveled once around the sun. At night if you look out in the same direction in space as you did a year earlier, you will see the same stars.

You can see how the stars and constellations change through the year by looking at the star charts in Appendix E. Note how different constellations move across the charts from the left (or east) to the right (or west) as you go from chart to chart through the months of the year, as the earth goes around the sun.

You know that the earth must move through 360 degrees in revolving once around the sun during a year. How many degrees will the earth move in one day, or 24 hours, from midnight to midnight? Can you see, then, why the stars seem to move toward the west almost one degree each day?

4–3 About motion: Let's get this straight.

The natural state of any body or object is *motion*, not *rest*. In fact, if you think it over, you will see that there is no such thing as rest. If you are at rest as you

Figure 4–4 *The stars appear to be circling the North Pole in this time exposure. What does this circular pattern suggest? Can you tell how many minutes the film was exposed? (See Section 3-3.)*

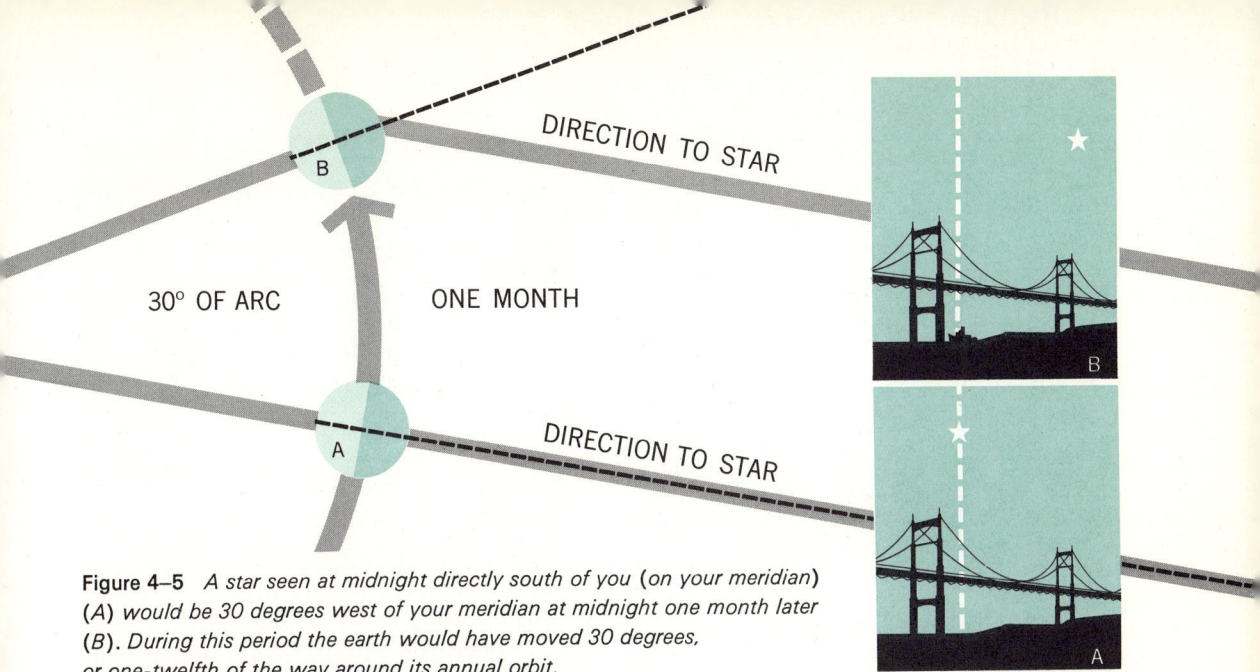

Figure 4–5 *A star seen at midnight directly south of you (on your meridian) (A) would be 30 degrees west of your meridian at midnight one month later (B). During this period the earth would have moved 30 degrees, or one-twelfth of the way around its annual orbit.*

sit in a chair, this means only that you and the chair have the *same* motion. For you and the chair are turning with the earth at several hundred kilometers per hour. You are also moving with the earth around the sun at almost 30 kilometers (18 miles) per *second*. Finally, you are going along with the sun and earth around the center of our Milky Way galaxy at hundreds of thousands of kilometers per hour. This sensation that

Figure 4–6 *Scorpio of the summer sky (left) is replaced by Orion in the winter sky. The earth has moved around to the opposite side of the sun and its night side faces a different part of the sky.*

you are at rest comes only from the fact that you and most things in the room have the same motion; you and all of the things around you are at rest in relation to each other.

The ancient thinkers believed that the earth was at rest in space. They even considered the earth to be the stationary center of the universe! They believed, too, that *rest* was the natural state of things. They thought that a rolling ball had to stop. Does it really have to? You know that it does stop, but if the floor were made smoother and smoother, until it was like the slickest ice, the ball would roll on much farther. Why does it stop sooner or later? What would happen to the ball in truly empty space? Do you think it would go on and on forever? On earth something must happen to the ball to speed it up or to slow it down.

Suppose we say the ball is moving steadily at three meters per second. Three meters per second with respect to what? To you? To the room? To the sun? Motion has meaning only when it is measured *with respect to something*, a frame of reference. When astronauts "walk in space," they "walk" with respect to the spacecraft. But both they and the

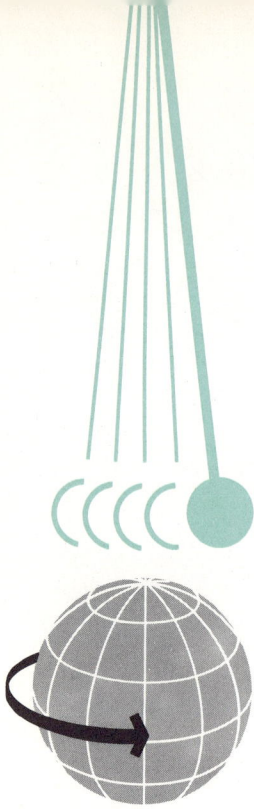

Figure 4–7 *A ball swinging back and forth above the earth (left) would swing in the same plane, but the earth would rotate under it.*

Figure 4–8 *The earth's rotation is proved by observing the Foucault pendulum. The earth rotates beneath the swinging ball (right, above) in the Smithsonian Museum, Washington, D.C. (Right, below) The ball at the Boston Museum of Science knocks down another peg every few minutes.*

spacecraft are hurtling around the earth at about 28,000 kilometers per hour, and around the sun at 108,000 kilometers per hour! The background of stars against which motion is measured is a frame of reference for the motion of the astronauts, the spacecraft, and the earth itself.

So, let's remember that motion is the natural state of things. Nothing in the universe is at rest. Objects are always moving with respect to something. If two objects are moving at the same speed and in the same direction with respect to something else, then the two objects are at rest with respect to each other. This is why an astronaut and his capsule are at rest in relation to each other, even though they are speeding through space in relation to the earth.

4–4 How do you know that the earth rotates?

Everyone agrees that the earth rotates. But do they really *know* this, or have they merely been told that it does? Suppose you were asked on a quiz program to prove that the earth rotates. Could you? even if you were contesting for a prize of $1000?

If you gave as evidence the fact that the sun appears to rise and set each day, your answer would be wrong and you wouldn't win the money. The ancient peoples watched sunrise and sunset, yet they firmly believed that it was only the sun moving, and not the earth. The ancients were convinced that the earth was flat and stood quite still at the center of the universe. As you saw in Section 3–4, a few of them, like Eratosthenes, thought the earth to be round. Most of them would have been shocked, however, by the idea that it was the turning of the earth that made the sun rise and set.

What is good evidence that the earth rotates? How can you prove it? Imagine this experiment: A large balloon is positioned directly over the North Pole of the earth. From this stationary balloon let down a heavy ball attached to a thin wire. Then let the ball swing back and forth like a pendulum, right above the North Pole. The ball will not change its direction of swing, but if the earth is indeed rotating, it will turn under the swinging ball. (See Figure 4–7.)

Now suppose you are an explorer, standing right at the North Pole. What would you think is happening? You would not realize that *you* are turning, but you would think that *the pendulum is slowly changing its direction of swing!* If, at the start, the ball swings over you from left to right, and right to left, six hours later when the earth has made one-quarter turn, it will seem *to you* to swing over you from front to back and back to front.

You can see for yourself in class, or with friends at home, how this pendulum works. Have someone stand on a chair, hold a ruler on the end between finger and thumb, and swing the ruler back and forth like a pendulum over another person's head. Now have the second person slowly turn around while remaining on the same spot on the floor. The ruler will seem to change its direction of motion *for the turning person*. In reality, it remains swinging back and forth in its original direction.

The famous Foucault (Foo-koh) pendulum shown in Figure 4–8 works on this principle. Its operation is somewhat more complicated elsewhere on the earth than at the North or South Poles, but it is a direct proof that the earth rotates.

Another proof is given by the apparent path of artificial satellites. A satellite is like a pendulum in that the plane in which it orbits remains unchanged for a relatively long time. Imagine an orbit around the poles, like that shown in Figure 4–9. Suppose this satellite has a period of two hours, that is, the satellite takes two hours to go completely around the earth and back to the same position in its orbit from which it started. In A,

The French scientist Jean Foucault (1819–1868) invented the gyroscope. He also accurately measured the speed of light and devised the first practical demonstration of the earth's rotation.

The Foucault pendulum, named after its inventor, was suspended from the ceiling of the dome of the Panthéon in Paris. It consisted of a cannon ball hanging from a 219-foot wire, its upper end fastened to a freely rotating swivel.

The great pendulum came within inches of the Panthéon floor. When Foucault set the ball in motion, a thin pointer attached to it traced out the path of its swing in a layer of sand on a low platform. It was known that a swinging pendulum would move in a constant plane unless deflected by some outside force. Amazingly, the Foucault pendulum slowly rotated at the rate of 360° in about 31 hours.

While the phenomenon seemed eerie, its explanation was simple. A pendulum dangling from a free, nearly frictionless swivel does continue to swing in the same plane. However, the rotation of the earth beneath it produces an apparent rotation of the pendulum instead. Scientists of Foucault's day knew that the earth turned on its axis, but it had never before been shown so clearly. This device still today fascinates visitors to science museums and university campuses around the world.

Jean Foucault

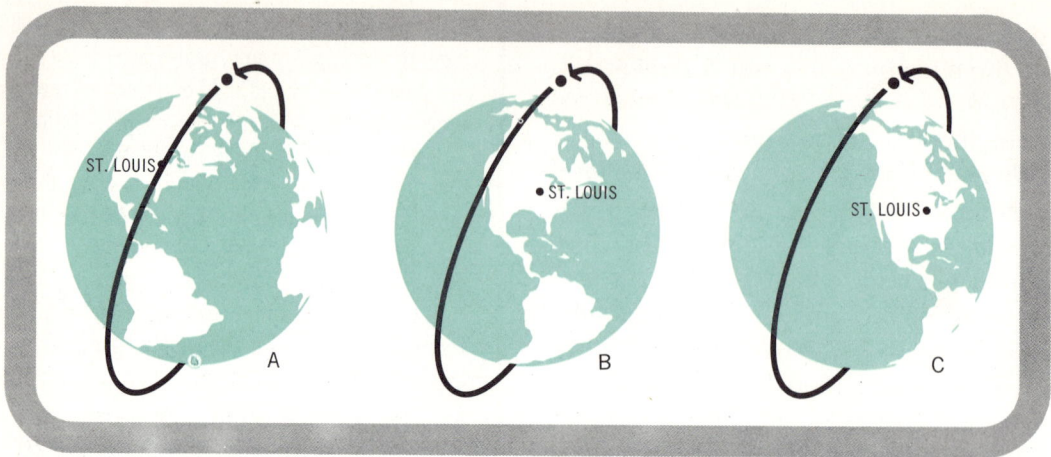

Figure 4–9 *A satellite in polar orbit maintains a nearly uniform path while the earth rotates beneath it.*

B, and C the satellite is shown during three revolutions. In A the satellite orbit is over St. Louis, in B it is over California, and in C it is over the Pacific. The orbit has not changed, but the earth's turning has brought first St. Louis, then California, and then the Pacific Ocean *under* the satellite's orbit. The gradual "slipping westward" of satellites is thus a good, modern proof that the earth rotates on its axis. (See Figure 4–9.)

4–5 How do you know that the earth revolves around the sun?

Now you come to the second great motion of the earth—its yearly journey around the sun. On your imaginary quiz program how could you prove that this occurs? Proofs are complex, but you can try another activity like the one you used to show how the pendulum works. You can also easily try this at home with your friends or family.

Put a bright, unshaded light in the center of an otherwise *darkened* room. Now take a small globe of the earth, or a ball on which you have marked the North and South Poles, and walk counterclockwise completely around the light. Make sure that the North Pole of the globe, or ball, is tipped from the vertical, just as the earth's pole is. (See Figure 4–10.) As you walk around the light, make sure that the North Pole of the globe always points in the same direction. This gives **parallelism** to the globe's axis; that is, the direction of the axis in one position is parallel to its direction in all other positions. Hence, tracing the axis of the globe at any two positions

Figure 4–10 *Move the globe around the light (far left), holding the globe as shown (left) and keeping the axis in the same direction in space. Notice that the globe is always half illuminated.*

would result in parallel lines. Notice that the North Pole will sometimes be tilted toward the light, and at other times away from it.

The light and the globe, of course, are models of the sun and the earth. Notice how the light strikes the Northern Hemisphere of the earth-globe when the axis of the globe is tipped toward the light. It is then summer for the northern part of the globe and winter for the southern part. The situation is reversed when you have walked halfway round the light. Keep the globe tilted exactly the same way as you walk around.

Now imagine yourself on the globe. How could you prove that it was really going around the light and that the light was not going around the globe? Notice that as you carry the globe around the light, part of the time you are going *toward* one of the walls of the room and part of the time *away* from that wall. In space there are no walls for a frame of reference, but there are stars. If you had some way of telling when the earth is going toward a group of stars, and when it is going away from them, then you could easily show that the earth must be going around the sun.

Astronomers can readily tell by the analysis of starlight whether the earth is going toward or away from a *group* of stars. Starlight is affected by motion, just as sound is affected by motion, through what is called the **Doppler effect.** You may have noticed how the sound of a horn or whistle moving rapidly toward you seems to have a higher pitch while approaching, and a lower pitch when moving away from you. Light is also affected by motion. Light from an object moving toward you appears bluer whereas light from an object moving away from you appears redder. By analysis of this Doppler effect in starlight,

LIGHT FROM STAR

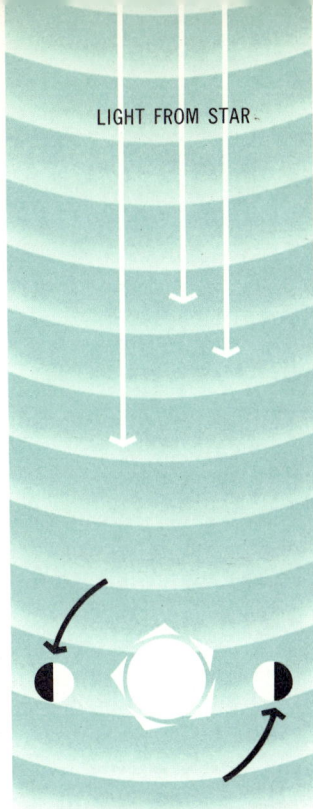

Figure 4–11
The Doppler effect offers additional proof of the annual revolution of the earth. During part of the year the earth is moving toward the light waves from a star, whereas six months later it is moving away from the light. An observer on earth could detect a slight change in color.

the revolution of the earth can be proved. (See Figure 4–11.)

An *effect* of the revolution of the earth about the sun, but not a *proof* of its revolution, is the slow westward shift of the constellations night after night. You can see why this must be. As you walk around the light with the globe, the night side of the globe, or the part facing away from the light, looks out toward different parts of the room, which represents the starry sky. This is why the stars of the summer sky are different from those of the winter sky. Why is this an effect, but not a proof, of the earth's revolution around the sun?

The activity with the light and globe is very important to the understanding of this chapter. It is so important that you can give it a special name: the Sun-Earth-Sunlight (S-E-S) setup. Make sure that you are doing the S-E-S demonstration properly. Repeat it until you thoroughly understand what is happening. It will give you an accurate picture of how the earth moves around the sun.

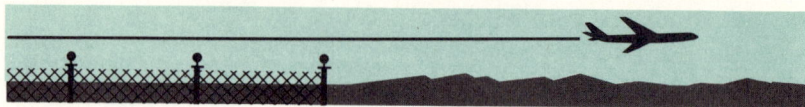

The sound of an approaching jet aircraft drops to a lower pitch as it passes over and streaks away, giving an example of the Doppler effect in sound waves similar to the effect in light waves.

Thought and Discussion . . .

1. What is the difference between rotation and revolution?
2. Why did it take so long for man to discover that the earth is neither stationary nor the center of the universe?
3. Ancient peoples used to speak of the "four corners of the earth." To what do you think they were referring?
4. The text states that the stars in the winter are different from those you see in the summer. Is there any place on earth where this statement is not strictly true? Explain.

Effects of Earth Motion

4–6 What would happen if the earth didn't move?

The motion of the earth affects us in many important ways. What would the effect be on us if the earth did not move? If the earth didn't rotate, or revolve, we would not have night and day, and one side of the earth would be intensely hot and the other very cold. There would probably be extremely violent storms and hurricanes as the hot air on one side interacted with the cold air on the other. The winds and temperatures would be so fierce that life might be impossible.

If the earth did not move around the sun, we would not have our seasons. We would never see the stars in one hemisphere of the sky because the sun would always appear there and the glare of daylight would blot out the stars. One of the most direct effects of the earth's rotation is, of course, the rising and setting of the sun. The place on the eastern horizon where the sun rises each day depends on the revolution of the tilted earth around the sun. When the Northern Hemisphere of the earth is tilted toward the sun, the sun rises in the northeast and sets in the northwest. In winter, when the North Pole of the earth is tilted away from the sun, the sun rises in the southeast and sets in the southwest.

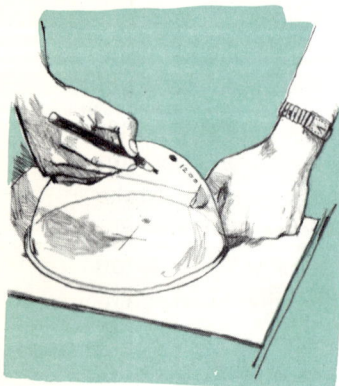

4–7 Investigating the sun's path – Sky Watch.

Figure 4–12

You are already familiar with this investigation because you started your Sky Watch several weeks ago. You are ready to make use of your earlier observations of the sun, along with those you will make now. Almost all progress in science comes from comparing observations made at one time with those made at another. Observations of the sun's position at different times show you how its path changes in the sky.

Procedure

Plot the position of the sun as you did in your Sky Watch observations in Investigation 1–9. (See Figure 4–12.) Once you have completed this, answer the following questions.

[1] How many degrees does the sun move in one hour? [2] What evidence do you have to prove or disprove the statement, "The sun is directly overhead at noon"? [3] What evidence do you have to prove or disprove the statement, "The sun always rises in the east and sets in the west"? [4] What was the altitude of the sun above the southern horizon at midday on the first day of your plotting in Investigation 1–9? What was the altitude of the sun at midday today? What caused this change of altitude? [5] In what ways can the duration of sunshine on the day of your observation be calculated? [6] How long was the sun above the horizon?

Place the transparent hemisphere on top of the globe so that the position of the North Star is again over the North Pole of the earth. [7] At what locations on earth is the sun exactly overhead today?

4–8 Why does the earth have seasons?

Recall the S-E-S demonstration when the North Pole is tipped away from the sun. When the North Pole is tipped toward the sun six months later, what is the season? Now back up to the place in between where the North Pole first receives sunlight. This occurs on our calendar about March 21. Six months later the sun sets on the North Pole for the first time since March. What would be the sun's path in the sky to an observer at the pole during all that time?

The revolution of the tipped earth around the sun causes the seasons. The reason is simple, as you can see from your S-E-S demonstration. During part of the earth's orbit (March to September) the Northern Hemisphere of the earth faces more directly into the sunlight than it does during the autumn and winter. Days are longer as well, and the greater total amount of sunshine the Northern Hemisphere receives heats it up. Our weather is warm, and we have spring and summer. In the other part of the earth's orbit (October to February), the Northern Hemisphere faces away from the sun, days are shorter, and the earth receives less sunlight. The weather is cold and we have autumn and winter.

If the sun should suddenly stop giving off energy, the earth would very soon become a lifeless, intensely cold, dark body. It has been shown from studies of the fossil record that the sun has been shining the way it does for over three billion years. Astronomers tell us that the sun will continue to shine for at least several billion years more.

The sun pours out its light and heat in all directions. Viewed from the sun, the earth would appear only as a speck in the sky, so small that it can capture only one two-billionth of all the light the sun sends out. Yet this seemingly small amount of radiation is enough to keep us alive, give us our seasons, and warm the entire earth.

How much radiation does the earth capture from the sun? This can be measured by instruments built especially to measure the sun's radiation. The amount of solar radiation received each second by a surface one centimeter square at the outer limit of the atmosphere and *turned perpendicular to the sun's rays* is called the **solar constant**. Can you say why the words "turned perpendicular

to the sun's rays" are emphasized? Only when the surface receiving the radiation is at right angles, or perpendicular, to the sun's rays does the surface receive the full benefit of the sun's energy. (See Figure 4–13.) This is part of the reason for the seasons.

When the earth is at that part of its orbit at which the North Pole is tipped toward the sun (see Figure 4–14), the sun's rays fall directly on the surface at 23½ degrees north latitude. What is this circle called on the globe?

A half-year later, when the earth is in position B, the North Pole is tipped away

(Below, left) How do you know the sun is at zenith in this photograph? Between what latitudes is this location? (Below, right) The sun rises perpendicular to the horizon. At what latitude was the photograph taken and at what time of year?

Figure 4–13 *The relative amounts of energy received from the sun at points A, B, and C, above, may be compared by counting the number of horizontal lines crossing each bar.*

from the sun. Now the direct rays of the sun fall at 23½ degrees south. This is the Tropic of Capricorn. Now the Tropic of Cancer is tipped away from the rays of the sun by twice 23½ degrees, or 47 degrees in all. Do you see why it should be twice 23½ degrees? Points on the Tropic of Cancer now receive only about two-thirds as much light and heat each minute as they did six months earlier.

A second factor causing seasons is that there are fewer minutes of daylight in winter time. (See Figure 4–14.) At the latitude of the United States, daylight lasts more than one half-turn of the earth in summer, but much less than one half-turn in winter. Because there is both less sunlight per minute and fewer minutes of sunlight, each hemisphere receives much less of the sun's warmth during its winter than during its summer.

ACTIVITY *Following the S-E-S demonstration procedure, set up the globe in the June 21 position with respect to an object representing the sun. Hold a pencil or pointer so as to represent the sun's rays striking the United States. With the globe on the other side of the "sun" in the December 21 position, show the angle at which the sun's rays strike the United States. Note the difference in the angle of incoming solar rays. About how many degrees difference is it? In which direction is the observer looking to see the sun in both situations?*

March 21 (or 22) is known as the **spring equinox** for the Northern Hemisphere. At that time the sun is directly above the equator, and days and nights are each 12 hours long the world over. *Equinox* comes from two Latin words meaning equal and night. On June 21 the Northern Hemisphere is tipped most directly toward the sun. (See Figure 4–15.) You might think it strange then, that this is the *first* day of summer with the hottest days coming in July and August. Why should this be? The reason is that it takes time to warm up the earth. Similarly, in winter we receive the least energy from the sun in the Northern Hemisphere on December 21, yet it is coldest in January or February. This is because we benefit from the heat stored in summertime well into the winter.

Passing from summer to winter is like going from a warm house to the cold outdoors. Your clothing and stored warmth protect you awhile, and you do not feel really cold until you have been outside for some time. When you come indoors it takes time to absorb the heat

and feel as warm as people who have been in the room. In the same way, on December 21, when you receive the least heat from the sun, the stored heat from summer acts as warm clothing, and you do not feel your coldest until several weeks later. This delay in seasonal temperatures is called the lag of the seasons.

4–9 What time is it?

The rotation of the earth causes day and night. The length of daylight depends on latitude and on where the earth is in its orbit, but day and night depend only on the earth's rotation. Study this with your S-E-S setup. No matter where the earth is in its orbit, it is *noon* along that meridian directly facing the sun and *midnight* 180 degrees away. Where is sunrise at this instant? Where is sunset?

Now use the S-E-S setup of globe and light again. Turn a globe that has cities marked on it so that it is noon in Chicago. Imagine that you are in Chicago. Then turn the globe toward the east until Chicago is in sunset position. It is now about 6 P.M. in Chicago. Continue to

Figure 4–14 *Compare the angle of the sun's rays that fall on a given point on the earth's surface on June 21 (A) and December 21 (B).*

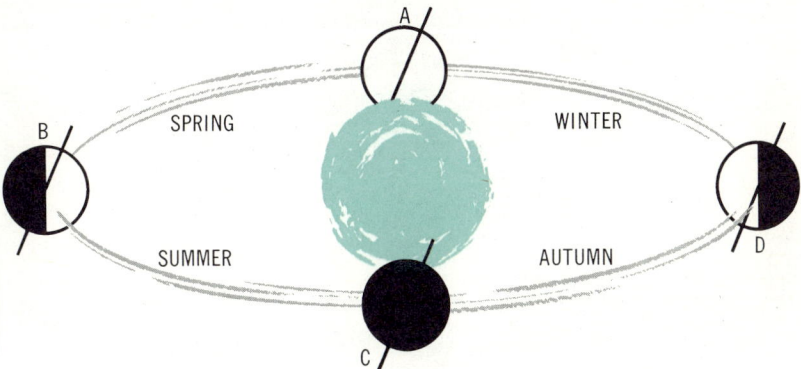

Figure 4–15 *Earth, sun, and seasons. (A) March 21, (B) June 21, (C) September 21, and (D) December 21. What season starts in the Southern Hemisphere on December 21?*

SPRING

WINTER

SUMMER

AUTUMN

turn the globe until it is midnight in Chicago. Now the next day is beginning for you there. Keep on turning the globe to sunrise of the new day. Then go on to noon. You have made time pass very rapidly, and it is now noon of the next day for you.

In the same way, each place on the earth moves around from the daylight side through the hours of night to dawn the next morning, and so on. *It is always midnight along the meridian directly opposite the sun.* As each place rotates past the midnight position, a new day begins at that place.

Now imagine a telephone game in which you are calling from Chicago at 6 P.M. on Wednesday. (See map, Figure 4–16.) The sun is just setting in the west. Turn the globe to this position. You rapidly call San Francisco, New York, Rio de Janeiro, London, Cairo, Manila, Tokyo, Sydney, and Honolulu. On each call you ask the time and day. Where would it be midnight? Where would the sun be rising? Here are the answers to your telephone calls.

City Called	*Time and Day*
San Francisco	4 P.M. Wednesday
New York	7 P.M. Wednesday
Rio de Janeiro	9 P.M. Wednesday
London	Midnight Wednesday
Cairo	2 A.M. Thursday
Manila	8 A.M. Thursday
Tokyo	9 A.M. Thursday
Sydney	10 A.M. Thursday
Honolulu	2 P.M. Wednesday

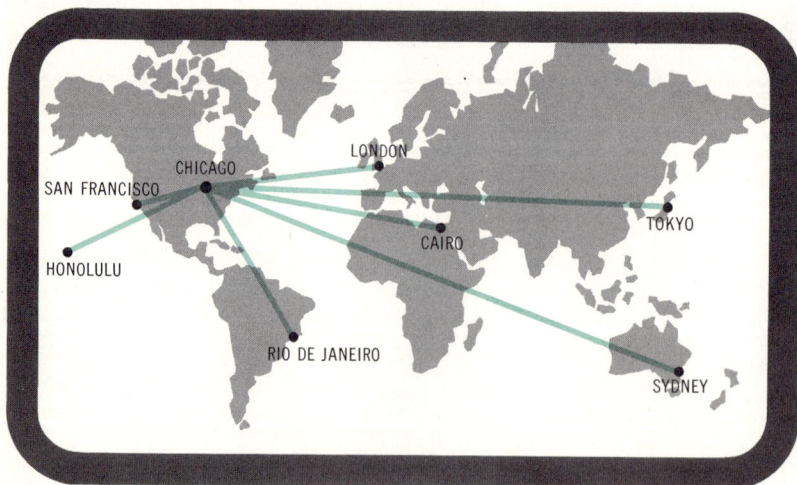

Figure 4–16 *The calls from Chicago to the other cities indicated on the map at the left show that the earth is in the time position at the right. When it is sundown in Chicago, the sun is still high above the beaches of California. Why are the time zone boundaries not straight lines?*

Where is it 3 A.M., or 5 A.M. on Wednesday? Nowhere. In fact, Wednesday morning no longer exists anywhere on earth. Can you see why? Where is it 3 A.M. on Thursday?

Suppose you take a trip around the world by jet and plan to travel westward at the same rate the earth is turning toward the east. In this way you could keep the noon sun always overhead. How fast would you need to fly if you were at the equator? How fast at the pole? If you start your world trip in New York at noon Wednesday, what time would it be then in Chicago? Flying at this speed it takes only an hour to reach Chicago, where you find that it is noon. Then New York will have 1 P.M., and San Francisco 10 A.M.

The midnight sun in Norway. The photographs were taken at one-hour intervals. Which one was taken at midnight? which at noon? If it is June 21-22, at what latitude were the photos taken?

Now imagine your progress as you fly across the country. In three hours from New York you reach the West Coast. What time is it there when you arrive? What time is it in New York? Six hours after takeoff you reach Hawaii. If you keep up the westward flight, eventually you will come back to New York. What time will it be? What day? But New York has already had noon Wednesday! When noon arrives at New York again, it will have to be noon Thursday. When did this change occur?

4–10 What day is it?

Somewhere in your flight westward, noon Wednesday must suddenly have changed to noon Thursday. And that place is, by international agreement, the **International Date Line.** As you traveled westward, your time automatically became the same time of the next day when you passed over the International Date Line. This line runs generally along the 180th meridian of longitude. (See the globe in Figure 4–16.) Noon Wednesday on the eastern side of the line becomes noon Thursday as the Date Line is crossed. One P.M. Wednesday

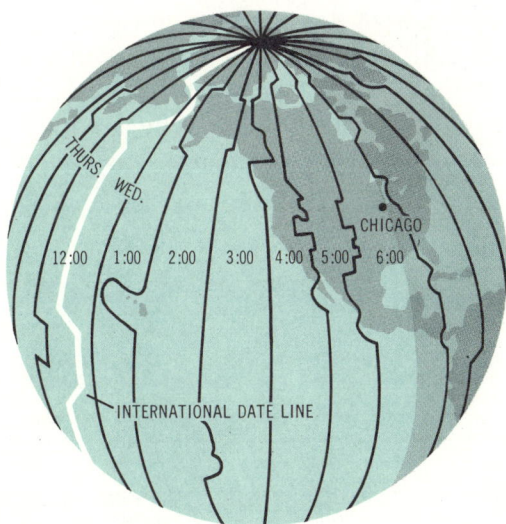

Figure 4–17 (Top) Clocks give time around the earth. (Bottom) Looking down on the North Pole as the earth rotates. (Left) The Date Line has rotated one hour past the midnight line. What day is it at A? Eleven hours later (center) Thursday has crossed the Eastern Hemisphere while elsewhere it is still Wednesday. (Right) What is happening to Wednesday?

becomes 1 P.M. Thursday on the western side of the line, and so on.

Travelers sometimes are puzzled by the Date Line. If you cross it going toward Japan, you find that Wednesday afternoon suddenly becomes Thursday afternoon. For you Wednesday evening will never exist. You have lost it. But coming from Japan to the United States, you will find just the opposite. In crossing the line on Thursday afternoon you find that it is Wednesday afternoon. If Wednesday is your birthday, you can celebrate two days in a row.

Remember that the date doesn't change at midnight only. No matter what time it is west of the Date Line, it is a day earlier east of the Date Line except when the midnight line is at the Date Line. At any given moment there are two lines on earth where dates change, as you can see in Figure 4–17. One of these is the midnight line, the other is the International Date Line.

The real time setter is the sun. When the sun is on the meridian in your town, it has not yet reached the meridian of a town just west of you. It would be very inconvenient if every town kept its own time, as was the case before 1881. In that year, Congress put an end to such confusion in the United States. The Eastern, Central, Mountain, and Pacific time zones were created. The Eastern time zone keeps the true time of the 75th meridian of longitude, the Central of the 90th, the Mountain of the 105th, and Pacific Time is the time at the 120th meridian of longitude. Why are these meridians 15 degrees apart?

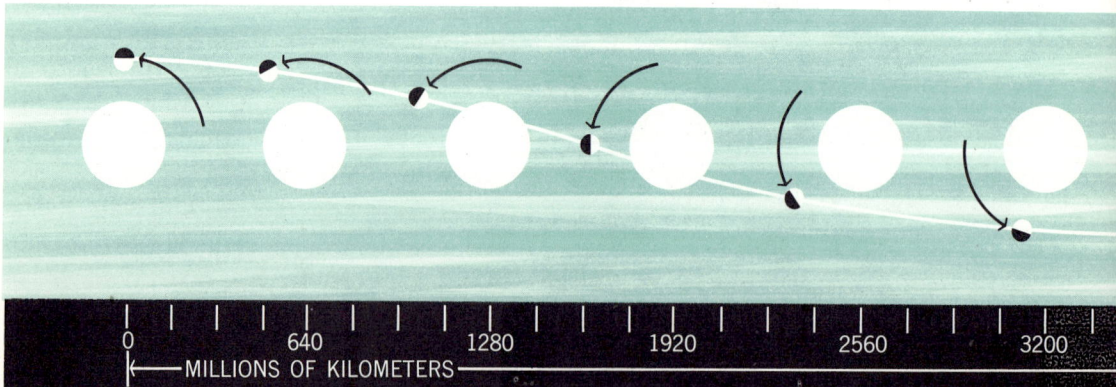

| 0 | 640 | 1280 | 1920 | 2560 | 3200 |

← MILLIONS OF KILOMETERS →

4–11 What time is it on the moon?

Time on the earth is governed by the spin of the earth. What then governs time on the moon? When astronauts reach the moon, how should they set their watches?

Probably astronauts will keep universal time, or Greenwich Mean Time. This is the standard time of the zero meridian of longitude on earth, the Prime Meridian. It is the time kept in Greenwich, England. All ships at sea also keep that time on their very accurate clocks, called chronometers. The difference in time between what the ship's chronometer reads and the local time on shipboard, which is obtained by observing the altitude of the sun, is used to determine the longitude of the ship. (See Section 3–3.) Do you see why?

Many scientific laboratories keep universal time. Astronomers record their observations in universal time. Then observatories all over the world can compare their observations directly without having to make troublesome changes from one time zone to another. In scientific work it is a nuisance to keep different times. So observatories and many laboratories keep universal time.

Universal time would be the most sensible time for astronauts to keep on the moon, too. If they do, they can set their watches by radio signals from earth. Of course, if people ever live on the moon for long periods of time, they should really keep clocks with moon time. Since a day and a night on the moon are 29½ times as long as an earth day and night, moon clocks would have to take this into account. Moon clocks would then read 12 o'clock at the lunar noon, when the sun is at its highest in the sky as seen from the moon.

ACTIVITY *Find out how long day and night are on Jupiter, Mars, and Saturn. How long is the year of these planets compared to the Earth's year?*

4–12 What causes the tides?

Up to now we have talked mostly about the effects of the two main motions of the earth, rotation and revolution. The earth has many motions. It accompanies the sun in its travel through space, and the sun is in turn revolving around the middle of the Milky Way Galaxy. (See Figure 4–18.) In addition, the earth has several small motions, such as the slow wobble of its axis, and its monthly dance with the moon as partner around the center of mass of the earth-moon system. The tides in the ocean are produced mainly by this action.

Some of you who live in the interior of the United States may scarcely have heard of tides. Those of you who live along the coast know very well what

Figure 4–18 *Relative positions of the earth and sun as the earth accompanies the sun on its journey around the center of the Milky Way galaxy.*

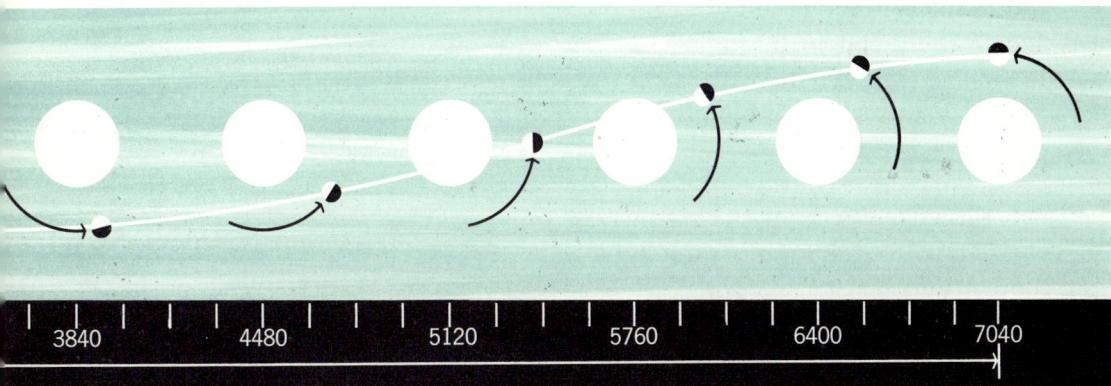

3840   4480   5120   5760   6400   7040

Figure 4–19   *Tides in the Bay of Fundy, Nova Scotia, may rise and fall over 17 meters in places.*

tides are and how important they are. Sometimes even human life depends on a knowledge of the tides.

If you live on the sea coast, or have visited there, you will know that *twice* a day (about every 12½ hours) the water rises, covering part of the beach. This is high tide. A quarter of a day later, you have low tide; the water level is below normal, and often wide stretches of the beach, generally under water, are uncovered. (See Figure 4–19.)

You probably already know that the moon is mainly responsible for the tides. (The sun is also, to a lesser extent.) The gravitational pull of the moon on the earth causes the oceans on the side of the earth facing the moon to be pulled toward the moon. This would explain *one* high tide a day, but why *two* high tides? Since there are two high tides a day, it means that one must occur on the side of the earth turned away from the moon. How is this possible? It results directly from the earth-moon dance.

Suppose we have two metal spheres with a hole bored through each so they can slide freely on a rod, as shown in Figure 4–20. Y, being lighter than X, has to be placed farther out on the rod to balance X, just as a small boy has to sit much farther out on a seesaw to balance a larger boy.

Now we have our model balanced. What happens if the rod now swings around B as in Figure 4–20? The faster X and Y revolve around B, the more quickly will they tend to slide off the ends of the rod, unless they are glued or fastened to the rod.

You have guessed, of course, that X and Y represent the earth and moon. What keeps the earth and moon from flying apart (as metal spheres X and Y would fly off the end of the rod) as they revolve around B? The pull of gravity is the answer. The earth is 81 times as massive as the moon. Consequently, the point of balance, or common center of mass, B, is within the earth as shown in Figure 4–21. The earth and moon pull on each other, and this exactly counterbalances the tendency of the earth and moon to fly apart—well, almost exactly! The side of the earth facing the moon is pulled more than the far side because it is closer. The solid earth cannot give very much, but the water on the near side is free to flow toward the moon. A person on this side of the earth would see a rise in water level, called high tide. (See Figure 4–21.)

Figure 4–20   *If the model rotates around pivot B, X and Y would tend to slide outward on the rod.*

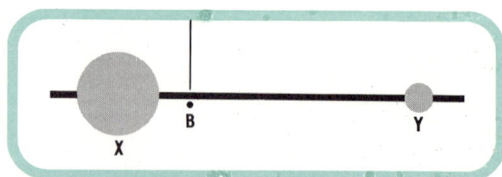

On the far side, both earth and ocean are pulled less than on the near side because they are both farther away. But *because* the pull of gravity is less on the far side, it does not exactly balance the tendency of water and earth to fly away from the moon (as the ball X would slide off the end of the rod if it were not fastened). The solid earth under the ocean on the far side cannot respond very much to the tendency to fly off, but the water, because it can flow freely, does respond, and that is why we have a high tide on the far side of the earth as well as on the near side. Can you see from Figure 4–21 why there is a low tide between the high tides?

The tides cause friction between water and land. Energy is lost by friction, so the earth's rotation is slowed. How will this affect the length of our day?

Thought and Discussion . . .

1. Do you think we know today all that there is to know about the motions of the earth? Explain.
2. If the earth's axis were tilted at an angle of 30 degrees, at what latitude would the following parallels lie: Tropic of Cancer, Arctic Circle, Tropic of Capricorn, Antarctic Circle?
3. What is the meaning of the "first day of spring"? Does spring always come on March 21 in the Northern Hemisphere regardless of latitude?
4. What time is it at the North Pole?
5. If an astronaut, traveling from west to east around the earth, wanted to have his watch keep the same time as that shown by the watches of the people on earth directly below him, how often would he have to set his watch ahead an hour? Suppose that it takes him exactly two hours to make one orbit.

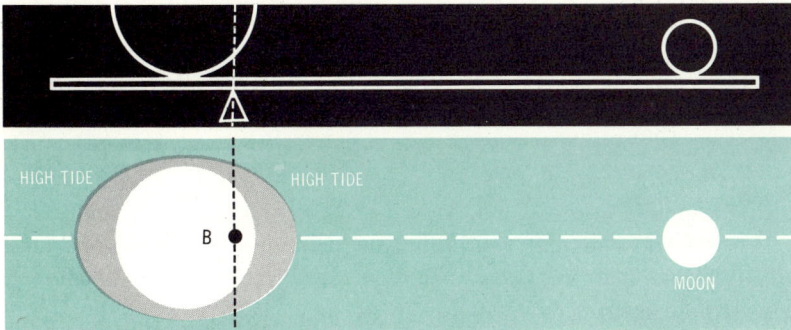

Figure 4–21 *The earth and moon complete a turn around their point of balance, B, about every 27 days and 8 hours. Tides are caused by gravity that keeps earth and moon from flying apart. As the earth rotates, the tides appear to move around it.*

HIGH TIDE   HIGH TIDE   B   MOON

Unsolved Problems Why do seasons vary from year to year? Why are some summers hotter than others and some winters colder than others? The seasons are caused by the motion of the earth around the sun. But this motion repeats itself with almost perfect exactness year after year. Why aren't all summers exactly alike, and all winters exactly alike? Why, in the course of long periods of time, have there been Ice Ages?

Why are there small changes in the period of rotation of the earth? The earth is slowing down in its rotation by one-thousandth of a second per century. This slow, steady change is caused by the drag of the ocean tides. There are other small changes—speedups and slowdowns—that happen in much shorter times. What causes the earth to be a little behind or ahead of schedule at various times?

CHAPTER REVIEW

Summary

The two primary motions of the earth are its rotation, turning about an axis through the North and South Poles, and its revolution, or almost circular yearly journey around the sun.

If the skies were always cloudy so that you could never see the stars, you could still demonstrate the rotation of the earth in several ways, one of which uses the Foucault pendulum.

The stars are necessary as a frame of reference to establish the earth's motion about the sun. One way this can be done is to show that at one time of the year the earth is moving toward the stars in one part of the sky and away from those in the opposite part of the sky. Six months later, the situation is reversed. Motion toward or away from stars causes the Doppler effect, which can be detected by examining the spectra of starlight.

Seasons are related to the earth's revolution around the sun. As the earth goes around the sun, its North Pole points in the same direction in space, a condition known as parallelism of the axis. At one part of the earth's orbit, the North Pole is tipped toward the sun, and summer results in the Northern Hemisphere. At the opposite part of the orbit, it is tipped away, so it is winter in the Northern Hemisphere.

Day and night and the telling of time are related to the *rotation* of the earth. The twenty-four hours of daylight are evenly distributed around the earth. It is one hour earlier in clock time for every fifteen degrees of longitude westward.

Tides occur on the earth because the moon's gravity attracts the near side of the earth more strongly and the far side less strongly than the earth as a whole, and because the earth and moon revolve around a common center of mass.

Questions and Problems

A

1. If you observe a particular star, such as Vega, for a period of one hour, you will notice that its position in relation to you will change. In what direction will its position change?
2. Why are the stars of the winter sky different from those of the summer sky?
3. If you were at a place where Polaris was at your zenith, what animals would you probably see?
4. The North Star, Polaris, is a valuable aid to navigation. Can you think of one factor that limits its use as a worldwide navigational landmark?
5. While you are sitting here doing this work, you think of yourself as being at rest. Are you really at rest or are you in motion? Explain your answer.
6. What proofs can you give that the earth rotates?
7. What proof can you give that the earth is revolving?
8. Why were the time zones created?
9. What factors cause the earth's seasons?
10. What causes the lag of the seasons?
11. Why is it necessary to have the International Date Line? Why isn't it a straight line on the earth's surface?

B

1. What is your frame of reference when you are the driver of an automobile?
2. If you are walking at a rate of 8 kilometers per hour toward the rear of a train that is traveling 70 kilometers per hour, describe your motion relative to the engine of the train, and relative to the telegraph poles beside the tracks.
3. Relate the various motions of the earth to the effects they produce.
4. How could you prove by using the Doppler effect that Mars is rotating?

5. At 15 degrees north latitude there are two periods during the year when temperature maxima occur. Locations at latitudes greater than $23\frac{1}{2}$ degrees north experience only one such period. Explain.

6. What would be the effect on the seasons if the earth's axis were perpendicular to the plane of its orbit?

7. If a certain star appears 5 degrees to the east of your meridian at midnight on Tuesday, where will it appear to be at midnight on Wednesday? Explain. On what day will it appear directly on your meridian at midnight?

8. Why is it that the moon has a much greater influence in producing tides on earth than does the sun considering that the sun's size is so many times greater than that of the moon?

9. It is found that high tides occur on opposite sides of the earth at the same time. What causes these tides on both the near side and far side of the earth with respect to the moon?

10. The gravitational forces of both the sun and moon affect tides on the earth. Explain why, at certain times each month, high tides are considerably higher and low tides lower than at other times during the same month.

C

1. Is it possible to launch a satellite which would, when in orbit, always be located over an identical spot on the earth's surface? Explain.

2. What difficulty would you encounter in attempting to prove the earth's rotation by using the pattern traced in the sand by a swinging pendulum suspended over the equator?

3. A sound has a higher pitch when the source of the sound approaches you, and a lower pitch when the source is moving away. How can this effect be used to determine whether you are moving toward or away from a source of light? How can the information be used to prove the earth revolves?

4. If it were 4:00 P.M. Wednesday at a location with a longitude of 165 degrees west, what would be the time and day at a location with a longitude of 165 degrees east?

5. How important is the varying distance between earth and sun in producing the seasons?

6. If the earth didn't rotate, would we still have tides? Suppose the earth kept the same face toward the moon in the same way that the moon does toward us. Would there be any tides?

Suggested Readings

BOOKS

Armitage, Angus. *The World of Copernicus.* The New American Library of World Literature, Inc., New York, 1947. Chapter 1, Planetary Theories Before Copernicus.

Gamow, George. *A Planet Called Earth.* The Viking Press, Inc., New York, 1963.

Hawkins, Gerald S. *Stonehenge Decoded.* Doubleday & Company, Inc., New York, 1965.

Koestler, Arthur. *The Watershed: A Biography of Johannes Kepler.* Doubleday & Company, Inc., New York, 1960. Paperback.

Strahler, Arthur N. *The Earth Sciences.* Harper & Row, Publishers, New York, 1963. Chapter 2, The Rotating Earth.

Trinklein, Frederick E. and Charles M. Huffer. *Modern Space Science.* Holt, Rinehart & Winston, Inc., New York, 1961. Chapter 6.

Whipple, Fred L. *Earth, Moon, and Planets,* rev. ed. Harvard University Press, Cambridge, Mass., 1963.

PERIODICALS

Cohen, I. Bernard. "The Man Who Looked to the Stars." *New York Times Magazine,* February 9, 1964.

Gamow, George. "Gravity." *Scientific American,* March, 1961.

Ronan, C. A. "Galileo Galilei." *Sky and Telescope,* February, 1964.

When you dive into a pool, you have a sense of freedom and excitement as you fall through the air. With a splash, you knife into the cool water. If the dive takes you deep into the pool, the weight of the water presses on your body and your ears may hurt. As you scramble out of the water, you may shiver with cold if the air is cool or the wind is blowing briskly.

During your dive, you were in contact with two common earth materials, air and water, and you crossed the interface between them in an instant. You felt the air rushing past as you dived, and the wind as you came out of the water. There was a sharp change in temperature as you plunged into the water, and later as you felt the wind on your wet body. You also sensed a change in pressure between the air and the water as well. Were these the only factors acting on you?

You could not have dived at all, unless the unseen force of gravity had pulled you down through the air and into the water. Gravity acting on the water created the pressures that you felt. Gravity was a factor even in creating the wind across the pool. You could not feel the magnetic field that was all around you in both the air and the water. You cannot observe magnetism directly with any of your senses.

Earth materials and the forces acting on them are the two main elements that determine any environment in which you find yourself. Both the kinds of matter and the conditions of matter are important. Some conditions of matter are its temperature, its pressure, and its motion. You learned in Chapter 2 about the kinds of materials composing the earth. Now you will learn how to describe and measure the conditions of these materials, and in the next chapter about the energies underlying all changes.

The motion of material, which includes not only the motion of a diver, but the motion of the air around him, and the motion of the earth and other planets, is a condition of materials that is a result of forces. Gravity is only one of these forces, but it acts throughout the entire universe. The turning of a compass needle and a flash of lightning are the result of other forces, magnetism and electricity, at work all around you.

You start now by investigating a field and discussing what a field is. Then you turn to the motion of objects in fields and the cause of motion. You will investigate two of the earth's force fields, gravity and magnetic force.

Chapter 5 Fields and Forces

Fields, Motions, and Forces

5–1 Investigating a temperature field.

What does the word field mean to you? Perhaps the first thing you think of when you hear the word is a portion of farmland with a fence around it, where a particular crop is grown, like a corn field or wheat field. Or maybe you think of a playing field for baseball or football. How would you describe these fields? Are they two- or three-dimensional?

Scientists use the word field when describing variations in conditions within a given portion of space. Think of a three-dimensional field as occupying a given portion of space. How would you describe the boundaries of such a field? What are the qualities of such a field? See if you can find answers to these questions during this investigation.

Procedure

Measure and record the temperature near your desk at: (a) floor level, (b) desk-top level, and (c) two or three meters above the floor.

Your teacher will give you the necessary instructions for making these measurements.

Figure 5–1

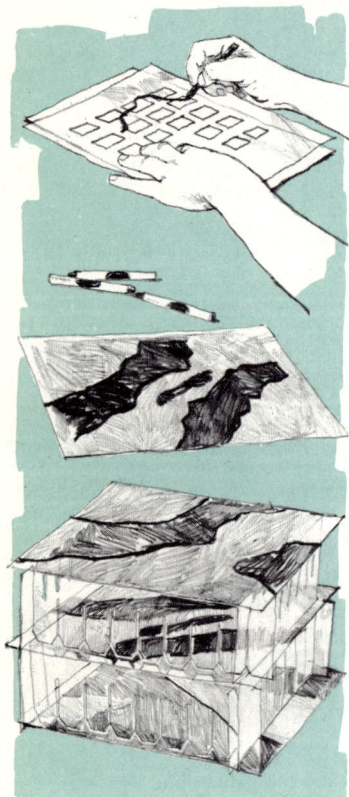

Make a map of the room temperature at each level. (See Figure 5–1.) Once this is done, place a clear plastic sheet over one of the maps and connect all the points of equal temperature with smooth lines. Do this for each temperature value on your map for each level. Color the spaces between the lines so that areas of the same temperature range are all the same color. Stack the sheets for each level to form a fence diagram and answer the following questions.

(1) What factors do you think cause the variations within the temperature field?

(2) Would the field have the same variations tomorrow at the same time? Explain.

(3) If there were any other fields in your classroom at the same time you were measuring the temperature field, how could they be detected and described?

You have drawn three maps that show for each level the lines that pass through points where the temperature is the same. Such lines are called isotherms. *Iso* comes from the Greek word meaning equal and *therm* from the Greek word for hot. An **isotherm** is a line in space along which temperatures are equal. The map in Figure 5–2 shows the temperature field of the air near the ground across the United States at one particular time. Do you think the readings for this map were made in summer or winter?

How is a field defined? Within a portion of space it is possible for you to measure many quantities that tell you about conditions in the space. With proper instruments you can measure air temperature and pressure. Plotting the measurements defines a temperature or pressure field.

You can measure the density of air. In another environment you might measure the density of a liquid, like water, or a solid, like rocks under the earth's surface. You can measure the speed and direction of motion of a moving object. You can measure the forces that are acting on matter in space. You would find a definite value at every point for the quantity you measured, as you did when you investigated the temperature field in your classroom. When you were finished you would have a representation of a field. A **field** is a portion of space where there is a value for a measurable quantity at every point in that space. Can you name and describe other fields?

Would you expect a field to change as time passes? Is the temperature or the pressure at a place always the same? The prediction of changes of temperature and pressure fields in the atmosphere is part of the job of weather forecasters.

Figure 5–2 *Air temperatures in the United States at a particular time.*

ACTIVITY *As part of your Weather Watch, you have been posting a daily weather map. Observe the atmospheric pressure field around your locality on some of these maps. What characteristics does it have that allow it to be described as a field? Describe the motion that is a result of the pressure field.*

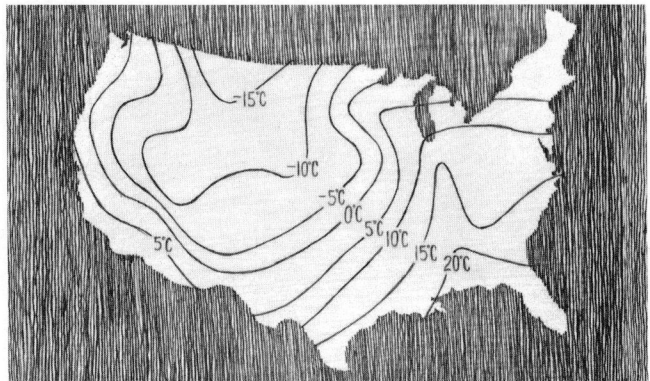

5–2 Investigating the behavior of a falling object.

Another field that filled your classroom as you investigated the temperature field in Section 5–1 was the gravitational field. You were born in the gravitational field of the earth and you will probably never escape it in your entire lifetime. When you release an object and it drops to the ground, it is gravitational force that causes the motion. It required the genius of men like Galileo and Newton to be able to look at

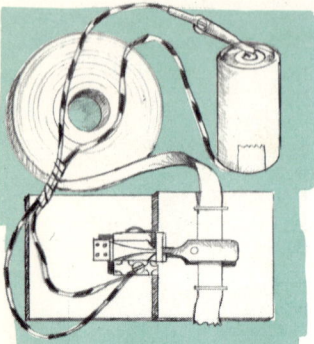

Figure 5–3

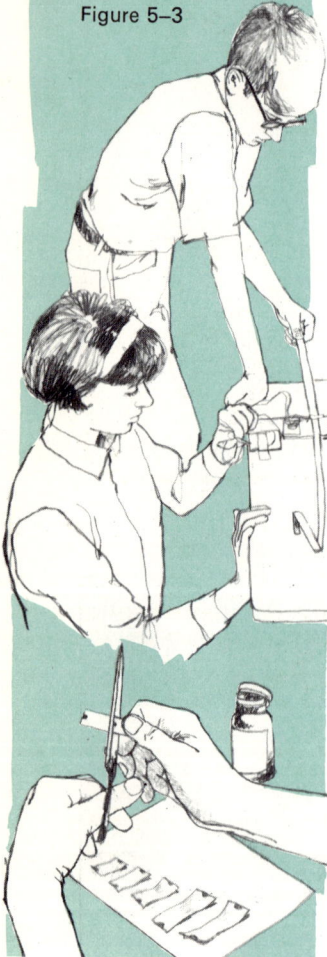

Figure 5–4

the motion of objects in the world around them and see that all these objects behave in a similar manner. Motion is everywhere. As you watch a ball arc through the air or a plane streak across the sky you observe motion. And yet motion is seldom described with care. Once the motion of objects is described and understood, evidence can be gathered that will provide insight into the nature of the gravitational field.

In this investigation you first examine different kinds of motion and rates of motion. Then you observe the way objects behave as they fall freely. By determining the behavior of a falling object, you will be able to understand certain characteristics of the gravitational field.

Procedure

Part A · Determining rate of motion.

Set up the equipment as shown in Figure 5–3.

Pull the tape through the timer at: (a) a steady rate, (b) a speeding-up rate, and (c) an irregular rate.

Cut each tape at the dots (Figure 5–4). Paste the pieces of tape down in correct order. The result will be a graph of the rate at which the tape was pulled through the timer.

Part B · Behavior of a falling object.

Feed the tape through the timer and attach a weight to the end of the tape. Allow the weight to drop off the end of the table.

Make a graph of the rate at which the weight falls. Compare this graph with your graphs from Part A.

(1)What force pulled the tape through the timer in Part A? in Part B? (2)Your graph for Part B closely resembles which of your graphs in Part A? (3)How does your Part B graph compare with the Part B graphs of other groups? (4)What can be said about the behavior of the falling object in Part B in different parts of the room?

The **speed** of an object is the distance it moves in a certain time. If you measure the distance in meters and use one second as the length of time, the speed will be in meters per second. (5)If the time that elapsed between the dots on the tape is one hundredth of a second, what is the speed of the tape in centimeters per second in your steady-rate graph?

5–3 How is motion described?

From your observations, do you think that just knowing the location of an object gives enough information to describe its motion? Is just knowing the speed enough? The direction of the motion is important as well. Do you also need to know how the speed and direction of motion changed while the object was moving?

If you know that an object moved 10 meters in 1 second, you know its average speed was 10 meters per second. If you know the object traveled at this speed in a definite direction, say to the north, you have a more complete picture of its motion. Speed and direction together make up the **velocity** of the moving object.

The velocity of the car in Figure 5–5 changes as it speeds up, slows down, or changes direction. You can see that knowing the velocity at one instant, therefore, still does not completely describe the motion. You must include the way in which the velocity changes. Velocity may change slowly or rapidly. The speed of a car may be reduced by applying the brakes or running it into a solid wall.

The change in velocity of an object in a certain amount of time is called **acceleration.** You know that velocity includes speed and direction. Thus, a change in *either* speed or direction results in a change in velocity. The car in Figure 5–5 (above) and (below), for example, changes its velocity in both cases. In Figure 5–5 (above), the car accelerates by changing speed but not direction. In Figure 5–5 (below), the car is accelerating, but it does not change its speed.

Rate of change of velocity is called acceleration. If speed is given in meters per second, then the acceleration will be

This hot rod is getting off to a fast start. Do you think its acceleration is constant?

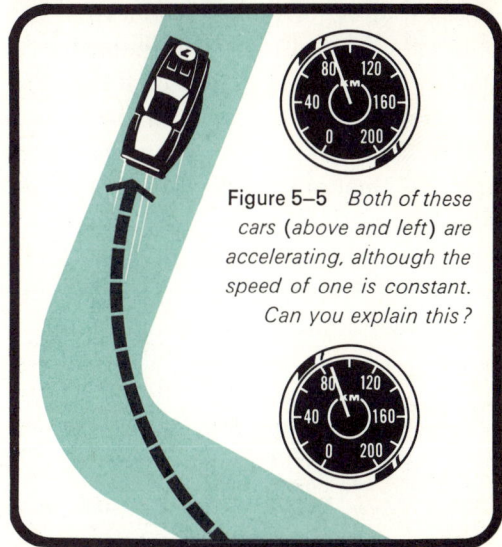

Figure 5–5 *Both of these cars (above and left) are accelerating, although the speed of one is constant. Can you explain this?*

the number of meters per second that this speed changes in one second. Acceleration is measured in meters per second per second, which is expressed as meters per second squared and written as

$$\frac{m}{sec^2} \text{ or } m/sec^2.$$

Refer to the graphs you constructed as part of Section 5–2, Investigating the behavior of a falling object. Which of the graphs represents uniform speed? uniform acceleration?

5–4 Forces are the cause of motion.

If a car is stalled in the middle of a street, how does the driver get it to the curb? Perhaps some helpful people will push it for him, or another motorist will use his car to push the driver's car to the nearest service station. What must be done to put any object in motion or to change the speed and direction in which an object is moving? A push or a pull must be exerted on it. This push or pull is called a **force.** Some forces act by direct contact between two objects, such as the force your hands exert if you are one of those who help push the car. Other forces act without contact between objects. Can you name some forces that act without contact between objects? What forces caused acceleration in your investigation of motion?

Isaac Newton stated three basic laws that tell us the relation between forces and the motions that forces produce. The laws of motion are based on thousands of observations of different kinds of motion. We accept these laws because they successfully describe our observations of motion, and they also success-

fully predict motions. However, there are motions to which these laws do not apply. For example, they fail to describe the motion of objects at velocities near the speed of light. But the laws work very well for all motions with which you are familiar.

The first of Newton's three laws of motion is that if no force acts on an object, or if a number of forces act that exactly balance each other, the motion of the object will not change. If the object is at rest, it will remain at rest. If the object is moving, it will continue to move in a straight line with the same speed. (See Figure 5–6.)

The second law tells us that if the forces acting on an object are not balanced, the motion of the object is changed in a very definite way. If you push an automobile and a bicycle with the same amount of effort, which one will accelerate faster? The effect that a given force has on the motion of an object depends on *how much mass the object has.* The mass of an object determines how much the object resists a change in its motion.

Figure 5–6 *An object at rest (top) remains at rest and an object in motion (bottom) continues in motion under Newton's first law. Are there forces acting on a motionless object?*

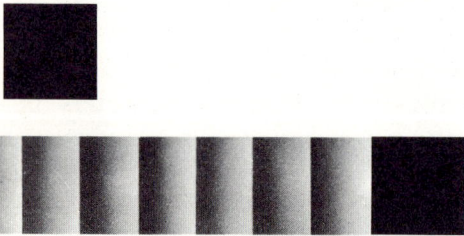

Figure 5–7 *Can you see how these objects represent the relationship between force, mass, and acceleration under Newton's second law of motion? Each arrow represents an equal force acting for the same amount of time.*

The second law of motion relates the force that is acting on the mass of an object and the change in the velocity, or the acceleration, of the object. The law says that as long as the mass remains the same, the acceleration is proportional to the force, and is in the same direction as the force. Force is another quantity that needs a direction as well as an amount to describe it completely. If two forces, one twice as strong as the other, act on equal masses, as shown in Figure 5–7, the stronger force will cause twice the acceleration. If forces of equal strength act on objects of unequal mass, the object with less mass will be accelerated more. As long as an unbalanced force continues to act, the object will con-

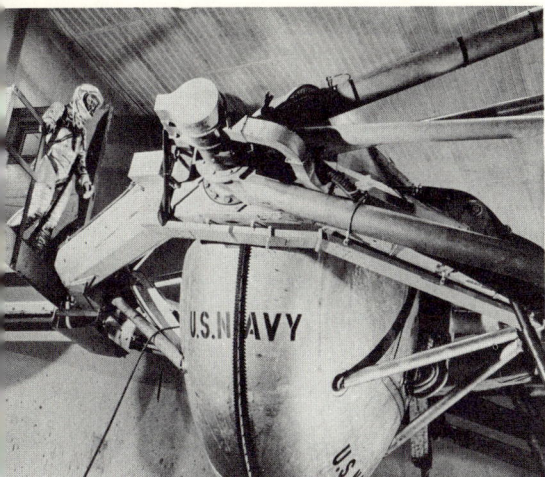

Figure 5–8 *The astronaut enters a giant centrifuge (left) to test his reactions to great forces of acceleration like those he would experience in space flight. In which direction does the ball fly when the hammer thrower lets it go? Is the ball accelerating while the thrower is holding it? after he releases it?*

tinue to accelerate, that is, the velocity will change.

We can write the second law of motion as a formula, in which F stands for the force, M stands for the mass, and a is the acceleration that the force causes. The formula is

$$F = Ma.$$

If the mass is measured in kilograms and the acceleration in meters per second², the force will be in kilograms times meters per second². Scientists have named this unit of force the newton in honor of the discoverer of the laws of motion. One *newton* equals one kilogram times one meter per second². The sample problem illustrates this:

Sample problem: What force acting on a mass of 20 kilograms would produce an acceleration of 15 meters per second²?

Solution: $F = Ma$
$\quad\quad = 20\,\text{kg} \times 15\,\text{meters per second}^2$
$\quad F = 300\,\text{newtons}$

If either the speed of an object, the direction, or both change, then a force has acted on the object. If a body moves in a circle with constant speed, is a force acting on the body? Whirl an object on the end of a piece of string. The pull you feel in the string is the force needed to make the object move in a circle. If the string were to break, the pull would no longer act on the body. In which direction would the object fly? The first law of motion gives you the answer. An example of this situation appears in Figure 5–8.

The third law tells us about forces rather than motion. When you push on a car, the car pushes back on you with equal force. When one object exerts a force on another which is at rest, the second object exerts an equal and opposite force on the first. When a book lies on a table, it exerts a force downward on the table because of its weight. The table exerts an equal and opposite force (upward) on the book.

Every particle of matter in the earth is acted on by forces all the time. Gravity, magnetism, and electricity have already been mentioned as common earth forces. Other kinds of forces that affect the behavior of earth materials are the forces that exist inside of bodies because the parts of the bodies exert pushes or pulls on the other parts. If you stretch a rubber band, each part of the rubber band exerts a pull on the part next to it.

The internal force is called the *elastic force* in a solid material. You feel the elastic force in a rubber band when you stretch it. These internal forces are important because they balance external forces that tend to change the shape of objects by squeezing, stretching, and twisting them. They are the forces that must be overcome when a solid object is deformed or broken.

Of all the forces that have been active in moving earth materials, gravity is by far the most important. How does gravity move earth materials?

Thought and Discussion . . .

1. When does a field exist in a given region?
2. Name at least two fields that have a major effect on your personal comfort.
3. What is the difference between speed, velocity, and acceleration?
4. Describe the motion of an object if the forces acting on it are exactly balanced.
5. What three quantities are related to each other in the second law of motion? How do they affect each other?
6. Why is the motion of the moon around the earth an accelerated motion?

The Gravitational Field of the Earth

5–5 The law of gravitation applies to all matter.

What do the tumbling of water over a waterfall and the motion of the planets around the sun have in common? The nature of the force that is responsible for most of the natural motions we see every day was first discovered by Newton. Newton was searching for an explanation of the motions of the planets. He had already discovered the three laws of motion discussed in Section 5–4. The one thing he didn't know was the strength and direction of the force that would account for the observed motion of the planets. After much thought, he finally came to the conclusion that a force must exist that has the following three properties:

1. The force is an attraction that pulls the planets toward the sun, and the sun toward the planets. The force acts along the line between the center of the planet and the center of the sun.

2. The force is proportional to the product of the mass of the sun times the mass of the planet.

3. The force is smaller the farther the planet is from the sun. In fact, the force decreases as the square of its distance from the sun.

Newton also found that the same kind of force acts between the planets themselves. In a bold step, he stated that this force acts between all pieces of matter in the universe. He could not prove this last conclusion, nor can we, but a great deal of evidence supports it.

The force is called gravitation. The law that Newton discovered which tells the direction and strength of the force is called the **law of gravitation.** Because there is evidence that the law applies to all matter, from deep within the earth to the most distant galaxies observed, it is called a universal law. We do not yet know what *causes* gravity, but we know what gravity *does*. For every two objects in the universe, the larger their masses, the greater the force of attraction between them. The greater the distance between the two objects, the smaller the force of attraction between them. Actually, Newton found that the attraction between the two objects varies directly with the product of their masses and varies inversely with the square of their distance from each other.

In order to calculate the strength of the gravitational force between two objects, we must describe the force more specifically than we have done so far and in mathematical terms. The formula involves four quantities:

1. the force, F,
2. the masses of the two objects, M_1, and M_2, and
3. the distance between the masses, d.

In addition, there is a constant, G, which makes the force come out in newtons, when the masses are measured in kilograms and the distance in meters. The value of G is 6.67×10^{-11} cubic meters per kilogram seconds^2. The formula for the universal law of gravitation is

$$F = \frac{GM_1M_2}{d^2}.$$

It is important to fully understand what this mathematical statement of the law expresses. Look carefully at the formula. The expression, $\frac{GM_1M_2}{d^2}$, is obviously a fraction. What happens to the value of a fraction if the numerator alone

Sir Isaac Newton (1642–1727), a brilliant English astronomer and mathematician, from early childhood showed a talent for invention.

Newton's genius brought him a mathematics professorship at 27, and a fellowship in the Royal Society at 29. His major contribution to this field was the calculus, a branch of mathematics that deals with rates of change and the areas of irregularly shaped figures. Newton's Optics, published in 1704, contains his theories of light and color. Most of this work had been done earlier, however, while Newton was still in his twenties. At that time Newton had developed a telescope that produced images with the aid of a curved mirror. Such telescopes, called reflectors, are still in use today.

Newton's Mathematical Principles of Natural Philosophy, printed in 1687, established the basic laws of modern physics, which today are still phrased almost in his own words. In it Newton dealt with the motions of heavenly bodies and introduced his three laws of motion, as well as the universal law of gravitation.

Newton's theories provided the basis for work in physics and astronomy for over 200 years. Even Einstein, while disputing Newton's explanation of gravity, depended on the foundation laid down by his seventeenth-century predecessor.

increases? What happens to its value if the denominator alone increases? Remember that *G* is a constant, so its value remains the same. Will the force of attraction, *F*, increase or decrease if the distance between the two objects, *d*, becomes larger? Will *F* increase or decrease if one of the masses decreases? Writing Newton's law as a formula is a way of combining the influence of mass and distance.

You studied the motions of the earth around the sun in Chapter 4. Compare the path of the earth around the sun with that of the car rounding the curve, in Figure 5–5. Is the earth accelerating? It certainly is. To have acceleration there must be a force and you know that the force between the planets is the force of gravity. (See Figure 5–9.)

Actually every object in the solar system, and in the universe for that matter, attracts every other object. Can you see why the attraction between the earth and a distant star is very small compared with the attraction between the earth and sun? (See Figure 5–10.)

5–6 How does gravity affect earth materials?

The earth can be thought of as many millions of small pieces of matter, each attracted to the others by gravitational

GIVEN MASS & DISTANCE—GIVEN ATTRACTION

SAME MASS, GREATER DISTANCE—LESS ATTRACTION

LARGER MASS, SAME DISTANCE—GREATER ATTRACTION

Figure 5–10 *Every object in the universe attracts every other object. The force varies directly as the products of the masses and inversely as the square of the distance between the masses.*

force. The combination of all these forces produces the gravitational force that the entire earth exerts on any object. Which will have the greater effect on the gravitational force on an object at the earth's surface, the rocks just beneath it, or rocks of the same mass on the other side of the earth? Remember the formula in finding the answer.

It is possible to calculate the approximate pull of the earth on an object at the earth's surface by considering the earth as a single mass rather than as millions of little masses joined together. In other words, if you calculate the total force with which the earth attracts an object on its surface by adding together the forces exerted on the object by each part, the result is about the same as if the whole mass of the earth were lumped together at its center. You can get a rough idea of the strength of the earth's gravitational pull by using the approximate radius of the earth, 6400 kilometers, as the distance (d) from the center of the earth to the object. The mass of the earth (M_1) is about 6.0×10^{24} kilograms.

Figure 5–9 *Gravitational attraction causes the earth to accelerate. (See also Figure 5–5.)*

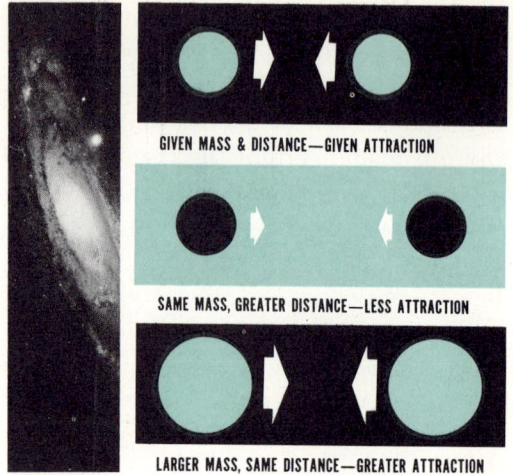

You can now calculate the approximate force with which the earth attracts a mass of one kilogram (M_2) located on the surface of the earth. First express the earth's radius in *meters:* 6.4×10^3 kilometers multiplied by 10^3 (1000 meters per kilometer) is 6.4×10^6 meters. Putting these values in the formula $F = \dfrac{GM_1M_2}{d^2}$, and making the calculations, gives you:

$$F = \frac{(6.67 \times 10^{-11}) \times (6.0 \times 10^{24}) \times (1.0)}{(6.4 \times 10^6)^2}$$

$$= \frac{40.02 \times 10^{13}}{40.96 \times 10^{12}}$$

$$= 0.98 \times 10^1$$

$$F = 9.8 \text{ newtons.}$$

So the force with which the earth pulls on a mass of one kilogram is about 9.8 newtons. This value, 9.8 newtons, is important in the discussion of the acceleration of falling bodies. Note that the force on a person with a mass of 50 kilograms is 50 times as great, or 50 multiplied by 9.8 newtons, which is 490 newtons. Look at the three different masses hanging from identical springs in Figure 5–11. The law of gravitation states that the amount of force depends, in part, on the mass. Can you see in Figure 5–11 that the force on the three-kilogram mass is three times the force on the one-kilogram mass?

Suppose you took a one-kilogram mass to various locations on the earth's surface and weighed it very carefully, that is, measured the downward force on the mass with a sensitive spring scale. Would the force be the same in every case? Remember the factors that went into the original calculation. Are all points on the earth's surface at an equal distance from the center of the earth?

What about the equatorial bulge mentioned in Chapter 3? Would it have an effect? Would differences in elevation have an effect?

Consider the following point: When you made the calculation of the force with which the earth attracts a one-kilogram mass, one of the underlying assumptions was that the earth is a perfectly uniform, homogeneous sphere. Is the earth homogenous? Is water evenly distributed over the surface? How

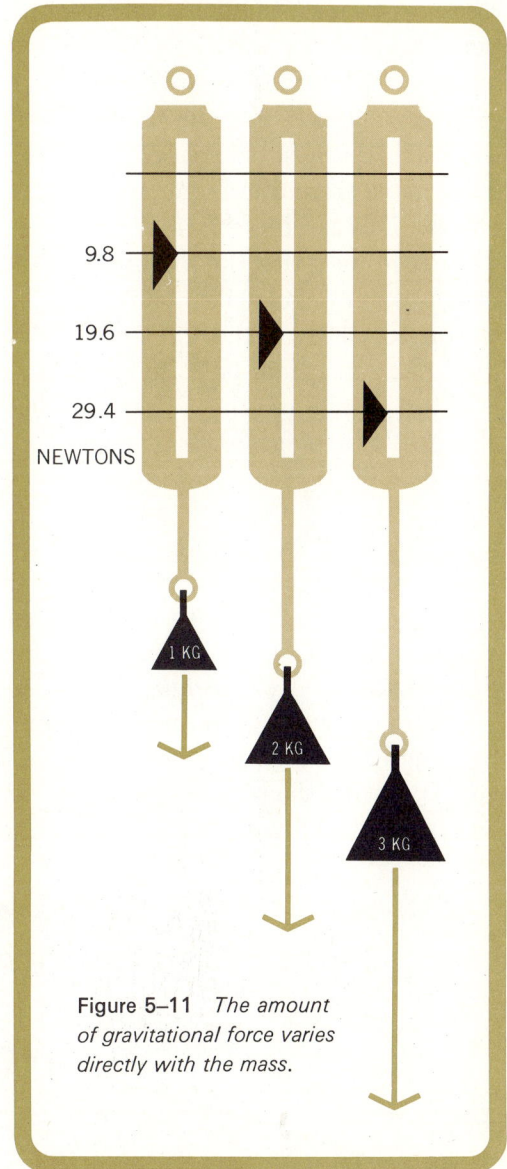

Figure 5–11 *The amount of gravitational force varies directly with the mass.*

would the uneven distribution of earth materials affect your measurements?

Another factor affects your measurements of gravitational attraction. In Section 5–4 you learned that motion around a circle is an accelerated motion that requires a force. You know that, because of the earth's rotation, every object on and in the earth travels in a circle around the axis once every day. This acceleration uses up part of the force of gravitational attraction. As a result, in most cases, your measurements of gravitational force at the earth's surface would be a little lower than expected. The effect of rotation is not the same all over the earth, because some points on the earth move around in larger circles than others. This can be seen in Figure 5–12. The net result is that the rotational effect *increases* in a regular fashion from poles to equator. Hence, the force of gravity itself *decreases* from poles to equator.

As a result of these factors that change the average force of attraction, the idea of the force of gravity was developed. The **force of gravity** is the force measured by weighing a standard mass at various locations, exactly as you visualized yourself doing with the one-kilogram mass. The common name for the force of gravity is *weight*.

Mass and weight are not the same thing and should never be confused. As you have seen, the second law of motion tells us that **mass** is a measure of how much an object resists a change in its motion. **Weight** on the other hand is the name of a force that acts on an object; for example, the earth's force of gravity. To better appreciate the difference between mass and weight, consider an astronaut with a mass of 80 kilograms. Will his weight and mass be the same on the moon as they are on the earth?

If the force of gravity is measured (as 9.8 newtons, for example) and the mass is known (as 1 kilogram), the downward acceleration can be calculated from Newton's second law of motion, which states that force (F) equals mass (M) times acceleration (a), as follows:

$$F = Ma$$
$$9.8 \text{ newtons} = 1 \text{ kg} \times a$$
$$a = \frac{9.8 \text{ newtons}}{1 \text{ kg}}$$
$$a = 9.8 \text{ meters/sec/sec.}$$

This acceleration is known as the *acceleration of gravity*. Note that if the mass being weighed were doubled, the force of gravity (the weight) would double, but the acceleration would not change. The force of gravity on a mass of one kilogram at any point, whether below, above, or on the earth's surface, is called the *gravity field intensity*. Would the gravity field intensity vary from point to point? Can you think of any place where the earth's gravitational attraction would be zero?

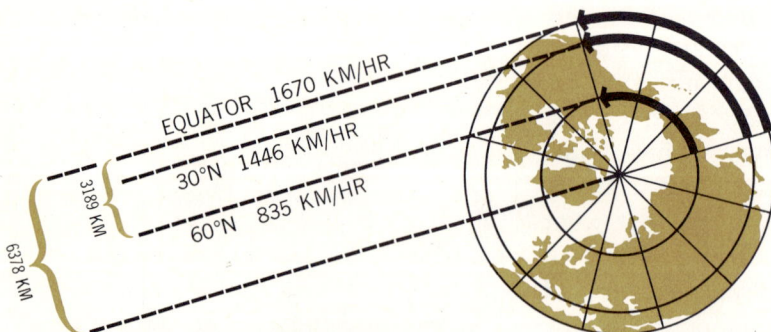

EQUATOR 1670 KM/HR
30°N 1446 KM/HR
60°N 835 KM/HR
3,189 KM
6378 KM

Figure 5–12
Except for the two poles, all points on the earth make a circle around the axis every day. Why do points on the equator move faster?

The ski jumper (far left) is experiencing the effects of the earth's gravitational field. The drivers of these gravity-driven vehicles (left) are waiting to be released. Will they accelerate as fast as the skier? Why?

Sample Problem: The force of gravity on the moon is one-sixth that on earth. If an astronaut's mass is 80 kilograms, what would be the downward force on him at the moon's surface?

Solution: If the downward force on the earth is 9.8 newtons per kilogram, then on the moon it must be $\frac{1}{6}$ of 9.8 or 1.63 newtons per kilogram. On 80 kilograms, therefore, the downward force would be 80 × 1.63 or 130.4 newtons (about 30 pounds).

Sample Problem: What is the force of gravity on an object with a mass of 20 kilograms at a place where the acceleration of gravity is 9.81 meters per second²?

Solution: $F = Ma = 20 \text{ kg} \times 9.81$ meters per second² = 196.2 newtons.

5–7 Measuring the earth's gravity.

The amount a spring stretches can be used to measure the force of gravity. This is the principle on which the ordinary bathroom scale works. Earth scientists use instruments similar to spring scales to measure gravity, but they are more sensitive. (See Figure 5–13.) The springs are arranged so that a very small change in gravity can be detected.

A *gravity meter* is an instrument used for measuring gravity field intensity at different places. Modern gravity meters are lightweight, portable, and very sen-

sitive. Changes in gravity as small as 0.0000001 meters per second² (10^{-7} meters per second²) can be detected. Such tiny variations provide useful data for earth scientists who investigate the earth's crust by interpreting slight differences in the gravity field intensity.

If gravity-meter measurements are started from a place at which the value of gravity has been determined by some other means, the readings of the gravity meter can be used to find the value at other places by adding or subtracting the changes measured. For example, if you start at a place where the acceleration of gravity is 9.80 meters per second² and then move to a place where the gravity meter shows a reading corresponding to an increase of 0.03 meters per second²,

Figure 5–13 *The simple spring scale (left), like those in Figures 5–11 and 5–14, measures the pull of gravity directly. Geophysicists use gravity meters (right) to detect differences in the gravitational attraction at the earth's surface.*

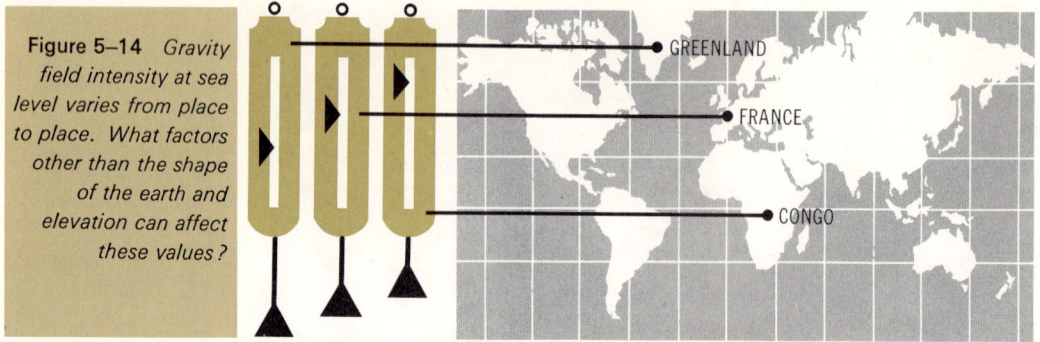

Figure 5–14 *Gravity field intensity at sea level varies from place to place. What factors other than the shape of the earth and elevation can affect these values?*

the value at the second place is 9.83 meters per second². This is a large change in gravity.

A few values of the gravity field intensity are given in Figure 5–14. The values for sea level at the latitudes of the locations shown are 9.82600 meters/second² at 70 degrees north latitude in Greenland, 9.80621 at 45 degrees in France, and 9.78039 at 0 degrees latitude in the Congo. As you would expect from the previous discussion, gravity is greater at the poles than at the equator by about one-half percent, a change easily detected by a gravity meter. Calculate the difference in your weight at the equator and your weight at the North Pole.

The way in which measurements of gravity can be used to investigate the earth's crust is illustrated in Figure 5–15. In the situation shown, even if all the factors that can affect gravity, such as rotation of the earth, its shape, and the elevation of the surface at that location are taken into account, there is still a small local irregularity in gravity. This results from a hump in the buried igneous rock surface. This hump brings high-density material closer to the earth's surface. If you measure the gravity field intensity in this region, you can locate the high place in the igneous rock even though it may be hidden under many meters of low density sedimentary rocks.

If a block of low density material is present under the surface, the gravity field intensity will be lower than in the surrounding area. Gravity measurements across a large salt dome in Texas produced the results shown in Figure 5–16.

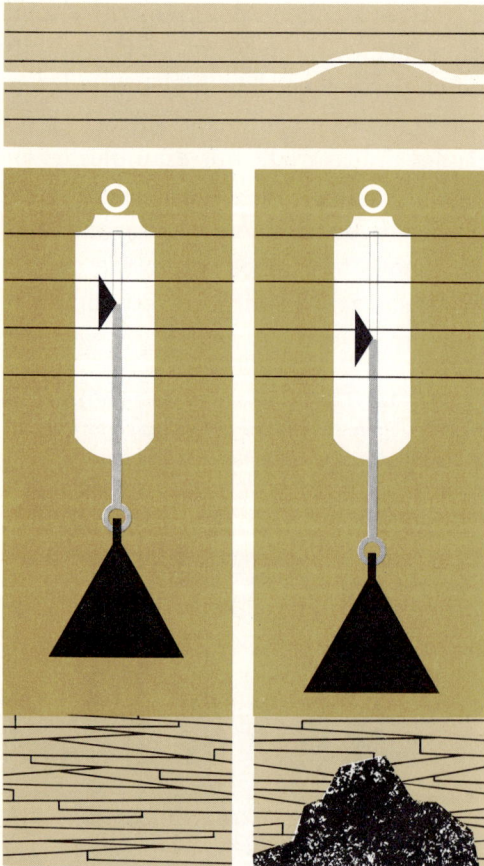

Figure 5–15 *The dark-colored mass under the earth's surface is denser than the surrounding rocks and causes a variation in the gravitational attraction. Although the denser mass may be buried under many meters of lighter rock, gravity measurements can detect it.*

You can see in the drawing how the gravity field intensity decreases toward the center of the area above the dome. The zero value on the gravity scale corresponds to the normal reading in the region. The negative values show that gravity over the dome is less than normal. The dome is capped with high density rock, which was formed on top of the salt as it pushed upward through the sedimentary rocks. How does this cap rock affect the gravity values? From such measurements, geophysicists have located many salt domes and other subsurface features that could not be detected from surface evidence. A mine in such a dome is shown in Figure 5–17.

Scientists can learn a lot about the nature of materials in the earth's crust by studying variations in the earth's gravity field. There is another force field that aids them in learning about conditions under the crust and in the atmosphere—a field that is all around you but which you cannot detect with any of your senses. This is of course the field of magnetic force. Can you think of any ways in which the magnetic field acts on your environment?

Thought and Discussion . . .

1. How does the mass of an object affect the gravitational attraction it produces?
2. How does the distance between objects affect the gravitational attraction between them?
3. Why does the shape of the earth make gravity at the poles greater than at the equator?
4. What is gravity field intensity, and how is it useful?
5. Would you expect a buried deposit of lead ore to cause gravity to be relatively higher or lower on the surface above it?
6. Does the earth exert a pull on an astronaut in orbit? Explain.

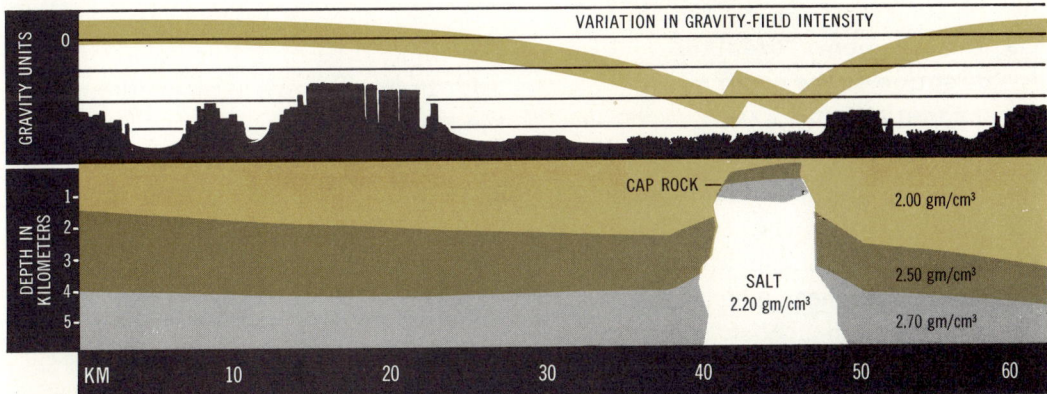

Figure 5–16 (above) Gravity measurements can be used to find a buried salt dome. Oil is frequently found with salt domes near the Gulf Coast.
Figure 5–17 (right) This salt mine near Grand Saline, Texas, is about 6 meters high. Note tractor tracks.

The Magnetic Field of the Earth

5–8 Investigating the magnetic field.

Gravity is a force that affects your life in many ways. Other fields surround you also, but they are not as noticeable because their effect is not the same on all kinds of matter. One of these is the magnetic field. In this investigation you will learn more about how a piece of material with the property of magnetism influences its surroundings.

Procedure

Using the equipment as shown in Figure 5–18, investigate the nature of a magnetic field. Locate the poles of the field and mark their positions on the sphere.

Answer the following questions about the field: [1]What evidence do you have that the field is three-dimensional? [2]Draw a picture of what the magnetic field would look like if you could see it. [3]How could you distort the field?

Take a compass outdoors to the place on the school ground where the north-south line was constructed in Investigation 1–9. [4]What is the relationship between the compass indication of north and the north-south line? Explain your observations. [5]How could you determine whether or not the earth's magnetic field is three-dimensional?

Figure 5–18

5–9 Measurements reveal the direction of the earth's magnetic field.

Thousands of years ago the Greeks knew that certain types of natural materials can attract iron. The word *magnet* comes from Magnesia, an ancient city in the Middle East near which rocks with the property of magnetism were found. The mineral causing this behavior is an oxide of iron, known as magnetite, which these rocks contain.

Although the ancient Greeks and Romans knew about magnetic materials, they did not know about the earth's magnetic field. Apparently the Chinese were the first to discover that if they suspended a piece of magnetic material

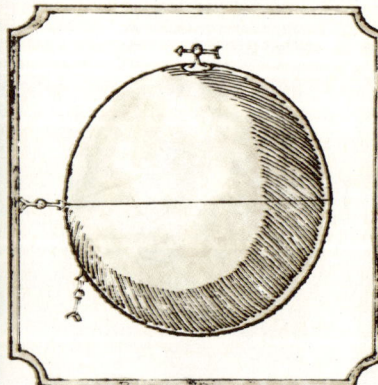

(*Far left*) A magnetic compass such as mariners used for centuries.
(*Left*) Gilbert used his terrella, an earth model made of magnetic lodestone, to study lines of force.

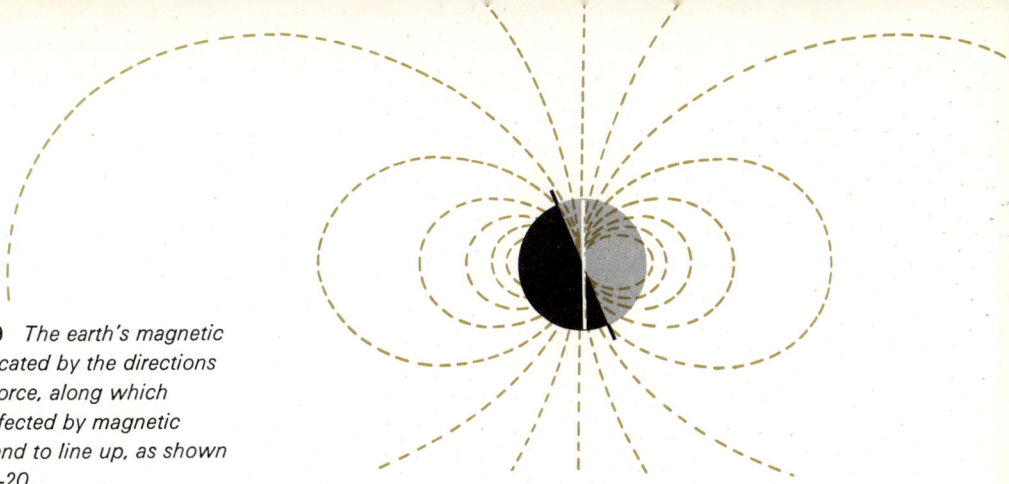

Figure 5–19 *The earth's magnetic field as indicated by the directions of lines of force, along which materials affected by magnetic force will tend to line up, as shown in Figure 5–20.*

so that it could swing freely, it would line up in a general north-south direction. Therefore, they called one end of the magnetic material the north-seeking, or North Pole, and the other the south-seeking, or South Pole. Chinese writings of the eleventh century A.D. mention using a magnetic needle to show direction. The magnetic compass has thus been an important aid to navigation for nearly a thousand years.

Scientific understanding of the behavior of the compass did not come until the seventeenth century when William Gilbert demonstrated that the earth itself acts as a magnet and is surrounded by a magnetic field. Figure 5–19 shows the magnetic field of the earth. The magnetic force acts to pull a magnetic needle so that it lines up with the earth's magnetic field as shown in Figure 5–20. Although scientists know the shape and strength of the earth's magnetic field near the earth, they are still trying to solve the problem of what its nature is and how it is produced.

The place on the earth's surface toward which a compass points is called a *magnetic pole* of the earth. The magnetic poles of the earth are located near the north and south geographic poles. The map in Figure 5–21 shows the location of the earth's north magnetic pole on Bathurst Island, near 75 degrees north latitude, 100 degrees west longitude. This location, pictured in Figure 5–22, is about 1900 kilometers from the north geographic pole. Since present theories hold that the magnetic field is related to the earth's rotation, it may not be a coincidence that these poles are close together.

The compasses in Figure 5–21 point toward the north magnetic pole. At

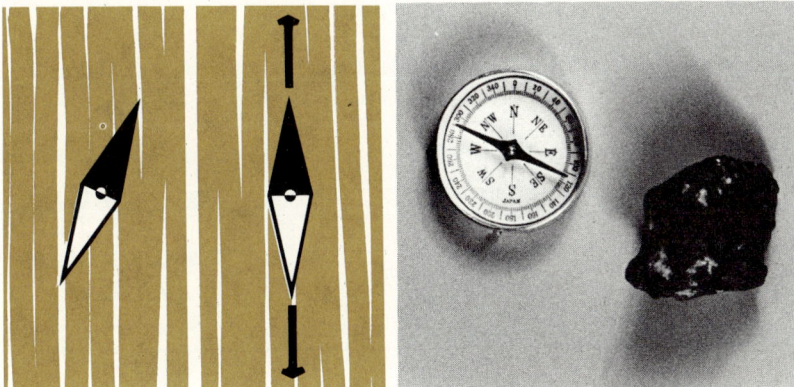

Figure 5–20 (*Far left*) *Lines of force on the earth's magnetic field cause the free-swinging magnetic needle to line up in the field.* (*Left*) *The needle of the compass is being deflected from north by the piece of natural lodestone.*

many places in the Northern Hemisphere this is also roughly the direction to the north geographic pole. At most places, however, there is an angle between the direction of geographic or true north and the direction indicated by the compass needle. This angle between the magnetic and geographic north pole is called the **magnetic declination.** Note the magnetic declination at places in the United States on the map in Figure 5–23. You can see that the declination can be either to the east or west of true north. What was the declination you detected answering question 4 in Investigation 5–8? How does this value compare with the declination of your area as shown in Figure 5–23? Find the line connecting places at which the declination is zero.

If you have a good compass, made for use in the Northern Hemisphere, you will find a small weight on the end of the compass needle that points south. If you removed this weight, the north-seeking end of the needle would dip down. What does this indicate about the direction of the magnetic field? If the needle dips, it must mean that the magnetic force that acts to turn the needle is not horizontal, but points down at an angle.

To test this idea, we can use a magnetic needle that is supported on a horizontal axis, like the one shown in Figure 5–24. In the Northern Hemisphere, you find that the north-seeking end of the needle points down. If you turn the base of this device, called a *dipping needle,* until it points toward magnetic north as well as down, you can measure the angle between the needle and the horizon. This angle, which is the angle between the direction of the magnetic force and a horizontal position, is called the **magnetic inclination.**

If you measured the angle of inclination at many places on the earth's surface, you would find two places, one in the Northern Hemisphere and one in the Southern Hemisphere, where the inclination is 90 degrees. The dipping needle points straight down, no matter how you turn its base. These points are the magnetic poles of the earth, to which the compass needle points.

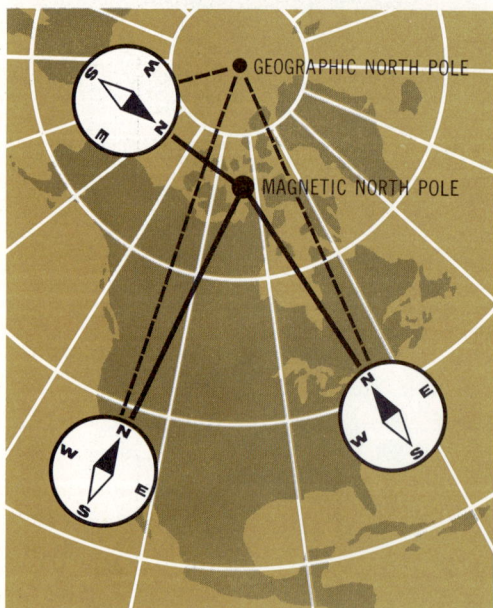

GEOGRAPHIC NORTH POLE

MAGNETIC NORTH POLE

Figure 5–21 (*Left*) In the Northern Hemisphere magnetic needles point to the earth's north magnetic pole.

Figure 5–22 A recent location of the north magnetic pole on Bathurst Island (*right*), from an altitude of 6000 meters.

Figure 5–23 (*Far right*) The curved lines on this map are lines of equal magnetic declination. Any point on a line has the same declination.

Taken together, the angles of declination and inclination as determined by a compass and a dipping needle give the direction of the earth's magnetic field with reference to north-south, east-west, and up and down.

ACTIVITY *The south magnetic pole is on the edge of the Antarctic continent, at 66 degrees south latitude, 140 degrees east longitude. Use a globe or map to find the distance from the south magnetic pole to the south geographic pole. Can you calculate this distance, using the length of one degree of latitude given in Chapter 3? A straight line drawn between the magnetic poles will pass close to but not exactly through the center of the earth.*

5–10 The earth's magnetic field changes constantly.

Although the different magnetic properties of subsurface rocks may cause the magnetic field of the earth to vary from place to place, differences are also evident at the same points at different

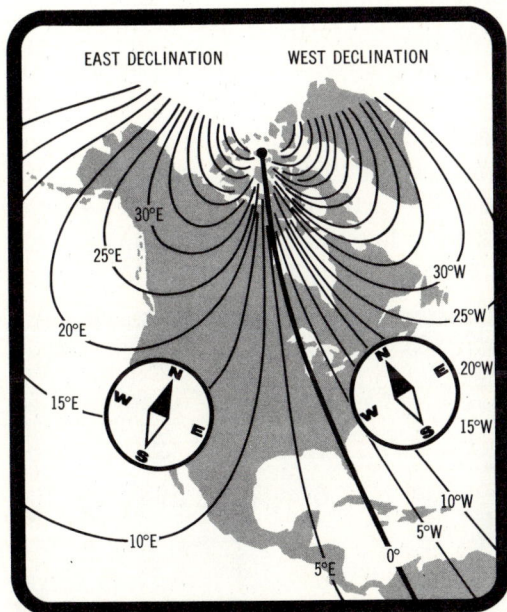

Figure 5–24 *The inclination of the magnetic field can be determined with a magnetic needle that turns on a horizontal axis. Needles that measure inclination are called dipping needles.*

times. Some of the ways in which scientists measure magnetic fields today are shown in Figure 5–25. Measurements made at one place over a long period show both rapid, sometimes cyclic, changes, as well as slow changes of the magnetic field. The rate of change is unpredictable, however. Since neither the strength nor direction of the variation is constant, magnetic field maps must constantly be redrawn to take these variations into account. Readings taken in London since 1576, for example, have shown radical changes in the magnetic field over the last four centuries. Indeed, the earth's magnetic field has been changing during the earth's long history, and evidence has been found indicating that the magnetic poles have wandered far from their original locations. Such slow, gradual changes are related to the processes causing the earth's magnetic field, which are thought to take place in the earth's central core.

More rapid changes also take place in the earth's magnetic field. Charged particles thrown off by the sun travel to the earth through space in a matter of hours or days. This phenomenon is called the solar wind and its arrival produces wild fluctuations in the strength and direction of the earth's magnetic

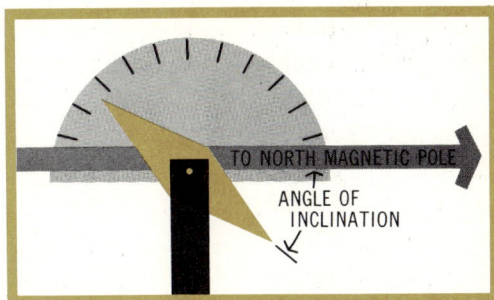

Figure 5–25 *The IMP satellite (below, left) measures magnetism in space. The airplane (right) trails a magnetometer to locate iron ore deposits. Magnetism is measured on the ground (below, right), and (far right) magnetic intensity values are mapped.*

field for short periods of time. These sudden and erratic variations in the earth's magnetic field, which often interrupt communications all over the world, are called *magnetic storms*. Records of a magnetic storm are shown in Figure 5–26. The streams of charged particles causing magnetic storms are probably also responsible for the **auroras,** brilliant displays of many-colored lights in the atmosphere surrounding the north and south magnetic poles. The *aurora borealis* or Northern Lights of the Northern Hemisphere (see Figure 5–27) and the similar *aurora australis* of the Southern Hemisphere occur at about the same time as magnetic storms and are accompanied by changes in the earth's magnetic field.

The charged particles entering the earth's magnetic field and causing it to fluctuate, however, are in turn affected by this field. Many of them are temporarily trapped and controlled by it, becoming concentrated in the outer part of a doughnut-shaped zone of radiation that surrounds the earth in the region high above the magnetic equator. This radiation zone is called the **Van Allen belt** after the scientist who discovered its existence in 1958 by analyzing data sent back to earth by an early space probe. As they lose their energy, trapped particles eventually leak out of the zone.

Figure 5–26 *Magnetic disturbances recorded on the magnetometer at College, Alaska, show large sudden changes in magnetic intensity at the earth's surface caused by solar events.*

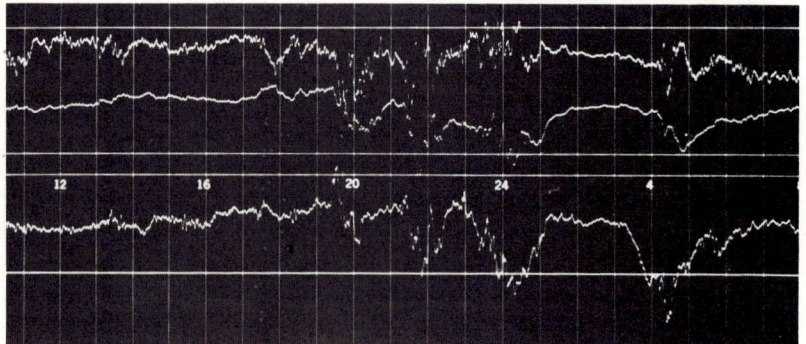

The conditions of matter, such as motion, temperature, and pressure, show that earth materials contain energy. Earth changes involve a loss or gain in the energy of materials. Where does the energy come from, and how is it transferred in earth processes?

Thought and Discussion . . .

1. How does a compass work?
2. Why are some materials naturally magnetic?
3. Why is it that a compass does not always point *true north?*
4. Explain the difference between magnetic declination and magnetic inclination.
5. What is the inclination at the earth's north and south magnetic poles? at the magnetic equator?
6. How is it possible for the sun to affect the earth's magnetic field?

Figure 5–27 *Unusual displays of aurora borealis, commonly called Northern Lights, accompany magnetic storms, which are related to disturbances at the sun's surface.*

Unsolved Problems What *is* gravitational attraction? Scientists know much about this force in terms of what it does, but no one knows why a body like the earth is surrounded by a field of force that pulls on other objects. How can one object exert a pull on another when there is no physical link between them? This question puzzled Newton and it remains unanswered today.

Many scientists believe that the earth's magnetic poles have moved, wandering from place to place throughout the earth's history. The evidence is based on how magnetic particles in rocks lined up along the lines of force as the rocks formed. Large variations in the lineup of these particles may mean that there have been complete flips in the earth's magnetic field that reversed the magnetic poles, the north magnetic pole becoming the south magnetic pole and vice versa. The theory of magnetic pole reversal is now being investigated.

CHAPTER REVIEW

Summary

Earth science is concerned not only with the kind of materials that the earth contains, but also with the condition of these materials. Earth changes, which go on all the time, involve changes in these conditions. The conditions of the material in a region can be measured and described by using the idea of a field. At every point in a field there is a value for the particular quantity being measured. Changes in a field reflect changes in earth materials.

Motion is a condition of earth materials that is produced by various forces acting on matter. Describing motion involves finding the velocity, the speed and direction of the motion, and the acceleration, the rate at which the velocity changes. Since forces cause motion, it is important to know the kinds of motion a force will produce; these are defined by Newton's laws of motion. When a force acts at every point in a given region, a force field exists.

Two of the most important force fields in earth science are those of gravity and magnetism. Newton's universal law of gravitation describes the way in which the masses of two bodies and their distance apart affect the force of gravity between them. The universal law applies to all bodies anywhere in the universe. Gravity is the force responsible for most of the motions seen in nature. The earth's gravitational and magnetic fields change from place to place on the surface of the earth. The shape and rotation of the earth affect the gravitational field. Both gravity and magnetism are affected by materials in the interior of the earth. Hence the study of both fields gives clues about those materials under the earth's surface. What would changes in the intensity (strength) of these fields indicate about materials below the surface?

Questions and Problems

A

1. Name two conditions of matter that affect your environment.
2. Is the illumination produced by a lamp a field? Explain.
3. What force, when acting on a mass of 6 kilograms, will produce an acceleration of 5 meters per second squared?
4. If velocity is plotted against time, what does a graph showing accelerated motion look like? uniform motion?
5. What force causes the moon's motion around the earth to be an accelerated motion?
6. A car changes its velocity from 20 meters per second to 30 meters per second in a period of 5 seconds. What is its acceleration?

7. How is the gravitational force between two objects affected if the distance between them is doubled? tripled? halved?
8. If a force of 12 newtons acts on a mass of two kilograms, what will be the acceleration of the mass?
9. The gravity field intensity at place A is 9.80 meters per second^2, and at place B it is 9.83 meters per second^2. What could cause this difference?
10. If the magnetic declination is N 13° E, is true north to the east or west of that direction? Explain.

B

1. Explain why two isothermal lines can never cross.
2. Which of the following is a field: the amount of salt in each cubic centimeter of seawater, the intensity of sunlight on the earth's surface, the ages of the students in your earth science class, the amount of moisture in each cubic centimeter of soil, and the speed of an airplane?
3. Why does motion at a constant speed around a circle require a force to maintain it?
4. What is the force of attraction between two objects, one with a mass of 10 kilograms, the other of 20 kilograms, if they are 10 meters apart?
5. What is the value of the gravity field intensity at a distance from the earth's center equal to twice the earth's radius? (Use 9.8 newtons as the value on the earth's surface.)

C

1. The radius of the giant planet Saturn is 9.5 times the radius of the earth. Its mass is 95 times the mass of the earth. Show that the surface gravity on Saturn is almost the same as it is on earth.
2. How many times greater is the gravitational attraction between a person with a mass of 50 kilograms and the earth than the attraction between two people each with a mass of 50 kilograms who

are 5 meters apart? Use the values given in the text for the mass and the radius of the earth. (Remember that it has already been shown that the force of attraction between the person weighing 50 kilograms and the earth is 490 newtons.)

3. What is the force of attraction between the earth and an artificial satellite with a mass of 2000 kilograms orbiting the earth at a height of 200 kilometers?

Suggested readings

BOOKS

Bates, D. R., ed. *The Earth and Its Atmosphere.* Basic Books, New York, 1957. Chapter 6, Geomagnetic Field.

Beiser, Arthur. *Our Earth.* E. P. Dutton & Co., Inc., New York, 1959. Chapters 1 and 6.

Harland, W. B. *The Earth.* Franklin Watts, Inc., New York, 1960. Chapters 5 and 19.

Physical Sciences Study Committee. *Physics,* 2nd ed. D. C. Heath & Company, Boston, 1965. Chapters 3 through 6 deal with motion and its measurement.

Scientific American. *The Planet Earth.* Simon and Schuster, Inc., New York, 1957. Part 1: III. S. K. Runcorn, The Earth's Magnetism.

Strahler, Arthur N. *The Earth Sciences.* Harper & Row, Publishers, 1963. Chapter 9, The Earth as a Magnet.

PERIODICALS

Dadin, Michael. "The Earth's Wandering Pole." *Science World,* March 7, 1962.

Elsasser, Walter M. "The Earth as a Dynamo." *Scientific American,* May, 1958. (Also Scientific American Offprint #825, W. H. Freeman & Co., Publishers, San Francisco.)

Heiskanen, Weikko A. "The Earth's Gravity." *Scientific American,* September, 1955. (Also Scientific American Offprint #812.)

Artificial magnets have many uses, like this electromagnet lifting a heavy iron beam. Will the magnet lose its magnetism when the power is turned off? Would the magnet lift the beam if it were aluminum?

Trace the flow of energy
from left to right in
the above illustration.

Chapter 6 Energy Flow

A landslide crashes downhill into the valley below. A tornado sweeps a path of destruction as it roars through the heart of a town. A mountain glacier tears out the floor and walls of the valley through which it flows. Ocean waves pound a grounded ship to splinters. A raging stream cuts into its bed, laying bare the rocks beneath. Strong winds shift sand from place to place. Energy is acting at or near the earth's surface in each of these examples. Energy in many forms powers natural processes.

Changes taking place today, like all changes throughout time, require energy. The changes described in Chapter 1 could not take place without energy. The history of the earth and its inhabitants and the story of earth processes operating today are really part of the story of energy. Change is accompanied by a flow of energy.

Energy is what makes things move or change. You can't see energy, but you can see its effects all around you. Energy's effects on matter tell you about the behavior of energy. In Chapter 5 you learned that a force was required to move an object. How are energy and force related? What do motion, gravity, and magnetism have to do with energy?

You can't see a breeze, but you can see the effects of the breeze as it surges across a field of rippling wheat or fills the billowing sails of a boat. You can't see the energy of a boulder resting on a hillside, but if the soil beneath it were to give way the boulder would tumble downhill without being pushed.

Energy powers the world of life—just as it powers winds and waves. A field of corn, a flock of geese, and a football team depend as much on energy as do automobiles and ocean currents. A nation's energy sources include manpower, waterpower, coal, petroleum, and nuclear power. What is energy? It is easy to describe the effects of energy but can energy itself be defined?

Energy and Change

6–1 What is energy?

In the language of science, **energy** is said to be the capacity to do work. Work has been done when an object moves because a force has been exerted on it. The push or pull that is called **force** requires energy. You can see an object at rest set in motion. You can see a moving object being speeded up or slowed down. You can sometimes see a moving object such as a tennis ball deflected from its course. Each of these observations tells you that a force has acted.

Work is a measure of the amount of energy that has been converted to provide the force to move an object. You measure work by multiplying the force times the distance the object moves in the direction of the force. (Work = Force × Distance.) For example, in Figure 6–1, the work done by the man pulling on the rope equals the force he exerts, times the distance moved or height to which he raises the weight. If the mass of the weight were doubled, it would require twice the work or energy to move the mass to the same height. When the man has raised the mass halfway to the pulley, he has done half the work, or transferred half the energy it takes to raise the weight all the way to the pulley. The weight could not do any work while it was on the floor. In a raised position, however, it can pull up some other object; it has energy transferred to it by the man.

The fact that work, the measure of energy, can be given in terms of force times distance has some interesting results. If you push against a boulder that does not move, then the distance moved is zero and so force times distance is also zero. (Force × 0 = 0.) Therefore, you have done no work on the boulder

Figure 6–1 An energy system at rest: a man with a hand on a rope strung over a pulley to a mass resting on the floor. The man has stored chemical energy in his muscles. However, this energy is only potential.

Chemical energy is being converted to work by the man to raise the mass. As the mass moves up, it gains potential energy.

The mass has come to rest in this position and its kinetic energy has become zero. Its potential energy equals the work done to raise the mass from the floor.

When the mass falls, its potential energy is converted to kinetic energy. Vibrations and heat resulting when the mass hits the floor are forms of energy that can be traced back to the man's storage of chemical energy.

(Force × Distance = 0 = Work), so you have not transferred any energy to move it. Of course, you have used energy in other ways, but none of it has moved the boulder. Where has your energy gone?

The transfer or flow of energy needed for work comes from changing one type of energy to another. In an automobile engine, for example, the stored chemical energy of gasoline is changed to heat or thermal energy which in turn is changed to the mechanical energy of the moving wheels. The transfer of energy can involve several types of energy or just one type. Energy is transferred from moving water in a stream to loose particles on the bottom and then in turn from particle to particle as they collide. This is mechanical energy.

Energy flow can be compared to the way we exchange money. French francs, English shillings, and American dollars are all used in the same way in each country. Each has buying power, and can be exchanged for the other types of money. The same thing holds for energy. One type can be exchanged for an equivalent amount of another type.

6–2 Investigating flow and change in energy.

Since you cannot see energy, how can you observe and analyze the flow of energy and its change from one form to another? You will see one method in this investigation. Perhaps you will be able to think of other ways yourself.

Procedure

Figure 6–2

Part A • Using the equipment as shown in Figure 6–2, turn on the light and record the temperatures each minute for 10 minutes. Turn the light off, remove it without disturbing the cans, and record the temperatures each minute for 10 more minutes. Draw a graph for the temperature change in each can. From your results answer the following questions: (1)Which can heats faster? (2)Which can cools faster? (3)Which can absorbs energy better? What is your evidence? (4)Which can loses energy faster? How do you know? (5)How was the energy transferred in this investigation? (6)List and describe the forms of energy you observed.

Figure 6–3

Part B • Start the investigation by putting boiling water (100°C) in one calorimeter and water at room temperature (approximately 25°C) in the other. Figure 6–3 shows the setup of the calorimeters. These containers are insulated to prevent a gain or loss of heat. Record the temperature reading of each thermometer at four-minute intervals for 20 minutes. Graph your results for both calorimeters. Answer the following questions. (1)In which direction does the energy flow? What is your evidence? (2)Does energy loss equal energy gain? Explain why. (3)Describe the kinds of energy flow you observed in this investigation. (4)What could you do to make the final temperature readings in Part B higher?

6–3 How is one form of energy related to another?

Your observations in Investigation 6–2 have given you some insight into energy flow and conversion. Both of these ideas are key concepts in science. To understand energy conversions better it is necessary to classify energy into different types. In Investigation 6–2 you saw evidence that there are several kinds of energy. Now you can compare the kinds of energy you identified with those recognized by scientists.

The types of energy are mechanical, heat or thermal, radiant (such as light), chemical, electrical, and nuclear. A boulder rolling down a hillside has *mechanical energy*. A warm ocean current has *heat* or *thermal energy* as well as mechanical energy. The sun's *radiant energy* travels through space to light and warm the earth. *Chemical energy* is the energy stored in fuels, and the energy of food that your body converts into the energy for all of your activities. *Electrical energy* lights your home and is also involved in many important ways in the behavior of matter. *Nuclear energy* gets its name from the nucleus of the atom and results from the conversion of matter to energy. Now that you know the names for the types of energy look again at Question 6 in Part A and Question 3 in Part B of Investigation 6–2. Would your answers to these questions be the same as they were before?

Engines are devices for changing or transforming energy. A gasoline engine transforms the chemical energy of gasoline into mechanical energy. Is all of the chemical energy of the fuel transformed into mechanical energy? The oceans and the atmosphere may be thought of as

Can you identify the different kinds of energy related to the pictures on the left? Is more than one kind of energy apparent in any one picture?

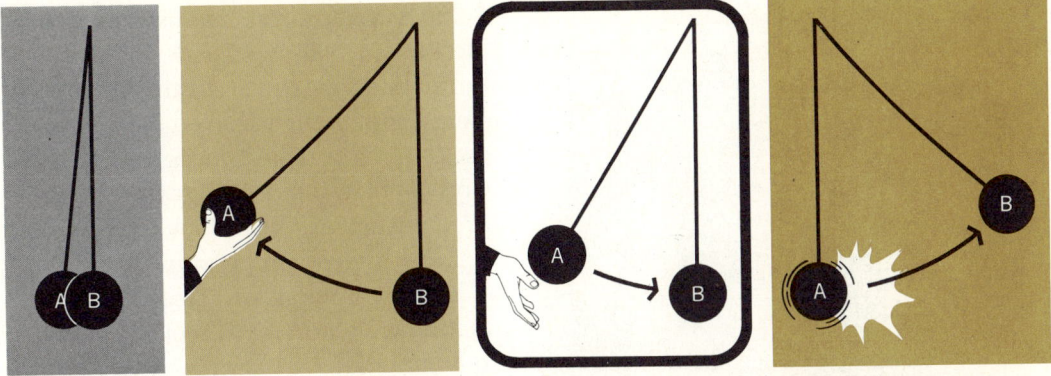

Figure 6–4 *Describe the energy transfer shown in this figure in terms of potential and kinetic energy.*

great engines powered by heat from the sun. You may already know that plants and animals are able to transform and store energy. *Fuels,* like gasoline and coal, contain stored chemical energy. The energy that was used in the formation of fuel molecules is released when they are taken apart in burning.

Another useful way to think about energy is to divide energy into two classes, kinetic and potential. **Kinetic energy** is energy of motion. **Potential energy** is stored energy. In effect, kinetic energy is energy flowing whereas potential is stored energy that could flow. All six types of energy named can be regarded as kinetic or potential energy, or some combination of the two.

Fuels contain potential energy. Rocks under great pressure in the earth may store energy just as a wound clock spring does or a stretched rubber band. A boulder sitting on top of a hill has potential energy in relation to the bottom of the hill. The boulder's potential energy becomes kinetic energy when the boulder rolls downhill. Relationships between kinetic and potential energy are illustrated in Figure 6–4.

What types of energy are involved in making this thunderhead above the plains?

6–4 Natural processes require energy flow and conversion.

How do the energy transfers and conversion demonstrated in Investigation 6–2 apply to earth processes? In Figure 6–5 you can get some idea of the tremendous variation in the amount of energy acting in different places in our world and in the universe. What does a volcano or a towering thunderhead have to do with energy flow and conversion? In what sense could the oceans and the atmosphere be considered engines?

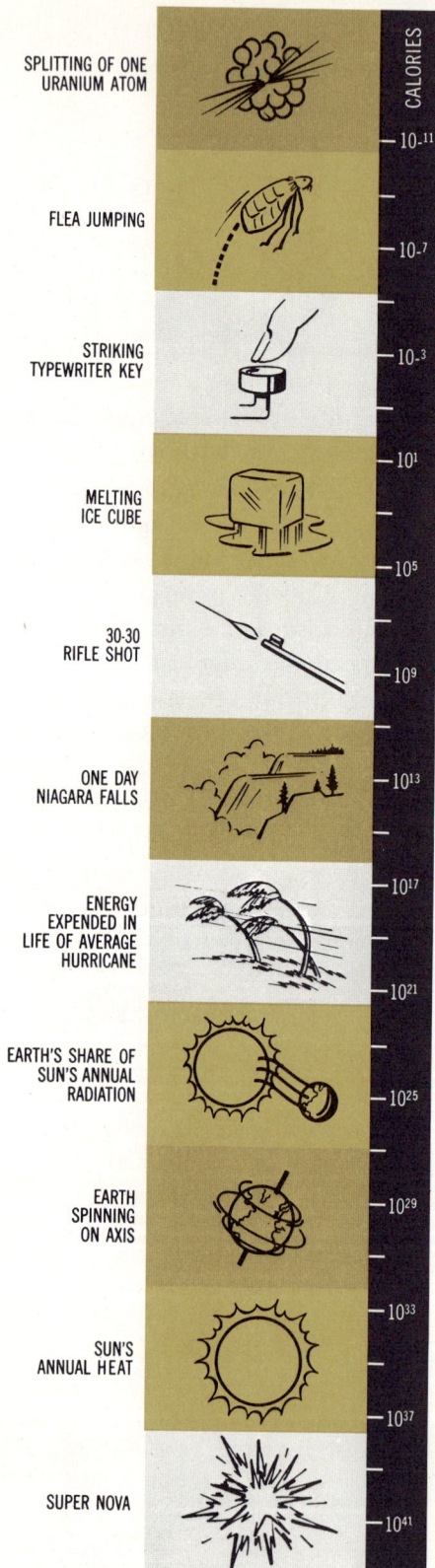

	CALORIES
SPLITTING OF ONE URANIUM ATOM	
	10^{-11}
FLEA JUMPING	
	10^{-7}
STRIKING TYPEWRITER KEY	
	10^{-3}
	10^{1}
MELTING ICE CUBE	
	10^{5}
30-30 RIFLE SHOT	
	10^{9}
ONE DAY NIAGARA FALLS	
	10^{13}
ENERGY EXPENDED IN LIFE OF AVERAGE HURRICANE	10^{17}
	10^{21}
EARTH'S SHARE OF SUN'S ANNUAL RADIATION	10^{25}
EARTH SPINNING ON AXIS	10^{29}
	10^{33}
SUN'S ANNUAL HEAT	
	10^{37}
SUPER NOVA	
	10^{41}

You can get a start in answering these questions by first considering heat or thermal energy because this is a form of energy commonly involved in earth processes. Heat can be transferred in three ways, as illustrated in Figure 6–6. In all three instances, heat moves from material at higher temperature to material at lower temperature. Heating by **conduction** involves the direct warming of cool material by warm material when they are in contact. (See Figure 6–6.) Hot lava bakes adjoining rocks by conduction and causes seawater to boil by conduction if the lava flows into the sea. Warm air heats cool air simply because the higher energy (more rapidly moving) molecules in the warm air batter the low-energy (slowly moving) molecules of the cooler air into more rapid motion. In doing this, the higher energy molecules transfer energy to the lower energy molecules. Because of these collisions some of the higher energy molecules lose energy and become lower energy molecules. In this process the warm air is cooled and the cool air is warmed, until the average kinetic energy of the molecules is the same throughout. This is another way of saying that heat energy flows through the air until the temperature is the same throughout.

Heating by **radiation** is also illustrated in Figure 6–6. Energy is transferred by radiation through space when an electric lamp lights a room. Energy can be radiated as well as conducted through

Figure 6–5 *A ladder of energy. Examples of energy transfer are here arranged in increasing order from the top down. One flea jump involves 10,000 (10^4) times as much energy as the splitting of one uranium atom. The average hurricane involves about 10^{24} times as much energy as a flea jump. The sun's annual heat energy is 10^{20} times as great as the average hurricane's energy.*

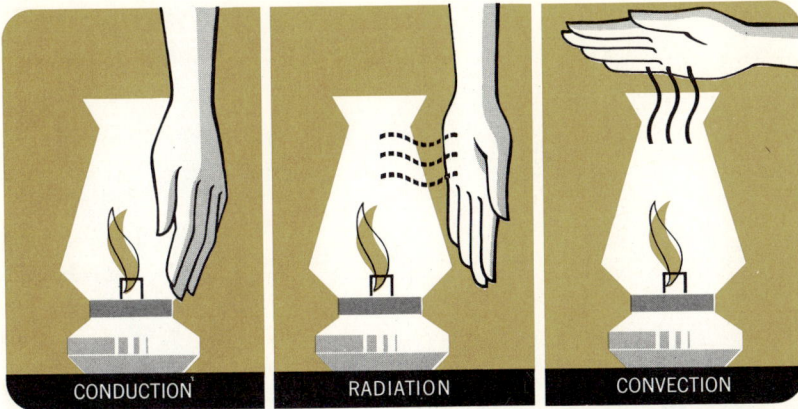

Figure 6–6 *Three ways by which heat energy can be transferred. Which of these involves the movement of air?*

some materials like air, glass, and water. Water is partially transparent to light but absorbs thermal radiation. Can you recall from swimming in a lake or in the ocean which type of energy penetrates farther into the water, heat or light?

When air is heated by the earth's surface, it expands. Why would the warm expanded air be less dense than the cooler air surrounding it? The denser, cooler air sinks under the influence of gravity and forces the less dense, heated air to rise. The effect is commonly described by the phrase "warm air rises." Thus there is a tendency for gravity to eliminate or smooth out temperature differences by mixing the warm and cool air. The smoothing is accomplished by the movement of air. This process is

called **convection** and the motions it produces in materials are called **convection currents.** Some effects of convection currents are shown in figures 6–6 and 6–7. Convection can also occur in liquids, as in lakes or in the ocean. There is even a possibility that convection can occur over very long periods of time in materials that you think of as being solid. It is possible that convection occurs even in the rock beneath the crust of the earth.

Energy tends to flow from materials of high potential energy to materials of low potential energy. Streams flowing downhill, landslides roaring down a slope, and

Figure 6–7 *This glider would follow a gentle, straight path if there were no convection. Different types of surfaces contribute heat at different rates causing convection currents.*

An iceberg in the Atlantic. Is the iceberg a heat source or a heat sink?
How can the material in this suit protect the man from the intense heat of the fire?

glaciers scraping down their valleys all illustrate the flow from higher to lower potential energy. Without friction all of the potential energy lost could be converted to kinetic energy. Because of the friction between moving masses of water, rock, and ice, much of the energy may be converted to heat. How do glaciers, landslides, and streams differ?

You can also think about the flow of energy in terms of energy sources and energy sinks. An **energy source** is a region that has a higher average energy than its surroundings. An **energy sink** is a region that has a lower average energy than its surroundings. As you can see in Figure 6–8, energy always flows *from* a source *to* a sink. How does an open refrigerator illustrate this?

A flame under a pot of coffee is a thermal energy source. An ice cube dropped into a cup of hot coffee is a thermal energy sink. Lava flowing over cooler rock is a thermal source. A mountain glacier would ordinarily be thought of as a thermal sink. Can you think of conditions in which it would become a thermal source?

6–5 Total energy remains the same.

Whether you keep your money in one or two pockets, in a wallet or a handbag, under a mattress or in an attic trunk, the total amount remains the same—as long as you don't add to it or take some away. The total is not changed by moving the money from place to place, by taking it out and counting it, or by changing it into shiny new coins.

The **law of conservation of energy** states that total energy, no matter what type, remains constant if there is no flow of energy into or out of the system. (See Figure 6–9.) The universe is considered

Figure 6–8 *An energy source and an energy sink. The flame gives off heat energy, the ice cube absorbs heat energy from its surroundings.*

Figure 6–9 *The snow's potential energy has been transformed into the avalanche's kinetic energy. The avalanche continues for a distance up the opposite valley wall. What prevents the ball (right) from rolling to a higher position?*

to behave in this way, on a grand scale, but the law applies as well to the smallest drop of water.

This fundamental law allows you to use a convenient device—the energy budget—to help you understand the flow and storage of energy. Family and government budgets tell us how much money is available for needs. Similarly, the *energy budget* tells how much and what kinds of energy there are available to be spent. However, unlike money you cannot use or waste more energy than is available.

Could a boulder rolling down a valley wall roll up the opposite valley wall to a height greater than that at which it started? (See Figure 6–9.) You know that the boulder will probably stop far short of this height. The reason is that not all of the potential energy released is used to move the boulder. Some is used by friction, breaking of rock, squeezing the ground, kicking up rocks and clods of dirt, and making noise. The amount of energy wasted in these actions plus the kinetic energy of the boulder must equal the boulder's original potential energy. Thus, according to the law of conservation of energy, the more energy that is wasted, the less there is available for moving the boulder. The law of conservation also tells you that the wasted energy has not been destroyed. This "wasted" energy has simply been converted into other types of energy and scattered about. How is energy "wasted" when an engine is used to convert chemical energy into mechanical energy?

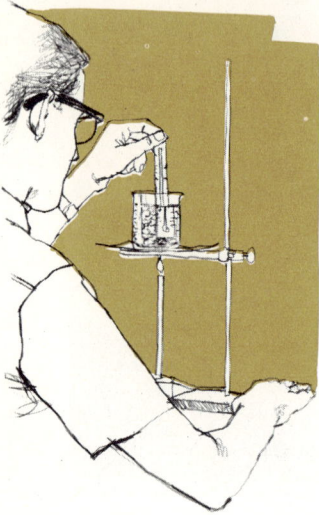

Figure 6–10

6–6 Investigating where energy goes and what it does.

In this investigation you will be adding energy to a common earth material. As you do so, you will be measuring the effects of this addition of energy. Try to relate what you observe to the principle of conservation of energy.

Procedure

Set up the equipment as shown in Figure 6–10. While stirring the ice *gently* with the thermometer, read and record the temperature at one-minute intervals.

Continue adding energy (heat) until the water boils. Make three readings after the water begins to boil. Graph your results.

(1)What is the relationship between energy input (heat) and temperature change?

(2)When did the greatest temperature changes occur?

(3)What do you think caused the changes in the slope of the line on your graph?

6–7 What is the difference between heat and temperature?

During Investigation 6–6 you discovered that a constant input of heat energy did not result in a uniform temperature change. These results might have surprised you. Heat (thermal energy) and temperature are often thought to be the same. The results of your investigation should have proved that they are not. Why didn't the temperature increase steadily as you added energy?

The distinction must be made between temperature and heat. **Temperature** depends on the *average* energy of motion of molecules and **heat** depends on the *total* energy of motion of the molecules. The terms average and total apply only to the kinetic energies of the molecules.

To illustrate the distinction between temperature and heat, two glasses of water can yield twice as much heat as one glass of water at the same temperature. Combining the water from the two glasses does not raise the temperature, but the water from both glasses can melt twice as much ice as the water from one.

Look at Figure 6–11 and see if you can answer the question in the caption.

Actually, heat also depends on potential energy. In the case of a gas, this potential energy is determined by the spacing between its molecules. The three states of matter are gas, liquid, and solid. *Changes of state* of matter, from

Figure 6–11 *The temperature of the water in these two beakers is different. Which contains more heat?*

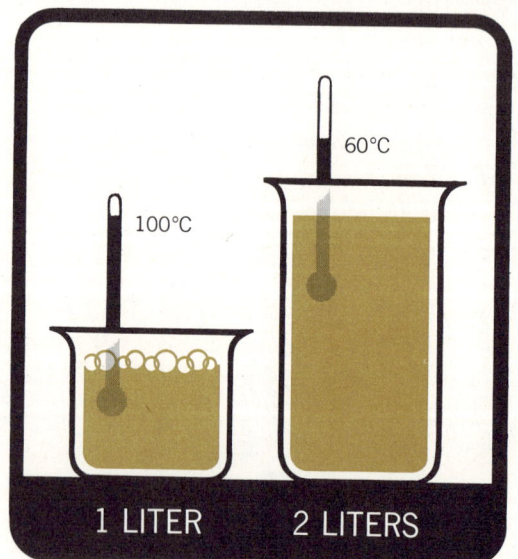

100°C

60°C

1 LITER   2 LITERS

Figure 6–12 *Gas molecules (left) receive energy from a heat source and move faster. Heated air (above) expands and fills a balloon.*

solid to liquid, or the reverse, and liquid to gas, or the reverse, require the flow of energy. As you discovered in Investigation 6–6, changes from ice to liquid water (melting) and from liquid water to gas or water vapor (vaporization) require the addition of heat. The change from liquid water to ice (freezing) releases heat. Water vapor changing to the liquid form also releases heat. The heat required for all of these changes is called **latent** (hidden) **heat.**

The interesting fact is that the temperature does not change as the solid changes into the liquid form or the liquid to vapor. Do the graphs of your results in Investigation 6–6 indicate this? Each change of state requires the flow of energy into or out of the material because each change of state involves a change in stored or potential energy. For example, the change from liquid water to water vapor is nothing more than the effect of increasing the spacing of molecules. When the spacing is increased enough, the molecules break free from the liquid and it becomes a gas. Increasing this spacing requires energy. What

happens when water boils? The temperature of water and steam in a container are equal because the average kinetic energy of the molecules remains the same. The heat used in this change of state is called latent heat and affects the spacing of the molecules but not their kinetic energies. Can you think of any way in which this latent heat could be recovered from the gaseous water?

The molecules of a gas in a container at room temperature are moving about. They collide with each other and with the walls of their container. Because they are moving about, the molecules have kinetic energy. Gas molecules with different amounts of kinetic energy are shown in Figure 6–12 (left). The *temperature* of a gas is a measure of the average energy of motion (kinetic energy) of the gas molecules; hence the two drawings represent different temperatures. The *heat* of the gas is related to the total kinetic energy of all of the gas molecules. If the amount of gas (the number of gas molecules) is increased, what do you think the effect will be? The average kinetic energy of each molecule does not change with gas added, but the amount of heat that can flow from the gas will be increased. However, the temperature of the gas will remain the same.

From what has been discussed here, can you guess how thermal energy is stored in the water vapor of clouds? Do clouds store large amounts of energy and if so, where does this energy come from? How do changes of state and latent heat affect the weather? You will find these topics discussed in the next two chapters. However, with what you know about energy you can begin to answer the questions for yourself.

Thought and Discussion . . .

1. What is the difference between work and energy?
2. What is the amount of work you do on a rock while holding it at arm's length over your head?
3. Why does freezing water release heat?
4. Why do you feel warmer in sunlight than in shade?
5. Show how the water in a mountain stream has acquired the energy that causes it to flow.
6. Why should thermometers be much smaller than the objects or materials whose temperatures they measure?
7. What type and class of energy is present in a can of gasoline?

The Earth's Sources of Energy

6–8 Heat flows from the interior to the earth's surface.

Although the sun's radiant energy is the most important source of energy at and above the earth's surface, this energy penetrates only a very short distance into rocks and soil. Does the earth have another source of heat? (See Figure 6–13.) What is known about the possible energy sources in the earth's interior?

The increase of temperature with depth in wells and mines averages about 1°C for every 30 meters (about 100 feet). (See Figure 6–13.) In a deep hole drilled in west Texas the temperature was 178°C at a depth of about 8 kilometers. It is believed that the temperature does not continue to increase at this rate all the way to the center of the earth, 6400 kilometers (about 4000 miles)

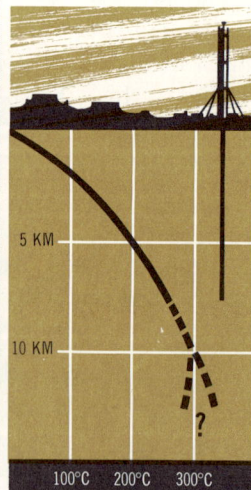

5 KM

10 KM

?

100°C   200°C   300°C

Figure 6–13 *If the temperature continues to increase, as indicated on the graph, what would the temperature be at the center of the earth?*

An offshore drilling rig (left) of the type that could be used to probe the earth's crust.

Water below the earth's surface encounters rocks at high temperatures and steam is produced. This energy can be harnessed, as it is here on North Island, New Zealand.

down. If the temperature did increase at this rate, what would be the temperature at the center of the earth? Recent theoretical studies suggest temperatures of 4000°C or less at the center of the earth. How does your calculated figure compare with the recent estimate? What do you conclude from this?

Calculating the temperature of the earth's center from our figure of 1°C per 30 meters of depth is like calculating the expected weight of an adult from the growth of a baby. An average-sized baby of about 3.5 kilograms gains about 7 kilograms during his first year. If he were to gain weight by the same amount each year, at age 21 he would have gained 147 kilograms and at age 70 he would weigh about 490 kilograms (over 1000 pounds). What is wrong with predicting weight in this way?

Our deepest penetration into the earth is only $\frac{1}{800}$ of the distance to the earth's center. It is not surprising then that what has been measured for a very small depth at the outer edge of the solid earth is not typical of what is happening at greater depths.

From what you learned about the direction of heat flow in Investigation 6–2 you know that the heat of the deep interior of the earth cannot come from the cooler surface. Why? Where does it come from then? One assumption is that the heat of the earth's interior was there

when the earth was formed and that heat has been flowing outward ever since.

A famous British physicist, Lord Kelvin (1824–1907), made a calculation of the age of the earth based on the assumption that the heat of the earth's interior was there when the earth formed. He also reasoned that no heat had been added since the time of the earth's beginning. By assuming that the earth had lost heat by radiation at a nearly constant rate since it was formed, he estimated that the earth was about 40 million (4×10^7) years old.

Kelvin's calculations did not take into account the possibility that the heat flow measured at the earth's surface could have a source other than the heat that was present when the earth formed. About 1900 it was found that the earth has a source of internally produced heat. Such a source was recognized with the discovery of radioactivity. The radioactive decay of unstable atoms could give the earth a continuing supply of internal thermal energy. Today it is believed that the age of the earth is about 4.5×10^9 years, which is far greater than Kelvin's estimate. This is a good example of the way an idea changes as new information is discovered.

The radioactive decay of atoms is a nuclear reaction. As you learned in Chapter 2, **nuclear reactions** are those in which atoms of one element change into isotopes, or into atoms, of another

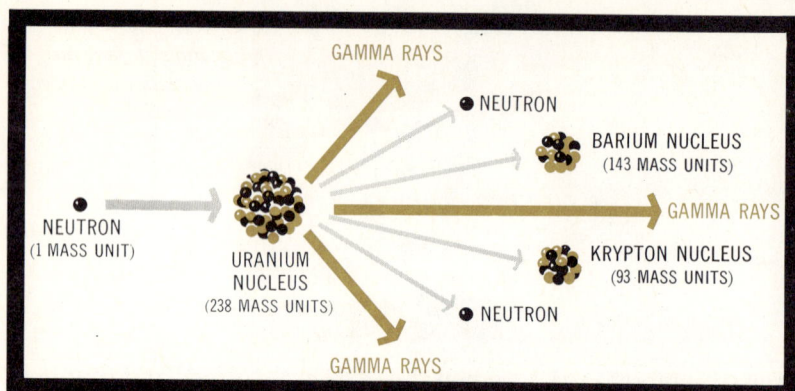

GAMMA RAYS

NEUTRON

BARIUM NUCLEUS
(143 MASS UNITS)

NEUTRON
(1 MASS UNIT)

GAMMA RAYS

URANIUM
NUCLEUS
(238 MASS UNITS)

KRYPTON NUCLEUS
(93 MASS UNITS)

NEUTRON

GAMMA RAYS

Figure 6–14 (*Left*) *The radioactive decay of uranium (U 238) to barium and krypton results in a loss of mass.*

Figure 6–15 (*Right*) *A highly magnified section of the sun's surface.*

element. (See Figure 6–14.) In these nuclear reactions the mass at the end of the change is smaller than the mass at the beginning. The mass represented by this small difference is converted to energy according to Einstein's famous equation $E = Mc^2$. In this equation E represents energy, M stands for the amount of mass converted to energy, and c is the speed of light. You know that the speed of light is a large number, 3×10^{10} centimeters per second, and squaring this gives 9×10^{20}. It is not hard to see from the equation that even a very small amount of mass will produce a tremendous amount of energy.

ACTIVITY *Using a cloud chamber containing a piece of radioactive earth material, watch for evidence of emission of particles from atoms within the material.*

The flow of heat from the earth's interior is small compared to the amount of radiant energy arriving from the sun. When the sun is overhead, 25,000 (2.5×10^4) times as much energy falls on the earth's surface as flows from the earth's interior. Therefore, the earth's surface temperature and surface changes in the hydrosphere and atmosphere are controlled by solar energy.

6–9 The sun's surface shows evidence of enormous energy output.

Our planet receives only a small part of the sun's total energy output. About one two-billionth (5×10^{-10}) of the light and heat pouring out from the sun falls on the earth but this contributes the major part of the energy supply at the earth's surface. The sun warms the earth as a bonfire warms a mosquito flying around it 30 meters away. The mosquito gets only a small portion of the bonfire's energy, just as the earth receives only a very small part of the sun's total radiant energy.

A photograph made with a telescope, Figure 6–15, shows that the surface of the sun is mottled and granular in appearance. Photos taken one after the other, like frames of a moving picture, show that the observed mottling is due to a boiling motion in the material on the surface of the sun.

Sunspots, the dark spots that appear on the sun's surface, are also evidence of energy transformation in the sun. They last only a few days or weeks and are carried around with the sun's rotation. The smallest sunspots are several hundred miles in diameter. Sunspots often come in groups, and, as you found in Chapter 1, the total number seen each year changes. You can observe sunspots

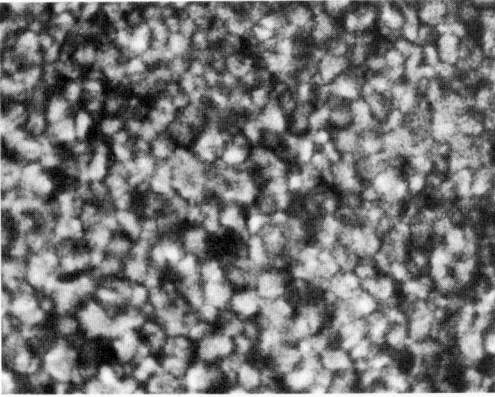

by projecting the sun's image on a sheet of white paper held behind the eyepiece of a telescope. NEVER LOOK DIRECTLY AT THE SUN.

The sun's red rim or inner atmosphere is the site of occasional brilliant flares often associated with sunspots that suddenly become intensely bright and then dim back to normal after a few minutes. At times, huge tongues of hot gas like those shown in Figure 6–16 rise hundreds of thousands of kilometers above the sun's surface before falling back into the sun. Figure 6–16 also shows the sun's outer atmosphere or **corona** as seen during an eclipse of the sun.

Some of this solar material is blown completely out of the sun. This causes **solar wind,** consisting mostly of protons and electrons that stream out into space in all directions. Some particles strike the earth, often producing magnetic storms. Other particles become trapped in the earth's Van Allen belts discussed in Chapter 5. The aurora borealis and the aurora australis are caused by these high-speed solar particles colliding with oxygen and nitrogen molecules hundreds of kilometers above the earth's surface.

All of this activity on the surface of the sun made scientists curious about the energy output of the sun. Does the sun like the earth have a source of internal heat? How can we measure the amounts of energy the sun radiates?

6–10 How much energy does the sun produce?

The sun's energy output can be calculated from the following measurements:

1. the distance from the sun to the earth, which has been calculated and found to be about 1.5×10^{13} centimeters (1.5×10^8 kilometers), and also

2. the radiant energy from the sun arriving at the earth, which has been determined to be about 2 calories per square centimeter every minute. One **calorie** is defined as the amount of thermal energy necessary to raise the temperature of one gram of water one degree Celsius. The calorie is a unit of both heat and energy.

You can think of the sun as being at the center of an imaginary hollow sphere, like a marble inside a beach ball. The

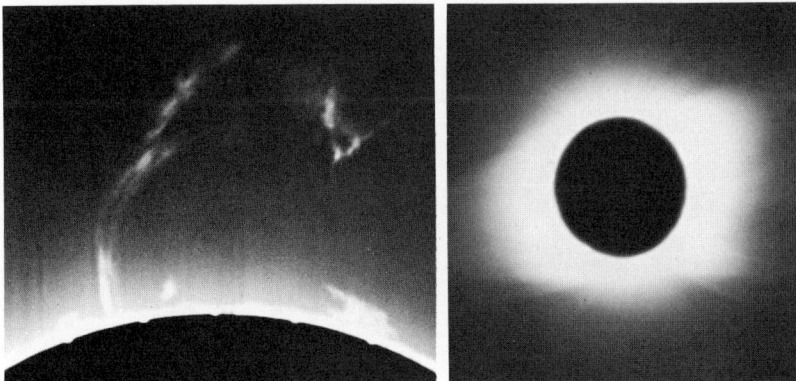

Figure 6–16 *A great eruption of hot gases above the sun's surface (far left), and the bright solar corona as photographed during a total eclipse of the sun (left).*

imaginary sphere is much larger than a beach ball for its radius is equal to the earth-sun distance. (See Figure 6–17.) Since the sun radiates energy in all directions, each square centimeter on the imaginary sphere should receive the same amount of energy, namely two calories per square centimeter per minute.

How many square centimeters are there on this imaginary sphere? You can figure this out by looking back to Figure 3–13, which shows the relationship between parts of a sphere. The surface area of a sphere is equal to $4\pi R^2$. In this case R is equal to 1.5×10^{13} centimeters and you learned that π is a constant equal to about 3.14. Multiplying $4 \times 3.14 \times (1.5 \times 10^{13})^2$, you find that the area is 2.8×10^{27} square centimeters.

How much total energy is the sun radiating each minute? If each square centimeter at the earth distance is receiving two calories per minute, then the total energy radiated must be $2 \times 2.8 \times 10^{27}$ or 5.6×10^{27} calories per minute.

This is a very large amount of energy. If all of the earth's other energy sources

Figure 6–17 *The earth receives only a very small fraction of the sun's total radiation. What happens to solar energy not received by the earth?*

were to produce heat at this rate, they would last but a few days. Even more startling is the realization that the sun has been producing such large amounts of energy for about three billion years. How do we know this? The remains of life called fossils that are found in rocks record the existence of animals and plants that could not have survived at temperatures very different from those at the earth's surface today. The age of rocks in which fossils are found can sometimes be determined. Since the oldest known rocks containing fossils are about three billion years old, scientists have concluded that the sun has been pouring energy on the earth at about the same intensity for at least that great length of time.

If the sun has been glowing with about the same intensity for three billion years or 1.5×10^{15} minutes, its total output in this period is equal to the output per minute (5.6×10^{27} calories) times the total number of minutes (1.5×10^{15} minutes). This is about 8×10^{42} calories. To bring this large number into focus, it can be expressed in terms of the output per gram of the sun's mass. It turns out that the sun has radiated over 4×10^9 (four billion) calories per gram during the last three billion years.

Where does all this energy come from? Can it be from burning as the early scientists speculated? The burning of even such a powerful fuel as gasoline yields only 3000 or 3×10^3 calories per gram. Compare this with the figure of 4×10^9 calories per gram. A century ago scientists speculated that the sun's energy output was caused by contraction or shrinkage of the sun. Although shrinkage could account for the energy output over a relatively short period, it completely fails to explain the total energy output of 4×10^9 calories per gram.

(Far left) Debris thrown up from a nuclear explosion in a drill hole in Nevada. The explosion made the crater shown at the left.

A gram of mass falling or contracting all of the way from the farthest planet, Pluto, would account for only $\frac{1}{90}$ of this energy output.

You have already learned that nuclear reactions produce great amounts of energy. When hydrogen is converted to helium, an amount of mass equal to 0.0072 gram is lost for each gram of hydrogen. Yet even this small quantity of mass can be shown to produce 1.5×10^{11} calories according to Einstein's formula, $E = Mc^2$. Could this nuclear reaction account for the sun's energy output?

6–11 Mass is converted into energy in the sun's interior.

Nuclear reactions within the sun provide the only acceptable explanation of the large output of energy from the sun. Analysis of sunlight shows that the sun's surface layers consist of 70 percent hydrogen and 25 percent helium. The energy released when one gram of hydrogen is converted to helium (1.5×10^{11} calories) is over 30 times what is needed to account for the amount of energy output of the sun per gram over the last three billion years. Hence, the hydrogen-helium reaction is more than adequate as a source of the sun's radiant energy. The great energy of the hydrogen bomb and of atomic reactors comes from the same type of reactions.

Having found a possible source for the sun's tremendous energy output, we must determine whether this reaction can take place in the sun. The conversion of hydrogen to helium requires very high temperatures—higher than those at the sun's surface. Are these high temperatures found in the sun's interior? What can be determined about temperatures inside the sun?

Physicists and chemists have constructed mathematical models of the sun's interior, by using what they have discovered about gases at high temperature in the laboratory. From this it is possible to form a mental picture or model of the sun's interior. According to the models the pressures and temperatures inside the sun are great enough to convert hydrogen to helium.

The *rate* at which energy is produced in this nuclear reaction can be calculated from the results of laboratory experiments. The calculated value of energy produced per minute equals the observed output of the sun per minute.

How long can this great outpouring of energy last? How much mass is the sun losing? Theoretically the sun probably has enough hydrogen in its interior to continue generating nuclear energy at its present rate for 60 billion years. (See How Much Mass Does the Sun Lose?) But scientists know that the conversion of hydrogen to helium changes the composition of the gas in the sun's core. This will cause structural changes in the sun that will probably reduce its energy output 5 to 10 billion years from now. From the study of other stars that produce

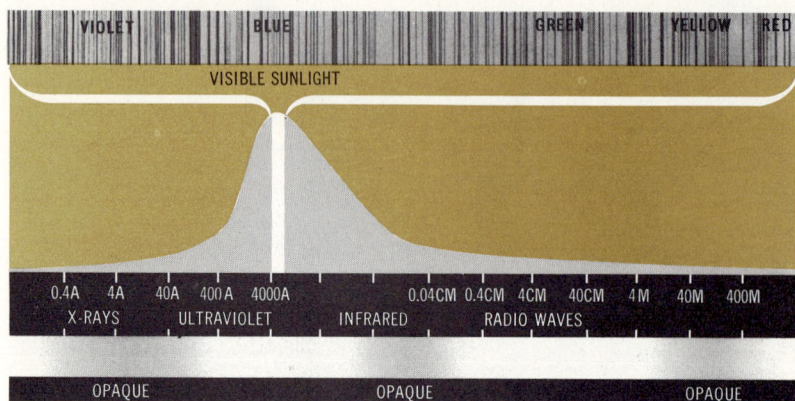

VIOLET   BLUE   GREEN   YELLOW   RED

VISIBLE SUNLIGHT

| 0.4A | 4A | 40A | 400A | 4000A | 0.04CM | 0.4CM | 4CM | 40CM | 4M | 40M | 400M |
| X-RAYS | | ULTRAVIOLET | | | INFRARED | | | RADIO WAVES | | | |

OPAQUE   OPAQUE   OPAQUE

Figure 6–18 *The energy spectrum of the sun. The earth's atmosphere filters out certain wavelengths indicated by the dark bands marked "opaque." A = Angstrom $(1 \times 10^{-8} cm)$, CM = centimeters, and M = meters.*

energy in the same way, astronomers hope to learn more about changes that accompany the aging of the sun.

How Much Mass Does the Sun Lose?

Earlier we calculated the energy output of the sun to be 5.6×10^{27} calories per minute (cal/min).

We can calculate that for each gram of hydrogen converted to helium there is a loss of .0072 (7.2×10^{-3}) gram (gm) of mass, and that this change yields 1.5×10^{11} calories.

Using these data the number of grams lost by the sun is found to be $\dfrac{5.6 \times 10^{27} \text{ cal/min}}{1.5 \times 10^{11} \text{ cal}}$ $\times 7.2 \times 10^{-3}$ gm $= 2.65 \times 10^{14}$ gm/min.

In more familiar terms, the mass lost is 265 million metric tons per minute, or about 4 million metric tons per second. One metric ton $= 2205$ lb. $= 10^6$ gm. About 600 million metric tons of hydrogen are converted to helium each second.

How long can this go on if the sun continues to burn at the same rate? The sun's total mass is 2×10^{33} grams. If half of the sun's mass is potential hydrogen fuel, then the sun's fuel storehouse can generate a total of $1 \times 10^{33} \times 1.5 \times 10^{11}$, which equals 1.5×10^{44} calories.

With an energy output of 5.6×10^{27} calories every minute, this process could continue for 3×10^{16} minutes or about 6×10^{10} years (or 60 billion years).

6–12 The sun's radiation is a source of information.

The small fraction of the sun's energy received by the earth carries with it important information about the sun. Just as a musical instrument can be identified by the quality and loudness of its sound, so too can the surface temperature and composition of the sun be calculated from the color and brightness of its light.

To carry the comparison with sound still further, we know that musical instruments and other sources of sound can produce tones or sound waves that are out of the range of the human ear. Similarly, the sun produces radiant energy such as X-rays, ultraviolet rays, infrared rays and radio waves, that the human eye cannot detect. The relative intensities of the various forms of radiant energy produced by the sun are shown in Figure 6–18.

Even though some of the sun's energy is filtered out by the earth's atmosphere, the portion that gets through provides useful information about the sun. The sun's radiant energy can be studied with a variety of instruments. Visible light from the sun can be studied with a spectrograph, an instrument that spreads out the different colors of light in a rainbow-like spectrum as shown at the top in Figure 6–18.

ACTIVITY *Using a spectroscope look at the spectrum of sunlight. How are the colors arranged in the spectrum? In terms of color, which wavelengths are longest? Which are shortest? (See Figure 6–18.)*

Physicists learned many years ago that light can be studied in terms of wave motion. Different colors of light represent different wavelengths, just as different tones in sound are related to wavelength. The **wavelength** is the distance from crest to crest in a wave. As shown in Figure 6–18, the wavelength of blue light is shorter than that of red light. Somewhat longer waves make up invisible infrared (heat) radiation with wavelengths about 10^{-4} centimeters. Somewhat shorter waves make up ultraviolet radiation.

In a hot material there are small charged particles such as electrons moving at high speeds and colliding with each other. These collisions shake the charged particles, and the shake produces waves called *electromagnetic radiation*. High-speed particles get shaken rapidly and produce short waves; lower speed particles produce longer waves.

All of these electromagnetic waves travel at the same speed of 3×10^{10} centimeters per second or 300,000 kilometers per second in empty space. X-rays, light, radiated heat, and radio waves are all part of the family of electromagnetic radiations shown in Figure 6–18. These radiations and the others shown make up the *electromagnetic spectrum.*

Material at high temperature, like that in the sun's bright disk, contains electrically charged particles moving at many different speeds. Because the particles move at different speeds, they radiate electromagnetic waves of many different wavelengths. The curve in

From mid-1957 to the end of 1958, sixty-seven countries joined forces in a remarkable assault on the unknown in a project called the International Geophysical Year (I. G. Y.).

The I. G. Y. was characterized by the tireless participation of members of the world community of science. These scientists obtained data on the sun, cosmic rays, ocean currents, and earthquakes, which helped them gain new insights into the way the earth's crust has been deformed—how mountains and oceanic trenches have developed.

I. G. Y.'s great strength came not only from assembling talented teams from all over the world, but also from making simultaneous observations of complex changing features, such as the atmosphere and ocean currents, that need to be studied over broad areas and for long periods of time to yield useful results.

The I. G. Y. has been the largest international venture of its type, although the International Polar Year, in 1882–1883, was the first. Fifty years later, in 1932–1933, the second International Polar Year was undertaken. The I. G. Y. was first thought of as a third polar year, but was wisely broadened to include studies of the entire earth.

The I. G. Y. was so successful that other large-scale international projects have since been undertaken, such as the recent Indian Ocean Expedition.

Figure 6–18 shows how much energy is radiated at each wavelength by the sun. Note that most energy is radiated as light at wavelengths in the region of 5×10^{-5} centimeters, most of which can travel through the earth's atmosphere. Do you think it is a coincidence that the eyes of men and animals are tuned in exactly on the part of the electromagnetic spectrum that penetrates the atmosphere?

From the curve of brightness for each wavelength in Figure 6–18, the surface temperature of the sun can be calculated. The temperature of a distant radiating body can be determined from its color. At low temperatures the wavelength radiated most brightly is long and the color reddish. At higher temperatures the wavelength radiated most brightly is shorter and the color yellow to blue. Red hot coals are not as hot as yellow-hot coals. Both theory and laboratory studies show that a curve like the one in Figure 6–18 comes from an object with a surface temperature of about 6000°C, which is the sun's surface temperature.

This conclusion is strengthened by results from another important relationship. The amount of energy radiated depends on an object's surface temperature. A small increase in surface temperature will produce a very large increase in the amount of energy radiated. From the amount of energy radiated by the sun, it can be calculated that its surface temperature is about 6000°C. Hence, the amount of radiated energy and the sun's color indicate the same value for the sun's surface temperature.

The sun is a powerful energy radiator not only because it is big but also because it has a high surface temperature (6000°C). If it were at the temperature of boiling water (100°C), this would be a very cold world indeed, and we would not be here to speculate about the nature and life span of the sun.

6–13 Without sunlight the earth would be very different.

Most changes and processes on the earth depend in some way on the great energy received from the sun, demonstrated in Figure 6–19. The sun warms the solid earth, the atmosphere, and the oceans. The transfer of energy within each of these three spheres and from one to the others results in movement of earth materials and shaping of earth features.

The sun's energy can also be stored in a variety of ways. For example, water vapor in the atmosphere that has been

Figure 6–19 *Sunlight on the solar cells atop the car (left) makes the electricity to run it. The solar cooker (right) concentrates the sun's energy.*

raised far above sea level has potential energy. If the vapor falls to the earth as rain or snow, this potential energy becomes the kinetic energy of streams that carve the landscape and literally carry mountains, bit by bit, to the sea. Here, the sun's energy has been stored as mechanical potential energy, just as you store mechanical potential energy in a rubber band as you stretch it. In addition, water vapor in the air carries large amounts of stored thermal energy, which also affects earth processes. Solar energy is stored for long periods as coal or petroleum in the upper lithosphere.

Life on earth, now and in the past, has been dependent on solar energy. Sunlight provides the energy for life, and indeed life is delicately tuned to the particular type of energy that comes to earth from the sun through the partly shuttered window of the atmosphere.

Without sunlight this would be a very different planet. The earth would be dead not only in terms of life as we know it, but also in terms of many of the processes that shape the landscape and produce the features about us. The fascinating story of surface and atmospheric processes, as told in the chapters that follow, would have to be rewritten.

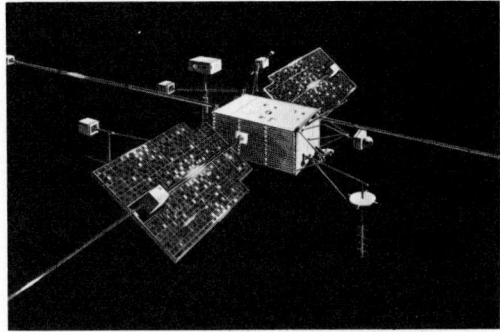

The large solar-cell panels on this satellite (OGO) transform solar radiation into electricity to operate the spacecraft's scientific instruments.

Thought and Discussion . . .

1. Why does a very small loss of mass result in the production of a large amount of energy in nuclear reactions?
2. What is probably the chief source of the sun's energy?
3. If the earth were twice as far away from the sun as it actually is, what would be the amount of the sun's radiant energy (in calories per square centimeter per minute) arriving at the earth?
4. If all of the material in the sun were cooled down sufficiently so that the sun became a solid body, what would its mass be?
5. If you continue heating a red-hot poker or branding iron to raise its temperature, will it become blue-hot? Explain.

Unsolved Problems One of the major problems related to the earth's thermal history is the present temperature of the earth's deep interior. Information about the temperature of the interior comes only from laboratory studies and mathematical models. Constructing such a model requires making certain assumptions about the heat of the earth when it was formed, the concentration of radioactive materials inside the earth, and the physical properties of materials in the earth's interior. Of course, these assump-

tions are not merely wild guesses, for they are consistent with what is known. Much is yet to be learned, however, because no model has yet been found that is consistent with all the facts.

Although the sun is the nearest star, and the only one whose surface can be examined in detail, there are many things about it which are not understood. What are sunspots and why do they come and go? Why do flares suddenly appear on the sun's surface? How is material ejected as solar wind?

CHAPTER REVIEW

Summary

The general discussion of energy has centered on flow and storage of energy. The transfer or flow of energy is one of the most important concepts of science. All earth changes result from the flow of energy. The understanding of any process depends in part on how far you can go in tracing the flow of energy through the process. All forms of energy can be changed to other forms with all of the energy accounted for. Changes of state of matter require the flow of energy. The total energy in a material remains constant if there is no flow of energy into or out of the materials.

The discussion of the earth's energy budget has centered largely around its thermal energy. The earth's surface radiates energy into space. A small amount of this radiated energy comes from inside the planet. Some is inherited or original heat but most is new heat generated by the decay of small amounts of radioactive elements. Many other forms of energy are involved in earth processes, and these processes involve the change of one type of energy to another. Energy is not lost in these changes but very frequently is changed to heat.

The sun's energy output is produced by the conversion of matter into energy. By studying radiation from the sun, we have learned about the sun's temperature and composition.

The sun radiates tremendous quantities of energy into space and the earth receives a small part of this energy. This fraction, small as it is when compared to the sun's total radiation, accounts for most of the continuing energy supply at the earth's surface. The energy from the sun directly affects only the outer part of the planet earth. The sun's energy heats the atmosphere, the hydrosphere, and the solid surface, moving earth materials, changing the earth's features, and providing a comfortable temperature for life as we know it.

Questions and Problems

A

1. Which of the following are examples of work being done: (a) writing an examination using a pencil, (b) jumping over a fence, (c) standing on your head, and (d) drinking with a straw?

2. Heat is transferred by the processes of conduction, convection, and radiation. Which of these processes is *most* effective in each of the examples below: (a) cooling of a cup of hot chocolate, (b) heating a skillet, (c) warming your bed with an electric blanket, and (d) getting a suntan?

3. Which of the places listed below are examples of energy sinks? Which are energy sources? (a) a glacier in summer, (b) the shade of a tree, (c) a concrete sidewalk in direct sunlight, and (d) the open refrigerator that is on display in a store?

4. You have often heard that machines or engines are inefficient—that they waste energy. Does this mean that the energy is lost? Explain.

5. A calorie is a unit of heat energy. How many calories are required to raise the temperature of 10 grams of water from 50°C to 80°C?

6. What type of energy is always involved when a substance changes state?

7. Why do substances containing radioactive elements tend to become warmer than their environment?

8. Since the earth radiates thermal energy, why is it not listed as a contributor to the sun's heat?

9. What do the following phenomena have in common: X-rays, light, radiated heat, and radio waves?

B

1. Describe the energy conversions that occur when electric power is produced in a power plant using coal.

2. List three examples of kinetic energy and three examples of potential energy.
3. If convection involves the transportation of energy by the material containing it, is the flow of gasoline from the gas tank of a car to the engine an example of convection? Why?
4. Is it possible for an object or a substance to contain both kinetic and potential energy at the same time? Explain.
5. Why doesn't the heat released when water freezes to ice cause the ice to melt again?
6. How does the fact that cold air is denser than warm air aid in the heating of the atmosphere? What would happen if warm air were more dense than cold air?
7. Water vapor (gas) changes state to form clouds (liquid) in the atmosphere. How might this affect the temperature of the surrounding air? Explain.
8. What have we learned about the sun by studying its electromagnetic radiation?

C

1. Trace the heat energy of your body back to the sun as a source.
2. Why does the bathroom floor feel cold though the rug lying on the floor feels warm?
3. Calculate the amount of solar energy radiated to Mars. Compare this result to the corresponding figure for the energy radiated to earth.

$$\frac{\text{Sun-Mars distance}}{\text{Sun-Earth distance}} = 1.5$$

$$\frac{\text{Radius of Mars}}{\text{Radius of Earth}} = 0.54$$

You will find other data that you need for this problem in the text.

Suggested Readings

BOOKS

Chemical Bond Approach Committee. *Chemical Systems.* McGraw-Hill Book Company, New York, 1964. Chapter 8.

Editors of *Scientific American. The Planet Earth.* Simon and Schuster, Inc., New York, 1957. Paperback. Pages 29–38, "The Earth's Heat."

Menzel, Donald H. *Our Sun.* Harvard University Press, Cambridge, Mass., 1959.

Page, Thornton, ed. *Stars and Galaxies.* Prentice-Hall, Inc., Englewood Cliffs, N.J., 1962. Chapter 4.

Physical Science Study Committee. *Physics,* 2nd ed. D. C. Heath & Company, Boston, Mass., 1966. Chapters 23, 24, and 25.

Rogers, Eric M. *Physics for the Inquiring Mind.* Princeton University Press, Princeton, N.J., 1960. Part III, Molecules and Energy.

Aerial photograph with infrared film (above) reveals high temperature areas in the Halemaumau crater on the Kilauea volcano in Hawaii. (Below) The same location photographed with normal film.

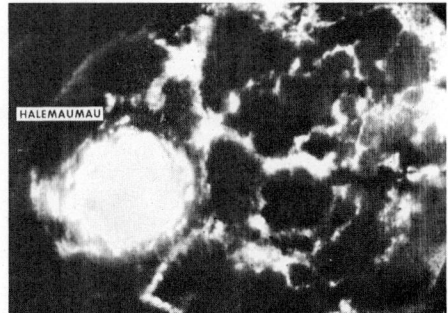

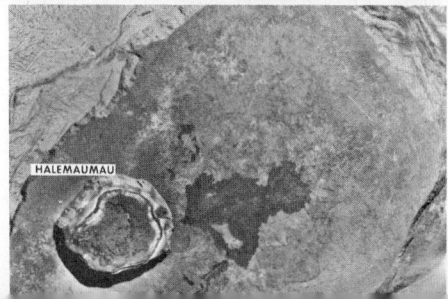

UNIT **II** *Earth Cycles*

To the ancient Greeks the world was a less hostile place than to the Egyptians. The Greeks felt more at home and found satisfaction in the world around them. Unlike the Egyptians, they thought of the gods in their own image, and were more at ease with them. The Greeks, too, searched for an explanation of events in the earth and sky. To them, the great gods had divided up the universe among themselves, each having power over certain natural events. These humanized gods were still to be feared for they were powerful and dangerous when angry, and their actions were often unpredictable.

Zeus was the master god in Greek mythology. He was lord of sky, wind, and rain. Rocky Greece needed rain more than sunshine and, of course, only the greatest of gods

could bring it. When Zeus hurled his thunderbolts from the sky or from his home on Mount Olympus, the lightning flashed and the world shook with his fury. Sometimes in his anger he brought too much rain. Floods resulted and lightning burned vast forests.

Hephaestus was the god of terrestrial fire and volcanoes. Unlike other immortals he was lame. Banished from Olympus, Hephaestus toiled in his workshop deep in the volcano of Mt. Etna. With hammer and tongs, he forged works of metal for the gods on a huge anvil. Ill-behaved gods held in his prison under Mt. Etna would occasionally try to break loose, causing earthquakes and eruptions of lava.

Poseidon, ruler of the sea, was Zeus' brother and second only to him in importance. With trident in hand he rode through the sea in a chariot drawn by monstrous creatures —half horse, half serpent. Poseidon ruled sea and shores, troubling the waves and bringing tempests and earthquakes or calming the towering waves of the raging sea when he passed over them in his chariot.

In Unit II on earth cycles you will gain a deeper understanding of the processes of nature that the Greeks sought to explain with stories and legends of the gods.

Chapter 7 Energy and Air Motions

Palm trees bend low before the rushing wind, waves dash upon the beach, and spray flung from the waves into the air mingles with rain. A giant storm is spending a small fraction of its energy against the shore. Southward along the coast, people returning from inland shelters see homes washed from foundations, power lines tangled, and the familiar beach replaced by an arm of the sea. Hundreds of miles to the north, where the storm has lost its fury, farmers see welcome rain falling upon dry fields.

No one saw the birth of this storm far out over the calm waters of the Atlantic, between the equator and the Tropic of Cancer. Water vapor from the warm sea was carried upward by unseen eddies in the wind. White puffs of cloud appeared in the sky. All at once, many of the cloud puffs seemed to erupt. The vapor, changing into cloud, began to release its internal energy in tremendous quantities. Towering columns of cloud billowed upward; in the vast expanse of ocean no one saw them.

The next day, however, a plane bound from Lisbon to Brazil spotted the clouds, which covered an area several hundred kilometers across. The pilot flashed a weather message. An analyst in one of the world's weather centers read the message and sorted through the latest photographs from a Tiros weather satellite. He found the area of clouds and thought he could just detect a band of cloud that seemed to spiral into the center of the area. He handed the picture to the hurricane forecaster on duty.

The forecaster could imagine the storm five days later, pounding the beach and flooding the low-lying coastal area. He issued a warning, giving the location of the beginning storm and its probable path. A few days later, the pilot of a hurricane-hunter plane saw below him the swirling clouds of the hurricane —the equivalent of a dozen atomic bombs exploding every second!

Although hurricanes often bring great destruction to the land areas they strike, storms are essential parts of the circulation of air and water. The atmosphere is always in motion. No word describes the atmosphere better than *restless*. If the atmosphere should come to rest and all air motions stop, the water cycle too would end. There would be no more rain, and life on earth would be quite different, if it could exist. What keeps the air and water moving? How is the energy of great storms produced?

You know that almost all of the energy reaching the earth's surface and the atmosphere comes from the sun. Somehow the sun's radiation must be the source of energy for storms and all the motions of the atmosphere.

Solar Radiation and the Earth

7–1 Investigating radiant energy.

Suppose the earth were so cold that its water supply was locked up in ice or so hot that all the water was in the form of vapor. The earth's water cycle requires not only an atmosphere in motion, but also one that is neither too warm nor too cold for water to exist in all three states—liquid, vapor, and ice. The temperatures of the earth's surface and of the atmosphere are within the range needed for water to occur in its three states. What determines this range?

Procedure

Set up the equipment as shown in Figure 7–1. Read and record the temperature in each can before the lamp is turned on. Call this beginning temperature (BT). Turn the lamp on and observe the change in temperature until the temperature in each can stabilizes (stops rising).

Record the stabilized temperature (ST) for each of the four cans. (1)Why did the temperature eventually stabilize?

Subtract the beginning temperature (BT) from the stabilized temperature (ST) to get the observed temperature change (OTC). ($ST - BT = OTC$.) Plot the values for the OTC of each can on a graph of temperature change versus number of distance units between the lamp and the can. Connect the points on your graph with a smooth curve.

The curve you have drawn indicates that the temperature change is related to the distance from the lamp. It has been theorized that the change decreases with the square of the distance. For example, knowing the temperature change in the nearest can, we can theorize that the temperature change in a can twice as far away should be one-fourth as much as in the first can rather than one-half as much. In a can three times as far away the temperature change should be one-ninth that of the first can, and so on.

With this theory you can predict the temperature change in each of the outer cans if you know the temperature change in the first can. Use the following formula:

$$\text{Calculated Temperature Change of Can} = \frac{\text{Observed Temperature Change of nearest can}}{\left(\substack{\text{Number of distance} \\ \text{units to can } (d)}\right)^2}$$

$$CTC = \frac{OTC_1}{d^2}$$

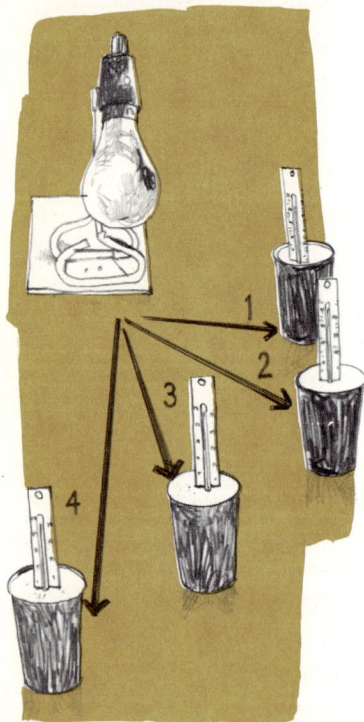

Figure 7–1 *The numbers 1, 2, 3, and 4 refer to the number of distance units from light to can.*

Plot the theoretical values for the four cans on the same graph on which you plotted your observed values.

(2) Does the evidence you obtained from your temperature readings in the cans tend to support the theory or not? (3) How do the two curves you have constructed compare with the curve in Figure 7–2? (4) In what state (solid, liquid, or gas) would most of the earth's water exist if the earth were (a) one-half its present distance from the sun, or (b) twice its present distance from the sun?

Figure 7–2 (*Below*)
If the planets absorbed and emitted all the solar energy reaching them, they would have the temperatures shown by the curve. One Astronomical Unit is the average distance from sun to earth.

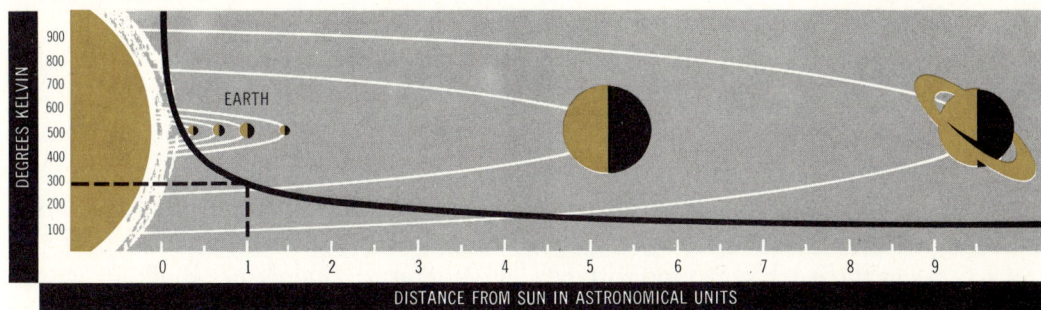

DISTANCE FROM SUN IN ASTRONOMICAL UNITS

7–2 Earth's energy balance and distance from the sun.

During the past 60 million years, the earth's average surface temperature is believed to have fallen from a warm 22°C to about 2°C when the polar ice sheet made its farthest excursion toward the equator. Over the past few centuries, however, records show that the temperature has varied little from its present average value of 15°C. Does this mean that the earth is now emitting the same amount of energy that it receives from the sun?

An object is said to be in **radiative balance** when it is emitting the same amount of energy that it absorbs. The radiation emitted by an object increases as its surface temperature increases. If the energy emitted is constant, then the surface temperature must also be constant. If an object is in radiative balance, and has a constant energy source, its temperature is constant.

Distance from the sun and the amount of the sun's energy output determine the temperature the planets would have if they absorbed and emitted all the energy received. (See Figure 7–2.) The earth's surface receives enough energy to maintain its average temperature above the freezing point of water, but much lower than the boiling point. Would you expect this to be true on other planets of the solar system?

The earth's distance from the sun gives it the right amount of energy for a climate favorable to our form of life. This distance varies slightly during the year, because the earth's orbit is not exactly a circle.

The earth is farthest from the sun in early July and closest early in January. But this difference could produce only a slight temperature change. The reason that the earth's average temperature remains about the same year after year is that it is very nearly in radiative balance with its surroundings. The sun's energy output is almost constant, varying perhaps by only one or two percent. Of course the earth also has its own source

Figure 7–3 *The Athabaska Glacier (far left) has been receding at the rate of about 15 meters per year since 1952. Can you also see evidence of recession in the Saskatchewan Glacier (left)? Both glaciers are in the Canadian Rockies.*

of internally produced heat. But, as you learned in Chapter 6, this internal heat created by radioactivity contributes very little to the earth's surface temperature.

Changes in the earth's average surface temperature show that the earth may not be always in exact radiative balance. The most marked changes are evidenced by the discovery of remains of tropical plants in areas that are now covered by ice and snow. These changes take place over millions of years. But there are also shorter periods when the earth seems to be gaining or losing heat. At present many of the earth's glaciers are decreasing in size (see Figure 7–3) which suggests that the earth is gaining heat.

The calculations for Figure 7–2 were made according to a model that represents a solid that absorbs and emits all the radiation received. However, the solid earth is surrounded by a thin layer of gas, the atmosphere. Do you think that the atmosphere itself, as well as distance from the sun, influences the earth's surface temperature?

7–3 How does the atmosphere affect incoming energy?

The incoming energy from the sun is called **insolation,** a contraction of the three words INCOMING SOLAR RADIATION. What happens to insolation as it enters

the atmosphere? You learned in Section 6–2 that matter can absorb, transmit, or reflect the radiant energy that reaches it. Only if matter absorbs energy does its temperature increase. Radiant energy can pass through some materials without being absorbed by them. Does a window absorb energy?

The atmosphere is composed of different kinds of material: several gases including water vapor, the liquid water of clouds, and dust particles of many sizes. These materials absorb, transmit, and reflect radiation in different ways, depending on the wavelength of the radiation. The sun radiates nearly half of its energy at the wavelengths of visible light. (See Figure 6–18.) The only gas in the atmosphere that absorbs much energy at these wavelengths is water vapor. High in the atmosphere is another gas, a form of oxygen called **ozone** (O_3), that absorbs practically all of the energy in the ultraviolet part of the solar spectrum. Even the small amount of ultraviolet radiation that penetrates the atmosphere can give you a severe sunburn. All of the gases in the atmosphere, together with clouds and dust, absorb only about 19 percent of the energy coming in, as shown in Figure 7–4.

The earth's cloud cover reflects about one-fourth of the incoming solar radia-

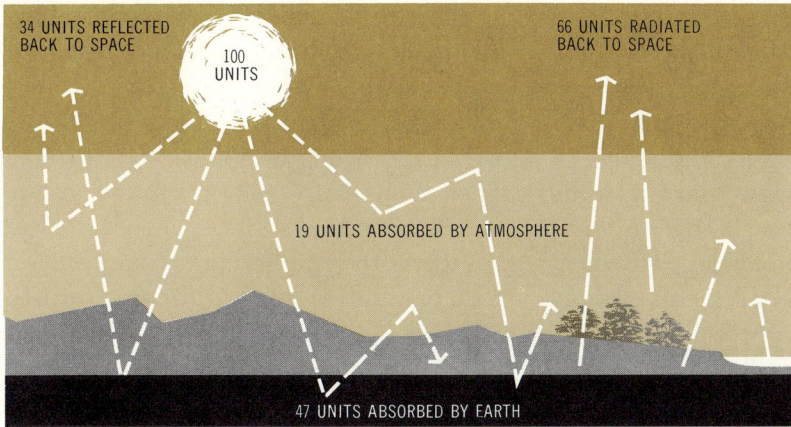

Figure 7–4 *Energy budget of the earth and its atmosphere. Some energy (34 units) is reflected directly to space from the atmosphere and the earth. The remaining 66 units (19 for the atmosphere and 47 for the earth) are absorbed, then finally radiated into space.*

tion back to space so that it plays no part in warming the earth. Some of the radiation is reflected by gas molecules in the atmosphere and some by materials at the earth's surface. Water surfaces, rock, soil, vegetation, and especially snow and ice reflect solar energy, as shown in Figure 7–4. Clouds, the atmosphere, and the earth's surface materials together reflect about 34 percent of insolation.

The remaining 47 percent of insolation is absorbed at the earth's surface. Thus, most of the insolation that is not reflected and lost to space is used to heat the land and ocean surfaces of the earth.

Since the earth is in overall radiative balance, the total energy absorbed is sent back to space at the same rate. If this were not true, the earth could not maintain a fairly constant temperature. Can you determine from Figure 7–4 how much energy the earth and its atmosphere emit to space by radiation? Does

the energy emitted from the earth and atmosphere plus the energy reflected equal the amount coming in?

7–4 The atmosphere keeps the earth warm.

The temperature at which energy is emitted determines the wavelength of the radiation. The sun glows white-hot, and its energy, centered in the visible part of the spectrum, is called **short-wave** radiation. The earth and its atmosphere, absorbing the short-wave radiation, become warm, but they do not receive enough energy to become very hot. Consequently, the earth and its atmosphere radiate at a much lower temperature than the sun, and the radiation emitted is **long-wave** radiation in the infrared part of the spectrum. (See Figure 6–18.) Radiation by the earth and its atmosphere is felt as heat rather than seen as light. You may have felt heat

Solar energy is reflected back to space principally by (A) cloud cover, but also by (B) water surfaces, sand, and soil, by (C) vegetation, and by (D) ice and snow fields.

radiating from pavement, the soil, or other surfaces in hot weather.

Between the times energy is absorbed as short-wave radiation and sent back to space as long-wave radiation, it warms the earth's surface and the atmosphere and powers the circulation of air and water in the water cycle. Since heat represents the *flow* of energy, the energy is not lost in powering air and water circulation. If energy flows twice over the same path instead of only once, the work done or the heat emitted somewhere along the path can be doubled.

If this idea seems strange to you, ask yourself how much a dollar might buy in the course of a day. One dollar's worth, or more? At the grocery counter, the dollar may buy a pound of meat; perhaps the grocer gives the dollar to a delivery boy as part of his wages; perhaps the boy uses it to go to a movie the same evening. The dollar represents one token of energy, but its use depends on the number of times it changes hands. The solar energy absorbed by the earth may circulate several times between the atmosphere and the earth's surface before it returns to space, as shown in Figure 7–4. The earth's surface and the atmosphere gain in this exchange, just as many people benefit when money circulates freely. **Heat** is energy in transit.

The exchange of energy between the earth's surface and the atmosphere is largely the result of the way the atmosphere absorbs short-wave and long-wave radiation. Water vapor and carbon dioxide absorb some short-wave solar radiation, but they absorb much more of the longer waves emitted by the earth. In fact, water vapor and carbon dioxide absorb most of the radiation emitted by the earth's surface. These gases re-emit radiation, so that some energy given off by the surface is returned to it.

Thus the earth's surface receives energy both from the sun and from the atmosphere. The atmosphere acts like an invisible blanket to keep the earth's surface warm, trapping and turning back some of the energy that flows upward from the surface. In dry, clear weather the nights are cool, but in cloudy weather the nights are warmer. What is the reason for this?

The **energy budget** of the earth and the atmosphere is illustrated in Figure 7–4. The exchange between the atmosphere and the earth's surface does not all take place through radiation. Heat is lost from the earth's surface when liquid water becomes vapor. Why is this so? The same amount of heat is gained by the atmosphere when the water vapor becomes cloud and the latent heat is released. Some heat is lost by the earth's surface through conduction to the air resting on it, and this heat is transferred upward by air motions.

Would you expect the temperature to decrease with increasing altitude? The absorption of ultraviolet solar energy in the upper part of the ozone layer, at about 55 kilometers above the earth's surface, keeps this level almost as warm as the earth's surface. If the temperature does decrease above the earth's surface, then at some higher level it must begin to increase again up to the top of the ozone layer. The diagram in Figure 7–5 shows that this is indeed the case.

The change of temperature with height in the atmosphere, illustrated in Figure 7–5, is one basis for classifying the different layers of the atmosphere. The **troposphere**, the layer next to the earth's surface, is kept warm at the bottom. When air is heated from below, convection can take place, for the colder, denser air at the top of the layer tends to sink, forcing the heated air upward.

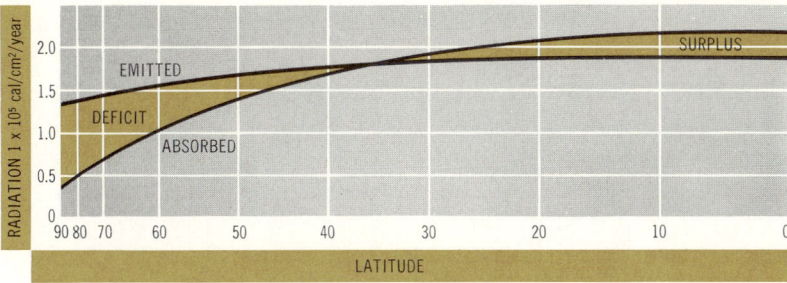

Figure 7-6 *More radiation is emitted than absorbed at high latitudes (deficit) and more is absorbed than emitted at low latitudes (surplus).*

(See Section 6–4.) Thus you can see why the troposphere gets its name from a Greek word meaning turning or changing. Most of the earth's weather occurs in the troposphere. The **stratosphere** above is warmed at the top by direct solar radiation. The two layers are separated by a cold interface called the **tropopause.** Because the stratosphere is warm at the top and cold at the bottom, much less convection takes place than in the troposphere below.

7-5 How is insolation distributed on earth?

Because the earth's surface is warmer than the overlying air, the surface is an energy *source* compared with the colder atmosphere above. Can you think of another set of energy sources and sinks and why they exist?

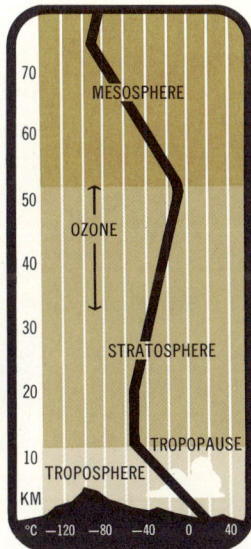

Figure 7–5 *Variation of temperature with height in the earth's atmosphere. Why is it warmer at the earth's surface than at 10 kilometers above the earth? Can you explain the sharp breaks in the temperature curve at the top of the troposphere and at the top of the stratosphere?*

Why is the equatorial region warm, and why are the polar regions cold? You saw in Figure 4–13 how the earth's spherical shape causes the insolation to be distributed unequally with latitude. The higher the latitude, the greater the area over which the solar beam is spread on the earth's surface, so the amount of radiation received on each unit area decreases from the equator to the poles.

The rotation of the earth brings each point on a circle of latitude into sunlight for the same period each day. In the course of a day, insolation is spread equally around a circle of latitude. What would happen if the earth rotated more slowly, always keeping the same side toward the sun? What would happen if the earth didn't rotate at all?

One of the curves in Figure 7–6 shows the average amount of energy *absorbed* by the earth and atmosphere at each latitude during the year. The other curve shows the amount of energy *emitted* (leaving the earth and atmosphere). *On the average,* the earth and its atmosphere emit to space all of the energy absorbed. However, the regions at low latitudes absorb more energy than they emit and those at higher latitudes emit more energy than they absorb. The regions at low latitudes must lose heat, and those at high latitudes must gain an equal amount of heat by some process other than radiation. Can you suggest how this energy is transferred from the low to the high latitudes?

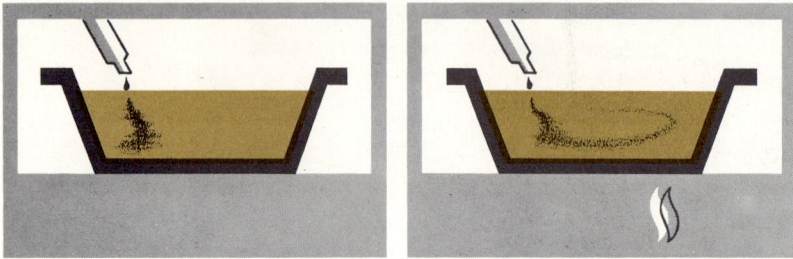

Figure 7–7 *Heating the bottom of a tank of water at one end produces convective circulation. Is movement away from or toward the heat source? Explain.*

7–6 What causes convection in the atmosphere?

What happens if a tank of cold water is heated at the bottom of one end and a little dye is introduced into the water at the other end? (See Figure 7–7.) The dye shows that the water sinks and moves along the bottom toward the warm end of the tank. There, it rises and flows back along the upper surface toward the cool end of the tank, where it sinks and thus completes a **convective circulation.** Why do you suppose that this occurs? Is the moving water transferring heat from the warm to the cold part of the tank? Does the same kind of convection account for the atmosphere's motions? Which end of the tank might be considered to represent the equator? Which might represent the pole?

Many of the physical laws that apply to water apply also to air. Air and water are both fluids. A **fluid** is a substance that tends to flow and take the shape of its container. Can the tank be used to find how the atmosphere moves?

The direct cause of the motion is the unbalanced pressure resulting from heating at the end of the tank. Pressure in the atmosphere or the tank of water is equal to the weight of the fluid above the point at which the pressure is measured. Knowing that fluid pressure represents the weight of the fluid, can you explain the way in which convection is related to gravity?

When air, water or any other fluid is cooled its density increases, and when it is warmed its density decreases. (See Figure 7–7.) The cooler fluid therefore tends to sink as gravity has more effect on it than on the warmer, less dense fluid. This allows fluid near the top to flow into the area above the cold, dense portion. This flow increases the mass of fluid at the cold side, causing the pressure to increase at the bottom of the cold side, and at the same time decrease

(*Near right*), *Cold, dense air lies on the earth's surface in early morning hours. One hour later (far right) the sun has warmed the earth, causing the air to expand and rise, dissipating the smog.*

on the warm side. The fluid near the bottom is thus forced toward the warm side, creating a **convective current.** (See Figure 7–7, right side.) If convective flow makes a complete circuit, it is referred to as a **convective cell.** It is known that convection takes place not only in the atmosphere but also in the oceans and perhaps within the earth.

What would the atmosphere's circulation look like if the differences in heating were the only factor controlling the air's motion? Air heated at the equator would rise and flow along the meridians toward the poles, where it would cool and sink and flow back to the equator along the earth's surface, as shown in Figure 7–8A. At the earth's surface the pressure would be greatest at the poles and least at the equator. If you drew lines connecting points of equal pressure, on a map of the hemisphere, these lines would be circles running around the earth on parallels of latitude, as shown by the wavy lines on Figure 7–8B. Lines through points of equal pressure like these lines are called **isobars,** just as lines of equal temperature are called **isotherms.** The flow of air under these conditions would everywhere be directly across the isobars from high to low pressure or from pole to equator. How would you describe the atmosphere's

pressure field at the earth's surface under these conditions?

But if this simple convection model accounted for the atmosphere's circulation, the surface wind in the Northern Hemisphere would always blow from the north and from the south in the Southern Hemisphere. Having observed the wind velocity, including its direction, for several weeks in your Weather Watch, you know that the wind blows from all points of the compass. What does the atmosphere's general circulation really look like?

Thought and Discussion . . .

1. Twice each day when the earth's surface is absorbing and emitting the same amount of energy, the temperature is constant for a brief period. Can you relate these temperatures to temperatures in the daily weather report?
2. During the long winter night one of the earth's poles receives no radiation from the sun. If there were no atmosphere to transfer heat to the pole, is there another way it might receive heat?
3. Can convective circulation result from cooling at one place?
4. What effect do you think a great increase in water vapor in the earth's atmosphere would have on the average surface temperature?

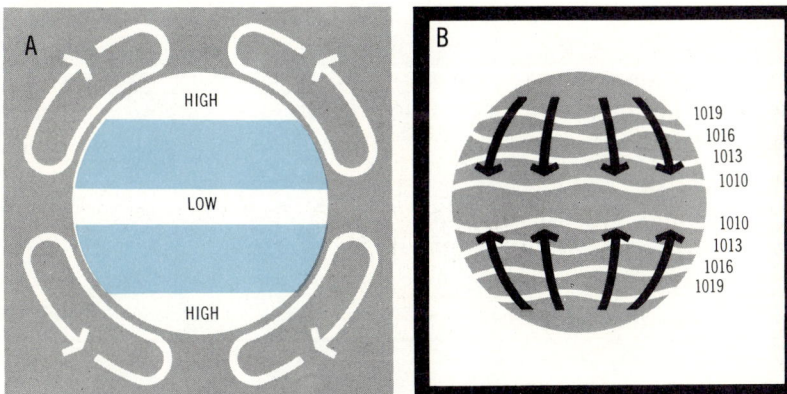

A

HIGH

LOW

HIGH

B

1019
1016
1013
1010

1010
1013
1016
1019

Figure 7–8 *Convective circulation as it might occur on a nonrotating earth. A cross section of the flow of air at the earth's surface and aloft appears in (A), and its movement across isobars at the surface is shown in (B).*

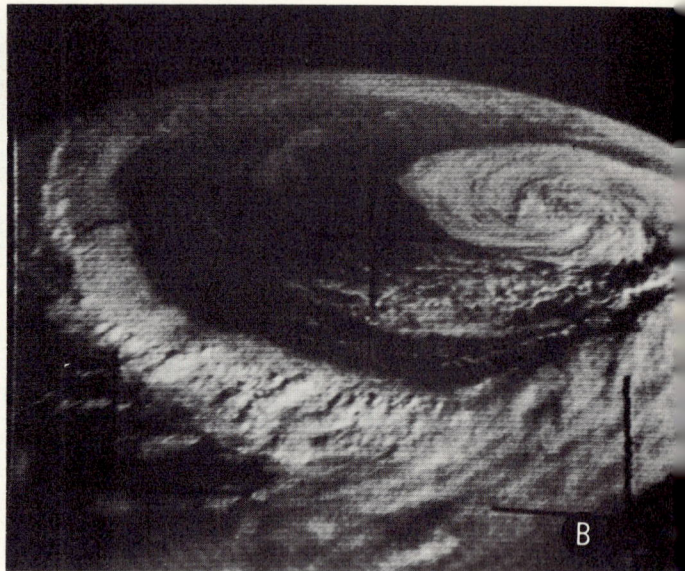

The Atmosphere in Motion

7–7 World patterns of wind and pressure.

There are many scales of motion in the atmosphere. The smallest are unseen whirls or eddies in the wind. Sensitive wind instruments show that the wind changes direction and speed every few seconds because of these whirls or eddies carried along with the wind. Larger, but still invisible eddies are felt by the passengers of an airliner as it descends into the "bumpy" air near the earth's surface. If the airliner came down through the billowy clouds called **cumulus,** the passengers may have experienced even more bumpiness, or turbulence. This turbulence is caused by upward and downward moving air currents that together create a predominantly vertical cell, as shown in Figure 7–9. Larger circulations, such as Hurricane Betsy, have mainly horizontal circulation. Why are some circulations like those producing cumulus clouds (see Figure 7–10A) nearly vertical, whereas others are nearly horizontal? Are the types of motion patterns that you see in clouds related in any way to their size?

Most of the atmosphere's mass is spread in a very thin shell over the earth's surface. Figure 3–22 shows that 99 percent of the air is below an altitude of 32 kilometers. If you take the depth of the atmosphere as 32 kilometers and its horizontal extent as the circumference of the earth (40,000 kilometers), the horizontal dimension is about 1250

Figure 7–9 *A cumulus cloud is evidence of upward flowing air currents in a vertical convection cell. Where is air descending in the photograph?*

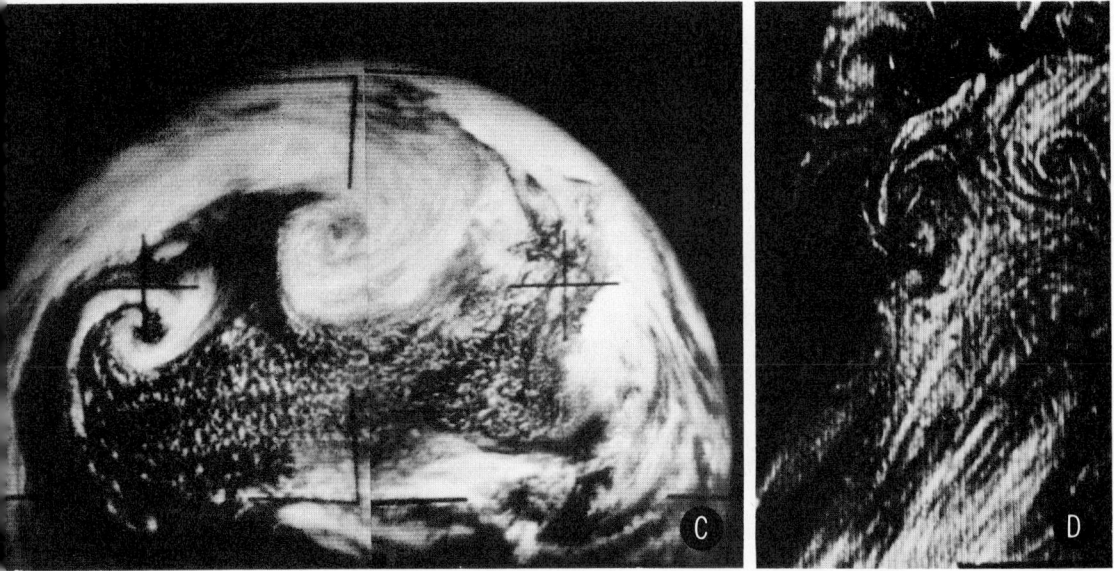

Figure 7–10 *Cloud patterns suggest some of the many motions of the atmosphere. (A) Gemini 4 photos of cumulus clouds over Florida. (B) Cyclone over the North Atlantic photographed by a weather satellite. (C) What region is shown in this photograph? Why do the two cyclones spiral in directions opposite to that of the cyclone in (B)? (D) Eddy patterns downwind from the Canary Islands televised by Tiros 5.*

times as great as its depth! When the pattern of air movement is very large, the air has a lot of room to move horizontally but not much room for vertical motion. On the other hand, when the pattern of motion is small, the vertical path is about the same length as the horizontal path. Large-scale air motions are nearly horizontal but small-scale motions are more nearly vertical.

The many-sized motion patterns made by the moving air range in scale from the small turbulent eddies a few centimeters in diameter to immense circulations that whirl around the earth's poles. Turbulent eddies, cumulus clouds, thunderstorms, and larger eddies called **cyclones** form and travel in the thin shell of air surrounding our planet. A cyclone is a sort of giant whirlwind in a low pressure area. As vapor changes into cloud in some of the circulations, the clouds reveal the varied patterns of motion. Some of these patterns of motion shown by clouds are illustrated in the photographs of Figure 7–10. Is there an even larger pattern underlying the restless motions of the moving eddies? Does such a pattern appear in the picture of the entire

earth's cloud cover on a single day, shown in Figure 7–11?

When the atmosphere's motions are averaged for many days, an orderly pattern of motion does appear. This motion is called the atmosphere's **general circulation.** Strangely enough, the general world pattern of air motion near the earth's surface was fairly well understood before it was realized that storms are eddies that move across the earth's surface. The general circulation was far better understood than were the causes of day-to-day weather changes.

The explorers who followed Columbus took great care to observe the winds and ocean currents during their voyages. Their chances of sailing home safely depended on the winds and currents they encountered. These voyagers, including

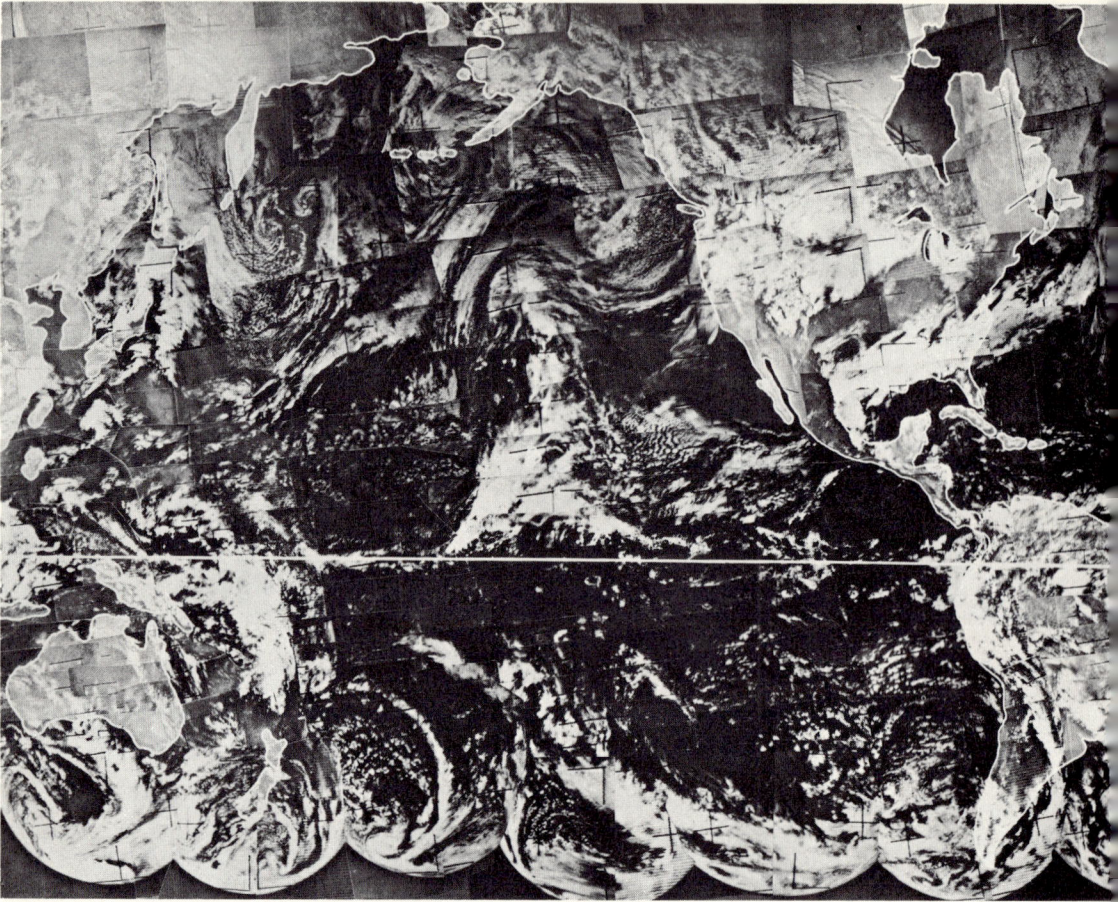

Figure 7–11 *This picture of the earth's cloud cover on February 13, 1965, consists of 450 photographs received from the weather satellite Tiros 9 as it orbited the earth from pole to pole.*

a famous English buccaneer named William Dampier, brought back accounts of the winds. From their accounts came the first attempt, by the English astronomer Edmund Halley in 1686, to relate the atmosphere's general circulation to the distribution of solar radiation.

Nearly everyone has heard of the trade winds. The **trade winds** are broad, steady air currents that blow toward the equator from the northeast in the Northern Hemisphere and from the southeast in the Southern Hemisphere. Halley suggested that the trades are caused by the rising of heated air near the equator where the sun's heat is greatest. This rising air must be replaced by the air of the trade winds blowing toward the

equator from the cooler region of each hemisphere. The zone where the trades meet is a region of calm air which mariners called the **doldrums,** and which today is called the **Intertropical Convergence Zone** by some earth scientists. Halley had hit upon *convection* as the basic cause of the air's motion. Although he had discovered the *cause* of the trade winds, Halley could not account satisfactorily for their direction. If the air moved from the cold region of each hemisphere toward the hot equator, shouldn't the trades blow from the north instead of the northeast and from the south instead of the southeast?

Since Halley's time, much more information on winds has been obtained. These data have been averaged to show the atmosphere's motion near the earth's surface in Figure 7–12. The wavy lines

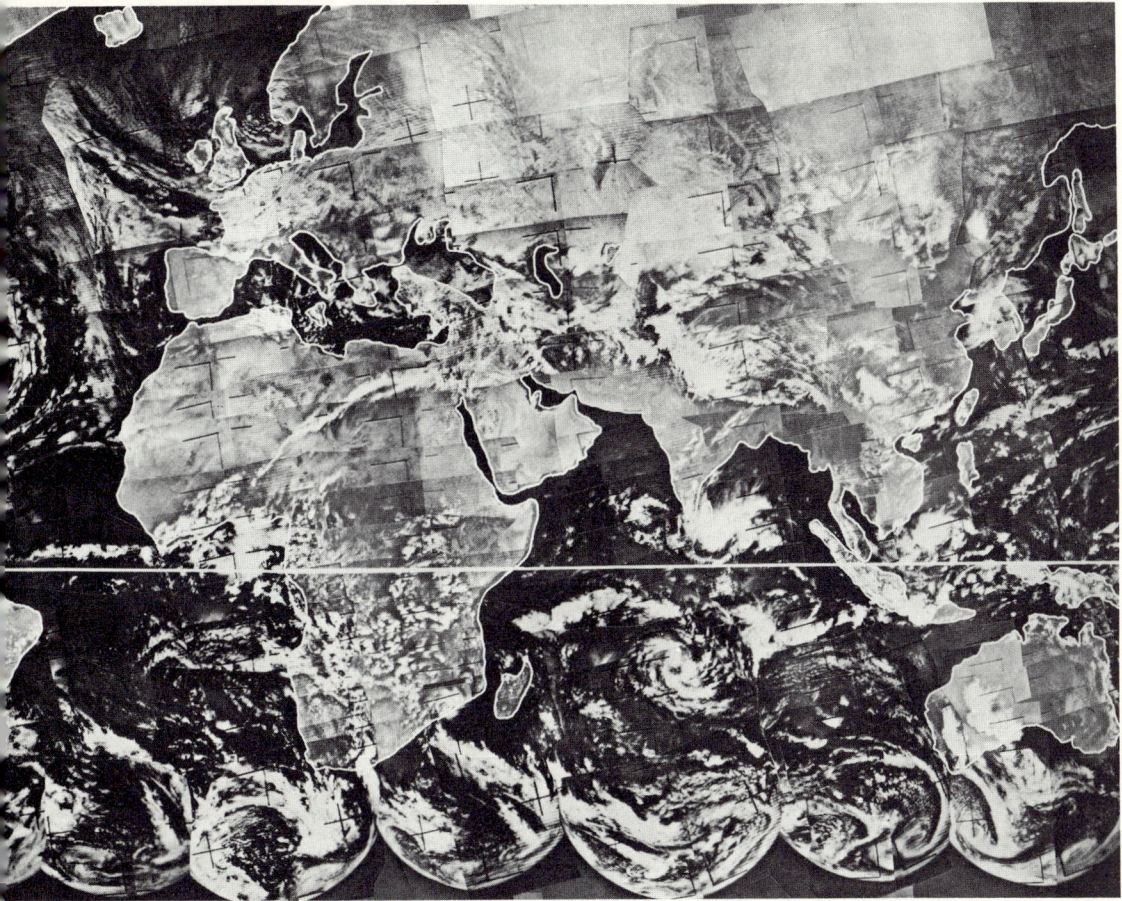

on the map are isobars of the average pressure at sea level. At first glance this map appears to be an unorganized maze of lines and arrows. Look back at Figure 7–8. In what ways does the actual pattern of the general circulation resemble the theoretical model of convection? Can you see in both figures the equatorial belt of low pressure where the trade winds meet? Can you see the polar high pressure area of cold, sinking air in both figures? However, in between equator and pole many things are happening in the atmosphere that Figure 7–8 does not explain.

The patterns of pressure and motion in Figure 7–12 are simplified in Figure 7–13. Does the model of the circulation

Figure 7–12 *Average annual sea-level pressure and generalized wind patterns near the earth's surface.*

in Figure 7–13 bring out more clearly the big features of the actual world patterns of air motion and pressure? What causes the high-pressure pattern at about 30 degrees latitude? What makes the trade winds and other winds blow at an angle across the isobars?

The missing argument in Halley's explanation came in 1735 from another English scientist, George Hadley. Hadley recognized that unequal heating of the earth must be the basic cause of the trades. He introduced a new idea to account for the fact that the trades blow from the northeast instead of from the north, and from the southeast instead of from the south. He said that the air moving toward the equator would be deflected by the earth's rotation so that it would approach the equator at an angle. The air rising at the equator doesn't travel all the way to the pole. Instead, it sinks back to the earth's surface near 30 degrees latitude. (See Figure 7–13.) From there, most of the air sweeps back toward the equator to rise again and make another circuit. Thus, the trade winds are a part of a huge cell of air motion that is known by earth scientists as the **Hadley cell.**

Hadley explained that the trades blow at an angle to the equator because of the earth's rotation. You can see from Figure 7–12 that other winds blow at an angle to the pressure belts instead of straight down the pressure gradient from high to low pressure. Why is this so?

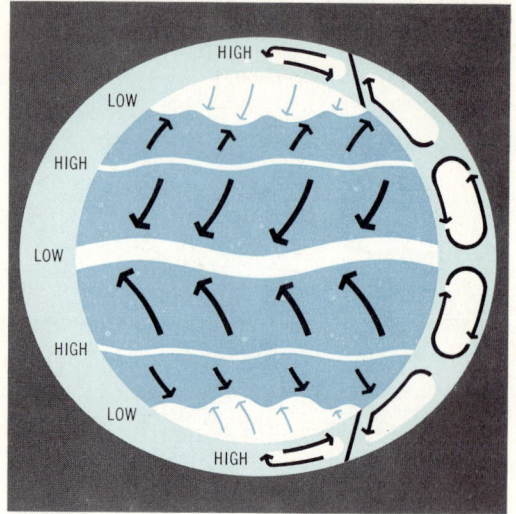

Figure 7–13 *Simplified wind belts and pressure belts. The westerlies blow in belts between the trades and the polar winds.*

7–8 How does the earth's rotation affect the winds?

The influence of the earth's rotation on objects moving over its surface is called the **Coriolis effect,** after Gaspard G. Coriolis, the French physicist who first explained the effect mathematically in 1835. The nature of the Coriolis effect can be demonstrated simply, without the aid of mathematics.

You learned in Chapter 5 that an object accelerates in the direction of an unbalanced force acting on the object. However, this direction is the *direction of the force in space.* If an unbalanced force is directed toward the North Star, an object acted on by the force accelerates toward the North Star. Remember

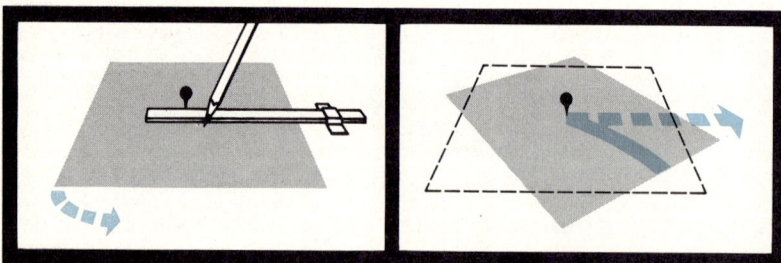

Figure 7–14 *The trace of the pencil on the paper represents the path of the wind on a rotating earth.*

also that you live on a "spherical merry-go-round." (See Section 4–2.) Your merry-go-round, the earth, turns under the object that is accelerating in the direction of the North Star.

If you were at the center of a merry-go-round that was rotating counter-clockwise, and threw a ball toward a friend seated at the rim, would he catch the ball? No indeed, but not because your aim is bad. By the time the ball reached the rim, the merry-go-round would have carried him around to a point at the left of the point toward which you aimed the ball. If the path of the ball were traced on the floor of the merry-go-round, it would appear to be curved to your right.

This effect can be demonstrated with the aid of the simple equipment shown in Figure 7–14. Rotate the sheet of paper around the thumbtack and at the same time draw a line from the center outward along the sheet of paper. Use the ruler as a guide for a straight line. If you rotate the paper counterclockwise (the direction of rotation in the Northern Hemisphere as viewed from above the North Pole), your pencil line will curve to the right when you look in the direction the pencil is moving. What happens when you draw a straight line and rotate the paper clockwise? This represents motion in the Southern Hemisphere. Even though your pencil moved in a straight line, the trace of the line was deflected and resulted in a curved line. You can see from the wind arrows in Figure 7–12 that this deflection substantially affects global winds blowing over long distances. Consequently, the Coriolis effect has widespread influence on the world's weather.

The effect of the earth's rotation on moving air is the same as its effect on projectiles or other objects that are trav-

Edmund Halley (1656–1742) is perhaps best known as the astronomer who discovered the comet bearing his name. It was he who persuaded Newton to publish his Principia. Halley was a great scientist whose interests covered many fields. He traveled widely to investigate the earth's magnetism. He published the first map of the winds and laid the groundwork for the study of weather by relating the winds to the way in which the sun's heat is distributed over the earth.

Halley's contribution to our understanding of the winds is especially notable since so little was known about the causes of air motion at that time. It is natural for us to think of the wind as air in motion. Yet, in Halley's time, some scientists still held to Aristotle's notion that wind was produced by a kind of "breathing" from the earth! In 1686, in a paper before the Royal Society, Dr. Martin Lister referred to the trade winds as the "constant breath" of the seaweed in the tropical ocean. He held that the trades were "constant and uniform" because the wind came from the breath of only one plant, unlike the confused winds from the many plants and trees of the land!

Halley's explanation of the trade winds, published with his map in 1686, gave a much more scientific and accurate account of their cause than did Lister's paper of the same year.

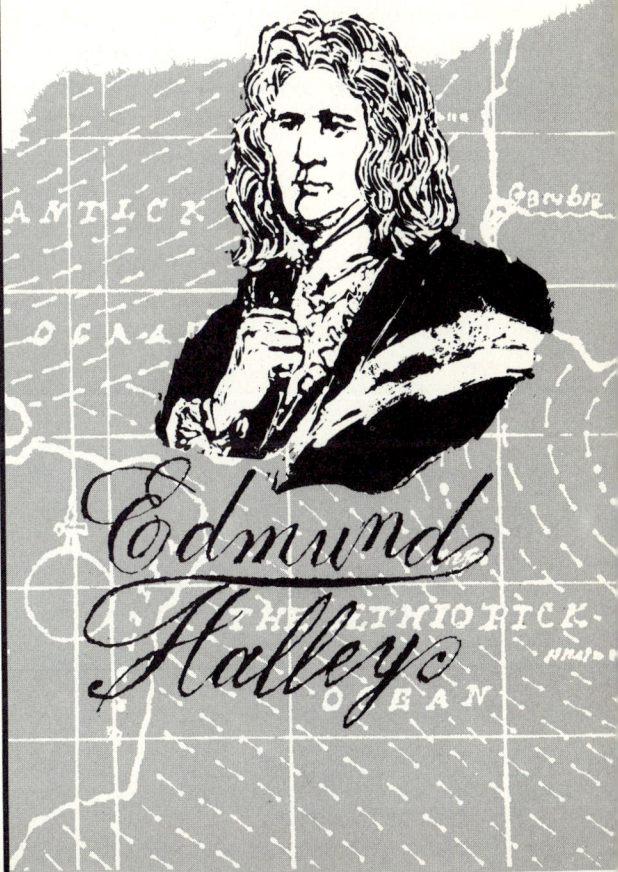

eling above the earth's surface. If such objects were to travel far enough, their deflection would be as noticeable as the deflection of the wind is. In the Northern Hemisphere the Coriolis effect tends to deflect an air current to the right of its path, as one looks in the direction of the air flow. In the Southern Hemisphere the effect is to deflect an air current to the left of its path.

7–9 Rotation introduces zonal motion.

Convection sets the air in motion. The air starts moving directly across isobars to areas of lower pressure. (See Figure 7–15.) The Coriolis effect deflects the winds and causes them to blow at an angle to the isobars as shown in Figure 7–15. The motion becomes somewhat parallel to the latitude lines. Motion along the parallels is called **zonal** motion.

Instead of one convective cell circulating air between the equator and the pole, three cells appear, as shown in Figure 7–13. As a result of rotation, zonal motions develop.

Meteorologists explain the picture of the general circulation (Figure 7–13) in the following way: As heated air rises at the equator, it begins to flow poleward high in the troposphere. As it does so, the air is deflected by the Coriolis effect and becomes a west wind with only a slight poleward motion. Moving away from the equator, the air cools rapidly by radiation to space, becomes

denser, and sinks to the earth's surface near latitude 30 degrees north or south.

Part of the sinking air near latitude 30 degrees turns back toward the equator as it reaches the earth's surface. Part continues toward the pole. The current moving toward the equator is deflected to become the trade winds. The trades of each hemisphere meet near the equator and begin to rise, thus completing the circulation of the Hadley cell. The trade winds sweep across about half of the earth's surface. (See Figure 7–13.) They are the steadiest winds in the lower atmosphere, showing little change in direction or speed from day to day. The Hadley cell is a permanent and steady feature of the general circulation.

Try to visualize in three dimensions the pattern of this huge cell of air in motion rising all around the earth near the equator, moving aloft toward the pole to settle at about 30 degrees latitude and flow back toward the equator. The amount of air moving through this pattern, according to some estimates, is an incredible 200 to 250 million tons per second in each of the hemispheres, north

Figure 7–15 *Earth's rotation causes air currents to curve to the right in the Northern Hemisphere. What direction do they curve in the Southern Hemisphere?*

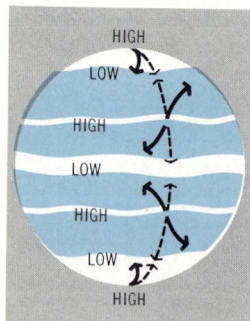

(Left) Pirates like Dampier recorded air motions. (Right) Modern programs like the Global HOrizontal Sounding Technique (GHOST) continue the work. (Top right) Balloon carries an instrument (below, right) powered by solar cells. A sun sensor locates the balloon. (Far right) Numbers on a map show the position each day after launch from New Zealand.

and south. Remember, however, that the vertical rise may be about 12 to 15 kilometers or less, while the horizontal flow is 2000 to 3000 kilometers.

Part of the sinking air at latitude 30 degrees continues poleward but is deflected to become the *westerlies* of middle latitudes at the earth's surface, as shown in Figure 7–13. Over the polar region, where there is little or no solar radiation most of the year, the air also cools and sinks. This sinking air flows equatorward at the earth's surface and is deflected by the Coriolis effect to become the belt of *polar easterlies*. The polar easterlies occupy a very thin layer next to the earth's surface.

The polar easterlies and the mid-latitude westerlies are not steady winds, blowing in the same direction day after day as the trades do. Only the average motion resembles the pattern of Figure 7–13. As you observed the wind direction from day to day in your Weather Watch, did you notice that the wind is quite changeable? What causes the continual changes in wind direction at middle and high latitudes?

Look at Figure 7–13 again. The middle latitudes, where the warm subtropical air of the westerlies is thrust directly against the contrasting cold air coming from the polar region, is the most turbulent zone on earth. The boundary where they meet is called the **polar front**. A **front** is an interface between two large air masses of differing densities. The intersection of the polar front with the earth's surface is shown as the irregular line in Figure 7–13 separating the westerlies from the polar easterlies. This front is forced back and forth from north to south. The temperatures of places within that broad zone are alternately warm and cold as the polar and subtropical air masses surge back and forth. Eddies called **polar-front cyclones** develop along the front and are carried eastward by strong westerly winds.

The cyclones that move along the polar front and the circulation of the Hadley cell transfer heat poleward. This transfer of heat allows the higher latitudes to radiate more energy to space than they receive from the sun, as you can see by studying Figure 7–6.

Look back at Figure 7–12. Can you identify the trade winds, the westerlies, and the polar easterlies? the equatorial low-pressure belt, and the zone of high pressure near latitude 30 degrees? Notice how the winds blow from high to low pressure and veer to the right in the Northern Hemisphere. Does Figure 7–13 suggest where the air near the earth's surface comes from to supply the high pressure zone, and where it goes out of the low pressure areas?

In the map of Figure 7–12, notice how the zone of high pressure near latitude 30 degrees appears to be interrupted where it crosses the continents. Can you suggest a reason for this interruption in the pressure pattern?

7–10 Investigating land and water temperatures.

The island of Bermuda is both a winter and summer resort. People from the United States travel to Bermuda in the summer to escape the heat, and in the winter to escape the cold. Can you explain why this is possible?

Procedure

Set up the materials as shown in Figure 7–16. Place a light source 30 to 40 cm directly above the containers.

Turn the light on and record the temperatures of the containers each minute for 10 minutes. After 10 minutes have passed, turn the light off and again record the temperatures each minute for 10 minutes.

Make a graph to summarize your observations. Plot the values for all four thermometers on the graph. Connect the plotted points for each thermometer with a smooth curve.

Answer the following questions: (1)Does the air heat up faster over the soil or the water? Why? (2)Why was there so much difference between the rate of temperature change of the soil and the rate of temperature change of the water? (3)Which received more heat energy from the lamp, the soil or the water? Why? (4)Which lost heat faster, the soil or the water? Why? (5)Which (soil or water) might be considered a heat source during the winter? Explain. (6)How would air pressure over a warm portion of the earth's surface compare with that over a cooler area? Why?

Figure 7–16 *Equipment setup for investigating the heating of earth materials.*

7–11 Land and water modify air motions.

Now look again at the map in Figure 7–12 and compare it with those in figures 7–17 and 7–18. The latter figures show the average winds and sea-level pressures for July when insolation is high in the Northern Hemisphere, and for January when insolation is low. Can you see the influence of the greater heat-ing and cooling rates of the continents? Look especially at Asia. Why are the July and January maps different? What causes the low pressure over south Asia in summer and how does the low pressure affect the air flow?

It takes three to five times as much energy to heat a gram of water 1°C as it takes to heat a gram of soil by the same amount. For this and other reasons, a land surface heats and cools rapidly, compared to a water surface. Can you think of other reasons related to investigations 6–2 and 6–6 that explain why soil is more readily heated by solar radiation than water is? What effect would mixing of waters in the oceans have on rate of heating and cooling? What effect would the transparency of water have?

Thus the land heats more in summer and cools more in winter, while the ocean tends to keep a more even temperature throughout the year. In summer, the land becomes a heat **source,** whereas the ocean may act as a heat **sink** to the overlying air. Does this mean the air density will be lower over the continents than over the ocean in summer? During the winter the situation is reversed: The ocean is a heat source and the continents become heat sinks, places where heat is removed from the atmosphere.

A barograph records atmospheric pressure. The drum at left rotates once in seven days while the pen rises and falls with changing air pressure, leaving a trace on the graph paper.

ACTIVITY *Look in figures 7–17 and 7–18 at southern Asia, largest of all land masses. Explain the change in pressure and wind patterns from summer to winter in terms of heat sources and sinks as related to land versus water. Your explanation should run through these steps: (1) difference in heating due to land versus water, which produces (2) difference in air density, which produces (3) difference in air pressure, which produces (4) air motion.*

Figure 7–17 Sea-level pressure and wind patterns near the earth's surface in July.

Figure 7–18 Sea-level pressure and wind patterns near the earth's surface in January. What are the main differences in the patterns shown in Figure 17 and Figure 18?

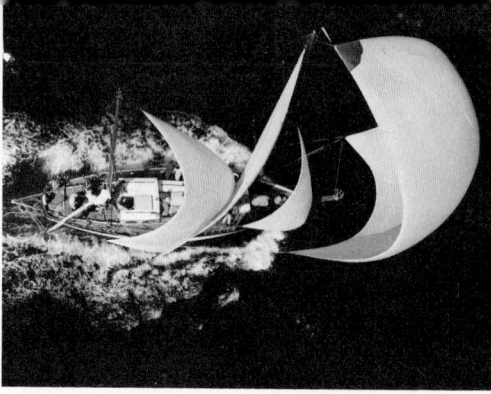

Wind serves man in many ways. Here a yacht, long-distance racing in trade winds, sets a huge sail area for maximum speed.

These land-to-water and water-to-land circulations, changing their direction from winter to summer, are called **monsoons.** Do you think the same kind of in-and-out flow of air might occur from day to night along a seacoast?

Seasonal wind changes, as in India, may dominate other features of the atmosphere's circulation. For example, can you find the trade winds over the Indian Ocean? In summer, the monsoon transports vast quantities of vapor from the ocean to the land. Over land, the air near the earth's surface becomes warmed and rises, causing the vapor to change to cloud.

Cumulus clouds develop in rising air currents when the underlying surface is quite warm compared with the air above. Figure 7–10A shows thousands of such clouds scattered in a beautiful pattern over the lower part of the Florida peninsula. Can you explain why there is a big blank space, free of clouds, over the peninsula? This space marks Lake Okeechobee. The lake surface is much cooler than the surrounding land.

Note in figures 7–17 and 7–18 how the broad belts of high pressure located near latitude 30 degrees in both hemispheres seem to be broken up where they cross the continents. Air over the land alternates between high and low pressure, while the subtropical high pressure area remains over the oceans all year long.

The high-pressure belts break up into areas of high pressure with their centers over the oceans, two in the Northern Hemisphere and three in the Southern Hemisphere. These high pressure areas are the **semipermanent subtropical highs.** The winds blow out of the high pressure areas and are deflected to the right in the Northern Hemisphere and to the left in the Southern Hemisphere. Consequently, on the eastern sides of the highs the flow is toward the equator, and on the western sides it is toward the pole. The air moving toward the equator is cool and tends to sink, but at the other side of the high the air is warm and tends to rise. Would the weather be quite different at the eastern and western ends of the subtropical highs?

The distribution of land and water is only one of the factors that modify the circulation, producing the many-sized motion patterns of the atmosphere. The great variety of motion patterns is in part the result of water in the air, as you will discover in the next chapter.

Thought and Discussion . . .

1. When air currents near the earth's surface meet or *converge,* what do you think happens to the air? When air currents flow out of a region or *diverge,* where do you think the air comes from?

2. A high-pressure area is called an **anticyclone,** or high, and a low-pressure area is called a **cyclone,** or low. Knowing the relation between the pressure and wind fields in the atmosphere, can you give a more complete description of cyclones and anticyclones?

3. Do you think that tropical cyclones or hurricanes are a necessary part of the general circulation? Suppose that man found it within his power to destroy them as soon as they appear? Do you think he should do so? Why?

Unsolved Problems Accurate prediction of the atmosphere's motions is one of the unsolved problems of earth science. However, scientific prediction of the air's motion patterns, made possible by electronic computers, has revolutionized weather prediction. With more advanced computers, meteorologists believe that they can put more data into the machines and get fairly accurate predictions of the large-scale motion patterns a week or more in advance. To attempt this, however, they need to have a close network of observations over the entire world. Can you suggest how weather and communications satellites might supply the data needed for more accurate predictions?

Northern Hemisphere weather drawn by a computer. (Left) Wind velocity is shown by the length and direction of the barbs, which point in the direction of the air flow. (Right) Isobars show surface pressure. Wind circulates differently around high and low pressure centers.

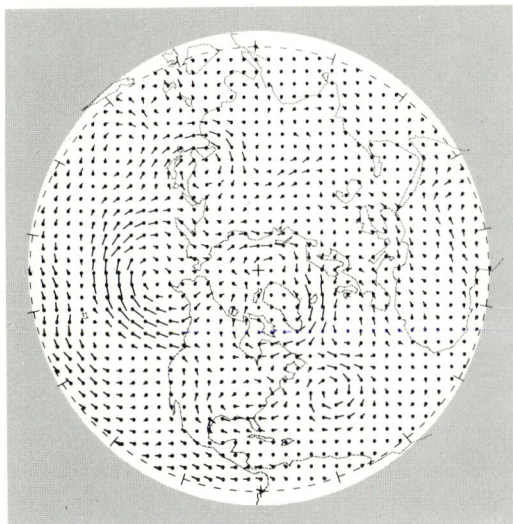

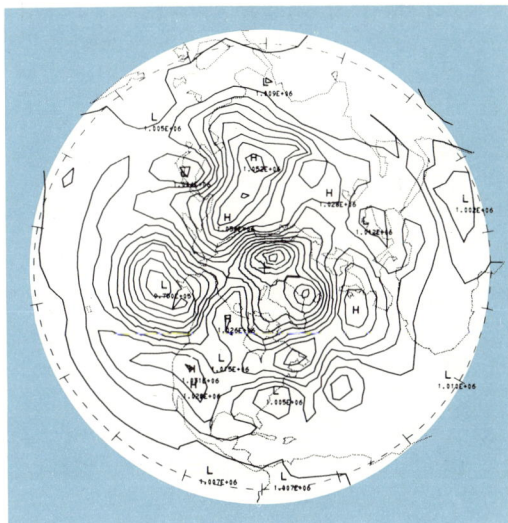

CHAPTER REVIEW

Summary

Energy from the sun and the way this energy is distributed are responsible for the circulation of air and water in the atmosphere. The earth is in radiative balance, emitting about the same amount of radiation it absorbs from the sun. The resulting temperature, determined largely by the earth's distance from the sun, is within the range necessary for water to occur in all three states and thus to move through the water cycle.

The earth and its atmosphere absorb about two-thirds of the incoming energy, the rest being reflected to space by clouds, air molecules, ice and snow, and other materials at the earth's surface. The atmosphere absorbs only a little of the incoming energy, but the earth's surface absorbs far more. The earth's surface emits long-wave radiation, the greater part of which is absorbed by water vapor and carbon dioxide in the atmosphere. These gases radiate downward as well as upward, so that the earth's surface receives energy from the atmosphere as well as from the sun. As a result, the earth's surface is warmer than the atmosphere above and is much warmer than it would be if there were no atmosphere to trap the energy.

The earth's spherical shape results in a distribution of incoming energy that decreases between the equator and the poles.

This produces an energy source at the equator and energy sinks at the poles. The higher latitudes emit more energy than they absorb, whereas the lower latitudes absorb more energy than they emit. The excess energy absorbed at the lower latitudes is transferred to the higher latitudes by the motions of the atmosphere.

Convection is caused by unequal heating or cooling which brings about density differences in the fluid. These density differences result in the unbalanced pressure forces that drive air from high to low pressure. If the earth did not rotate, air might rise at the equator, flow to the poles, sink, and then return to the equator near the earth's surface. However, the earth's rotation causes the air currents to be deflected so that they tend to flow parallel to the latitude circles instead of directly across them.

The poleward moving currents, leaving the equator, lose heat by radiation and sink near latitude 30 degrees, creating the subtropical high-pressure belts. One branch of the sinking currents turns equatorward as the trade winds. Another branch continues poleward where it encounters colder air, producing the polar front. The polar front is an interface separating the tropical and polar air masses. Immense eddies called cyclones, powered by the density contrast between the air masses, develop along the polar front and travel in the westerly current of middle latitudes.

Land heats more rapidly than water because the energy does not penetrate deeply into the soil or rock. In water, heat may be carried downward by the water's motions. Moreover the temperature of soil or rock increases much more than that of water when a given quantity of heat is absorbed. For the same reasons, the land also cools more rapidly than the oceans. Energy is also used to evaporate water, resulting in the more even temperature of the oceans. The land and water contrasts produce seasonal circulations called monsoons.

Small-scale convection, the polar front, and land and water contrasts create a variety of motion patterns in the atmosphere, ranging from small turbulent eddies to that of the general circulation. These motion patterns, powered by solar energy, are necessary links in the water cycle, and depend for their development in part on the energy released during the water cycle.

Questions and Problems

A

1. If an object is radiating the same amount of energy it is absorbing, does its surface temperature rise, fall, or remain the same?

2. If the earth were twice its present distance from the sun, what would be its approximate temperature?

3. How do water vapor and carbon dioxide keep the earth's surface warm?

4. If a pan containing water is heated at the rim and cooled at the center, what motion takes place?

5. If a projectile is fired in the Northern Hemisphere, does it appear to curve to the right or left of the direction in which it was fired?

6. What causes zonal motion in the earth's atmosphere?

7. What is a monsoon?

B

1. When the air is very dry, the minimum temperature just before sunrise tends to be lower than when the air contains a lot of water vapor. Can you explain why?

2. Can you show how temperature differences can produce a horizontal pressure field in a fluid?

3. At which place on earth would you expect to find the greatest annual range of temperatures?

C

1. In Chapter 5 you learned that physical quantities can be represented as *fields*; what is the relation between motion and pressure if the fluid is not rotating?

2. Explain how the dimensions of the atmosphere are related to the air's patterns of motion, namely, vertical cells and horizontal eddies.

3. Records show that the entire earth's average temperature is higher during the Northern Hemisphere summer when the earth is farthest from the sun than it is during the Northern Hemisphere winter when the earth is closest to the sun. Knowing that the major part of the earth's land masses is in the Northern Hemisphere, can you suggest why the earth's average temperature is higher when it is farthest from the sun?

Suggested Readings

BOOKS

Battan, Louis J. *The Nature of Violent Storms.* Doubleday & Company, Inc. (Science Study Series), Garden City, N.Y., 1961. Paperback.

Blumenstock, David J. *The Ocean of Air.* Rutgers University Press, New Brunswick, N.J., 1959.

Harris, Miles F. *Man Against Storm: The Challenge of Weather.* Coward-McCann, Inc., New York, 1962. Chapters 1 and 2.

Lehr, Paul E., R. Will Burnett, and Herbert S. Zim. *Weather. A Guide to Phenomena and Forecasts.* Golden Press, Inc., New York, 1957.

Thompson, Philip D., Robert O'Brien, and the Editors of *Life. Weather.* Time, Inc. (Life Science Library), New York, 1965.

PERIODICALS

Jastrow, Robert. "Artificial Satellites and the Earth's Atmosphere." *Scientific American,* August, 1959.

Starr, Victor P. "The General Circulation of the Atmosphere." *Scientific American,* December, 1956. (Scientific American Offprint #841, W. H. Freeman & Co., Publishers, San Francisco.)

Sometimes the wind is detrimental to man, and he builds protective devices against its effects. (Right) A snow fence reduces wind velocity and causes the wind to drop some of the snow it carries, protecting a nearby road. (Left) A windbreak of planted trees is common on the plains of many countries and protects crops and homes.

Dry soil, blown by the wind, drifts around the farmhouse. The windmills pump no water, for the land has been scorched by years of drought. Yet, in the air above the farm, there is enough water to fill a large lake.

The earth is surrounded by an invisible ocean of water. Even over the Sahara desert, the water in the air could supply a heavy rainfall. Suppose the ocean in the air could give up all its water in one big storm. The resulting rainfall, if spread evenly over the earth, would amount to 25 millimeters or one inch of water. This may seem insignificant compared to the oceans, but the reservoir in the air provides nearly the entire supply of fresh water.

The atmospheric reservoir doesn't deliver water equally everywhere, however. In some areas, the atmosphere supplies ample water to the land and makes it productive. In other places the water supply comes in deluges. In March, 1952, on the island of Réunion, in the Indian Ocean off the east coast of Africa, over 1.8 meters of rain fell in 24 hours! In many places where there is usually enough rain for crops and man's other needs, occasional droughts lasting a season or a year, even several years, result in water shortages, ruined crops, and human suffering. Over much of the earth's surface a supply of fresh water is one of nature's least reliable gifts.

Carried in never-ending streams of air, the supply of water comes in showers or torrents, in steady rains that last for days, or in sprinkles lasting only a minute or two. Winter storms pile layer upon layer of snow, and spring brings warm air and rain to melt the snowpack. Then the water rushes into streams. The streams flow into the rivers, and the rivers overflow, flooding the land.

Why is the water carried by the atmosphere distributed so unevenly? What makes the atmosphere give up or retain its water supply? Under what conditions does the atmosphere give up the right amount of water to produce crops and fulfill man's other needs for water? How does the atmosphere influence weather, climate, and environment?

Chapter **8** Water in the Air

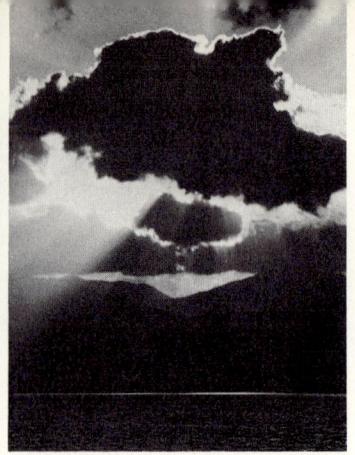

The Water Cycle

8–1 What is the water cycle?

Four centuries ago, the great artist-scientist, Leonardo da Vinci, observed that "the air moves like a river, carrying the clouds with it." Did Leonardo think of the rivers of the air as having their source in the ocean, and emptying into the rivers of the land?

The **water cycle** is often considered to have three basic stages, as shown in Figure 8–1. Water passes as vapor from the ocean reservoir into the atmosphere. The atmosphere transports water vapor over the land, where it may change to clouds and fall as precipitation. Rivers and underground flow carry the water back to the ocean, where it is ready to repeat the never-ending cycle. However, this is an oversimplification. Have you seen thin clouds of moisture rising from the surface of a freshly plowed field, or mist rising from the streets when sunshine follows the rain?

The water cycle, like the circulation of the atmosphere, occurs on many scales.

A puddle of water that you watch evaporate today may return tomorrow in a shower in the same area. Seawater, evaporated and taken up by the trade winds two weeks ago, may be the snow falling today over New England. Instead of the simple circulation indicated above, the water cycle is more like a series of sub-cycles, or separate exchanges of moisture between land, sea, and air. While moving across the interfaces between these three spheres, water is also changing between liquid, vapor, and solid states.

Can you find the sequence of events in Figure 8–1 that shows some moisture coming from the ocean into the air and then returning to the ocean directly as precipitation? Because the oceans are so vast, this sequence is a major sub-

Figure 8–1 *This simplified diagram of the water cycle concept shows the evaporation of water from the sea into the atmosphere, the transport of water to the land, by winds, precipitation upon the land, and stream flow to the sea.*

cycle in the water cycle. Some of the rainfall does not reach the surface. Some of the raindrops change back to vapor on their way earthward and remain in the atmosphere. This is another sub-cycle in the water cycle.

As water molecules journey through the water cycle, they may change their physical form many times. To escape from a glacier, they must **melt,** changing from a solid to a liquid state. To free themselves from a lake or pond they must absorb energy and **evaporate,** changing from a liquid to a vapor state. The molecules remain free vapor in the air until they **condense,** changing from a vapor to a liquid state. Droplets large enough to be pulled to earth by gravity may be formed. From the earth they may again evaporate into the atmosphere.

8–2 Investigating evaporation.

You often notice water evaporating, and you know that water gets into the atmosphere by evaporation, but do you know what makes water evaporate? Clothes on a line dry faster on some days than on others. What slows down evaporation and what speeds it up? In this investigation you will find some of the answers to these questions.

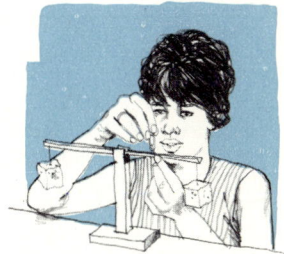

Procedure

With the equipment set up as shown in Figure 8–2, investigate the factors that influence the rate of evaporation. Try to determine the effect of one factor at a time. Answer the following questions: (1)What factors influence the rate of evaporation? (2)How do these factors operate in nature? (3)Which of these factors has the greatest effect?

Figure 8–2 *Equipment for investigating evaporation.*

8–3 How does water get into the air?

You learned in Section 6–6 that the change of state of matter from a liquid to a gas requires energy. However, you do not have to boil water to evaporate it. Did the investigation in Section 8–2 show that energy is needed to vaporize water? Some of the kinetic energy of the moving molecules changes into potential energy when a liquid becomes a gas. This energy is stored in the gas as *latent heat,* or hidden heat. It is a form of potential energy. When the gas changes back to a liquid, or condenses, the latent heat is released. Even during evaporation, some of the molecules of the gas are continually returning to the liquid surface. If more molecules are leaving a liquid than are returning to the liquid, then **evaporation** is taking place. Evap-

oration requires energy. Why do you feel cooler in a breeze when you are wet than when you are dry?

As water evaporates, the molecules of the vapor exert a pressure in the atmosphere that becomes part of the total atmospheric pressure. The reason for this is that the water vapor is now one of the gases in the atmosphere. The greater the number of molecules of water vapor per unit volume, the higher is the **vapor pressure** caused by the water molecules. When the vapor pressure increases until it is just balanced by the pressure from within the liquid driving the molecules away from the water surface, evaporation appears to stop. The vapor pressure at which this occurs is called the **saturation vapor pressure,** because the air is saturated and can hold no more water

Figure 8–3 *Because the saturation vapor pressure is higher near warm water, evaporation is greater. Can you explain how temperature controls evaporation?*

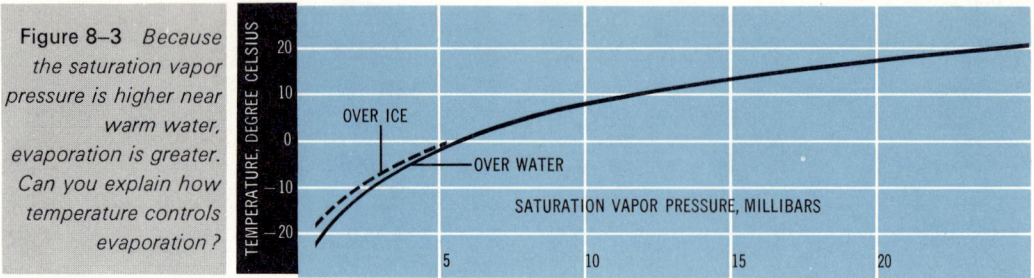

vapor. The saturation vapor pressure is greater over warm water than over cold water, as shown in Figure 8–3. As a result, evaporation is greater over warm water. *Air* temperature also controls evaporation. Warm air can hold more vapor than cold, and evaporation is more rapid in warm air.

In Investigation 8–2, did air motion have an effect on the rate of evaporation? Air is being continually moved about and mixed throughout a thick layer of the lower atmosphere. Dry air is transported from regions where there is less moisture and may replace moist air in the region above a water surface, so that evaporation can continue. Air motions are another control of evaporation. Did you discover all of these factors in the investigation?

Most of the water vapor gets into the air across the interface between ocean and air. Nevertheless, a great deal of water is evaporated over land as well, much more than you might expect from the basic water cycle—ocean to air to land to ocean.

Higher temperatures at the equator result in higher vapor pressure there than at other latitudes, as shown in Figure 8–4. Compare Figure 8–5 with Figure 8–4. Why do you suppose there is a dip in the evaporation curve over the oceans near the equator in Figure 8–5? Would the high vapor pressure there produce such an effect? Could it also be partly due to cloud cover? Is the air mo-

tion greater or less at the equator than in the trade wind regions on either side?

When the air is warm, you can feel the difference between high and low vapor pressure. We commonly think of the amount of moisture in the air in terms of relative humidity. **Relative humidity** is the ratio of the actual vapor pressure to the saturation vapor pressure. This is the ratio of the amount of moisture in the

Figure 8–4 *(Top) The average water vapor pressure in the atmosphere varies with latitude.*

Figure 8–5 *(Bottom) The amount of evaporation at a given latitude is related to the vapor pressure (see Figure 8–4) and is generally greater over the oceans than over the continents.*

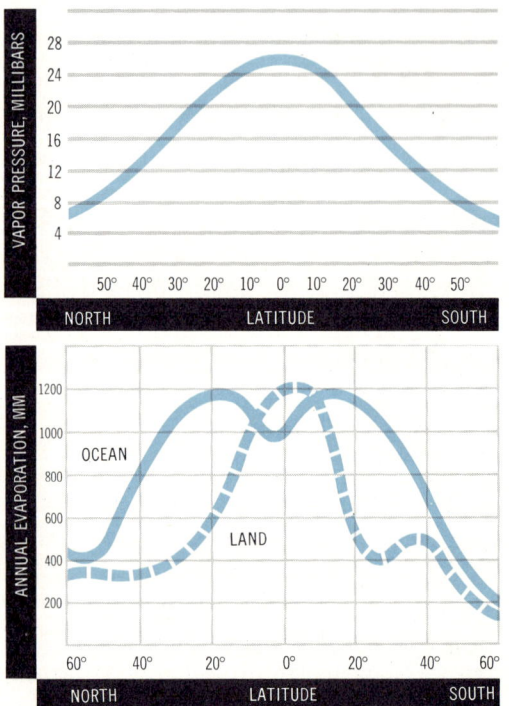

(*Right*) A pan of water is used to measure evaporation. The three-cup device measures wind speed.
(*Far right*) A hygro-thermograph records humidity and temperature.

air to the maximum amount it could hold under the same conditions. It is expressed as a percentage:

Relative humidity (%) =

$$\frac{\text{Actual vapor pressure}}{\text{Saturation vapor pressure}} \times 100.$$

For example, if the actual vapor pressure is 10 millibars and the saturation vapor pressure is 25 millibars, the relative humidity is $\frac{10}{25} \times 100$, or 40 percent. When the relative humidity reaches 100 percent, condensation can normally be expected.

Relative humidity is a convenient measure of how close the air is to saturation with water vapor. It is also a simple indicator of human comfort. When the relative humidity is high, evaporation of perspiration from your skin takes place slowly. Can you see why? Perhaps you have said, on such an occasion, "It's a sticky day."

8–4 What is condensation?

Water vapor changes to liquid water in the air by **condensation,** the change of state that is just the opposite of evaporation. Where do you suppose the water from the condensed vapor collects in the atmosphere?

Place a jar over a saucer of water and heat the water with a lamp. Leave the lamp on until evaporation ceases (when the water level in the saucer stops falling). Then turn the lamp off and observe what happens.

Water vapor must have a solid surface on which to condense. Condensation occurs when the relative humidity is near 100 percent. Since the glass of the jar cools more quickly than the air inside, water vapor condenses on the glass. If the air inside the jar cooled all at once, the vapor would condense on tiny particles and you would see a cloud, or fog, fill the jar. How can vapor condense in the air if solid surfaces are required? Small solid particles are always present in unfiltered air. Where do you think these particles come from? How do they get into the atmosphere? They are called **condensation nuclei** in the case of the formation of cloud drops. (*Nucleus,* the singular, is Latin for seed.)

Air can be filtered to remove all the nuclei from it. If the pure air is then saturated with water vapor and cooled, condensation may not take place until the relative humidity is 400 or even 500 percent! The atmosphere, however, may contain certain kinds of impurities that may cause condensation to take place well below 100 percent relative humidity. You have probably seen this as fog or smog, hanging in the atmosphere.

Water vapor collects on condensation nuclei to form tiny droplets. A salt crystal left drifting in the air from ocean spray that has been evaporated, a particle of ash or oil from the smoke of a fire, or dust particles may serve as condensation nuclei. Sea salt and smoke particles from burning are especially suited for condensation nuclei, since water vapor condenses on these particles at relative humidities less than 100 percent. Have you noticed that salt may clog a salt-shaker on a humid day?

When wind is blowing and the air is thoroughly mixed, air rarely becomes saturated with water vapor even above a large body of water. However, you have seen moisture condense on the side of a glass of ice water even though the atmosphere is not saturated. Why does dew form on blades of grass after nightfall as the temperature begins to drop?

When the temperature of the surface reaches freezing before saturation occurs, water vapor changes directly to ice and **frost** forms on the grass and other objects. The temperature at which saturation is reached is called the **dew point.** This is the temperature at which moisture condenses.

8–5 What causes condensation in the atmosphere?

While a number of factors control evaporation into the atmosphere, the cause of condensation can be summed up in a single phrase: cooling of the air. Condensation also depends on the presence of nuclei, but nuclei are always present in the atmosphere. So, the question is: How is the air cooled?

Cooling can take place when energy is transferred from a body to its surroundings by radiation, conduction, or convection. (See Section 6–4.) However, most condensation in the atmosphere results from rising air masses. How could this cause cooling and condensation? When you snap the top from a bottle of cold soda pop, releasing the pressure, vapor condenses in the neck of the bottle to form a cloud. Air in the neck of the bottle must have cooled to the dew-point temperature. What caused the cooling of the air? The temperature of a mass of air can be increased by compressing it and decreased by letting it expand.

Warming of a gas by compression, and cooling of a gas by expansion, are illustrations of the law of the conservation of energy, discussed in Section 6–5. If you have ever let air out of a bicycle tire, you have felt cool air rushing from the valve. If you have pumped air into the tire, you have noticed the pump getting hot as you compressed the air in the cylinder. In pumping up the tire, you were doing work on the air—packing or compressing it—and the energy you

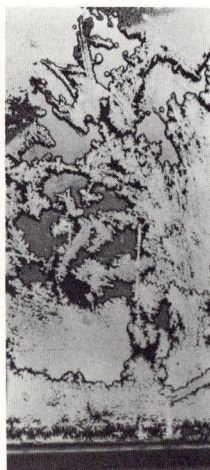

(Left) As the jar cools, water vapor from the air inside condenses on the glass. Why? (Center) What is the source of the moisture that condenses on the outside of a glass containing a cold drink? (Right) If window glass is very cold, what form will condensation take?

were exerting on the air became observable as an increase in its temperature. In escaping from the tire, the air did work by expanding against the atmospheric pressure and thereby lost energy, and cooled.

Suppose that you could take an inflated balloon high into the atmosphere where the pressure is much less than that at sea level. The air in the balloon would expand because of the lower atmospheric pressure around it. As it expanded, the air in the balloon would cool. In the same way, an air mass lifted into the atmosphere comes into regions of lower pressure where it expands and cools. This kind of temperature change—cooling with expansion, warming with compression—is called **adiabatic** (ay-dee-ah-BAT-ic) temperature change. An adiabatic process is one in which there is no heat flow into or out of the gas. The temperature changes only because the internal energy of the gas is changed as work is done on the gas, or as the gas itself does work.

We know the pressure of the atmosphere decreases upward at a certain rate. We can calculate the adiabatic temperature change of a bubble of air rising through the atmosphere. The adiabatic change in temperature of a mass of air lifted into the atmosphere depends on how high it is lifted. The adiabatic temperature change in the lower atmosphere is about 10°C per kilometer as shown in Figure 8–6.

The dew-point temperature also varies with pressure, so it too can be calculated for each kilometer the air is lifted. The dew-point temperature decreases in a rising air mass at the rate of about 1.7°C per kilometer. By finding where the temperature and dew point of the surface air are the same on the graph in Figure 8–6, you can determine the height

to which the surface air would have to be lifted in order for condensation to begin and clouds to form.

ACTIVITY *Suppose the surface temperature is 20°C and the dew-point temperature is 10°C. If the air is lifted, at what height will saturation occur? In Figure 8–6, find the point where the air-temperature line marked 20°C intersects the dew-point line marked 10°C. Move horizontally to the height scale at the right and read the height. This is how high the air must be lifted for saturation to occur. Do this for several combinations of surface air temperature and dew point. (See Investigation 8–12.)*

If a mass of air continues to rise after condensation begins, what happens to its temperature? Remember that condensation releases latent heat and warms the air. Therefore, if the *saturated* air keeps rising, it will cool more slowly than 10°C for each kilometer it rises. The rate of cooling for saturated air varies with pressure and temperature. On the average it is about 6°C for each kilometer lifted.

This difference in the rates of cooling frequently results in the warming of air as it flows up over a mountain range. Clouds and rain commonly occur on the windward side of the range as the air is

Figure 8–6 *Rising air cools about 10° Celsius for each kilometer of altitude it gains, and the dew point drops about 1.7° Celsius for each kilometer the air is lifted. (The heavy blue lines on the graph relate to the activity above.)*

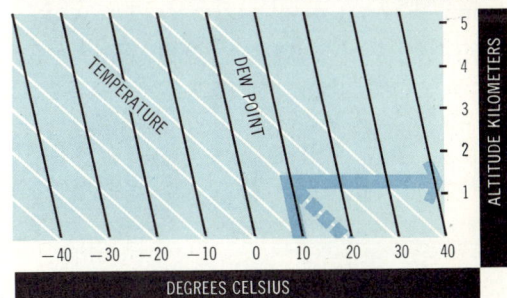

Figure 8–7 *Changes in the temperature of an air mass rising over a coastal mountain range (left) are shown in the graph.*

lifted and cooled. (**Windward** is the side against which the wind is blowing; **leeward** is the opposite side.) Once condensation begins, the air loses its moisture and gains latent heat corresponding to the amount of vapor that is condensed. When the air descends the leeward slope, it warms further by compression and reaches the valley as a warm, dry wind, sometimes called a chinook wind.

To see why this wind is warm and dry, look at the diagram in Figure 8–7. Suppose that the air's temperature is 20°C and its dew point is 11.7°C when it starts to rise over a mountain two kilometers high. When the rising air reaches a height of one kilometer, it becomes saturated, as you can determine from Figure 8–6, and condensation begins. Its temperature at this height is 10°C. Since this air is saturated, it cools thereafter at the rate of about 6°C for each kilometer it rises. At the top of the mountain its temperature is 4°C, and its dew point is also 4°C, since the air is saturated. But the air flowing down the other side of the mountain is no longer saturated and therefore warms at the dry adiabatic rate, 10°C per kilometer, during its descent. When it reaches the level at which it started to rise on the windward side

of the mountain, its temperature is 24°C. Compare this temperature with the air's original temperature. The dew point is 7.4°C because some of the moisture has been released. What effect do you think mountain ranges might have on the distribution of clouds and rainfall?

Rising air accounts for most of the condensation that occurs in the atmosphere. Since most clouds occur above the earth's surface, perhaps you could have guessed that most condensation occurs in lifted air.

Clouds that form at the earth's surface are called **fog.** Fog is usually caused by cooling of warm, moist air as it comes in contact with a cold land or water surface. The warm air loses heat to the cold ground or ocean surface below and cools to its dew point. Then the water vapor condenses to form fog.

You will recall from Figure 7–13 that there are two main regions of upward air motion in each hemisphere. Compare Figure 7–13 with Figure 8–8. These regions occur where air currents meet or **converge** near the earth's surface to force the air upward. Near the equator,

Figure 8–8 *In each hemisphere, the atmosphere's general circulation produces two zones of upward air motion and two zones of downward motion. Can you identify them on the diagram?*

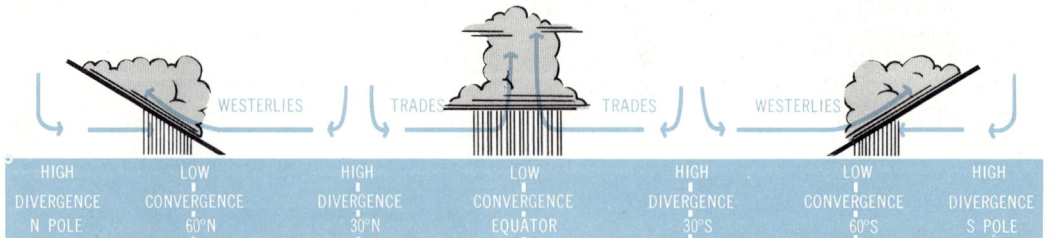

the air rises in the ascending part of the Hadley cell. In middle latitudes alternating upward and downward air motions occur where cyclones move along the polar front. Do you think that clouds could form in these zones of converging and rising air currents? Where do the zones of sinking air occur, and why? Would you expect many clouds in these regions of sinking air?

The air's upward and downward motions, together with the supply of water, largely control condensation in the atmosphere. If the water is to fall from the atmosphere, raindrops or snowflakes must form. Cloud droplets are so small that the resistance of the air helps keep them from falling. Raindrops are many times larger than cloud droplets and are pulled to the earth by gravity. What causes condensed vapor to precipitate?

Thought and Discussion . . .

1. Air that sinks to the earth's surface is usually quite dry. In what zone over the ocean would you expect the most evaporation?
2. If the earth's surface water were all ice, what would the water cycle be like? Can ice move?
3. If the earth's surface temperature were higher than 100°C, do you think liquid water might still exist in the atmosphere? Why or why not?

(Right) Great Plains where chinooks are important. (Far right) "Waiting for a Chinook" was C. M. Russell's reply to a rancher's inquiry about his cattle in the winter of 1886.

Clouds and Rain

8–6 Why do clouds differ?

You saw in Chapter 7 photographs of clouds taken from a great distance and you identified different kinds of cloud patterns. Some of the patterns were made up of many individual cumulus clouds. In cumulus clouds the vertical and horizontal dimensions are about the same. The other patterns were in the form of extensive layers of clouds of the size of cyclones, several hundred kilometers across. Long before such extensive cloud patterns could be seen, meteorologists had classified clouds on the basis of their appearance from the ground.

Can you detect the differences in clouds from your own observations? Although there are about 40 different recognized kinds of clouds, a few major types can be related to the processes that produce precipitation.

The different kinds of air motion discussed in Chapter 7 determine the kinds of clouds that form. Even when the motion is mainly horizontal, the whole mass of air may have a slight upward movement. The air mass may be gliding up the gradual slope of a front, the interface where the cold and warm air masses meet. (See Section 7–9.) Thus the whole air mass is cooled and condensation can occur throughout the rising air. If the upward motion is slow and gradual, a layer of cloud covering a wide area will be produced. Under these conditions the sky is said to be overcast.

On the other hand, small convective cells may form where the sun heats the earth's surface, indirectly warming the air. The entire air mass does not rise. Instead, bubbles of heated air are forced upward through the air mass. One reason why the whole mass does not rise is that the earth's surface is not uniformly heated. The air over a warmer spot becomes hotter and less dense than the surrounding air and rises in a big bubble like a balloon filled with gas. As the bubble rises, it expands and cools. If the air cools to its dew point, condensation takes place, and if the air continues to rise, a cumulus cloud forms. However, cumulus clouds can form in some air masses but not in others, even when the moisture in the air masses is the same and when the surface heating is the same. What do you suppose causes this to happen?

Look at the two diagrams in Figure 8–9 to see why convective clouds form in one air mass and not in another. The temperature of the air is represented by the solid lines in the diagrams. At the surface, the temperature of each is 20°C and each has the same dew point. However, in the left-hand diagram the temperature aloft is colder. The dashed lines show the temperature that a rising bubble of air would have if it were heated to 25°C at the surface. The moisture content of the two air masses is the same, so each bubble would reach saturation at the same height.

For a bubble of heated air to continue to rise, however, its density must be less than that of the surrounding air. Therefore it must be warmer than the surrounding air. Examine the diagram on the left in Figure 8–9. A parcel of air heated to 25°C at the surface would cool at 10°C per kilometer (dashed line) as it rises, until condensation occurs. Above that level, it would cool at about 6°C per kilometer. Can you see that the bubble will continue to rise in this situation because it remains warmer (dashed line) than the surrounding air (solid line)? Because it behaves in this way, such an air mass is said to be **unstable.**

How is this situation different from that in the air mass at the right in Figure 8–9? The heated parcel of air at the surface would rise and cool at the same rate, and so condensation would occur at the same level. Thereafter the rising air would cool at about 6°C per kilometer but would soon reach the same temperature as the surrounding air. Could it rise any farther? This type of

Figure 8–9 *The broken lines show how the temperature of a rising air bubble would change. The solid lines show the temperature of the surrounding air. The bubble on the left continues to rise because it is always lighter (warmer) than the surrounding air. What of the bubble on the right?*

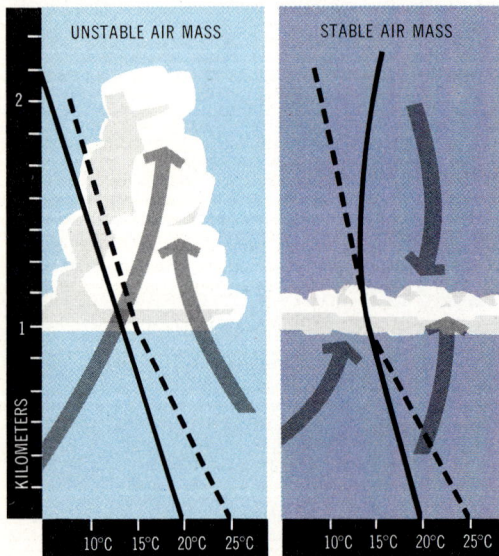

Figure 8–10 *Principal types of clouds are shown in the diagram at the left according to the heights where they generally occur. Letters on the diagram refer to the photographs of the same clouds shown on the right.*

mass is said to be **stable.** If the air mass is stable, it shows no tendency to produce cumulus clouds. Clouds formed under *stable* conditions appear as sheets or layers covering a large portion of the sky and are called **stratiform** or **stratus-type** clouds. These clouds give the sky an overall even, gray appearance and get their name from a Latin word meaning cover or layer.

Clouds formed under *unstable* conditions are usually well separated from each other and scattered over the sky with clear spaces between them. They often have a puffy appearance like a ball of cotton and are called **cumuliform** or **cumulus-type** clouds. *Cumulus* comes from a Latin word meaning pile or heap.

Both stratiform and cumuliform clouds are illustrated in Figure 8–10. Have you been able to identify the two main types of clouds in your Weather Watch? A great many clouds have some of the characteristics of both stratus and cumulus clouds. (See Figure 8–10F.) A common cumulus cloud of this type, called **stratocumulus**, consists of a layer of closely packed, globular masses of cloud caused by many vertical cells. A cumulus cloud may blow into a region where the air is sinking and change into a stratocumulus cloud. Or a stratiform layer may drift over a warm surface where rising air currents tear it apart.

Clouds are composed of water droplets or of ice crystals or of a combination of the two. It is sometimes difficult to determine the composition from the appearance of clouds. The thin wisps or faint sheets of clouds at high altitudes are usually made of ice crystals. If you have ever seen a halo around the sun or moon, it was probably caused by such a cloud. These ice-crystal clouds are called **cirrostratus.** (See Figure 8–10.) The white trails left across the sky by high-flying jet planes are true ice-crystal clouds. Ice-crystal clouds often have a fuzzy appearance at their edge in contrast to water-droplet clouds, which usually have sharp and clearly defined edges. In addition, clouds of ice crystals show no sign of grayness at their bases. However, water clouds, though white around the edges, usually have at least a faint smudge of gray at their bases.

8–7 Precipitation is related to cloud forms.

The presence of ice crystals in a cloud may determine whether or not the cloud precipitates its moisture. Different kinds of precipitation are formed in different ways. The size of precipitation particles, shown in Figure 8–11, and whether they are liquid water or ice, are important clues to their formation.

The maximum diameter of **raindrops** striking the earth is about 6 millimeters, about the size of a medium-sized pea. Raindrops larger than this can form in the atmosphere, but they are quickly broken up by air resistance as they fall. The largest drops fall from cumuliform clouds. **Drizzle** is composed of drops a half-millimeter or less in diameter (about

DRIZZLE RAIN AND SLEET HAIL

Figure 8–11 *Actual size of precipitation particles. Hailstones range from the size of raindrops to about 13 centimeters in diameter.*

the size of a period on this page), which fall from low stratiform clouds or from fog. Thus, the smallest drops of precipitation come from stable clouds, the largest drops from unstable clouds. The fine drops of drizzle are the only form of rain that can be caused by cloud droplets growing to raindrop size through continued condensation. Can you think of ways larger raindrops might form?

Snowflakes occur in the beautiful six-sided or hexagonal shapes you can see in the photographs of Figure 8–12. Snowflakes form when water vapor accumulates on ice crystals, going directly to the ice stage. **Sleet,** consisting of clear pellets of ice, is formed when raindrops fall through a layer of cold air and freeze. Another kind of frozen precipitation is hail, which usually falls from cumuliform clouds that have developed into **cumulonimbus** clouds or thunderheads. (See Figure 8–13.) **Hail** consists of balls or irregular lumps of ice. They are either transparent or composed of alternating layers of ice and opaque snow. The layers form as the hail is alternately lifted

Figure 8–12 *Although ice crystals are often pictured in perfect hexagonal shape, they seldom occur that way in nature. (Far left) Billions of such crystals cover a Colorado ski slope.*

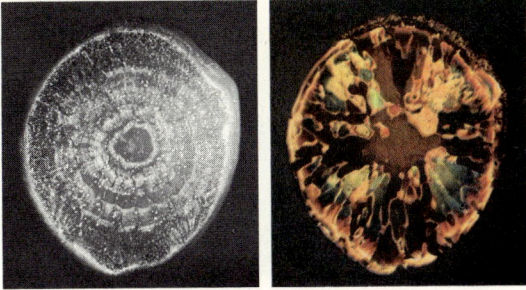

Figure 8–13 *Cross section of a hailstone seen by natural light (far left) and by polarized light (left).*
Figure 8–14 *(Right) Cloud droplet, drizzle, and a raindrop greatly exaggerated in size.*

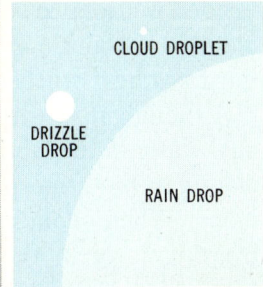

CLOUD DROPLET

DRIZZLE DROP

RAIN DROP

into a part of the cloud where snow and ice crystals become attached to it and then released into layers composed of water droplets. Hail the size of an orange is reported several times each year, usually in the mid-western states. Hailstones of this size and smaller ones, too, can do tremendous damage to crops, livestock, and automobiles, and can even seriously injure people.

8–8 How does condensed water get out of the atmosphere?

Since the tiny droplets that make up clouds are caused by condensation on small solid particles, it is natural to suppose that raindrops grow by further condensation on cloud droplets. Most raindrops cannot form in this simple way. It takes as many as a million cloud droplets to make one sizable raindrop! (See Figure 8–14.) Condensation on a cloud droplet takes place much too slowly to multiply its size a million times before the drop falls to earth.

Imagine a basketball and a number of BB's. The raindrop represents the basketball, the cloud droplets represent the BB's. It takes about a million BB's to fill a sphere the size of a basketball. Imagine the BB's drifting about like lazy flies in a large hall, each separated from the other by about a meter. When the BB's are brought together, it is probable that they will bounce apart rather than stick together. How, then, does the water from cloud droplets collect to form rain? There are two possible explanations or hypotheses. One suggests that water is transferred from liquid droplets to ice crystals that then melt as they fall. The other involves the collision of droplets.

How are water droplets converted to ice crystals in the atmosphere? Ice crystals are not always present when the temperature of the cloud is lower than freezing. Water can be much colder than 0° Celsius without freezing. When substance remains unfrozen at temperatures below its usual freezing point, it is said to be **supercooled.** An air mass can also be cooled below 0° Celsius without freezing the water droplets present. At least two conditions are

THERE'S THAT WHITE STUFF AGAIN.

GREAT ZOT! IT'S ONLY WATER!

-- IT'S AWFUL FAT FOR WATER.

WHY SHOULD I WASTE MY TIME ON FAT WATER?

Publishers Newspaper Syndicate 1966

needed in order to supercool water. The water must not touch any ice, and it must not be disturbed or jarred.

Although it is very difficult to supercool water in the laboratory, supercooled clouds in the atmosphere are very common. When clouds extend above the freezing level in the atmosphere, their tops are composed of both supercooled water droplets and ice crystals. The saturation vapor pressure is lower near ice than near water. (See Figure 8–3.) Therefore, water vapor in the surrounding air will tend to condense on the ice crystal rather than on the water droplet. (See Figure 8–15.) The loss of vapor causes the water to evaporate from the cloud droplets. The vapor continues to crystallize on the ice particles. The ice particles thus grow rapidly and become snowflakes. These flakes may melt in lower, warmer regions of the atmosphere and produce rain. If they do not melt as they fall, the particles reach the ground as snow or hail.

In many clouds the temperature is above freezing, so there are no ice crystals in these *warm* clouds. Raindrops can form in warm clouds if the cloud droplets collide and stick to each other. (See Figure 8–15.) The growth of

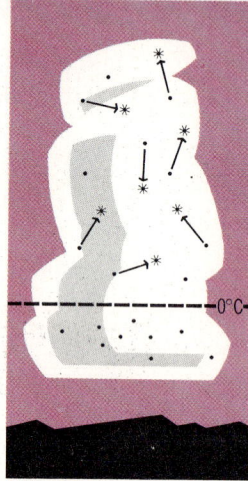

Figure 8–15 *Precipitation forms in supercooled vapor (upper part of cloud) when water from droplets crystallizes on ice particles. Precipitation forms in warmer vapor (bottom part of cloud) when water droplets collide.*

drops by collision is most effective when there are many drops of many different sizes, when the clouds are thick, and when the up-and-down motions are strong. Some clouds, mainly in the tropical zones, give up their entire supply of rain without ever reaching the ice stage. In these zones raindrops may form from collision alone.

TABLE 8–1 PRECIPITATION TYPES AS RELATED TO CLOUD TEMPERATURE AND CLOUD FORM

	CUMULIFORM (RAPID UPWARD MOTION OVER SMALL AREA)	STRATIFORM (SLOW UPWARD MOTION OVER LARGE AREA)
COLD CLOUDS (ICE CRYSTALS AND SUPERCOOLED WATER DROPLETS)	RAINSHOWERS AND THUNDERSTORMS	SNOWSTORMS OR CONTINUOUS RAIN
WARM CLOUDS (WARM WATER DROPLETS)	TROPICAL AND SUBTROPICAL RAINSHOWERS	DRIZZLE

The various types of precipitation depend, then, on the variety of cloud drop sizes, the vertical motions within the cloud, and the presence of supercooled water, ice crystals, or warm cloud droplets. Combinations of these conditions result in four main types of precipitation, summarized in Table 8–1.

The different types of precipitation are related to the different types of air motions. Vertical motion produces cumuliform clouds and heavy precipitation. Horizontal motions with a slight upward movement produce layer clouds and steady precipitation.

Thought and Discussion . . .

1. The large-scale motions of the atmosphere produce the large cyclones that last for days. Small-scale motions produce thunderstorms and have a lifetime of only a few hours. Do you think it should be easier to predict the pattern of precipitation that falls in cyclones or in thunderstorms?

2. Silver iodide crystals resemble ice crystals in shape. Why do you think silver iodide is sometimes released into clouds in an attempt to increase rainfall?

3. In what way is precipitation different from condensation?

Air Masses, Fronts, and Cyclones

8–9 Investigating the weather – Weather Watch.

In your Weather Watch, you have made daily observations of the most important weather elements and plotted each day's observations on a graph. Perhaps you have wondered about the weather changes represented by the graph and even tried to predict what the next day's weather would be. Since you began the Weather Watch, you have learned more about the way *solar radiation*, *air motion*, and *moisture* control the weather. You may now form some hypotheses about the relationships between various factors that influence the weather. Moving air carries heat and moisture, and the air's motion is related to the pressure pattern. Study the wall graph made from your observations in the Weather Watch begun in Chapter 1. See if you can discover relations between the following weather elements:

(1)*Wind direction* and changes in *pressure*.
(2)Change of *temperature* and changes in *pressure*.
(3)*Cloudiness* and changes in *pressure*.
(4)*Precipitation* and changes in *pressure*.

Select one week from the graph in which you can see a marked change in your local weather and compare it with the Daily Weather Map of the United States for the same period. Observe your locality with respect to the region around it. (5)Explain how the weather changes you graphed at your location fit into a broad, moving pattern of weather across the continent.

8–10 Air masses are formed at the earth's surface.

One of the effects of the atmosphere's general circulation is to bring warm and cold air masses together at the polar front. It is the back-and-forth conflict between the tropical and polar air masses at the polar front that brings the very changeable weather to the middle latitudes. Review the factors influencing this weather in sections 7–9 and 8–5.

An air mass may contain great quantities of water vapor, increasing the chances for clouds and rain. Or the air mass may be practically dry, and bring about clear, fine weather. What is the nature of an air mass and how does it acquire its characteristics?

An **air mass** is a body of air that has nearly uniform temperature and moisture content at any given altitude. It may cover several million square kilometers of the earth's surface. Essentially, an air mass takes its properties from the earth's surface with which it is in contact for days or weeks. In other words, it is mainly the earth's surface itself that gives an air mass its character. Suppose a mass of air remained in the tropics for a long time. (See Figure 8–16.) The tropics gain more heat from the sun than they lose to space. Would heat be transferred from the earth's surface to the air mass? How? Imagine a large mass of air resting on the earth's surface in a polar region, where the earth loses more radiation to space than it absorbs from the sun. (See Figure 8–16.) Would the air mass lose heat to the earth's surface?

What happens when a mass of air rests upon dry land? Could the air mass gain much moisture from such a surface? When an air mass remains over an ocean surface, moisture can enter the air until the humidity is very high. How is this

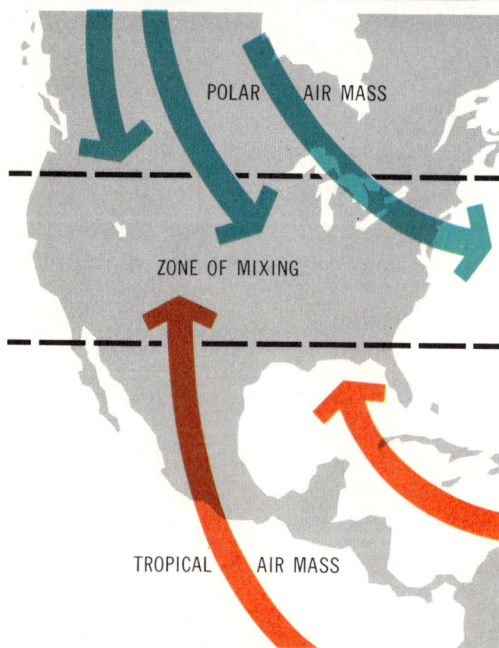

Figure 8–16 (A) Polar continental air mass develops over Canada. (B) A polar maritime air mass sweeps across the coast of Oregon from the Pacific. (C) A tropical continental air mass originates over Arizona. (D) A tropical maritime air mass crosses a Florida beach. (Below) Polar and tropical air masses meet and produce changeable weather.

moisture transferred from the water surface into the air?

An area over which an air mass acquires its properties of temperature and humidity is called its **source region.** Since the land is hot in summer and cold in winter, the continents may serve as source regions for either warm or cold air masses, depending on the season. The ocean, of course, is the main source region for moist air masses. Classifications of air masses include seven or eight types. However, the various combinations of cold, warm, dry, and moist conditions determine a simpler but very useful classification of four types of air masses: *polar continental, polar maritime, tropical continental,* and *tropical maritime.* Which air masses are cold and which are warm? Which are dry and which are moist?

The source regions of polar and tropical air masses, as illustrated in Figure 8–16, are nearly everywhere separated by a transition zone representing the belt in which the polar front moves southward and northward. In this transition zone the traveling air masses are changed by the properties of the surface beneath them. As they move from their source regions, polar air is warmed from below and tropical air is cooled from below. A polar continental air mass may pick up moisture from the ocean surface and become a polar maritime air mass.

When an air mass is warmed from below, the temperature at its lower level becomes much higher than that of the colder air above. The air mass becomes **unstable.** (See Figure 8–9.) A maritime air mass moving onto a continent in summer, for example, is warmed at the surface and becomes unstable. What would be the probability of precipitation? When an air mass is cooled from below, its temperature decreases only slightly or, if the surface cooling is great enough, may even increase with altitude. This kind of air mass is **stable.**

8–11 Cyclones develop at the polar front.

The polar front or boundary separating cold and warm air is shown as a line sloping upward and poleward in Figure 8–8. The surface of a front resembles the upper surface of a wedge. Have you wondered why a front slopes?

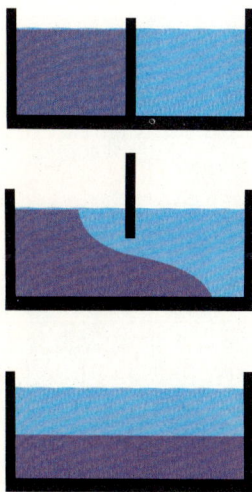

Figure 8–17 *Adjustment of fluid masses of different density takes place at an interface. Is a front an interface?*

ACTIVITY *With a rectangular container such as a plastic tank, or a glass dish used for baking, you can make a model of fluid masses and the boundary between them. Fill the tank or dish with water and make a wall of plastic or cardboard to separate the tank into two parts. (See Figure 8–17.) Pour salt into one half of the tank and then add food coloring to the water in this side. Allow the water in the tank to become quiet. Which water mass could represent a cold air mass? Carefully draw up the separating wall. Try not to disturb the water. Watch what happens in the tank and then describe what you see.*

In the activity you found that a front forms between the two water masses of different densities, and that the more dense mass slides under the less dense, so that the front becomes inclined. If enough time is allowed, the front will become horizontal.

When dense air lies in a horizontal layer under lighter air, the arrangement of air masses is stable. But the arrangement is unstable when a sloping surface separates the air masses. A slight disturbance that alters the delicate balance can start the dense air pushing the warm air upward.

This is what happens along the polar front. The disturbance appears first as a ripple in the front, as shown in Figure 8–18A. Driven by the westerly winds, the ripple begins to move eastward like a wave along the polar front.

As the cyclone develops, the *warm* air of the westerly winds is pushed against the front ahead of it. (See Figure 8–18B.) Because it is light, it tends to glide upward over the frontal surface. This part of the polar front is the **warm front** in the cyclone. The cold polar air to the north swings around behind and pushes the polar front southward. This

part of the polar front is called the **cold front** in the cyclone. While this is happening, the whole cyclone continues to move eastward. Since the air mass behind the cold front is dense, it moves faster than the warm front. This narrows the area of warm air, called the **warm sector,** between them. (See Figure 8–18C.) The narrowing of the warm sector means that the warm air is being pushed upward, while cold air is closing in at the surface to replace it.

Can you see a resemblance to convection in the development of a cyclone? In each case the pull of gravity on the denser part of the fluid causes it to move and push the less dense fluid upward. Potential energy is converted to kinetic energy as the cold dense air sinks and the less dense air rises.

As the cold front near the center of the cyclone overtakes the warm front, all of the warm air between the two fronts is squeezed upward. (See Figure 8–18D.) The overtaking of the warm front by the cold front and the squeezing of the warm air upward are called **occlusion.** When all of the warm sector has disappeared, the potential energy that was represented by the difference

(Left) An unusually well defined cold front. Wind blowing from the left in the cold air mass picked up yellow pollen that clearly defines the advancing front. Lower photo provides a closer view.
Figure 8–18 (Right) A ripple in the polar front develops into a polar front cyclone. (A through D.)

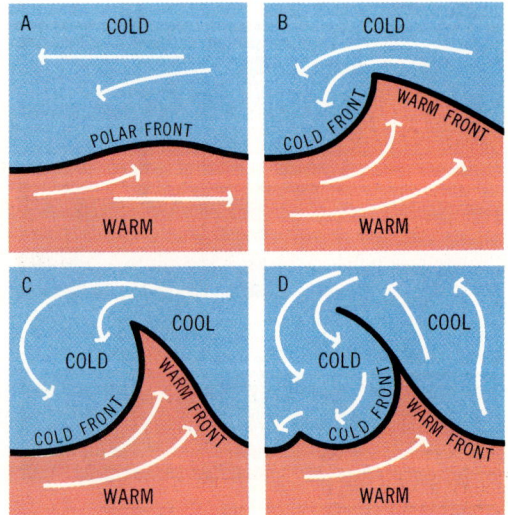

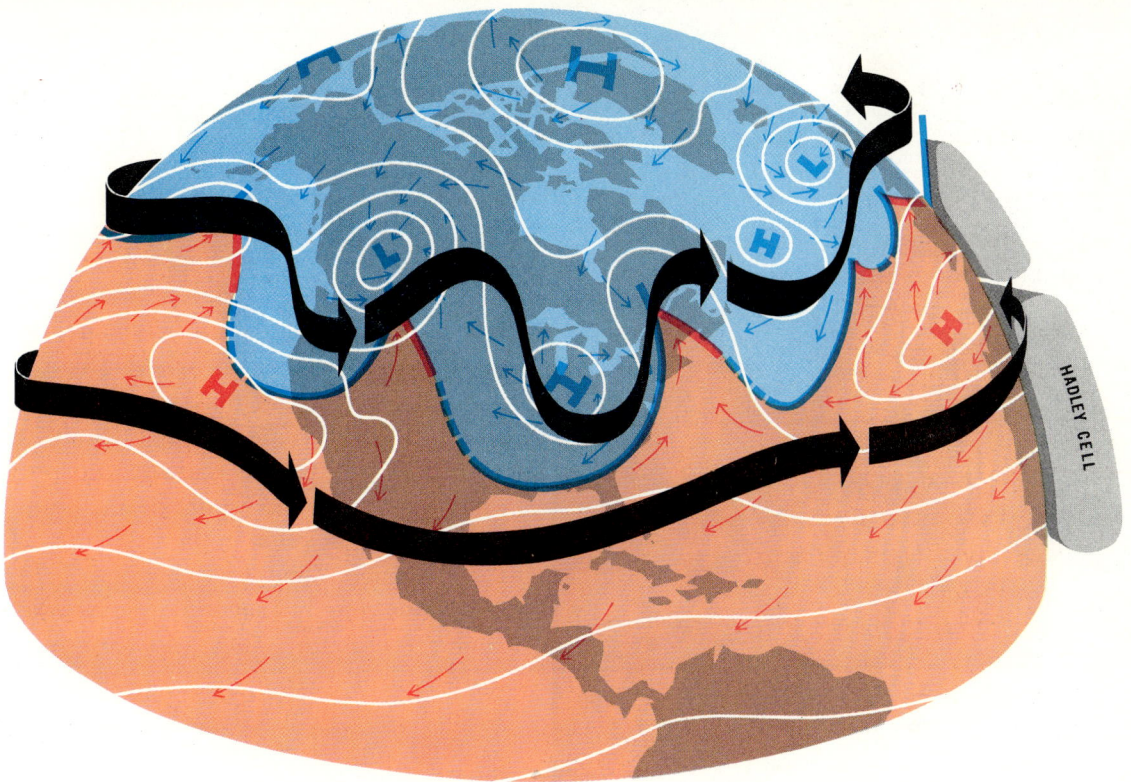

HADLEY CELL

Figure 8–19 *Polar front cyclones are closely related to the polar front jet stream (upper wavy black arrow). The small arrows represent surface winds in the warm and cold air masses. The lower black arrow represents the subtropical jet stream.*

in density between the warm and cold air masses has all been converted into kinetic energy. At this stage the cyclone begins to decay because friction with the earth's surface gradually slows the motion of the cyclone.

As a cyclone goes through its life stages, from wave disturbance to fully developed cyclone to occluded cyclone, it is steered by the strong westerly winds

(Right) The eye of hurricane Betsy seen from inside by "hurricane hunters." (Below) Twin tornadoes above the plains of Kansas.

high in the troposphere called **jet streams.** The wave moves rapidly, but the mature cyclone less rapidly. Finally, when occlusion has taken place, the cyclone almost stops. In the westerly air current at an altitude of five or six kilometers, there is first just a ripple in the current, then a deep wave or trough, and finally a big eddy marking the occluded cyclone. The relation between the moving cyclones near the earth's surface and the jet stream high in the troposphere is suggested in Figure 8–19.

The polar-front cyclone is only one among the many different-sized eddies that occur in the atmosphere. A **cyclone** is any large, nearly horizontal eddy in which the motion is *counterclockwise* in the Northern Hemisphere, around the center of an area of low pressure. In the Southern Hemisphere the motion is

Vilhelm F. Bjerknes

Vilhelm Bjerknes (1862–1951), a Norwegian physicist, by 1912 had become recognized as the founder of modern **physical hydrodynamics**, the study of forces and motion in fluids. In that year, on being named Director of the Geophysical Institute at the University of Leipzig, Bjerknes announced a new goal. He would consider his task done, he said, if in one year he could correctly calculate the change of weather during one day. "It may take a year to dig a tunnel through a mountain," he pointed out, "but, later, others may make the passage with an express train."

In 1917, Bjerknes returned to Norway to establish a geophysical institute at Bergen. There, with his son, J. Bjerknes, and Halvor Solberg, he laid the basis for a revolution in weather forecasting. During World War I, Norway was cut off almost completely from weather reports outside Scandinavia. Bjerknes was successful in establishing a network of many weather observing stations located close together along the Norwegian coast. His plan was to analyze the reports from this small network of stations intensively, applying his theories of fluid motion. Other young Scandinavian scientists joined the Bergen group. They would work enthusiastically far into the night, when V. Bjerknes might look into the map-room with his eyes gleaming and ask: "Are there any new discoveries tonight?"

clockwise around the center of a cyclone. Why is this true?

Polar-front cyclones occur mainly in middle latitudes. In the tropics another usually more violent kind of cyclone develops in quite a different way. This **tropical cyclone,** called a **hurricane,** develops over the oceans where there is only one kind of air mass. It draws its energy from the latent heat released in an area where the air is rising and producing clouds. (See Figure 8–20.) Tropical cyclones develop in the Intertropical Convergence Zone (see Section 7–7), when this zone lies several degrees away from the equator. They also grow from disturbances that appear in the trade winds. (See Figure 8–21.)

What kind of weather does a cyclone bring to an area? Look at Figure 8–22A. Would you expect to find flat, broad (stratiform) clouds along the cold front or warm front? Would you expect a steady drizzle or a heavy downpour under these stratiform clouds? Now, which front, warm or cold, forces air upward so abruptly that cumuliform clouds develop, producing heavy showers? The warm, moist air rises gradually over the gently sloping warm front as you see in Figure 8–22B. This broad lifting produces stratiform clouds and steady precipitation. The air ahead of the cold front is forced more rapidly upward, producing cumuliform clouds and heavy showers.

The cyclone moving toward the east and the associated weather pattern shown in Figure 8–22 represent a model. In looking at weather maps, you will find a great variety in the shapes of cyclones and their weather patterns.

In the sixteenth century, Leonardo da Vinci had speculated that warm air meeting cold would rise and produce rain. Until early in this century, meteorologists still had only vague ideas about

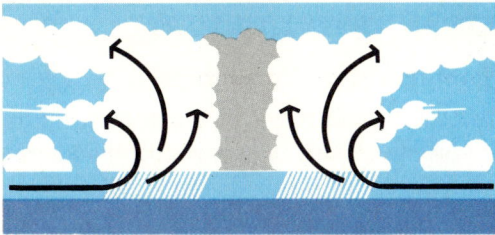

Figure 8–20 *The structure of a tropical cyclone.*
Figure 8–21 *The typical paths (right) of polar front cyclones (blue) and tropical cyclones (red).*

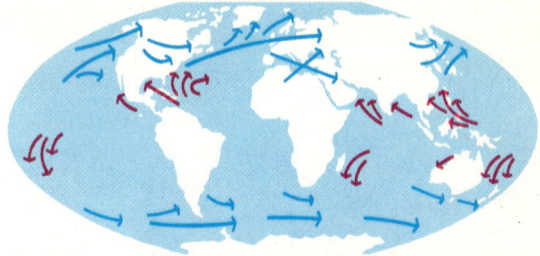

the conflict of masses of warm and cold air and the growth of cyclones. During World War I, a group of young meteorologists working under Vilhelm Bjerknes (Be-AIRK-ness) determined to apply physical principles to the old art of weather forecasting.

This group set aside the old traditions and looked at weather maps with fresh eyes. They discovered the existence of weather fronts, developed the method of air mass and frontal analysis, and identified the life cycle of polar-front cyclones. They related the development of cyclones to the conversion of potential to kinetic energy in the atmosphere.

Vilhelm Bjerknes lived to see his goal of scientific weather forecasting realized, in part, when a group at Princeton University used mathematical equations of fluid motion to produce a weather forecast on a computer in 1950. That first *numerical* forecast was far from perfect, but—the diggers were at least tunnelling through the mountain! (See the story of Vilhelm Bjerknes, page 198.)

Thought and Discussion . . .

1. How does a cyclone transfer heat, upward or downward? toward the pole, or toward the equator?
2. Explain how the polar front, the **Intertropical Convergence Zone** where the trades of the two hemispheres meet, the monsoons, and mountain ranges all contribute to the world's rainfall pattern.
3. What do you think the world's rainfall pattern would be like if the earth kept the same face toward the sun?

Figure 8–22 *(A) The relationship of air motion, cloud patterns, and precipitation in a polar front cyclone. (B) A vertical cross section through the cyclone. Identify cold and warm fronts.*

Additional Investigations

8-12 Investigating cumulus cloud formation.

In many parts of the country on a warm afternoon, cumulus clouds appear in the sky. The water vapor that forms these clouds comes from warm, moisture-laden air rising from the ground. As this air rises, it cools. When the air cools beyond a certain temperature, it can no longer hold all of its moisture, and thus at some point the water vapor must condense to form clouds. The temperature at which the water begins to condense is called the **dew point.** The dew-point temperature varies from day to day depending on the temperature and relative humidity. Knowing the temperature and the dew point for the day, you can calculate the height at which the temperature and dew point are equal, and cumulus clouds will form.

Procedure

Find the dew point in either or both of the following ways:

To measure dew point directly, slowly add ice to a can of water. (See Figure 8-23.) Record the temperature when drops of water begin to condense on the outside of the can.

To measure dew point indirectly, use the sling psychrometer as shown in Figure 8-24 and Appendix B.

When air rises, it cools 10°C per kilometer. The dew point decreases with altitude at the rate of 1.7°C per kilometer. [1]At what height will cumulus clouds begin to form on the day of your observations? (See Figure 8-6.)

8-13 Investigating weather maps.

Have you ever noticed that you see things differently after you get to know them better? This observation holds true also for such natural processes as the weather. You may realize how much more you know now about the weather if you examine some weather maps and see what they mean to you.

Procedure

Using the last two available U.S. Daily Weather Maps, study the weather developments over the country during the 24 hours between the maps.

[1]Identify highs, lows, air masses, and fronts. Compare the shapes of cyclones, and the cloud and precipitation patterns around them, with the cyclone model in figures 8-18 and 8-22. [2]Make a weather forecast for your area for the 24 hours following the time of the later map by estimating the direction and speed of movement of cyclones, frontal systems, and anticyclones from their past movement. Use the next day's weather map to check your forecast.

Note the uniform level of the cloud bases.

Figure 8-23 One way to determine the dew point.

Figure 8-24 Obtaining the dew point with the sling psychrometer.

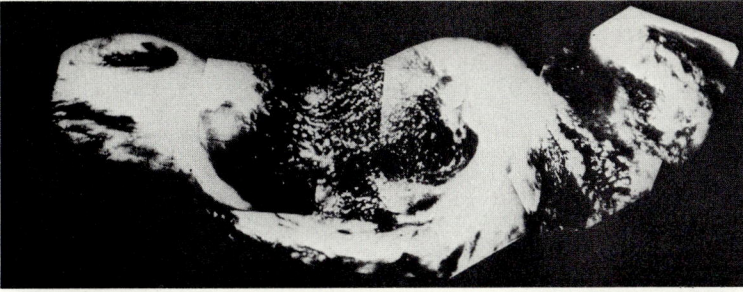

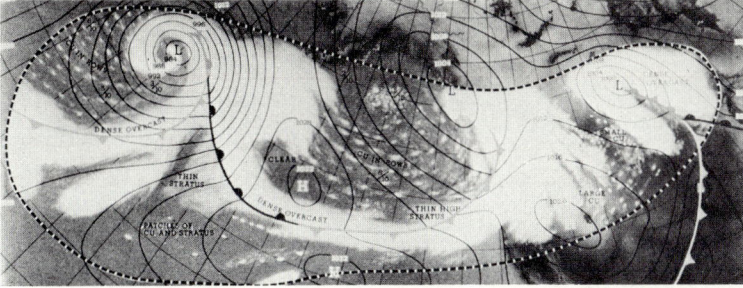

(*Above, left*) *Tiros 1 photographs from over the North Pacific taken May 19–20, 1960.* (*Below, left*) *A weather map of the same area at the same time.* (*Above*) *Tiros 9.*

Unsolved Problems   Ice crystals can form directly in the atmosphere in the same way cloud droplets form, if the temperature is low enough. Usually ice crystals will not form unless the air is cooled enough to bring the relative humidity to saturation (100 percent) with respect to water, although this is always a lower temperature than is needed to bring the air to ice saturation levels. If scientists could find some nucleus that would cause ice crystals to form at ice saturation levels, they could drop these nuclei into clouds and perhaps start the precipitation process when natural ice crystals are not present. However, there are still many unanswered questions about the formation of ice crystals in the atmosphere.

Recently earth scientists have discovered a rainfall cycle closely related to the moon's phases, which you will consider in Chapter 22. The moon and sun together produce tides in the atmosphere, just as they produce tides in the ocean. Very small up-and-down motions are caused by the atmospheric tides. Although the vertical motions are very small, they are periodic, whereas the rainfall produced by the motions of storms is not. Do you think that the tidal effect of the moon on the atmosphere could explain the observed lunar cycle in precipitation? Meteorologists are trying to find the explanation for the cycle, but for the time being its existence remains another of the unsolved problems of earth science.

CHAPTER REVIEW

Summary

Man looks to the shallow reservoir of water in the air for his supply of fresh water. This reservoir is constantly refilled by the ocean's surface water. The atmosphere acts as a pump and a condenser of water vapor, moving the water from the ocean to the land.

The water cycle in the atmosphere illustrates the flow of energy in earth processes. Solar energy heats the ocean surface. Most of this energy goes into the evaporation of water into the atmosphere. Evaporation is controlled primarily by the energy supply, but air motions are necessary to distribute the vapor so that evaporation can continue. Powered by the sun's energy, the winds transport the evaporated water to the continents. The motions within storms and other wind systems lift the water vapor into regions of lower pressure, causing the vapor to cool adiabatically and condense. This condensation releases the energy stored as latent heat in the vapor. Much of this released heat contributes to the energy of storms.

Water vapor condenses to form clouds, and the resulting cloud type depends on the kind of motion producing the cooling and condensation. The gradual upward movement of an air mass produces stratiform or layered clouds. Sudden upward motion and surface heating produce cumuliform clouds. When cloud droplets are formed, the water still has to collect in large drops or crystals to form precipitation. Precipitation does not form in all clouds.

The process by which raindrops are made is a part of the water cycle. Raindrops can be formed in two ways. In supercooled clouds, the water droplets evaporate and the water vapor crystallizes on ice crystals. In warm clouds, only the collision of droplets of many different sizes can account for the growth of raindrops. This process may also operate in cold clouds.

The vertical motions that bring about the condensation of water vapor and its release as rain and snow take place mainly at the polar front and in the equatorial zone. The polar front is an interface between warm and cold air masses. Air masses are large bodies of air that have nearly uniform temperature and moisture properties acquired at the earth's surface. The potential energy of air masses on each side of the polar front is converted to the kinetic energy of storms. Polar-front cyclones are the visible result of this energy transformation in middle latitudes. These cyclones go through a life cycle, beginning with a dis-

turbance on the polar front and often ending with the occluded cyclone that dies away because its energy source has decreased.

When water falls on the land, it enters another stage of the water cycle.

Questions and Problems

A

1. Describe some of the ways in which water can be diverted from the basic water cycle.
2. Trace the energy changes that take place in the evaporation and condensation of water.
3. Why is temperature an important control in evaporation?
4. If the actual vapor pressure is 10 millibars and the saturation vapor pressure is 20 millibars, what is the relative humidity?
5. What is the main cause of condensation in the atmosphere?
6. What is an adiabatic process?
7. What are the two main processes that appear to start the formation of raindrops in a cloud?
8. What are the wet and dry belts in the basic climatic pattern of the earth and how are they produced?

Various forms of condensation. (A) Mist. (B) Fog in a city street. (C) Frost on a sagebrush. (D) Dew on plant leaves.

9. Describe the stages in the development of a polar front cyclone.

B

1. The air temperature is 20°C and the dew point is 0°C. About how high must the air be lifted to reach saturation?
2. The polar front has been far north of its usual position for the past month. Was the rainfall during this period along the usual position of the polar front greater or less than normal?
3. A rapidly moving cold front is pushing unstable tropical maritime air ahead of it. What kind of clouds would you expect to find in the air ahead of it? What kind of clouds would you expect to find just in advance of the front, or at its leading edge?
4. A rapidly occluding cyclone has just passed over your area. Would you expect the forward movement of the storm to speed up or slow down during the next 24 hours?

C

1. Why do earth scientists speak of *the* water cycle, when water goes through so many different cycles?
2. Trace the flow of energy that takes place when you pump up a bicycle tire with a hand pump.
3. The air temperature at the earth's surface is 20°C, and at 3 kilometers it is 2°C. If you could carry a balloon containing air to 3 kilometers, would the air in the balloon be warmer or colder than the surrounding air?
4. In Problem 3 above, how high would you have to raise the temperature of the air in the balloon for it to rise freely to 3 kilometers?

Suggested Readings

BOOKS

Battan, Louis J. *Cloud Physics and Cloud Seeding.* Doubleday & Company, Inc. (Science Study Series), New York, 1962. Paperback.

Battan, Louis J. *The Nature of Violent Storms.* Doubleday & Company, Inc. (Science Study Series), New York, 1961. Paperback.

Battan, Louis J. *Radar Observes the Weather.* Doubleday & Company, Inc. (Science Study Series), New York, 1962. Paperback.

Lehr, Paul E., R. Will Burnett, and Herbert S. Zim. *Weather: A Guide to Phenomena and Forecasts.* Golden Press, Inc., New York, 1957.

Leopold, Luna B., Kenneth S. Davis, and the Editors of *Life. Water.* Time, Inc. (Life Science Library), New York, 1966.

Ohring, George. *Weather on the Planets —What We Know about Their Atmospheres.* Doubleday & Company, Inc. (Science Study Series), New York, 1966. Paperback. Chapters 1, 2, and 3.

Spar, Jerome. *The Way of the Weather.* Creative Educational Society, Inc., Mankato, Minnesota, 1957–62.

Stewart, George R. *Storm.* Random House, Inc. (Modern Library), New York, 1947.

Thompson, Philip D., Robert O'Brien, and the Editors of *Life. Weather.* Time, Inc. (Life Science Library), New York, 1965.

PERIODICALS

Malkus, Joanne. "The Origin of Hurricanes." *Scientific American,* August, 1957. (Also Scientific American Offprint #847, W. H. Freeman & Co., Publishers, San Francisco.)

Stong, C. L. "The Amateur Scientist. How to measure raindrops, make snowflakes, and simulate subatomic particle scattering." *Scientific American,* August, 1965.

Tepper, Morris. "Tornadoes." *Scientific American,* May, 1958. (Also Scientific American Offprint #848.

Terselic, Richard A. "The World Weather Watch—A Concept for Improvement." *Weatherwise,* June, 1966.

Woodcock, A. H. "Salt and Rain." *Scientific American,* October, 1957. (Also Scientific American Offprint #850.

Chapter 9

An individual water molecule may lead an adventurous existence within the water cycle. It may be bound up tightly in an alpine glacier for a long period of time, jammed in against other frozen molecules until freed by the sun to run down a glacial stream into a river. The molecule may be snatched up by a root of a stream-side tree before it ever reaches the ocean. It may accompany plant nutrients up through the tree to some growing woody part before escaping as vapor through a tiny opening in a leaf. Whisked away by the westerlies, the molecule may drift aloft for weeks or months before being caught up in a storm over the ocean or perhaps falling as rain where you live.

When you turn on a faucet for a glass of cold, clear water, where does the water come from? How does it get into the water pipe? How long will the supply last? Could the water you drank this morning have included some molecules from an alpine glacier, from a tropical swamp, or from the Volga River? Let your imagination roam and consider the possible adventures of the thousands of water molecules that were in that one glass.

People tend to take the supply of fresh water for granted. If you live in a city, water is brought to you

Waters of the Land

through careful planning, engineering, and construction. How did the engineers know where to drill the wells or build the dams? Did they know the water would continue to be available? What information did they need about the flow of water and its storage in and on the earth?

As far as our water supply is concerned, the amount of moisture in the air overhead is of secondary importance. Of greater concern to us is the amount of water that falls on the earth in places where we can use it and what happens to water that reaches the earth. Does it rush across the land in great floods, and sweep out to sea? Does it supply lakes and reservoirs? Or does the water seep into the soil and support plant life?

The scene on the right shows a river in India unable to contain the heavy downpour of a monsoon. The water flows across a patchwork of rice paddies and sustains life for many people. The hand pump on the left suggests another source of water from the land. Water drawn from under the surface supplies most rural communities, whereas most urban areas utilize surface waters. How does water enter and move through the soil? Why do streams continue to flow long after precipitation has ceased?

Moisture Income and Storage

9–1 Where does moisture come from?

The earth's main source of fresh water is the *precipitation* that falls from the atmosphere as rain or snow. In some parts of the earth, dew is a significant part of the moisture received. Dew forms when moisture condenses on solid surfaces such as leaves or rocks. During the time of the Roman Empire, people who lived in North Africa and the Middle East used large piles of rocks located over catch basins to collect dew for drinking water. Water condensed on the rock surfaces and dripped into the basin below. In the ancient city of Theodosia on the shores of the Black Sea, these basins, also called "surface wells," collected about 15,000 gallons of water a day.

In other places dense fogs form over cold ocean currents and are carried by the wind onto coastal hills and mountains. Moisture from the fog banks is caught by trees and shrubs and drips onto the ground below. This moisture is sufficient to keep plants growing in areas where rain seldom falls, as in the coastal desert of Peru. Along the coast of California fogs supply additional moisture to the dense forests growing there. (See Figure 9–1.) Under these conditions—rain, dew, or fog—water vapor in the air must condense to form droplets. As you know from Chapter 8, rain and fog form

Figure 9–1 *Fog rolling into a mountain forest along the coast of northern California. Trees and shrubs benefit from this additional moisture.*

Figure 9–2 *Of the total precipitation that falls on the continents, 64 percent (A) returns to the atmosphere through soil and plants. Eleven percent reaches streams by moving below the surface (B), and 25 percent runs off directly (C).*

on the tiny condensation nuclei that are always present in the atmosphere.

Precipitation varies from place to place, from one season to another, and from year to year. It also varies in form. Snow falls in colder seasons at high latitudes and high altitudes. Sleet and freezing rain may fall along the margins of a cold air mass. Hail is generally associated with thunderstorms.

Precipitation also varies in the rate and frequency with which it falls. As much as 150 millimeters of rain may fall in one hour, or only a few millimeters in an all-day drizzle. In some of the desert areas of the world, rain is so uncommon that the natives do not have a word for it in their vocabulary. Yet in tropical areas such as the Amazon basin it rains nearly every day. How often does it rain where you live?

Examine Figure 9–2 and describe what happens to precipitation reaching the earth. Consider a single raindrop. It might soak into the ground, run off, or evaporate. When you see a major flood, you might think that rivers and streams are the main carriers of water from the land in this part of the water cycle. However, only about 36 percent of the precipitation falling on the conti-

nents runs off in streams and rivers to the ocean. Almost two-thirds returns to the atmosphere by evaporation from soil and plants. The largest "river" in the world has no bridges, no banks, and no levees—it is the atmosphere!

All of the water received by the land masses eventually returns to the oceans. The return trip may be made through the atmosphere or in streams and rivers. If water were not delayed in its return journey, the land masses would be dry except when precipitation occurred.

9–2 How is moisture stored?

Where are the largest supplies of fresh water stored? Are they underground? in lakes and rivers? Or are they stored in the form of snow and ice?

The largest amount of stored fresh water on the earth is frozen in glaciers. These water supplies, locked in the ice caps that cover Greenland and Antarctica, could be used if a way were found to bring icebergs to places where water is needed. There are now over 25,000,000

Figure 9–3 *Water is temporarily stored in glaciers, snowfields, and lakes like these pictured in Alaska.*

because rates of evaporation and melting are low. It takes about 10 to 15 millimeters of snow to yield one millimeter of water, depending on the density of the snow. Much of the water melted from snow runs off the land surface into streams and lakes. This is especially true when the water in the soil under the snow is frozen.

If the soil beneath the snow is not frozen, melted water can move into the soil and add to the water supply in the ground. Rainfall also soaks into the ground. If rainfall is very light, most of it may return to the atmosphere directly through evaporation. If the rainfall is heavy and continuous, a considerable amount may filter into the soil and supply moisture for plants.

As water is added to the surface, it continues to move downward into soil pores. The solid rock below loose soil is called **bedrock.** Bedrock may contain fractures, cracks, and other openings that store water. In regions having only a thin layer of soil, such as New England, most of the subsurface water is found in the pore spaces or fractures in bedrock. Sandstone and other porous sedimentary rocks can store great quantities of water. Can you add water to a pail full of sand? In many parts of the world ground water is the principal source of moisture. In a large desert basin there may be more storage capacity underground than there is behind Hoover Dam. (See Figure 9–4.)

cubic kilometers of ice on the earth's surface. If all of the ice and snow on the earth were melted, the level of the ocean would rise an estimated 30 to 60 meters. (See Figure 9–3.)

In addition to the water stored in glacial ice, a considerable amount is also stored in the snowfields of the world. Snow accumulates during the cold season in each hemisphere. The greatest amounts of snow fall on margins of the cold polar regions and are quickly melted in the spring. Only a small amount falls in the coldest areas of the earth, and most of this is held in storage

Figure 9–4 *Lake Mead (far left), which is formed by Hoover Dam, and the Sonoran Desert. Which of the two stores more water?*

Figure 9–5 *The water treatment plant under construction to the right of the pier processes one billion gallons of Lake Michigan water per day, serving most of Chicago and its suburbs.*

If the soil becomes saturated during a rain and infiltration cannot keep pace with the falling rain, water begins to run over the soil. Some of this runoff may flow into low areas and form lakes. Lakes are an important form of water storage in many parts of the world. (See Figure 9–5.) They regulate streamflow and provide water for agricultural and urban uses. Many natural lakes have been modified for greater storage capacity by controlling the amount of water that flows out of them. New lakes have also been created by damming rivers.

ACTIVITY *Find out about the source or sources of the water for your community.*

9–3 Investigating the movement of water in earth.

Have you ever seen water seeping or flowing from a hillside? How fast does ground water move through the pore spaces in earth materials? Can water move upward through soil? In this investigation you will find evidence to answer some of these questions by examining three properties of earth materials that affect the flow of water underground.

Procedure

Set up the column as shown in Figure 9–6. Your teacher will provide you with quantities of different-sized particles. Place 100 milliliters of uniform-sized particles in the column, making sure the wire screen is in position to prevent the particles from running out.

1. Record the amount of water necessary to *just* cover the upper surface of the particles.
2. Open the clamp and allow the water to run out. Record the amount of water retained by the particles.
3. Add 300 milliliters (ml) of water to the cylinder holding the grains. Record the time required for the water to drain through the particles.

Repeat the procedure using the other sizes of particles and answer the following questions.

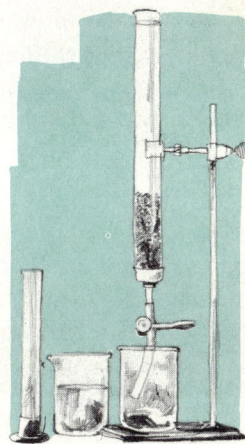

Figure 9–6 *Column for investigation of water flow.*

(1)What is the relationship between the water you add and **porosity,** the percentage of space between the grains? Make a graph showing the relationship between porosity and the diameter of the particles. Explain your results.

(2)Make a graph showing the relationship between grain size and the amount of water retained in the column after draining. What conclusions can you draw from the graph?

(3)Construct a graph showing the relationship between each of the grain sizes and the time required for 300 ml of water to run through them. Explain your results.

(4)**Permeability** is the rate at which water can pass through a porous material. What is the relationship between permeability and the size of the particles?

Set up the apparatus for investigating capillarity as indicated in the diagram. (See Figure 9–7.) Use 200 ml of fine dry sand in the tube. When your partner is ready to time, lower the tube into the water so that the base is *just* beneath the water surface. Time and record the changes in water level in the tube at 30-second intervals. Repeat this procedure with 200 ml of course sand in the tube.

(5)On the basis of your observations, what is capillarity?

Figure 9–7
Apparatus for investigating capillarity.

9–4 Water moves into the ground.

The entrance of water into the ground is called **infiltration.** What determines the rate at which water enters the soil? There are several factors. Water can enter the soil no faster than the water beneath the surface can move downward through the pore spaces. If the pore spaces are very small, like those in clay, the water moves very slowly. Water moves downward rapidly in sand because the pores between sand grains are large. For any movement to take place, the pore spaces must be connected to each other.

Most soils contain large amounts of clay as well as sand. Many of these particles are held together in clusters called **aggregates.** Raindrops hitting bare ground tend to break the aggregates, and soil particles fill the pore spaces to form a closely packed layer. (See Figure 9–8A.) This leaves a surface layer of low permeability and tends to reduce the infiltration rate.

Where plants cover the soil, their leaves absorb the impact of raindrops. Therefore, soil aggregates remain unbroken and the large pores in the soil are preserved. The rainwater quickly penetrates the soil. (See Figure 9–8B.) At a research station in Ohio it was observed that one bare soil had an infiltration

Figure 9–8 *Vegetation affects infiltration. When it rains, what happens to the pores of the soil that do not have a good cover of vegetation?*

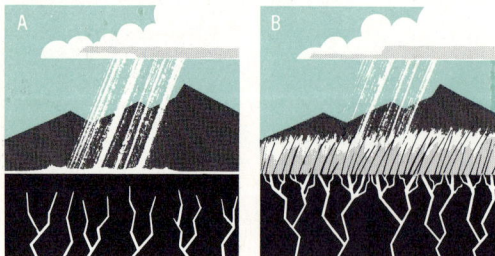

rate of only 0.7 centimeter per hour. By contrast, the same kind of soil protected by a layer of straw had an infiltration rate of 5.6 centimeters per hour, eight times that of the unprotected soil.

Farmers know the importance of having plant cover over the land during the time of year when the most intense rainstorms occur. The presence of vegetation on the land, whether on a farm or in the mountains, greatly lessens erosion and flooding because more precipitation enters the soil instead of running off.

Mixtures of sand and clay common in many soils have openings, like a bag of marbles of varying sizes. The larger openings permit water to move rapidly to lower levels under the pull of gravity. At each point of contact between particles, however, tiny droplets of water are retained by surface tension and by the molecular attraction between the water and solid particles. (See Figure 9–9.) The water stored in this way is called **capillary water.** How is this related to Investigation 9–3?

Capillary water cannot be drawn down by gravity. It can be removed only by evaporation into the air through soil openings or by absorption into plant roots. (See Figure 9–9.) Without this supply of capillary water in the upper few feet of soil, plants and crops might not survive long periods between rainfalls. The pores also serve as channels

Figure 9–9 *Particles of soil and a plant root with root hairs, greatly magnified. Capillary water clings to soil particles and to the root and cannot be drawn down by gravity. It can only be removed from the soil by root hairs or by evaporation.*

for the circulation of air which is vital to the growth of plants.

Which would hold more capillary water, a clay soil or a sandy soil? Study Figure 9–10. You can see that each 30 centimeters of clay soil contains about 100 millimeters of water when the soil is fully saturated. Thirty centimeters of sandy soil has only 25 to 50 millimeters of water when saturated.

Clay has more particles in a given volume and therefore more points of contact between the particles. Thus, clay can store more capillary water and hold it longer than sandy soil. A mixture of sand and clay is a **loam.** Would you prefer to have a sand, loam, or clay soil for your lawn or farm?

Some of the capillary water is used for plant growth and some evaporates. In dry regions the soil is rarely saturated.

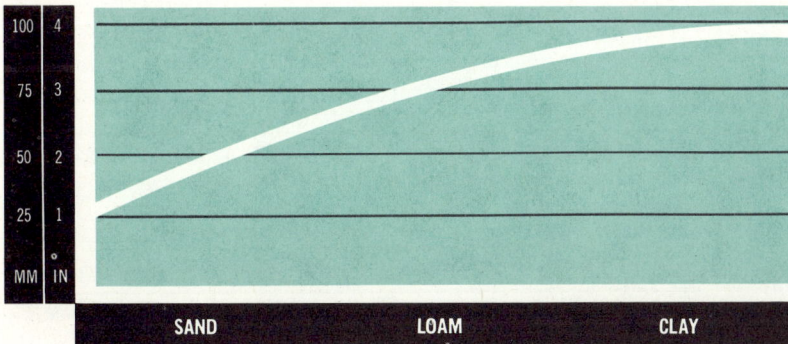

Figure 9–10 *Typical capillary water-holding characteristics of different kinds of soils. How much more will a clay soil hold than a sandy soil?*

(Far left) Fire has destroyed trees and undergrowth in this forest, exposing the soil to storms and runoff. (Left, above) A bulldozer cuts a contour trench on a mountain slope. (Below) Trenches hold water on a hillside after a storm.

In moist regions the soil water lost by evaporation and by plants is replaced by precipitation almost as rapidly as it is taken up by the atmosphere.

9–5 Water is stored at lower levels.

Water filling large pores in the soil is called **gravity water.** Like water dumped on a pile of marbles, gravity water drains through the surface pore spaces into the spaces below. When capillary water is removed by plants or by evaporation, it is replaced by downward-moving gravity water from precipitation. After a rain, when the pore spaces have received all the capillary moisture they can hold, gravity water filters to lower and lower levels. At some depth this gravity water accumulates and fills the available pore spaces. The top of this saturated zone is the **water table.** (See Figure 9–11.) Water below the earth's surface is known as **ground water.**

During the time of year when moisture income is greater than moisture removed by evaporation and by plants, the water table usually rises. If there were no way for the ground water to escape from the area, the water table would continue to rise until all the pore spaces were filled. What do you think happens when the water table is higher than a nearby stream or valley?

Ordinarily, ground water flows at very slow rates. Speeds commonly range from about 3 to 30 meters per day. This is approximately "a snail's pace." The characteristics of the pore spaces greatly influence the rate at which ground water moves. In a few instances, buried channels exist where loose gravel or cracks are found. The ground water flows much more rapidly through these channels than through most earth materials. Such underground streams are rare and ground water generally moves much more slowly than surface water.

Streams may be supplied continually by ground water moving directly into stream channels. During a dry period

SOIL WATER ZONE

WATER TABLE

GROUND WATER ZONE

ROCK

Figure 9–11 Gravity water seeps down into the ground water zone. What might happen to the surface of the water table during a long dry season?

when there is no moisture income, ground water may continue to discharge into rivers. Consequently, ground water storage decreases and the water table is lowered. In desert areas the water table is often lower than nearby stream beds. When this happens water moves from the river into ground water storage, often leaving the stream channel completely dry. (See Figure 9–12.)

Certain rocks with high permeability transmit large amounts of water and are called **aquifers.** Sandstone generally has abundant pore spaces that may contain air or water. Water seeps into sandstone easily but moves much more slowly through rocks composed of finer particles, such as shale. In igneous and metamorphic rocks, which have low porosities, the number of joints, cracks, and fractures determines the permeability and the amount of water they can hold.

In many parts of the world, porous and permeable rock layers extend away from mountainous regions underneath adjoining plains. Where the porous layer is confined by two nonporous layers, an **artesian system** may be created. In Figure 9–13 water enters the recharge area and flows underground to the points where wells tap the water confined in the aquifer. If the recharge area is in a region of high rainfall, the aquifer may carry large quantities of water. Wells tapping this aquifer may flow continuously at the surface, provided the water

Figure 9–12 *Ground water may move into streams or streams may supply water to the groundwater zone, depending on the season and location.*

pressure in the artesian system is great enough. Are there any flowing artesian wells in your locality?

Part of the underground moisture remains in storage, part of it moves into rivers on the way back to the ocean, and part is used by man. Water may be used several times by man before it returns to the atmosphere or ocean. For example, in some localities industries are required to pump the water circulated through industrial machinery into the ground to recharge the ground water supply.

Thought and Discussion . . .

1. Explain porosity, permeability, and capillarity.
2. Which lawn would need more frequent watering, one with sandy soil or one with clay soil?
3. How does vegetation influence runoff?
4. Distinguish between capillary water and gravity water.
5. How does a river continue to flow during times of no rainfall?

Figure 9–13 *Soil or rock layers may trap water under pressure. The outlet of an artesian well must be lower than the recharge area.*

Figure 9–14
Flooding of
Arkansas River
upstream from
Dodge City,
Kansas, on
June 20, 1965.
Normal river flow
appears on the
lower right. Three
minutes after the
photo was taken,
water covered all
but the treetops.

Moisture Outgo

9–6 Water flows over and through the ground.

Surface streams and ground water together carry about a third of the water that falls on the land. Rivers may occasionally become completely unmanageable, as you can see from the flood scene in Figure 9–14. What conditions might have caused this situation? The flooding of the Arkansas River was the result of many streams on the rampage across a broad region following a series of steady rains. Long after all the soil openings were filled to capacity, rain continued to fall. Infiltration could not keep pace with rainfall. Water began to collect in

streams and flow over the surface, covering many square kilometers of land.

Many intense storms die out before maximum runoff occurs. Look at Figure 9–15. About how many hours after the heaviest rainfall did the greatest runoff occur? There are three reasons for a delay between rainfall and its appearance as streamflow. One reason is the capture of the earliest rain by the many pore spaces in the soil. As pore spaces are filled, more and more rainfall becomes surface runoff as the storm continues. The second reason is that some time is required for water to run over the ground and collect downslope in

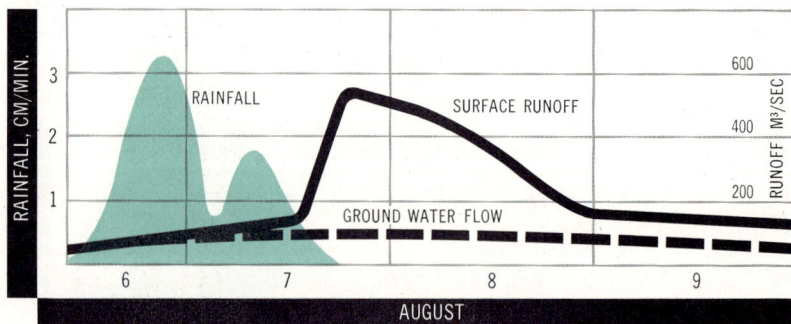

Figure 9–15 *The colored curve shows heavy rainfall on August 6 and 7. Maximum runoff occurred on August 7 after the rain had ceased.*

stream channels. The third reason is that ground water gradually contributes more and more underground flow to streams as gravity water raises the water table and causes ground water to flow into nearby streams.

Surface runoff varies greatly since it is closely related to the intensity of precipitation. Ground-water flow is generally more steady. (See Figure 9–15, broken line.) On an annual basis, it makes up more than half of the total annual flow of many rivers. In most cases streamflow is regulated by ground-water flow. Storage in swamps, marshes, and lakes also tends to regulate streamflow. Large storage areas such as these can keep streamflow nearly constant.

9–7 Evaporation and transpiration remove water.

You have seen moisture evaporate from wet surfaces when the sun comes out after a rain. Evaporation removes water from swamps, lakes, and wet soils. Vegetation also withdraws water from the root zone of the soil. This moisture is carried through the plants to their leaves, where it changes to vapor and escapes to the atmosphere through leaf openings. This process is known as **transpiration.**

Sometimes a single word, **evapotranspiration**, is used to refer to the processes of evaporation and transpiration together. Evapotranspiration is the only means by which capillary water can be removed from the soil. You will recall that about two-thirds of the precipitation received by the land is returned to the atmosphere in this way.

Most of the capillary water withdrawn by vegetation is transpired. Only a very small part is used in **photosynthesis,** the process by which a plant builds new plant tissue. The ratio between the amounts of water transpired and the amounts used to build new plant tissue is about 500 to 1, but varies greatly in different plants.

During both evaporation and transpiration, water changes from liquid to vapor. In Section 6–7 you learned that changes of state require energy. You know that the rate of evaporation depends on a number of factors. For a long time scientists have sought to determine the variables that affect the rates of evaporation and transpiration.

Some scientists have attempted to duplicate natural conditions by measuring water loss from tanks and pans. Some of these tanks contain soil and plants

ACTIVITIES *To see evidence for the transpiration process, obtain a green, potted plant, such as a geranium. Place a plastic bag around the plant so that it is airtight. The following day observe any changes within the bag.*

To record the amount of moisture lost, place two plants on a balance, one of them covered with a plastic bag. Set the plants in balance. The following day record any differences in the adjustment of the balance.

Repeat the activities, using two cactus plants and explain any differences.

A research forester in North Carolina prepares a leaf for weighing in an investigation of transpiration rates. Try to imagine the amount of water drawn from the soil by an acre of forest.

that are like those of the area being studied. The amount of water added to the tanks can be measured. This gives an idea of the amount of water needed to grow plants in that area. In addition, the Weather Bureau maintains evaporation pans at many of its stations. The amount of water lost from the pans over given periods of time is measured. (See photograph on page 183.)

In some irrigated areas rainfall, water outflow, and water used in irrigation are all measured. The amount of water that does not run off the surface or become ground-water flow is used in evapotranspiration. Thus, measuring the water used in irrigated areas is another way of approximating the amount of water lost by evaporation and transpiration.

Still other investigators have measured the amount of water that falls into the drainage basins of lakes in semi-arid regions. By measuring the amount of water flowing into these lakes, they can estimate how much is lost to the atmosphere by evapotranspiration.

Attempts have been made to develop theoretical models that can be used to estimate evapotranspiration. These models use such factors as air and soil temperatures, the availability of soil moisture, relative humidity, air speed and turbulence, the nature of the vegetation cover, and the amount of energy absorbed at the surface during the day. Scientists try to express the relationships between these factors in formulas. You can see why it is difficult to make a mathematical formula that will take all of these variables into account.

9–8 Energy and moisture regulate evapotranspiration.

The principal factor regulating the rate of evapotranspiration is the amount of energy supplied. The maximum amount of moisture that *could* be given off by evaporation and transpiration at a place is called the **potential evapotranspiration** (PE). Since air temperature is an indication of the amount of solar energy received, the PE at a place can be determined from the temperature.

A PE map of the world continents in Figure 9–16 shows a strong similarity to the insolation map. (See Figure 9–17.) Both maps show annual total amounts. The insolation map is given in calories and the PE map in millimeters of water that could be consumed.

Obviously water can be used only if it is available. There are many places in the world, especially in the middle latitudes, where *potential* evapotranspiration is higher than the amount of moisture supplied by precipitation. Does this mean that there is a water deficit? Would such an area support vegetation?

Precipitation and evapotranspiration are not often the same either in amount or in distribution throughout the year. In some parts of the earth more rain falls month after month than is lost by evapotranspiration. The surplus water moves into ground-water storage or flows toward the ocean as runoff. In other places there is less water in the soil at all seasons that could be used by evapotranspiration. In areas where there is barely enough precipitation to support vegetation, runoff occurs rarely, and then only after a heavy rainstorm. Still other regions have a surplus of moisture in one season and a deficit in another. Which description fits your own area?

The seasonal pattern of precipitation rarely matches the changing need for water through the year. Thus, the amount of water lost to the atmosphere over the continents is rarely equal to potential evapotranspiration because it is limited by the amount of water available

Figure 9–16
World map of
potential
evapotranspiration
in millimeters per year.
How many inches is
500 millimeters?
Black areas represent
mountains.

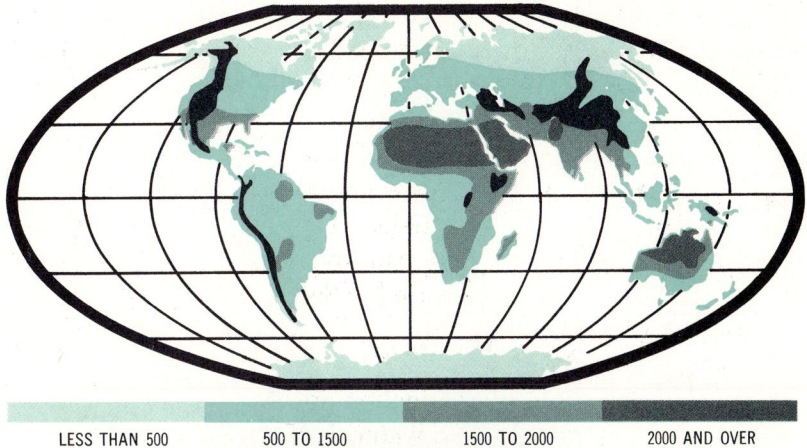

LESS THAN 500   500 TO 1500   1500 TO 2000   2000 AND OVER

Figure 9–17
World map of total
insolation in thousands
of calories per square
centimeter per year.
Black areas represent
mountains.

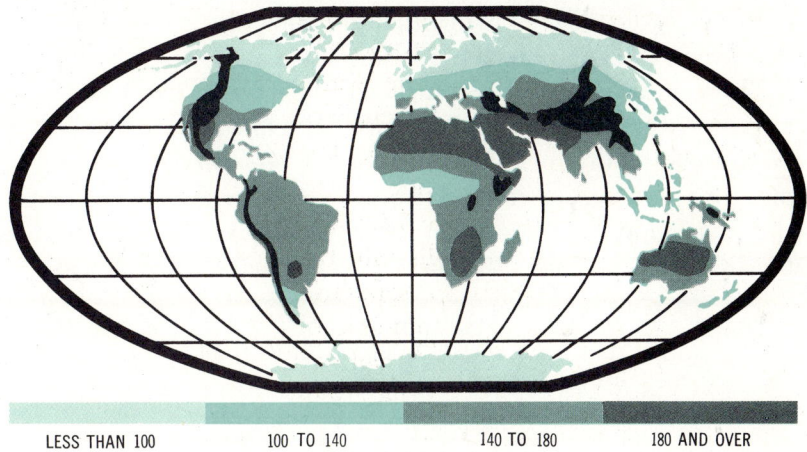

LESS THAN 100   100 TO 140   140 TO 180   180 AND OVER

from storage and precipitation during any given month. The amount of water actually lost through evaporation and transpiration is known as **actual evapotranspiration** (AE). It depends not only on the solar energy received but also on the amount of moisture available. Potential evapotranspiration is the amount of moisture that *could* be used at a place having an unlimited supply. Actual evapotranspiration, on the other hand, is the amount that a place *does* use.

Knowing the monthly values of actual and potential evapotranspiration permits you to determine whether a region is getting as much moisture as it can use. In order to obtain the highest yields from crops, additional water should be made available to plants during seasons with a water deficit. Do you know if your area receives as much moisture as the plants and soils can use?

Thought and Discussion . . .

1. What factors affect the amount and the rate of evapotranspiration in a particular area?
2. How do scientists try to measure water loss from the earth?
3. What determines potential evapotranspiration? How does it differ from actual evapotranspiration?
4. Why is it inadequate to say that a desert is a place that receives less than a certain amount of rainfall, such as 500 millimeters (20 inches) per year?
5. Is evaporation from open reservoirs great enough to cause concern?

The Local Water Budget

9–9 Investigating water budgets.

The water cycle is a general system of income, storage, and outgo of water in the hydrosphere, atmosphere, and lithosphere. You can account for moisture income, storage, and outgo at a particular place with the use of a convenient model called the **local water budget.**

Procedure

The water budget table provides the data for preparation of the water budget graph. Copy Table 9–1 on a separate sheet of paper and complete the table by filling in the missing numbers. Your teacher will provide you with the information needed to compute these numbers.

The values in the table will help you identify periods of moisture surplus and moisture shortage. On the basis of the average PE and precipitation income you will graph the moisture income, outgo, and storage at a certain place, in this case Houston, Texas. For convenience in computing the water budget, scientists use 100 millimeters of water as

TABLE 9–1 DATA FOR COMPUTING MONTHLY WATER BUDGET FOR HOUSTON, TEXAS

| | MILLIMETERS OF WATER MONTHLY | | | | | | | | | | | | |
	JAN	FEB	MAR	APR	MAY	JUN	JUL	AUG	SEP	OCT	NOV	DEC	YEAR
P	89	75	85	92	119	116	98	99	103	95	89	108	1168
PE	19	23	50	83	125	166	182	172	135	81	39	20	1095
P–PE					−6	−50							
ΔST					−6	−50							
ST				100	94	44							
AE					125	166							
D					0	0							
S					0	0							

LEGEND	PE, potential evapotranspiration; P, precipitation; P — PE, difference between P and PE; ΔST, change in soil-moisture storage since previous month; ST, soil-moisture storage at the end of the month; AE, actual evapotranspiration; D, water deficit; S, water surplus.

Cotton fields in the Houston area.

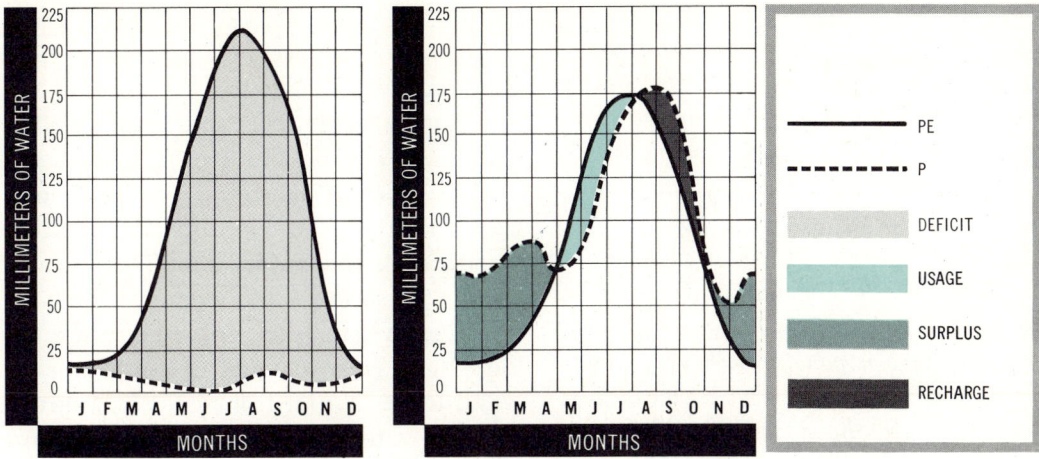

Figure 9–18 *Water budget graphs of Yuma, Arizona (left) and Savannah, Georgia (right).*

the maximum amount that can be stored in the soil. Obviously soil moisture storage varies from place to place depending on soil porosity and other factors, but 100 millimeters may be considered average storage capacity.

When you have completed the procedure for Houston, you will be given the data necessary to compute the water budget of your own geographic area.

After completing both water budget graphs, answer the following questions for each graph:

(1) How well does the precipitation pattern match the PE curve through the year?

(2) Why is PE so low in January and so high in July?

(3) During what months does a water surplus occur? Mark this on your graphs.

(4) How do you know when to end the water surplus period? What causes the surplus period?

(5) When did a period of water deficit begin? Mark this on your graphs.

(6) During what months is stored moisture drawn from the soil by plants and evaporation?

(7) During what months would you say that irrigation is most likely to be needed?

Compare your Houston graph with the two graphs in Figure 9–18, above.

(8) In what ways is the Houston graph different from or similar to each of the graphs?

(9) All of the locations represented in the graphs are on approximately the same line of latitude, about 30 to 32 degrees north. How do you account for the fact that such different water budgets exist along the same latitude?

ACTIVITY *If you have difficulty understanding the water budget concept, the following activity will illustrate the principles involved. Fill a graduated cylinder with 100 millimeters of water to represent the soil storage for the month of April at Houston, Texas. Add the amount of precipitation and subtract the amount of PE from the cylinder as required by the graph for each month. Place a pan beneath the cylinder to catch the surplus so that it can be measured. Record the deficit when it occurs. At the end of the 12 months, how much moisture will be in storage?*

9–10 Interpreting the water budget.

Over much of the middle latitudes, water storage decreases during the summer months because of high insolation, high evaporation, and transpiration. Consequently storage is at a minimum at the end of the summer season. Moisture income perhaps exceeds loss of moisture through evapotranspiration in autumn. Through the winter, soil and air temperatures are low, plants may cease to grow, and loss of moisture from the ground is slight. Snow may accumulate in mountainous areas; water seeps into the soil and into streams and lakes.

In late winter and early spring the melting snow cover releases large quantities of water. The surface layers of soil are soon saturated, and some of the water flows into the underground aquifers where it is stored for later use. Much of the water from the melting snow joins the surface runoff.

As the sun rises higher above the horizon each day, the air temperature increases. New clumps of grass appear and leaves sprout from trees and shrubs as soil water again starts moving upward through the plants. Transpiration losses once more become large. The increase in evapotranspiration creates great demands on the soil water reserves. If enough water is made available to plants, their growth rate increases. However, if summer rain is inadequate and soil moisture storage becomes depleted, plants wither and may even die. As crops are harvested and the growth rates of plants slow down, water losses due to evapotranspiration decrease. Autumn storms may bring water to fill the soil reservoir.

Drought or floods are expected as part of the annual pattern in many regions. In much of the eastern United States floods occur each spring as winter snowmelt coupled with spring rains covers

(Right) A recording rain gauge in North Carolina. (Far right) An electronic snow gauge being used at Donner Pass, California. (Below) A hydrologist rides this trolley to sample the Snake River in Idaho.

the land in greater amounts than can infiltrate the soil. Widespread runoff swells rivers beyond their capacity. (See Figure 9–14.)

In dry or arid regions long periods of summer drought are the rule as the PE curve rises high with summer heat, and rainfall (P) remains low for many months. The occasional convectional thundershower that does come is often too heavy for infiltration. Much of the water rushes across the land, washing away soil and cutting gullies.

Within the larger annual cycle of income, storage, and outgo are a number of smaller cycles that are repeated each time it rains. With the passage of each storm there is a period of soil moisture recharge followed by withdrawal. These shorter cycles vary considerably in length in the course of a year and from one year to the next. In most humid areas the annual cycle of moisture income and outgo repeats itself in much the same way year after year. Marked differences in the pattern of income and outgo may create extreme conditions like drought or flood.

High temperatures stimulate rapid plant growth, provided enough moisture is available. Thus, the higher the PE, the greater the potential rate of growth. In the humid tropics the combination of high energy and high precipitation produces conditions favorable to rapid plant growth. A great variety of trees and shrubs grows in abundance. In the southeastern United States a similar, though less marked, situation occurs. This region is represented by the Savannah water budget that you examined in Investigation 9–9.

In a dry region such as southern Arizona precipitation may be consistently less than PE. Types of plants completely foreign to humid regions are found.

International Hydrologic Decade

In recent years it has been recognized that the world's water is not inexhaustible and that a problem of both the present and the future is how to meet an increasing demand with a limited supply. Already many millions of people depend on water supplies that are either inadequate, unhealthy, or both. Within a few years, many more millions will have unsatisfactory or even dangerous water supplies unless great improvements are made.

This problem is one reason for the IHD, International Hydrological Decade, a program begun in January, 1965, under the sponsorship of UNESCO. Some 69 participating countries pledged to set up training schools, scientific missions, and scholarships, exchange professors and scientists, and work on textbooks adapted to the special needs of the less-developed nations of the world.

An important goal of the IHD, then, is to educate and train hydrologists and technicians. Equally important is that government leaders realize that the solution of water problems is vital.

A better understanding of natural processes that affect water supplies is necessary. Since the water cycle is closely related to atmospheric motion, more knowledge of the atmosphere should lead to a better understanding of weather and water transport.

For all these reasons, the IHD is expected to extend in some form well beyond the actual decade for which it was planned.

Figure 9–19
Farm and forest
land in the humid
area near
Savannah,
Georgia.

Compare the plants in Figures 9–19 and 9–20. Generally desert plants are widely spaced so that they do not have to share the limited water with so many competitors. Desert plants have evolved many modifications that allow them to adapt to a dry environment. Some are able to control the amount of water transpired by closing the pores in their thick-walled leaves. Many desert plants have the ability to store water for use during periods when there is little moisture. In Investigation 9–9 you noted from the Yuma water budget that precipitation is less than PE in every month. The area around Yuma is pictured in Figure 9–20. How do you account for the amount of vegetation that you see there?

It is possible to grow crops in a desert simply by importing water from an area of surplus. In this way the water shortage is overcome and the desert land takes on some characteristics of humid land. However, if the southwestern United States as a whole is a deficit region, where are the surplus areas from which to import water? Look at the region in the physical map on page 434. Notice the mountain ranges. For years these have been the major source areas for surplus water in the West. This is why mountain watersheds are so important to the livelihood of the region. How does solar energy work continually to restore the supply of water in mountainous areas? Is this supply limitless?

Figure 9–20 *Landscape near Yuma, Arizona.*

Thought and Discussion . . .

1. Like a bank account, the water budget involves three factors. What are they?
2. Does the wetting season of a place occur when the precipitation is lower or when it is higher than potential evapotranspiration?
3. Are there some plants in nature that actually thrive in areas where PE is greater than AE?
4. If PE is an index of maximum possible plant growth, where would you get the highest crop yields if water could be made available? What does this suggest about transporting water?
5. Might we eventually use up the world's supply of fresh water? Explain.

Unsolved Problems The circulation of the world's water produces a distribution of runoff that often does not match human needs. We have not yet found ways to overcome water shortages at reasonable cost. Basically, the problem is to distribute water more effectively on the land. The problem has been approached in many ways: cloud seeding to produce rainfall; extracting fresh water from seawater; decreasing evaporation from reservoirs; building reservoirs to hold seasonal excesses; transferring water from one basin to another; more efficient use of water; maintaining pure water in existing rivers; and planting types of vegetation on watersheds that will produce the most usable flows of water. It has even been suggested that coastal cities might acquire fresh water by towing icebergs from polar regions and melting them. Some of these proposals work well in certain local areas but none offers a complete solution.

The first two approaches are concerned with direct transfer of water to the land from another storage system in the water cycle. They are short circuits of a sort. The remainder are concerned with conserving the water resource by changing the amount, location, or timing of moisture released on the lands. All of these procedures are being used or experimented with today.

CHAPTER REVIEW

Summary

Water on the land is an important part of the water cycle. This cycle involves many processes and movements of water between all three physical states. Although more precipitation falls on the oceans than on the land, the most important circuit for water, with respect to its effect on the continents, is from the ocean to the atmosphere by evaporation; from the atmosphere to the land by condensation and precipitation; from soil to the atmosphere through evapotranspiration; and then to the ocean or land again by precipitation.

Water on the land can be considered in terms of income, storage, and outgo. Precipitation is the important source of income. Its distribution on the earth varies widely and depends on the season and geographic location.

Water reaching the land through precipitation may infiltrate, run off, or evaporate and transpire. Water may be stored on the land in snowfields, ice caps, lakes, and streams. Or water may be stored in the soil as capillary water in the root zone or as gravity water at lower levels. Water is removed from the land largely by evapotranspiration. Two-thirds of the precipitation falling on the continents goes into the atmosphere by this means. The other third leaves the continent as runoff in surface streams and ground water.

The local water budget is a convenient model to account for income, storage, and outgo at a particular place. By this means a value for deficit or surplus may be derived for each month. In adjusting to his environment and altering it for his convenience, man sometimes finds it necessary to change the patterns of water on the land.

Questions and Problems

A

1. What is the earth's main source of fresh water?
2. In what forms does water fall from the atmosphere?
3. During what season of the year does the most precipitation fall?
4. What happens to the precipitation that falls on the earth?

5. What is a pore space in a soil?
6. How is water held in soil?
7. How is bedrock able to store ground water?
8. How is water that falls on the land returned to the ocean?
9. Where does the heat come from when water is evaporated or transpired?
10. In which season of the year are evaporation and transpiration highest?

B

1. How is water stored on the earth?
2. How do plants protect the soil?
3. What is the ground-water table?
4. What is an aquifer?
5. How does an artesian system work?
6. How is moisture removed from the soil?
7. Why isn't there much runoff when it first begins to rain?
8. What factors govern the rate of infiltration of water into the ground? In addition to those mentioned in the text, can you think of any others?
9. Explain how the lack of vegetation reduces infiltration and causes runoff.
10. The seeding of clouds that are already overhead is a possible method of controlling the runoff cycle. If it were possible to produce precipitation reliably by this means, would it speed up the runoff cycle? Would more moisture be circulated to the places with greater precipitation?
11. How does air temperature affect evaporation and transpiration?
12. Explain what is meant by the local water budget.

C

1. During humid periods in the spring water condenses on snow surfaces. What effect does this have on the rate of melting? Do you think that this is a factor in spring floods?
2. Can ground water flow uphill? Explain your answer.
3. Do you think that large streams or small streams would vary more during and after a rain? Why?

4. Would more water evaporate from a pan of hot water or a pan of cold water? Why? Do you think that there is any difference in the rates of evaporation from large deep lakes and small shallow lakes? What differences would there be in winter and in summer? Why?
5. Is perspiration in humans related to transpiration in plants? What is the main function of each process?
6. Are evaporation pans a good way to measure the loss of moisture from a region? Explain your answer.
7. What effect do soil temperatures have on evaporation and transpiration?
8. Can actual evapotranspiration exceed potential evapotranspiration? Why or why not?
9. In your own words, define potential evapotranspiration. What factors determine how much it will be and why it is important?
10. The level in a wishing well is observed at Thomasville, Georgia, on a day in March and again on a day in August. The observations are recorded below. Determine which observations were made on the March day and which were made in August. Read all the observations before you write your answers. (a) Well level is 3.90 meters below the surface of the ground. (b) Well level is 5.10 meters below the surface. (c) Although rain fell into the well, its level dropped one millimeter today. (d) Nine millimeters of precipitation fell into the well, but its level dropped one millimeter today. (e) Seven millimeters of precipitation fell over the town today, but the water level in the well rose 12 millimeters.
11. Two watersheds in Connecticut have very different soils. In the flat Farmington River Valley, soils are deep and can store at least 100 millimeters of soil moisture in the root zone. The Naugatuck Valley is rocky and steep and has many areas with little soil depth. Its soils hold less than 100 millimeters of capillary water in the root zone. In

June and July of a recent year only 50 millimeters of precipitation fell each month. In August a hurricane dumped 400 millimeters of precipitation over both watersheds. Compare the factors affecting the runoff cycles in the two watersheds with respect to the flood conditions. (a) In which valley would there be a greater amount of standing water? (b) In which valley would there be more water for flooding and runoff? (c) Suppose that on July 5, 10, and 15, each valley had 25 millimeters of rain instead of a total of only 50 millimeters in the month. Is it likely that these storms would have had any effect on the August flood? (d) Which valley would need new bridges?

Suggested Readings

BOOKS

Bauer, Helen. *Water: Riches or Ruin.* Doubleday & Company, Inc., Garden City, N.Y., 1959.

Cocannouer, Joseph A. *Water and the Cycle of Life.* The Devin-Adair Co., New York, 1958.

Davis, Kenneth and John A. Day. *Water: The Mirror of Science.* Doubleday & Company, Inc., Garden City, N.Y., 1961.

Gresswell, Ronald Kay. *Physical Geography, Rivers and Valleys.* Hulton Educational Publications, Ltd., London, 1958.

Leopold, Luna, Kenneth S. Davis, and the editors of *Life. Water.* Time, Inc. (Life Science Library), New York, 1966.

Man has long been engaged in the transfer of water for his use. (Far left, above) Friant Dam and canal in California provide water for distant farms. (Below) Transported water supports citrus orchards in the desert of Coachella Valley. (Left) A 135-cm pipe carries water to San Diego.

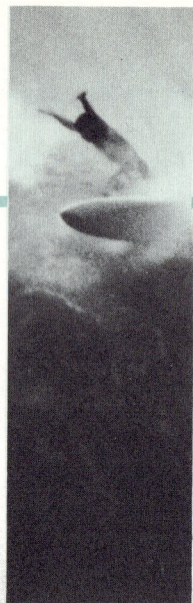

Chapter 10 Water in the Sea

Balancing on his surfboard, a surfer rushes toward the shore, racing the wave crest that rises in a threatening arch over his head. A veil of spray is tossed high into the air by the churning water. The surfer swoops at an angle in front of the crest of the wave, a wake spreading behind him. The wave seems to speed up and to rise higher, as if gathering strength to overwhelm him.

Although he may not think about it, the surfer is using the energy of the wave for his ride to the shore. If he loses his balance, he will feel the tremendous power of the sea wave as it crashes down on him. Sea waves have enough energy to provide power to heat and light the largest cities if man could find a way to harness them. Waves along the west coast of the United States release as much energy as 25 Hoover Dams. Where does this great energy come from? Could man ever find a way to use it for his own purposes?

The water in which the surfer is riding is warm, a comfortable temperature for swimming or surfing. However, at one time some of this water may have been flowing under the ice in Arctic regions. How does water travel from the polar seas to the Hawaiian Islands? What causes the temperature of the water to change?

If the surfer accidentally swallows a mouthful of seawater, he will experience an unpleasant sensation from its salty taste, so different from that of fresh water. Why is seawater unfit for drinking? Men adrift at sea have died of thirst, although surrounded by water. It is somewhat easier to stay afloat in the ocean than in freshwater lakes and pools. Why should this be so? How is fresh water changed to make seawater so different from water on the land?

Oceans cover most of the earth's surface and are the great reservoirs of the earth's water. In this unit you have studied the movement of water in the water cycle. You have seen that the atmosphere always contains a small amount of water, as compared with that stored in rivers, lakes, ground water, and ice on the continents. Is all this water really stored for very long on the land? Water in rivers is obviously on its way somewhere. Most lakes are really just wide places in a river. Even ground water and the ice in glaciers feed the rivers that flow to the sea. What are its activities in the sea? What happens to water molecules when they reach the sea? Do they remain there?

The Ocean in the Water Cycle

10–1 The water cycle makes the sea salty.

You often hear the expression "plain water," but is water really so plain? In many ways water is a very special substance. Remember the unusual properties of water discussed in Section 2–5. The fact that water exists in all three states, solid, liquid, and gaseous, on the surface of the earth makes it one of the most active of earth materials. Water is continually moving about in the atmosphere, on land, and in the ocean. It constantly passes through the water cycle, absorbing energy at some places, releasing energy at others, and moving materials about the surface of the earth.

What does it mean to say that the ocean is the great reservoir of the earth's water? If you were to follow a water molecule in its many trips through the water cycle, you would find that on the average it spends more than 98 out of every 100 years in the ocean. One year and eight months would be spent by the water molecule as ice on land, about half a month in lakes and rivers on the land, and less than a week in the atmo-

sphere. To a water molecule, going through the water cycle is like taking an occasional vacation from the ocean.

Seawater is different from the waters of the land. Men cannot drink it or use it to water their crops. Seawater destroys most metals in a short time unless they are protected from it. The concentration of earth materials dissolved in seawater makes it very different from fresh water. What are these materials? Where did they come from?

Men have known for thousands of years that if seawater is evaporated or boiled away, a quantity of white crystals will remain. This was one of the early ways used by men living near the sea to obtain salt for cooking. If 1 kilogram of water from almost any part of the sea is evaporated, about 35 grams of solid material are obtained. (See Figure 10–1.) The number of grams of dissolved material in 1000 grams of seawater is the **salinity** of the seawater. Thus the salinity of average seawater is about 35 grams per kilogram, or about 3.5 percent of seawater by weight. If all the dissolved salt from the oceans could be spread on the continents, it would form a layer more than 200 meters thick.

How did these dissolved materials get into the sea? Have they always been there? We do not know how old the oceans are, or how they were formed. How, then, can we find out how salt gets into the sea? Perhaps earth processes going on today can provide a clue.

Energy from the sun evaporates water from the sea. Wind carries the water vapor for great distances until it condenses and falls to the earth as rain or snow. The water from the rain and snow flows from tiny streams into rivers, and rivers flow back to the sea. Thus, water returns to the sea. How has it changed?

In flowing across the land, rivers pick up tiny particles of soil and rock that turn the water muddy brown. Rivers also contain material that has been dissolved from the land. Almost every earth material can be dissolved to some extent. This dissolved material occurs as ions in water. Do you remember why water is such an effective solvent? Because of gravity, particles of rock and soil eventually settle out and are deposited by rivers. Ions remain dissolved in the water until they are chemically removed.

How much earth material do rivers carry to the sea? The Mississippi River system collects runoff water, soil par-

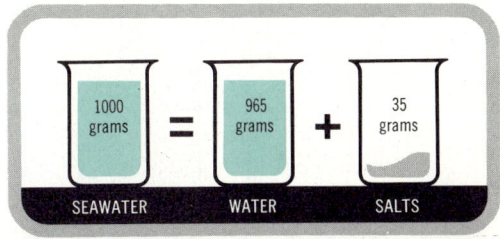

Figure 10–1 (*Top*) *Each kilogram of seawater contains about 35 grams of dissolved salts. Water from San Francisco Bay is pumped into ponds; it evaporates, leaving large amounts of salt.*

ticles, and its dissolved solids from 3,405,280 square kilometers of land. (See Figure 10–2.) Every year tons of sediment per square kilometer of this drainage area are carried to the Gulf of Mexico, resulting in an astounding total of over half a billion tons a year! The Mississippi also carries to the sea about 137 million tons of dissolved materials per year. Have the processes of evaporation, rainfall, and river flow always been going on? If so, how have these processes affected seawater?

Figure 10–2
Sediments are carried from the mouth of the Mississippi River into the Gulf of Mexico. Note how the several channels branch out across the delta.

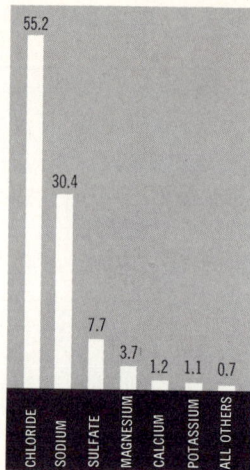

Figure 10–3 *Six kinds of ions make up over 99 percent of the salts in the sea. Scientists are not sure whether or not the average composition of ocean water is changing.*

10–2 What materials are dissolved in seawater?

Even just a taste of seawater suggests that it contains sodium chloride. Sodium ions and chloride ions make up about 85 percent of the material in seawater. Sensitive chemical tests have been devised to measure the amounts of about 60 different elements in seawater. However, as Figure 10–3 shows, ions of just six different elements make up over 99 percent of the sea salts. These ions exist in seawater because dipolar water molecules separate them and hold them in solution. (See Figure 2–16.)

Notice that the composition of sea salt is very different from the average composition of the earth's crust. (See Table 2–1.) If salts come from the land, why is the composition of the sea salt different from the average composition of the earth's crust?

Water that falls on the land as rain dissolves some of the chemical elements from rocks and soils. Certain elements are dissolved much more readily than others and enter streams and rivers along with sediments. Because of this, the composition of all the waters flowing to the sea does not reflect the average composition of rocks and soils.

Some chemicals are removed from the ocean waters by living organisms. Silicate minerals and calcium carbonate ($CaCO_3$) are abundant in the earth's crust. Calcium and silica (SiO_2) derived from silicate minerals are removed from seawater by organisms and become part of their shells and skeletons. Some elements that are very rare in seawater are commonly found in sea plants and animals. How can you account for this?

Sodium and chloride ions have been accumulating in seawater more than other chemicals because they are very soluble. They are carried from the land in great quantities and are used very little by sea animals. Because they are so soluble, sodium and chloride ions have not yet reached the saturation point in average ocean waters. In other words, the ocean could hold a great deal more of these ions.

An analysis of 77 samples of seawater collected from all parts of the world ocean during the cruise of the HMS *Challenger* (1872–1876) is shown in Figure 10–4. These samples showed that the most plentiful ions in seawater always occur in the same proportion. The amounts of these ions in a seawater sample can be found if the amount of just one type of ion is measured.

The less common ions in seawater are not always found in the same proportion because these ions are used by organisms living in the sea, just as minerals from the soil are used by plants living on land. Near the surface of the sea where tiny drifting ocean plants grow and are eaten by marine animals, these uncommon ions tend to be used up. They are carried to deeper water when the remains of dead marine animals sink and decay. It is known that the deep water therefore is richer in certain less common ions than the surface water.

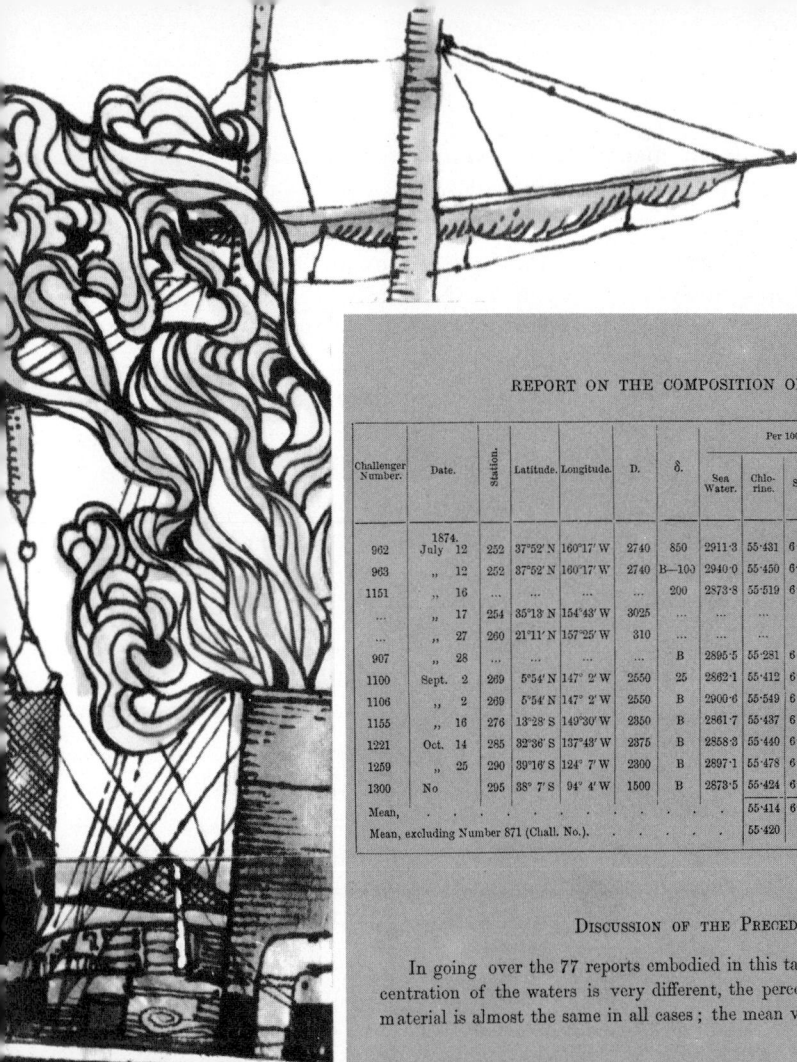

Challenger Number.	Date.	Station.	Latitude.	Longitude.	D.	δ.	Per 100 grms. of total Salts.							Alkalinity per kilo. in mils of Y place.	Sulphuric Acid per 1 grm. of Chlorine.	Laboratory Number.
							Sea Water.	Chlorine.	SO₃.	CaO.	MgO.	K₂O.	Na₂O.			
962	1874. July 12	252	37°52′ N	160°17′ W	2740	850	2911·3	55·431	6·372	1·725	6·227	1·316	41·429	2·60	·11496	50
963	,, 12	252	37°52′ N	160°17′ W	2740	B—103	2940·0	55·450	6·371	1·811	6·209	1·391	41·261	218	·11490	51
1151	,, 16	...	...	...	...	200	2873·8	55·519	6·388	1·664	6·194	1·316	41·446	149	·11506	62
...	,, 17	254	35°13′ N	154°43′ W	3025	...	...	...	...	...	...	...	...	...	...	...
...	,, 27	260	21°11′ N	157°25′ W	310	...	...	...	...	...	...	...	...	...	...	...
907	,, 28	...	...	...	...	B	2895·5	55·281	6·369	1·689	6·207	1·343	41·603	399	·11521	61 & 61A
1100	Sept. 2	269	5°54′ N	147° 2′ W	2550	25	2862·1	55·412	6·437	1·706	6·251	1·331	41·367	221	·11617	343
1106	,, 2	269	5°54′ N	147° 2′ W	2550	B	2900·6	55·549	6·434	1·717	6·216	1·355	41·261	79	·11582	344
1155	,, 16	276	13°28′ S	149°30′ W	2350	B	2861·7	55·437	6·428	1·726	6·242	1·319	41·358	207	·11595	345
1221	Oct. 14	285	32°36′ S	137°43′ W	2375	B	2858·3	55·440	6·471	1·721	6·200	1·278	41·401	157	·11672	346
1259	,, 25	290	39°16′ S	124° 7′ W	2300	B	2897·1	55·478	6·429	1·701	6·209	1·336	41·366	151	·11588	347
1300	No	295	38° 7′ S	94° 4′ W	1500	B	2873·5	55·424	6·434	1·713	6·187	1·333	41·409	189	·11609	348
Mean,								55·414	6·415	1·692	6·214	1·333	41·433	225	·11576	
Mean, excluding Number 871 (Chall. No.).								55·420	...	...	...	...	...	220	...	

DISCUSSION OF THE PRECEDING TABLE.

In going over the 77 reports embodied in this table, we see that although the concentration of the waters is very different, the percentage composition of the dissolved material is almost the same in all cases; the mean values being as follows :—

(In 100 parts of Total Salts.)

Chlorine,*	55·420
Deduct basic oxygen equivalent to this chlorine,	− 12·503
Muriatic acid, Cl_2-O	42·917
Sulphuric acid, SO_3	6·415
Lime,	1·692
Magnesia,	6·214
Potash,	1·333
Soda,	41·433
	100·004

* Excluding the abnormally low value in Challenger number 871.

(PHYS. CHEM. CHALL. EXP.— PART I.—1884.)   A 4

Figure 10–4 *What important finding is illustrated on this page (above) from the report of the data gathered during the cruise of the H.M.S. Challenger?*

Oceanographers have not been measuring the salinity of seawater long enough to know whether or not it is changing. Seawater could hold more of nearly all kinds of ions, with the exception of calcium. Seawater contains nearly all the calcium it can hold. This means that although there is less calcium available in seawater than some other salts such as sodium chloride, it is more easily removed from solution. In some areas near the shore where seawater becomes warm, it is unable to hold all of its calcium, and calcium carbonate is deposited. What type of sedimentary rock do you think might be formed from this material?

Because seawater contains small amounts of almost all the elements, men have long dreamed of obtaining valuable materials from the sea. Ordinary salt has been obtained from seawater for many centuries (see Figure 10–1), but only recently has it become possible to remove such other materials as magnesium and bromine.

10–3 The sea and the atmosphere exchange matter and energy.

Dissolved solids remain in the sea when water evaporates. However, some salt does move from the sea into the atmosphere. Breaking waves toss water droplets into the air. The smallest droplets may completely evaporate before they can fall back into the sea. (See Figure 10–6.) The salts that had been in these droplets remain in the air and are carried by the wind as tiny crystals. These crystals may become the nuclei on which atmospheric moisture condenses. Some scientists believe that most of the chloride ions in rivers come from salt washed out of the atmosphere by rain.

Gases as well as solids are also exchanged across the sea-air interface. The most important are oxygen and carbon dioxide. These exchanges are very important to life in the ocean. All animals must have oxygen uncombined with other elements to live. When fish or other animals use oxygen in the water, oxygen from the air replaces it.

In some cases, oxygen can also pass from the sea to the atmosphere. Growing plants release oxygen near the sea surface just as on land. Oxygen can be carried to the depths of the ocean by currents, while some may escape to the atmosphere. Surface water is usually saturated with oxygen. However, oxygen may pass in either direction across

Figure 10–5 *(Left) FLIP, or FLoating Instrument Platform can be "flipped" vertically to provide a stable research platform.*
Figure 10–6 *(Center) Salt may enter the atmosphere as spray from waves evaporates.*
Figure 10–7 *(Right) Sea smoke or fog forms when cold air flows over warmer water.*

the sea-air interface, depending on the time of year and geographic location. Altogether, there is about 200 times as much gaseous oxygen in the atmosphere as in the oceans of the earth.

ACTIVITY *You can see for yourself that water contains dissolved gases. Fill a tall glass or bottle with cold water and put it in a warm place or heat it gently. Explain what you see happening.*

One of the most important materials that crosses the sea-air interface is water. The atmosphere receives about 80 percent of its water vapor from the evaporation of seawater. When the sea is warmer than the atmosphere, as in Figure 10–7, water vapor passes rapidly from the sea to the air. Much of this water vapor condenses and falls as precipitation on some other part of the ocean. It also supplies most of the water for precipitation on the land masses. In spite of the great amount of water in the ocean, even the small amount that evaporates affects the local salinity.

The water that evaporates from the sea contains no dissolved salts. What happens to salinity in the ocean when pure water is added or taken away?

George Wüst, a German oceanographer, concluded that the salinity of surface seawater must be controlled chiefly by two things: the total amount of salt in the ocean and the exchange of fresh water across the sea surface. A water budget may be computed from the balance between precipitation and evaporation at a particular location on the ocean as well as on the land. If Wüst's idea is correct, the surface water of the sea should have higher than average salinity at latitudes with greater evaporation than precipitation. At what lati-

tudes would the salinity of surface waters be lower than average? Evidence to support Wüst's idea is shown in Figure 10–8. Look at 30 degrees north and south latitude. Can you see that salinity is higher than average where evaporation is greater than precipitation? Look back at Figure 8–8 (page 186) and explain how it relates to Figure 10–8.

Most of the water evaporated from the sea condenses in the atmosphere and returns directly to the sea as precipitation. It might seem that this part of the water cycle is not very important for life on the continents. Recall, however, that energy is used in evaporating water. Water vapor passing from the sea to the atmosphere takes energy with it in the form of latent heat. When the water vapor condenses to form clouds and rain, the energy remains as heat in the atmosphere. This is the source of much of the energy of wind and storms.

As shown in Figure 7–4, only about half of the energy coming from the sun is filtered out by the atmosphere before it reaches the surface of the earth. What happens to this energy over the three-fourths of the earth's surface covered by water? You can see in Figure 10–9 how

Figure 10–8 *The salinity of the ocean surface water is related to the local water budget. The upper graph shows salinity of the surface water. The lower graph shows evaporation minus precipitation. At what latitudes is evaporation greater than precipitation? less than precipitation?*

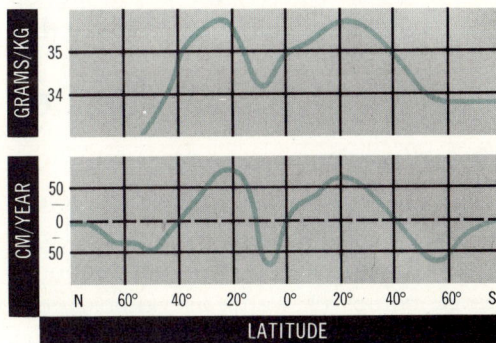

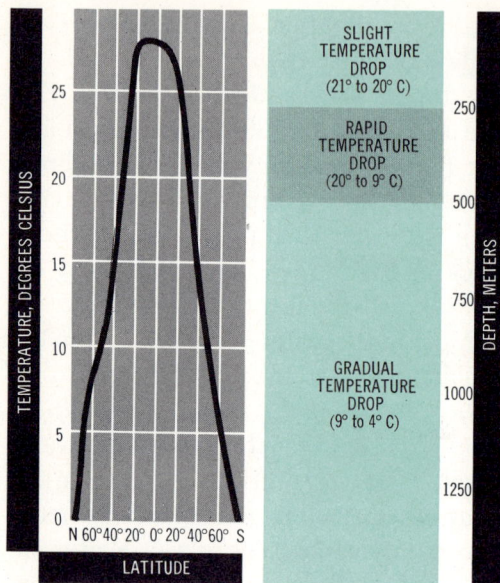

SLIGHT TEMPERATURE DROP (21° to 20° C)	250
RAPID TEMPERATURE DROP (20° to 9° C)	500
	750
GRADUAL TEMPERATURE DROP (9° to 4° C)	1000
	1250

Figure 10–9 (*Left, above*) *Ocean surface water is warm in the tropics and cold in the polar regions.*
Figure 10–10 (*Right, above*) *Even in tropical regions, the water in the ocean depths is very cold, about 4°C below 1000 meters.*

the average temperature of water at the surface of the sea changes with latitude. How does Figure 10–9 compare with Figure 7–6 showing the variation of solar radiation with latitude? The short-wave radiation that penetrates the atmosphere to reach the oceans is radiated back by the oceans at longer wavelengths. These longer wavelengths do not readily pass back through the atmosphere and therefore provide energy to heat the air. (See Section 7–4.)

Most of the shortwave solar radiation reaching the ocean is absorbed in the top few meters. Notice in Figure 10–10 that

there is a surface layer many meters thick with nearly uniform temperature. Because of vertical stirring action by waves and winds, some of the heat absorbed at the surface can be carried downward. Most travelers sailing on warm tropical oceans do not realize that less than a kilometer away from them (straight down) the water is nearly as cold as ice because warm surface waters do not reach these depths. Some heat is conducted directly from the warm sea to the colder atmosphere. Why would a better understanding of how matter and energy are exchanged across the interface between ocean and atmosphere improve weather forecasting?

ACTIVITY *Wet the back of your hand with water. Now wet the back of your other hand with alcohol. Can you explain the difference that you feel between the two? Repeat the activity and blow on the back of your hands. Is there a difference? Where did the energy come from to evaporate the water and alcohol?*

Thought and Discussion . . .

1. Why do hurricanes seem to lose energy, or "blow themselves out," when they pass over the land?
2. In what ways is the atmosphere heated by the oceans?
3. In Section 10–2 it is stated that if the amount of one type of ion in a seawater sample is known, amounts of others can be calculated. Why is this possible?

The Sea in Motion

10–4 Waves carry energy.

Have you ever seen water completely motionless at the seashore or in a large lake? If you have, it was not for long. Large bodies of water are almost constantly in motion. Most of what you

notice is wave motion. At the seashore you can hear the breakers roar as they slam against the rocks and sand, and you can watch them tossing clouds of spray high upon the cliffs. If you have ever been caught up, overturned, and smashed

Figure 10–11 *Ocean waves (above) are irregular, but their properties can be measured and described. Wave tanks (below) are used by oceanographers to study wave action.*

into the sand by a wave, you have experienced a wave's great energy. What kinds of energy does a wave have? Where does all this energy come from?

Most waves on water are caused by the wind. If you blow on the surface of still water, tiny ripples form. When you stop blowing, the ripples stop. The wind blows on the sea for a much longer time, however, and the ripples grow into small waves. The longer and harder the wind blows, the larger the waves become. Waves will continue even after the wind has stopped. They contain enough energy to continue traveling for many hundreds of kilometers across the ocean. That is why you may see waves at the shore even on a windless day.

What is a wave? It looks like a moving ridge on the water surface. (See Figure 10–11.) Waves obtain their energy from the wind and carry it across the ocean to distant shores. Spectacular effects of this energy are seen on seacoasts, where waves erode the cliffs and grind the rocks into fine sand.

How would you describe the waves you have seen to someone else? How high were they? how far apart? did the waves have pointed or rounded tops? and how fast were they moving? Sea or lake surfaces usually contain a mixture of waves of different heights and lengths so that no two waves look exactly alike.

Some things about all waves are the same, however. Each wave has a top, or crest, and a bottom, or trough. (See Figure 10–12.) The height of the crests above the troughs is called the **wave height,** and the distance between crests is called the **wavelength.** (See Section 6–12.) If you watch a group of waves pass a buoy or wash over a rock, you may notice that the time between passage of

Figure 10–12 *(Below) The terms used to describe waves. (Left) A surfer uses the tremendous energy of a wave that rushes toward the shore.*

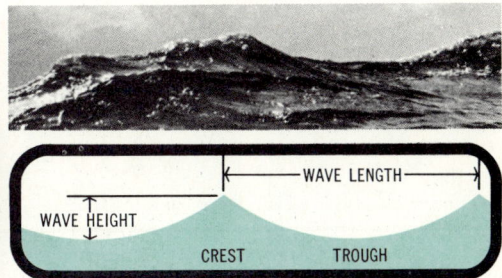

WAVE LENGTH
WAVE HEIGHT
CREST   TROUGH

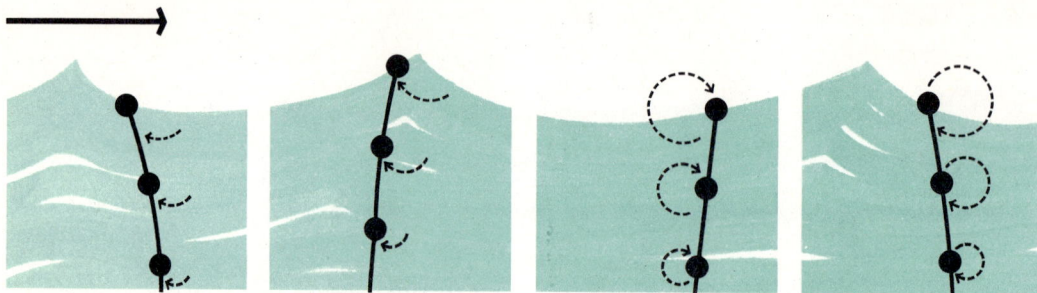

one crest and the next is always about the same. This time between crests is called the **period** of the waves.

If you know the wavelength and period of any wave, not just water waves, you can calculate its speed of travel with the formula:

$$\text{wave speed} = \frac{\text{wavelength}}{\text{period}}.$$

Thus, a wave having an average wavelength of 156 meters and a period of 10 seconds travels at a speed of $\frac{156}{10}$ or 15.6 meters per second.

ACTIVITY   *Tie one end of a rope with a knot tied in the middle of it to a doorknob. Extend the rope to its full length and jiggle it from the free end. Waves will pass along the rope toward the doorknob. How does the rope itself move? What is the motion of the knot? Is this a good model of the motion of water particles in a wave?*

Figure 10–13   *In deep-water waves, the orbital motion (arrows) of water particles (black dots) decreases below the surface.*

It may surprise you to learn that only the crests and troughs of the waves travel across the oceans, and not the water itself. The water particles move, as you will see, but they do not travel across the ocean with the wave motion. Try the Activity to help you understand this idea of wave motion.

How do the water particles move in waves? They move differently in deep water than in shallow water. Where the water is deep, the water particles near the surface move around in circles. The diameters of the circles, or orbits, are the same as the wave height. (See Figure 10–13.) Below the surface the water particles move in circles of smaller and smaller diameter. At a distance below

Figure 10–14   *In shallow water the orbital motion of waves becomes flattened as the waves reach to the bottom and move sediment.*

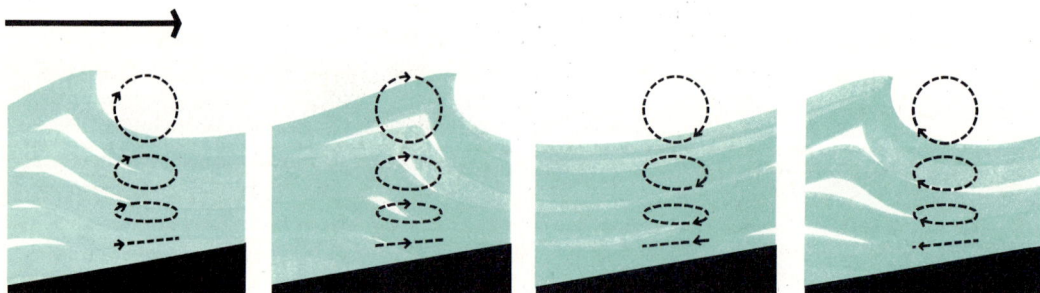

the surface equal to one-half wave-length, the diameter of the circular path is less than one-twentieth that at the surface. This is the reason why sub-marines can avoid stormy seas by diving beneath the surface.

In deep water, surface waves with long wavelengths travel faster than those with short wavelengths. Storms make waves of many wavelengths. These waves travel at different speeds. The longer waves race ahead, leaving the shorter waves behind. They may even run ahead of the storm itself. Long, low waves crashing on a beach often warn of the approach of a storm.

In water shallower than one-half wavelength, the waves begin to drag on the bottom. The circular motion of the water particles becomes flattened as shown in Figure 10–14. The bottom of the wave moves more slowly than the top of the wave, causing the wave to "break" on the beach and then flow back. This back-and-forth motion on the bottom stirs up sand and sediment. Even in places where the waves are not breaking, they can move sand along the bottom.

In shallow water the long waves travel at the same speed as the short waves, but the speed of all the waves changes with the depth of the water. The shallower the water, the slower the waves. Waves in deep water tend to catch up with the waves in shallow water. They can never overtake the waves ahead, but the wavelength be-comes shorter. (See Figure 10–15.)

Notice also that a wave in deep water travels faster than another part of the same wave in shallower water. Although most waves approach the beach at an angle, the influence of the bottom causes the waves to bend in toward the beach. This results in waves that are almost parallel to the shoreline.

Figure 10–15
(*Above and left*) *Near the beach, wavelengths become shorter because of bottom friction. Waves tend to break parallel to the beach.* (*Below*) *A U.S. nuclear-pow-ered submarine on the surface running at high speed.*

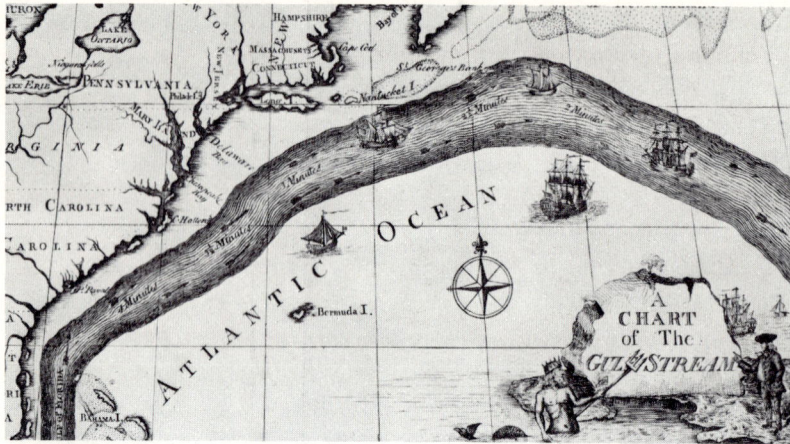

Figure 10–16
A portion of Timothy Folger's chart of the Gulf Stream off the East Coast. This map was drawn at the request of Benjamin Franklin.

10–5 Winds cause currents at the ocean surface.

When Benjamin Franklin was Deputy Postmaster of the Colonies, he asked his cousin Timothy Folger, a whaling captain from Nantucket, why mail packets (mail boats) took two weeks longer than merchant ships to make the voyage from England. Captain Folger replied that the whalers knew of a place in the ocean where the water flowed like a river. He went on to say that whalers

> . . . are well acquainted with the stream because in our pursuit of whales, we run along the side and frequently cross it to change our side, and in crossing it have sometimes met and spoke with those packets who were in the middle of it and stemming [going against] it. We have informed them that they were stemming a current that was against them to the value of three miles an hour and advised them to cross it, but they were too wise to be councelled by simple American fishermen.

Franklin asked Folger to draw a chart of this stream, now called the Gulf Stream, and had the chart printed by the General Post Office. (See Figure 10–16.) Since earliest times sailors have known of currents in the ocean and steered their ships so as to use or avoid them. Yet information on currents was not col-

lected in an organized manner until 1855 when an American naval officer named Matthew Maury compiled and published a complete collection of data on winds and currents.

Certain patterns in the flow of ocean currents over the globe became obvious from Maury's studies. You can see from Figure 10–17 that the currents in each of the ocean basins are similar. The water moves in large, almost circular paths north and south of the equator. These currents are somewhat like the winds. They are strong in some places and weak in others. Currents flowing away from the equator carry warm tropical water to higher latitudes. Currents flowing toward the equator carry cold water from higher to lower latitudes. What effect do you think ocean currents have on sea temperatures off Florida and off Baja California? Look again at Figure 10–9. What is the average ocean surface temperature at 25 degrees north latitude? Swimmers off Florida often find temperatures higher than 30°C at this latitude. At the same latitude off Baja California, the sea temperature is more likely to be near 15°C. Why such a difference? You can see in Figure 10–18 how the ocean currents, like the atmospheric circulation, carry heat from equatorial regions toward the poles.

What causes currents in the ocean? How do they obtain their energy? The sun is the basic source of energy for currents, but something must turn the sun's radiant energy into the kinetic energy of currents. This agent is the wind. As wind blows over the sea, it exerts a force on the water just as it exerts force on trees, houses, or blades of grass on land. Ocean water is not as firmly attached to the solid earth as trees or houses are. It is, therefore, free to flow.

When the wind applies force to the sea surface, the water will be pushed in the same direction that the wind is blowing. Compare the direction of the trade winds (Figure 7–12) with the direction of the equatorial currents. (See Figure 10–17.) Are the directions the same? Explain your answer.

Ocean currents, like wind, are affected by the rotation of the earth. They are deflected to the right of the average wind direction in the Northern Hemisphere. How do you think they are deflected in the Southern Hemisphere?

The steady trade winds blowing from the east pile up water on the west side of the oceans. Water does not pile very well, however, so it flows downhill and escapes in currents flowing away from the equator. Currents such as the Gulf

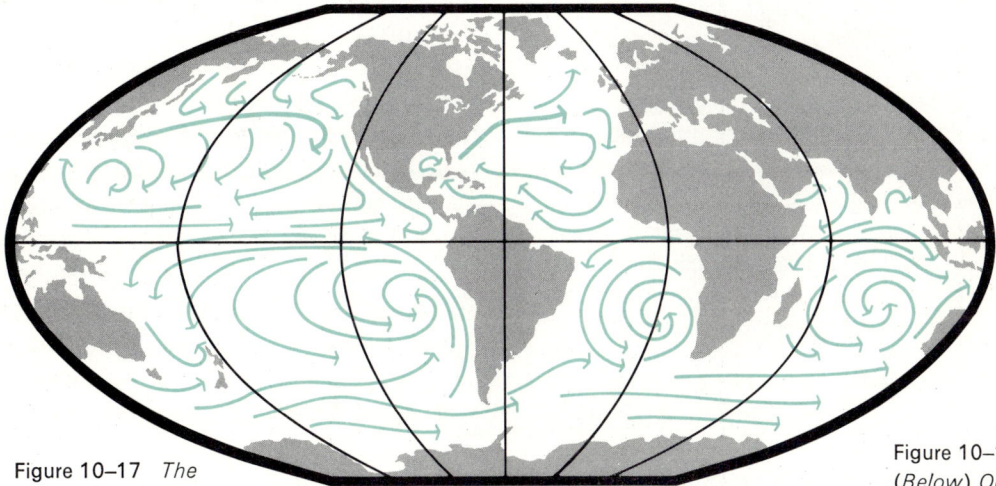

Figure 10–17 *The general pattern of currents at the surface of the oceans.*

Figure 10–18 (*Below*) *Ocean currents transfer heat from darker areas to lighter areas.*

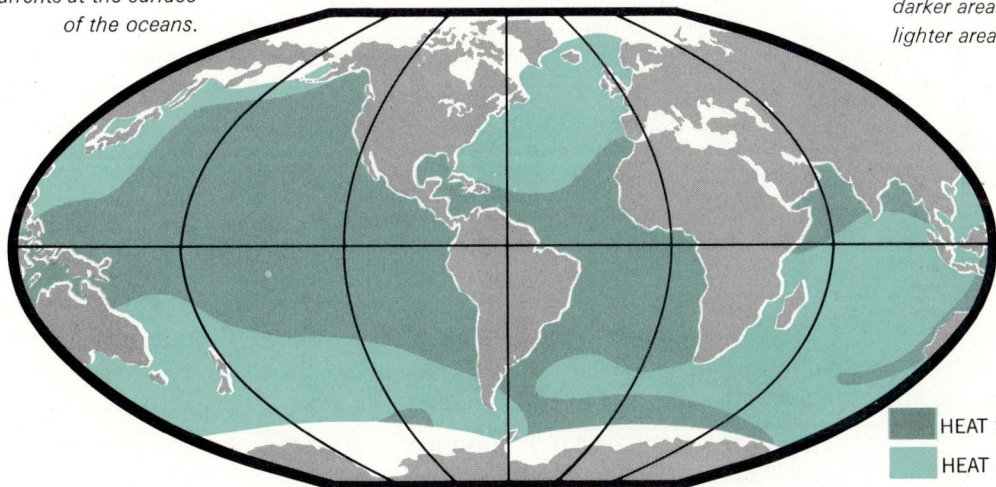

HEAT SOURCE
HEAT SINK

One of the founders of physical oceanography was a U.S. Navy officer, Lt. Matthew Fontaine Maury, who measured the depth of the sea floor by dropping a cannonball tied to a kilometer or so of line into the ocean off the deck of his ship. Crippled by an accident at the age of 33, Maury was forced into limited service. The Navy assigned him to its Depot of Charts and Instruments. In the Depot's dusty archives, Maury uncovered a treasure of long-neglected logbooks. These provided the initial data for a useful set of wind and current charts of the earth's oceans.

Through the years, Maury obtained from sea captains the most complete set of ocean data in the world. From these worldwide observations, he compiled a famous oceanographic treatise, Physical Geography of the Seas, and his office issued sailing instructions of great value to navigation and commerce.

Maury's early observations convinced him that the oceans of the world made up a sphere "with a system of circulation as complete, as perfect, and as harmonious as that of the atmosphere or of the blood."

One of the monuments to Lt. Maury's efforts to sound the sea is the Atlantic cable system. The first intercontinental telegraph cables laid in 1886 from Newfoundland to Ireland followed a route Maury had suggested years earlier.

Matthew Fontaine Maury

Stream in the Atlantic and the Kuroshio in the Pacific show this.

Ocean currents are not very fast when compared to the speed of the wind. In mid-ocean the speed of the current is usually less than two kilometers per hour. Narrow currents such as the Gulf Stream sometimes flow at a speed of eight kilometers per hour, which is faster than you ordinarily walk.

Where winds blow toward the equator along the west coast of continents, surface seawater is moved toward the equator by the winds. At the same time, the water is turned offshore by the Coriolis effect. Cold deeper water then rises to replace the water deflected offshore. The upward flow of deep water is called **upwelling.** Upwelling of cold water is the cause of the cool waters and fogs off the coast of northern California. This cold water is also rich in the chemicals needed by microscopic marine plants.

Upwelling is a regular occurrence along the coast of Peru. Here great amounts of dissolved nutrients are brought up into the sunlit surface water, and as a result marine life occurs in great abundance in these waters. Fishermen reap rich harvests off the coast of Peru. The dependence of sea life in this area on upwelling is dramatically shown every few years. For unknown reasons, the equatorial countercurrent turns and brings warm surface water along the coast of Peru. This is disastrous for fish and other marine life. Why? The sea becomes littered with the bodies of dead and dying creatures. Their decomposition produces poisonous hydrogen sulfide gas (H_2S), the same gas that gives rotten eggs their unpleasant odor. It can turn paint on ships black. One of Peru's seaports is named Callao. When H_2S is present, seamen say that the "Callao painter" has been at work again.

10–6 Investigating currents.

Wind causes currents at the ocean surface, but density differences cause circulation at depth. In this investigation, look for the factors that affect the density of seawater. See how density differences cause circulation deep in the ocean.

Procedure

Set up the equipment as shown in Figure 10–19. Mix two salt solutions of different densities. This will be your artificial seawater. Pour a test-tubeful of one of your samples of "seawater" into the sloping tube filled with fresh water. Measure the rate at which the salt solution travels down the tube. Put fresh water in the sloping tube and repeat the procedure with the other solution.

(1) Which solution traveled down the tube faster? (2) What kinds of processes in nature could produce differences in the density of seawater?

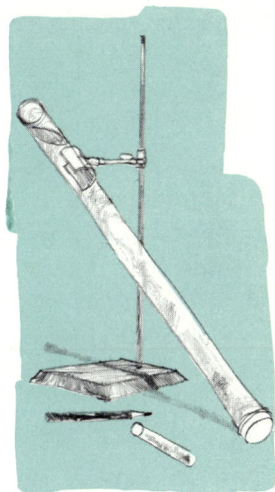

Figure 10–19
Density current apparatus.

Your teacher will give you a sample of artificial seawater. Use 100 ml of the solution and make it more dense without adding anything to it. Try some of the methods you suggested in answering Question 2. Keep a record of your methods and of the evidence that you actually *have* made the solution more dense.

The final part of this investigation is related to energy transfer through density differences. Set up a model ocean as shown in Figure 10–20. Put about 100 ml of ice in a paper cup that has several pinholes in the bottom and record the temperature changes shown by the thermometers. Drop a bit of paper on the surface of the water and a few soaked bits of paper inside the container.

(3) What kinds of energy transfer did you notice? (4) If you observed evidence for currents, what was the evidence and how did the currents behave? What caused the currents?

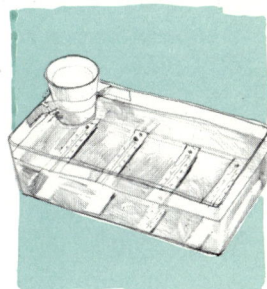

Figure 10–20 *A model ocean.*

10–7 Density differences cause currents in the ocean.

Little is known about currents beneath the surface of the ocean because they cannot be seen and are difficult to study. As recently as 1951 a new major current, the Cromwell Current, was discovered in the Pacific Ocean. It flows at speeds up to 5 kilometers per hour from west to east along the equator. Its existence was not even suspected until 1951 because it is covered by water 50 meters in depth

flowing more slowly in a direction opposite to that of the surface current.

It was once thought that the depths of the ocean were still and without life. Oceanographers have now taken pictures of, and even captured, animals in the very deepest parts of the ocean. This means that there must be some way for water rich in oxygen to reach these ocean depths. How does this occur?

The density of seawater depends upon temperature and salinity. The transfer of matter and energy across the air-sea interface changes the density of the seawater. Oceanographers believe that deep water moves in slow currents caused by density differences. Most of what we know about the movement of water deep in the ocean has been learned indirectly by the measurement of the temperature, salinity, and oxygen content of the deep water.

Partly because of their importance to ocean travel and fishing, currents in the Atlantic Ocean have been studied more than those in other oceans. The Gulf Stream carries relatively warm, salty water into the northern Atlantic near Greenland. There the water cools and increases in density. Some of the water from the Gulf Stream then sinks toward the bottom of the sea. This water then appears to move southward into the deep ocean basins at a speed of about 20 kilometers per year.

Notice in Figure 10–21 how the salinity patterns show where the currents flow. Along the way the cold, dense water mixes with the water above that is less salty. Mixing lowers the density of the current, and near Antarctica some of the mixture rises and returns to the North Atlantic with the surface currents. The rest flows around Antarctica as a deep current much like the surface cur-

rents shown in Figure 10–17. Some of it eventually passes into the Pacific and Indian Oceans.

The densest water in the ocean is around Antarctica. Freezing, like evaporation, leaves the salt in the unfrozen water. For this reason, when seawater freezes at the surface, the salinity of the remaining water is increased. The high salinity and low temperature produce extremely dense water that sinks to the bottom. Where it meets the slightly less dense North Atlantic water, the Antarctic water flows beneath it as shown in Figure 10–21. Perhaps the water at the bottom of all the great ocean basins of the earth comes from these two regions near Greenland and near Antarctica.

Ocean currents can also be measured in much the same way that meteorologists measure atmospheric currents. Oceanographers anchor buoys with current meters in the ocean and leave them for a month or more to record the speed of the currents. Another way of measuring currents is by releasing floats equipped with automatic radio transmitters. Some floats are designed to drift deep below the ocean surface. These must be traced by the use of sound waves rather than radio waves.

Deep currents in the ocean have been measured only a few times. These mea-

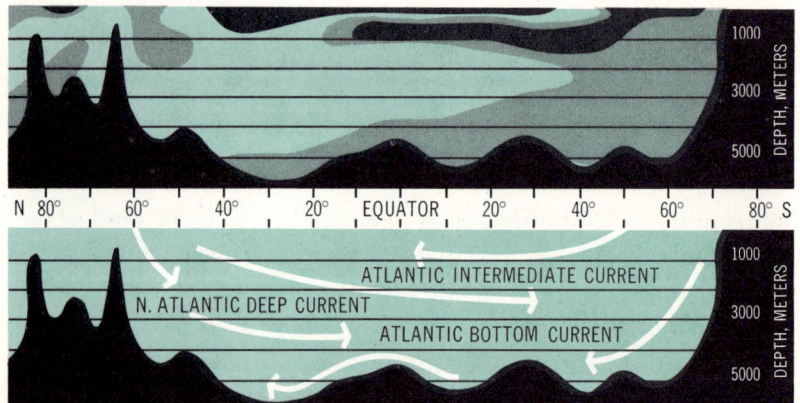

Figure 10–21 *How does salinity help identify ocean currents? In the upper graph, increasing salinity is indicated by the darker tones. The lower graph shows how the deep ocean currents move in this same area.*

N 80°   60°   40°   20°   EQUATOR   20°   40°   60°   80° S

DEPTH, METERS   1000   3000   5000

ATLANTIC INTERMEDIATE CURRENT
N. ATLANTIC DEEP CURRENT
ATLANTIC BOTTOM CURRENT

DEPTH, METERS   1000   3000   5000

surements were very puzzling to oceanographers because the currents moved as much as 100 times faster than expected. Furthermore, it was discovered that they frequently changed direction. It appears that the deep currents of the ocean may be as changeable as the air currents of the atmosphere.

Unsolved Problems One of the things that puzzle oceanographers is the way in which day-to-day currents combine to form the average currents. Why, for example, are the currents in the depths of the ocean so much faster than expected? If water is sinking to great depths near Greenland and Antarctica, then water must be rising from the depths somewhere else. At present no one knows where.

Even the most studied of all currents, the Gulf Stream, still holds many mysteries. Most ocean current charts show it as a broad stream. Recent research shows, however, that it is actually a narrow, winding stream. (See Figure 10–22.) For reasons still not understood by oceanographers, its position and speed change from month to month in an unpredictable manner.

Another major question is how fast carbon dioxide crosses the air-sea interface. Water vapor and carbon dioxide

Thought and Discussion . . .

1. Where do waves obtain their energy?
2. What are the differences between waves in shallow water and in deep water?
3. What causes ocean surface currents?
4. What causes deep currents in the ocean?
5. How is the Coriolis effect shown in ocean currents?

in the atmosphere act as a blanket, absorbing radiation and radiating it back to the earth's surface. What will happen then as man adds carbon dioxide to the atmosphere by burning great amounts of coal and other fuels? Some scientists think that the earth's climate may become much warmer, melting the Antarctic ice and causing the sea to rise 50 meters or more. Others think this change in the composition of the atmospheric blanket could start a new ice age by reducing the amount of insolation reaching the earth's surface.

However, the earth has a big safety valve for its carbon dioxide. Unlike oxygen, which is mostly in the atmosphere, there is about 60 times as much carbon dioxide in the sea as in the atmosphere. Most of the carbon dioxide added to the atmosphere ends up in the sea. It is important to know how fast carbon dioxide goes into the sea, for if it is exchanged too slowly, our climate may change.

Figure 10–22 (*Below*) The Gulf Stream boundaries (*white*) and the areas through which they may shift. How does this compare with Folger's map? (*Right*) A fishing vessel coated with ice after an Atlantic storm.

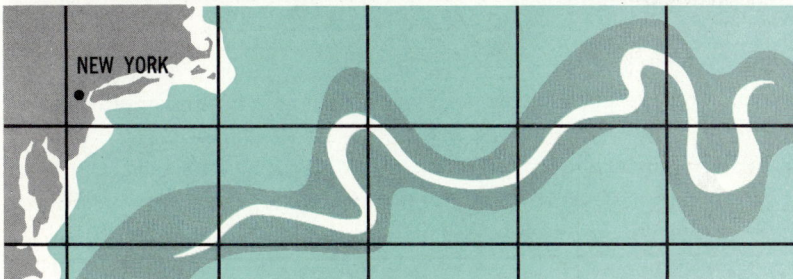

NEW YORK

CHAPTER REVIEW

Summary

One of the things that makes the planet earth different from the other planets of the solar system is the large amount of water on its surface. This water exists in all three states: solid, liquid, and gaseous. As it goes through the water cycle, water is continually being changed from one form to another, using and releasing energy.

Most of the water, however, is stored in one large, many-bayed basin—the ocean. Water circulates constantly, absorbing energy at some places and releasing it at others. The water cycle carries solid earth materials as well as dissolved ions down to the sea where they have been accumulating over countless ages.

Some solar energy passes through the atmosphere and is absorbed at the surface of the ocean. This energy is then passed on to the atmosphere by reradiation, by conduction of heat, and by the release of latent heat of vaporization in the atmosphere as part of the water cycle. Absorption of solar energy at the ocean surface does not cause much motion in the sea.

Waves in the ocean result from the transfer of kinetic energy from wind to water across the air-sea interface. Atmospheric winds also push the surface water along in currents. The ocean currents, like the atmospheric circulation, carry heat from equatorial to polar regions and thereby influence the climates of the earth. Increased density results from wintertime cooling of surface water at high latitudes, which in turn causes sinking and currents in the depths of the ocean.

One of the greatest climatic effects of the ocean may be that it is also a great reservoir of carbon dioxide, and therefore controls the radiation balance of the earth's surface by regulating the amount of carbon dioxide gas in the atmosphere. Scientists do not know how long it takes for excess carbon dioxide in the atmosphere to dissolve in the oceans.

Questions and Problems

A

1. What is salinity?
2. In what ways does seawater differ from fresh water?
3. Discuss two ways in which energy leaves the ocean.
4. What is meant by the wavelength and period of water waves?
5. Where is most solar energy absorbed in the sea?
6. What causes ocean surface currents?
7. What causes currents in the depths of the ocean?

B

1. How do salts get into the sea?
2. About how much seawater must be evaporated to obtain 453 grams (1 pound) of sea salts?
3. What factors determine the salinity of mid-ocean surface waters?
4. Name several things that are transferred across the air-sea interface.
5. What is the speed of travel of waves having a period of 6 seconds and a wavelength of 56 meters?
6. If one-half the radiation striking the sea surface is absorbed in the first meter, and one-half the radiation that passes through the first meter is absorbed in the second meter, and so on, what fraction striking the sea surface reaches a depth of 5 meters? 10 meters?
7. What is the relation between salinity and density of seawater?

C

1. How much seawater is needed to give 453 grams of magnesium metal?
2. Trace the flow of energy from the sun to a wave breaking on a beach.
3. What are some differences between deep and shallow water waves?
4. What causes the Gulf Stream? How was it discovered?

5. Are south-flowing currents warm or cold currents?
6. What effect has the rotation of the earth on ocean currents?
7. How would the speed and frequency of convection currents in the ocean compare with those of atmospheric currents? Explain your answer.
8. What determines seawater density?
9. How do we know about deep ocean currents?
10. How can the hypothesis that the deepest water in the oceans all comes from the region around Antarctica be tested?

Suggested Readings

BOOKS

Carson, Rachel L. *The Sea Around Us,* rev. ed. Oxford University Press, Inc., New York, 1961.

Coker, R. E. *This Great and Wide Sea.* Harper & Row, Publishers (Harper Torchbooks), New York, 1962. See Chapter 10 on waves, Chapter 11 on tides and internal waves, and Chapter 12 on heat and water balance.

Daugherty, Charles M. *Searchers of the Sea: Pioneers in Oceanography.* The Viking Press, Inc., New York, 1961.

Deacon, George E. R., ed. *Oceans, An Atlas History of Man's Exploration of the Deep.* Paul Hamlyn, London, 1962.

Engel, Leonard. *The Sea.* Time, Inc. (Life Nature Library), New York, 1961.

Pickard, George L. *Descriptive Physical Oceanography.* Pergamon Press, Inc., New York, 1964.

Stewart, Harris B., Jr. *The Global Sea.* D. Van Nostrand Co., Inc., Princeton, N.J., 1963.

PERIODICALS

Bascom, Willard. "Beaches." *Scientific American,* August, 1960. (Also Scientific American Offprint #845, W. H. Freeman & Co., Publishers, San Francisco.)

Bascom, Willard. "Ocean Waves." *Scientific American,* August, 1959. (Also Scientific American Offprint #828, W. H. Freeman & Co., Publishers, San Francisco.)

Bernstein, Joseph. "Tsunamis." *Scientific American,* August, 1954. (Also Scientific American Offprint #829, W. H. Freeman & Co., Publishers, San Francisco.)

Fairbridge, Rhodes W. "The Changing Levels of the Sea." *Scientific American,* May, 1960. (Also Scientific American Offprint #805, W. H. Freeman & Co., Publishers, San Francisco.)

Knauss, John A. "The Cromwell Current." *Scientific American,* April, 1961.

Kort, V. G. "The Antarctic Ocean." *Scientific American,* September, 1962. (Also Scientific American Offprint #860, W. H. Freeman & Co., Publishers, San Francisco.)

Munk, Walter. "The Circulation of the Oceans." *Scientific American,* September, 1955. (Also Scientific American Offprint #813, W. H. Freeman & Co., Publishers, San Francisco.)

Stommel, Henry. "The Anatomy of the Atlantic." *Scientific American,* January, 1955. (Also Scientific American Offprint #810, W. H. Freeman & Co., Publishers, San Francisco.)

Waves constantly pound the rock-bound coast of Maine.

Chapter 11 Energy, Moisture and Climate

Which of the three places in the photographs is a desert? People often think of a wide expanse of rolling sand dunes when the word desert is mentioned. A desert is an area with a particular kind of *climate*. Can you actually see a climate?

Climate may be described as the history of weather that has been recorded at a place. A history book cannot include all of the human events that have occurred. Neither is it possible to describe all of the weather events that have occurred at a place on the earth. Just as historians must summarize human events, so climatologists must *generalize* the weather events of a place in describing its climate. You cannot see history but you can see the *effects* of history. A people's past is reflected in their architecture, in their customs, and even in their way of dress.

Although you cannot see climate, you can see how the weather over the centuries has given the land a character of its own. The thick leaves of a desert cactus jealously guard its store of water. Brightly flowered plants of the tundra hug the earth closely to escape the strong winds that would tear them from the soil. Lush green leaves of jungle plants carelessly spend their plentiful water supplies. Over the land areas of the earth, vegetation reflects the weather of the past and maps the broad patterns of the earth's climates.

What are the patterns of the earth's climates and what causes them? The whole system of climates on earth can be traced back to energy from the sun as it powers the water cycle. Uneven distribution of solar energy over the surface of the earth is related to the earth's spherical shape and to its motions of rotation and revolution. Movements of the atmosphere that result from the unequal heating of the earth's surface transport energy and moisture from one part of the world to another in the water cycle. Some parts of the earth receive large amounts of energy and moisture, whereas other parts receive an abundance of one and not the other. The patterns resulting from the unequal distribution of energy and moisture over the earth's surface produce climatic regions.

Are there any other parts of the earth with a climate like that of your region? Do you think that the processes involved in the water cycle occur in an orderly fashion over the earth, or does weather occur in such a random way that no regular pattern of climates can be found? Suppose that all you knew about a place was its latitude, its location with reference to land and water bodies, and something about the surrounding terrain. Would you be able to describe its climate?

Men in various
regions must adjust to
different conditions of
energy and moisture.
(Left) A shepherd in
the desert of
Saudi Arabia.
(Right) A native
Jamaican guides
tourists down a
tropical river on a
bamboo raft.

Patterns of Energy and Moisture

11–1 Investigating the climates of an imaginary continent.

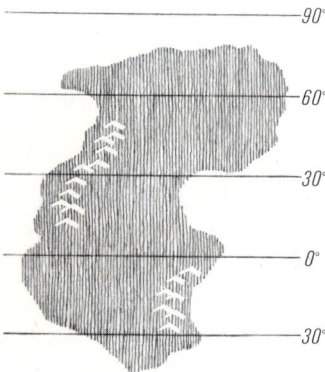

Figure 11–1

You learned something about the climate of your area from the Weather Watch investigation. Of course, other places on earth have climates different from that in your area. In previous chapters you have studied the processes involved in the movement of energy and moisture in the water cycle. Now, see if you can apply this knowledge in outlining the climates of an imaginary continent on the earth.

Procedure

On the outline map of an imaginary continent (Figure 11–1), which will be supplied by your teacher, sketch in what you believe to be the different climatic areas and label them. Explain the basis for your decisions.

11–2 Early ideas about climate.

Does your map of climates on the imaginary continent look anything like the map of climatic zones shown in Figure 11–2? In what way is your map similar or different?

This Greek map made about 500 B.C. by Hecataeus also shows an imaginary continent. The Greeks had no way of knowing what the world was really like. At the time that Hecataeus drew his map of the world, most people thought that the earth was a disk and that the continents were surrounded by the world

ocean. They thought that the sun revolved about the earth. By the time of Eratosthenes (276–196 B.C.), Greek scientists had been able to improve their knowledge of the earth and its climates. They had received reports from traders and explorers about weather conditions in the parts of the world where these men had traveled. They were thus able to make better interpretations of climatic conditions because they had more and better observations upon which to base their interpretations. Many people thought by then that the earth was round. Eratosthenes had made his famous estimate of the earth's circumference and had constructed his map of the world. (See Figure 3–12.)

The Greeks were able to measure the angle of the noon sun and to observe the arc of the sun's path across the sky. They had also found the length of daylight and darkness for the longest and shortest days of the year at various places on earth. From these observations, latitudinal zones called *climata* were established that had approximately the same period of sunlight on any given day of the year. (See Figure 11–3.) Eventually the word *climata* signified the temperature conditions in these zones also.

In thinking about the size and shape of the world and using the climatic data available to them, the Greek philosophers speculated that climatic zones similar to those they had observed in the Northern Hemisphere existed in the Southern Hemisphere. Some of them even thought that a continent must exist south of the equator. Out of these speculations came a division of the earth into five major climatic zones. The zones are identified in Figure 11–4.

As Greek ships sailed farther north and south and as Greek armies marched farther and farther from their homeland, they found that the temperate zone was more extensive than they had believed.

The Arctic and Antarctic circles and the Tropic of Cancer and the Tropic of Capricorn came to be accepted by the Greeks as the boundaries of the climatic zones. Why do you think they chose these lines for their boundaries?

Considering the small number of observations available to the Greeks, their system of climatic zones was really a remarkable achievement. It represented an idea that was changed very little until the nineteenth century when European scientists began to work together to collect weather observations from all over the world.

Today a great number of observations of atmospheric conditions are available to us. Twice each day, a weather map for the Northern Hemisphere is drawn by the United States Weather Bureau from hundreds of observations. Satellites send photographs of cloud patterns back to earth and special equipment on the satellites measures the flow of energy away from different parts of the earth. This is done by scanning with an instrument that is sensitive to heat (infrared) radiation rather than light. There are now so many observations that computers must be used to analyze the data

Figure 11–2 (*Left*) *Climatic zones as drawn by Hecataeus, a Greek, around 500 B.C.*

Figure 11–3 (*Right*) *Latitudinal zones or climata identified by the Greeks about A.D. 150.*

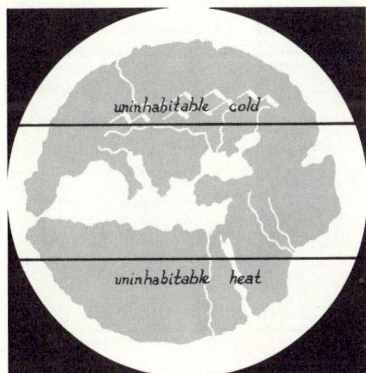

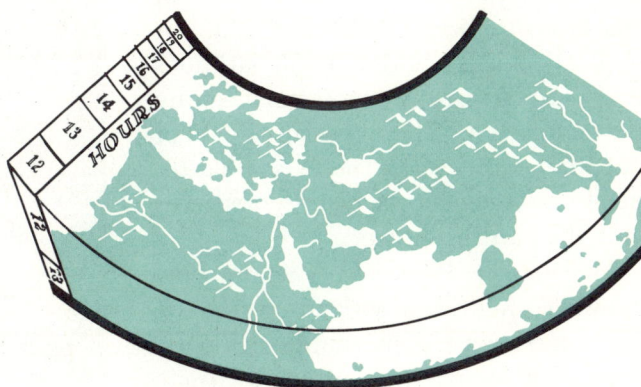

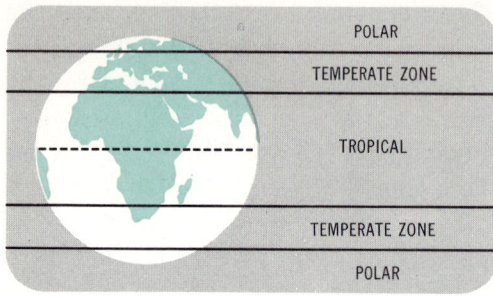

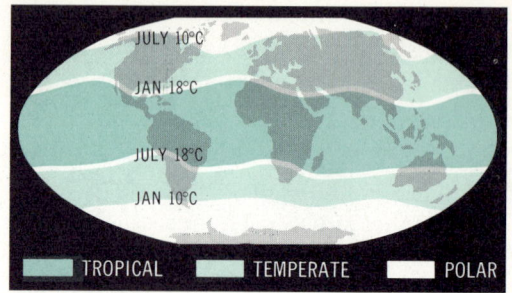

Figure 11–4 (Above) Climatic zones of the world as the ancient Greeks imagined them.
Figure 11–5 (Right) One way to classify climatic zones on the basis of temperature.

received. Our knowledge of the climates of the world is much greater than that of the Greeks. More is known about the reasons why climates differ from place to place. However, there are still many unsolved problems that climatologists are studying in order to explain why climates change in space and time.

11–3 Latitudinal patterns of energy.

Although the Greek system of classifying the climates of the world was devised over 2000 years ago, it is sometimes used today. Why do you suppose this is so?

The Greek system of classification was based on the idea that the principal control of the climate of a place was its latitude. How good was this idea? If you look at Figure 7–6 you will see the amounts of energy absorbed (income) and emitted (outgo) annually at various latitudes. There is a surplus of energy in tropical regions and a deficit in polar regions. In the middle latitudes the energy gained is almost balanced by the energy lost. These measurements of radiation verify that there is a latitudinal arrangement of energy patterns over the earth's surface.

The map in Figure 11–5 shows how the world might be divided into climatic zones making use of present-day climatic records of temperature. Does this map

look much like that of the climatic zones of the Greeks? The Greek system of climatic classification was based on the idea that the temperate zone was the only part of the earth in which man could live. The polar zone was too cold and the tropical zone was too hot.

As you learned in the introduction to this chapter, vegetation tells us something about the climate of an area. While there are many ways to define and classify climates, one approach is to use vegetation as an indicator. For example, the isotherm of 10°C for the warmest month of the year might be selected as the boundary of the polar zone. Where temperatures do not rise above this level, trees are not common because there is not enough heat during the short cool summer months for them to reproduce and grow. Consequently, the vegetation consists of small plants and shrubs.

The poleward boundary of the tropical zone is sometimes defined as the

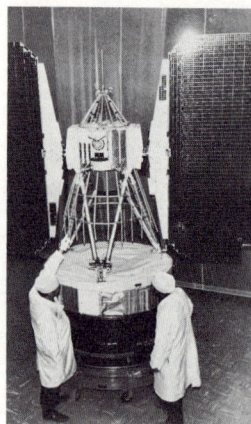

The Nimbus 2 weather satellite measures incoming solar radiation and outgoing radiation emitted from the earth. Because its orbit is over the poles, it can measure these quantities at all latitudes.

18°C isotherm for the coldest month. Tropical plant growth is generally restricted by colder temperatures. Between the isotherms of 10°C for the warmest month of the year and 18°C for the coldest month of the year lies the temperate zone. This temperate zone experiences considerable seasonal change from summer to winter. Although these boundary values are arbitrary, they are useful in studying the broad climatic zones of the earth.

What is it that produces these broad latitudinal temperature patterns? Over the earth as a whole, daily and seasonal temperature changes are related to earth motions that affect the amount of radiation received from the sun. Energy gained during the day causes temperatures to rise and reach their maximum shortly after noon. At night the loss of energy results in a cooling of the atmosphere. With the longer days and more direct rays of sunlight in summer, heat is accumulated from day to day and temperatures gradually increase. As winter approaches, more energy is lost at night than is received during the day. Average temperatures become lower.

As you know from chapters 4 and 7, the two most important factors determining the amount of solar energy received at a place on earth are the angle at which the sun's rays strike the area and the length of time the area is exposed to the rays—in other words, the **angle of incidence** and the length of daylight. Since both of these are related to latitude, the amount of insolation received is nearly the same along any given parallel. The vertical ray of the sun moves between 23½ degrees north

and south latitude. It is never directly overhead beyond those latitudes. The length of daylight is always 12 hours at the equator. It increases toward the pole in summer and decreases toward the pole in winter. (See Figure 11–6.)

On June 21, for example, the sun is directly overhead at 23½ degrees north

JUNE 21 SUMMER SOLSTICE	SEPT. 21 MAR. 21 AUTUMNAL & VERNAL EQUINOXES	DEC. 21 WINTER SOLSTICE	LATITUDE
24 HR. DAY		0 HR.	90°N
24 HR.		0 HR.	80°N
24 HR.		0 HR.	70°N
18 HR. 27 MIN.		5 HR. 33 MIN.	60°N
16 HR. 18 MIN.		7 HR. 42 MIN.	50°N
14 HR. 52 MIN.		9 HR. 8 MIN.	40°N
13 HR. 56 MIN.		10 HR. 4 MIN.	30°N
13 HR. 12 MIN.		10 HR. 48 MIN.	20°N
12 HR. 35 MIN.		11 HR. 25 MIN.	10°N
12 HR.	12 HOUR DAY—ALL LATITUDES	12 HR.	0°
11 HR. 25 MIN.		12 HR. 35 MIN.	10°S
10 HR. 48 MIN.		13 HR. 12 MIN.	20°S
10 HR. 4 MIN.		13 HR. 56 MIN.	30°S
9 HR. 8 MIN.		14 HR. 52 MIN.	40°S
7 HR. 42 MIN.		16 HR. 18 MIN.	50°S
5 HR. 33 MIN.		18 HR. 27 MIN.	60°S
0 HR.		24 HR.	70°S
0 HR.		24 HR.	80°S
0 HR.		24 HR. DAY	90°S

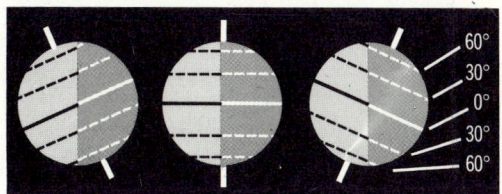

Figure 11–6 *Length of daylight as it relates to latitude and the seasons. How many hours of daylight will there be at your latitude on December 21? June 21?*

Wladimir Köppen

Wladimir Peter Köppen is considered the father of modern climatology. Born in Russia in 1846, Köppen spent his youth in the Crimea, where the mild climate and subtropical vegetation fostered an interest in the relationship between climate and vegetation. While he considered botany his first love, Köppen went on to spend nearly half a century as a meteorologist at the German Naval Observatory. There he produced a series of notable maps of the ocean winds. In 1924 Köppen went to the University of Graz in Austria. He died there in 1940.

Köppen's youthful interest in the relationship between climate and vegetation led to his classification of world climates on the basis of plant distribution. In 1918 he revised his classification, basing it more directly on temperature and precipitation values. The Köppen system divides the earth into five main zones, which are subdivided according to temperature and rainfall, seasonal variations, and effects on vegetation. Köppen's system is useful because it is both quantitative and fairly simple. Yet Köppen ignored physical factors that also affect climate, such as wind and pressure belts, frontal systems, or ocean currents. Expanding the basis for his climatic types to include such additional elements, however, would have defeated the advantage of simplicity that his system offers.

latitude and its rays become more slanted toward the North Pole. Yet the length of daylight increases toward the Pole. At what latitude are the combined effects of these two factors at a maximum during the northern summer? You can find the answer by looking at Figure 11–7. In July the latitude receiving the maximum amounts of energy is located between 30 and 40 degrees north. Where are the zones receiving the least energy at this season of the year? Why? Where are the maximum amounts of energy received in January? the minimum?

You can see that the zone of maximum energy income shifts back and forth across the equator with the seasons. It shifts more than the sun itself because of the longer days of summer toward the poles. In the tropical zones the amount of energy received does not vary much from one season to another, as shown in Figure 11–7, and there is always a surplus of energy income over outgo. Polar zones receive little or no insolation in winter months and only small amounts in summer so that there is nearly always a deficit of energy. Places in the middle latitudes experience great changes in the amounts of energy received during the course of the year. Look at 40 degrees north latitude, for example, to see how the surplus of energy in summer is replaced by a deficit in January.

One of the most convenient ways to show the effects of solar energy is by temperature maps. The temperature maps of the world for July and January are an indication of how much energy is received throughout the world and how much of it is used to heat the air above the earth's surface. (See figures 11–8 and 11–9.) If the amount of insolation received is related to latitude, why do the isotherms bend north and south across the maps?

Figure 11–7 *Net solar energy (difference between income and outgo) at various latitudes for July (solid line) and January (dashed line). What causes these variations?*

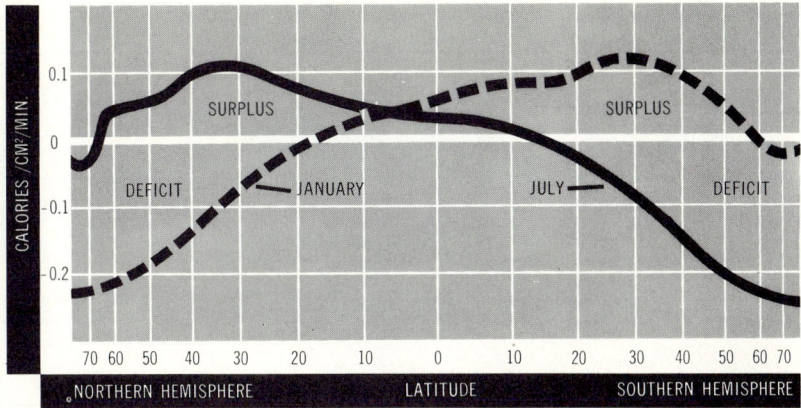

11–4 Latitudinal patterns of moisture.

The distribution of moisture in the atmosphere, like that of energy, is related to latitude. Recall that the atmosphere's ability to hold moisture depends on the temperature of the air. (See Section 8–3.) If temperature is arranged in broad zones of latitude, will moisture also be arranged in similar zones? What is the relation between temperature, moisture, and latitude?

The amount of water vapor in the atmosphere at various latitudes is given in Figure 11–10. If the atmosphere were a giant sponge and all of the moisture

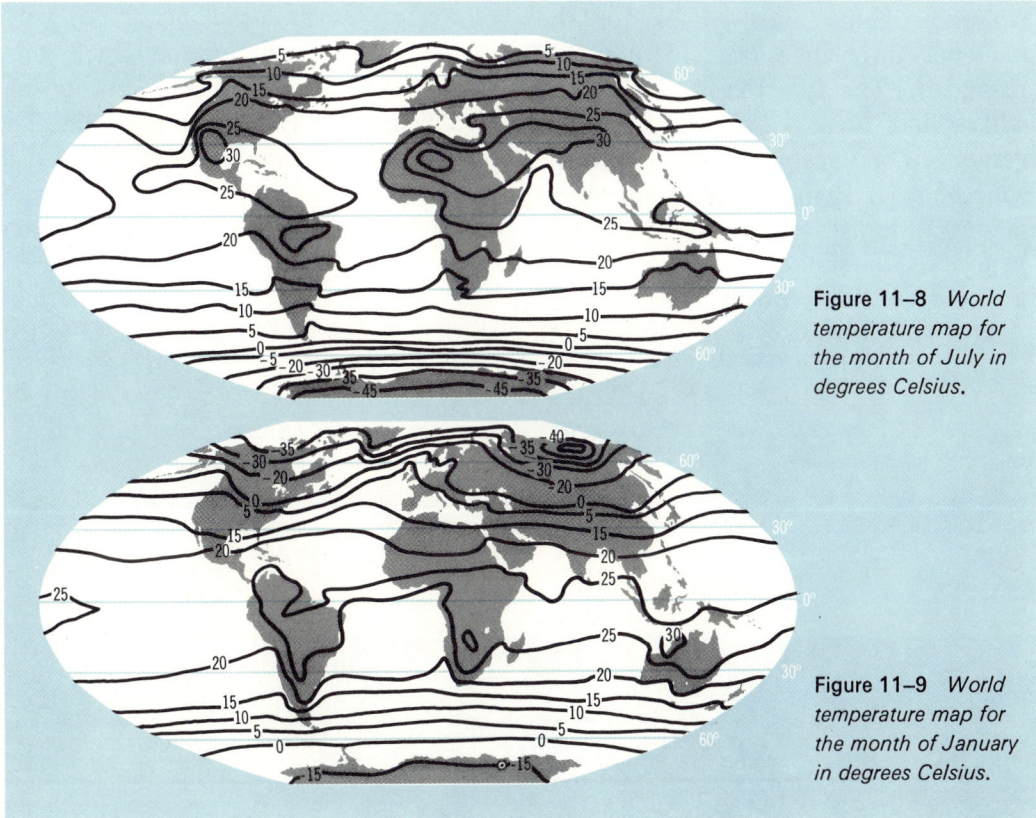

Figure 11–8 *World temperature map for the month of July in degrees Celsius.*

Figure 11–9 *World temperature map for the month of January in degrees Celsius.*

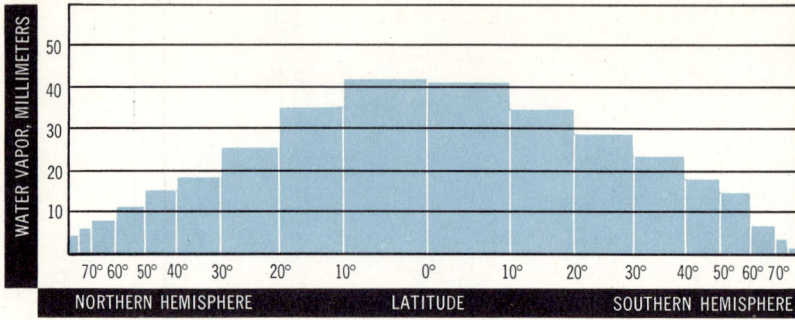

could be squeezed out of it over equatorial regions, about 40 millimeters of water would fall on the earth. Over middle latitudes and polar regions the amounts would be much smaller. At the North Pole it would be less than 5 millimeters. How much moisture could be squeezed out of the atmosphere at the latitude where you live?

The latitudinal distribution of precipitation and evaporation is shown in Figure 11–11. Concentrate first on the precipitation (blue line). Look for the influence of the zones of converging and rising air. The symbols at the bottom will remind you of the Intertropical Convergence Zone near the equator and the zone of polar front activity about 40 to 50 degrees north and south. What happens to the amount of moisture in the air as it rises in these zones?

Now look at the evaporation bars. At what latitudes is evaporation greatest, and why? What are the dominant air motions there? You can see from the graph that insolation is the principal factor controlling the amount and rate of evaporation on the surface of the earth. The curve sinks almost to zero at the poles where insolation is lowest. Air movement as a secondary factor helps to account for the higher evaporation rates at 10 to 20 degrees north and south latitude. How does air movement increase the rate of evaporation?

See if you can determine which zones of latitude have a water surplus and which zones have a water deficit. The zones of surplus moisture are related to converging and rising air and the zones with a deficit are related to sinking and diverging air.

Now look at the world map of precipitation shown in Figure 11–12. You can

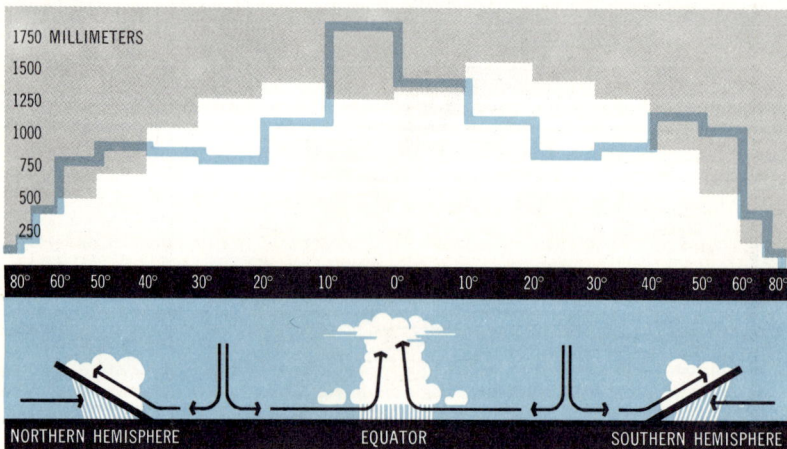

Figure 11–11 *Annual precipitation (blue line) and evaporation (white area) at various latitudes. The lower part of the diagram relates air movements to latitude.*

easily see the belt of heavy precipitation in the equatorial region. Can you see the zones of heavy precipitation at 40 to 50 degrees north and south? Notice the low rainfall zones at about 25 to 30 degrees north and south.

If you could lay the precipitation map on a map of potential evapotranspiration, you would have some idea of where the water deficit and surplus areas of the world are. What do we call a climate with a moisture deficit? Look at Figure 11–13. A **dry climate** is one in which precipitation is less than potential evapotranspiration. In other words it is where there is a moisture deficit for the year. A **desert** is a place with a large moisture deficit. Deserts are generally found in the core of dry climate regions. All places outside the

dry climates shown in Figure 11–13 have an annual moisture surplus and are considered humid.

Can you explain the location of the areas with a water deficit in Figure 11–13? Compare figures 11–12 and 11–13. Notice that the low precipitation zone of the desert regions extends across northern North America and northern Asia in Figure 11–12. The northern parts of these continents receive the same amounts of rainfall as the desert regions and yet do not exhibit a moisture deficit. The reason is that temperatures (and therefore evaporation) are so low that even the small amount of precipitation that does come is greater than the evaporation. Why is evaporation so low? Which part of Investigation 8–2 provided evidence for your answer?

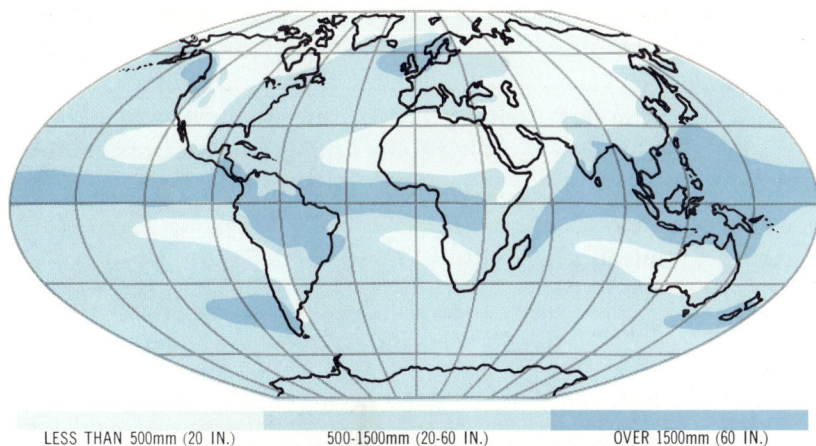

Figure 11–12 *Total annual precipitation of the world.*

LESS THAN 500mm (20 IN.)   500-1500mm (20-60 IN.)   OVER 1500mm (60 IN.)

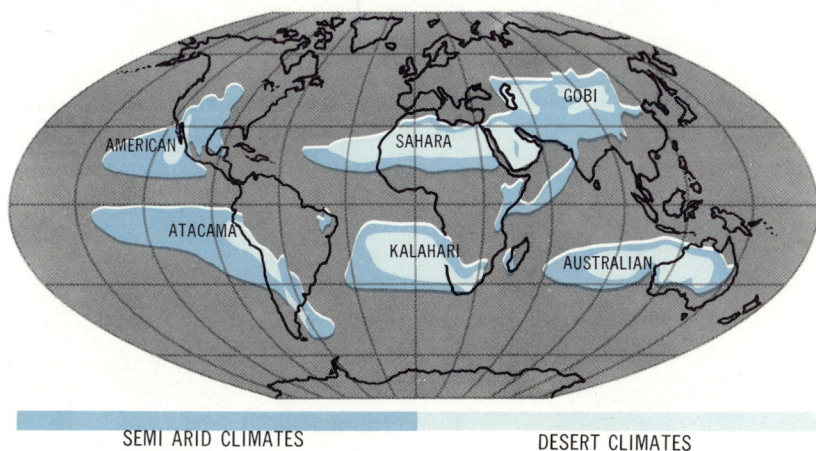

Figure 11–13 *Areas of the world with a moisture deficit, or a dry climate. Names of major deserts are given.*

SEMI ARID CLIMATES   DESERT CLIMATES

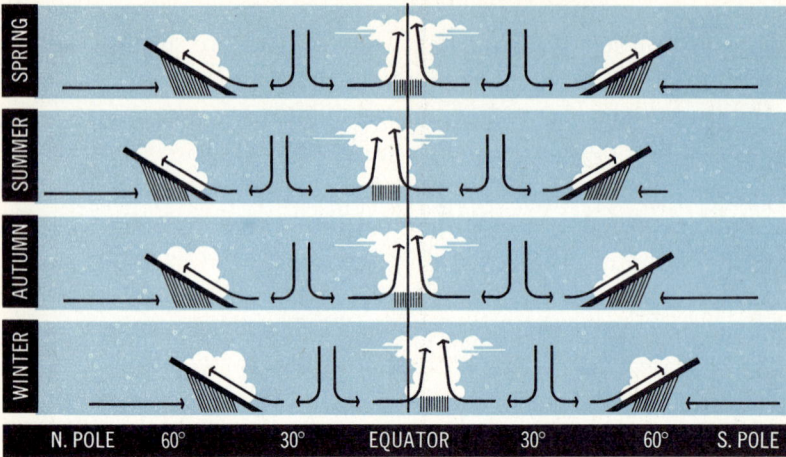

Figure 11–14
Seasonal shifting of the zones of convergence and divergence. (See Figure 8–8.) Names of seasons at far left refer to the Northern Hemisphere. Can you identify the seasons for the Southern Hemisphere?

You learned in Section 7–11 how the pressure and wind systems that produce the zones of converging and rising air follow the sun in its apparent motion north and south across the equator from season to season. (See figures 7–17 and 7–18.) While some parts of the earth remain constantly wet or constantly dry, the shift of the zones of converging and rising air produces zones of prevailing summer or winter rains. These are shown in Figure 11–14. The Intertropical Convergence Zone moves across the equator into the Northern Hemisphere as spring turns to summer. Tropical storms bring rain to regions that have been dry during winter months. At the same time, the subtropical high also shifts northward, bringing dry weather to areas that have been receiving rain from cyclonic storms moving along the polar front. These storms then in turn affect regions nearer the poles.

As summer passes and winter approaches the movement is reversed. The wind and pressure belts shift southward with their accompanying clear and cloudy weather.

The zones of converging and rising air masses are normally quite cloudy. As you know, clouds may reflect as much as three-fourths of all the insolation

reaching them. (See Section 7–3.) Areas that are continually cloudy receive less energy at the earth's surface than do areas that are generally clear. Can you see in Figure 11–11 the influence of the cloudy regions?

We have seen that energy and moisture are arranged generally in latitudinal belts around the world. There are also interruptions in their basic pattern. What causes the interruptions? Do they have an orderly pattern?

Thought and Discussion . . .

1. Explain why energy is so important in climatic patterns.
2. How is the distribution of moisture related to energy patterns?
3. Explain why the simple classification of climate into tropical, temperate, and polar zones is or is not an adequate system.
4. On the map of dry climates in Figure 11–13, what do the lines separating dry climates from humid ones represent in terms of annual amounts of P and PE?
5. If you were to visit the following places in North Africa, when would you go to avoid the rainy season? Zungeru (10 degrees N), Timbuktu (17 degrees N), Mogador (32 degrees N). Which of the three would have the most precipitation? the least?

Near the coast of Norway (far left) the temperature varies much less from winter to summer than it does in the heart of Siberia at the same latitude. (Left, above) A summer scene near Verkhoyansk. (Left, below) A winter reindeer race in eastern Siberia.

Latitudinal Patterns Are Modified

11–5 Land and water influence the pattern.

It should be apparent by now that the basic latitudinal pattern of climate is interrupted considerably by the influence of oceans and continents. Both temperature and moisture patterns are affected.

Looking first at temperature conditions, turn to Figure 11–8 and follow along the 60 degree north latitude line. Write down the July temperatures you read over the Gulf of Alaska, over Central Canada, the Atlantic north of Great Britain, and eastern Asia. Write the values for the same points in January. (See Figure 11–9.) Now compute the difference in temperature from July to January for each of the four points.

Which location has the greatest annual range? Which has the least? Why? Do you suppose the moderating influence of the ocean has any effect on the seasonal climate of island or coastal areas? Compare the seasonal temperatures along 60 degrees south latitude. Is the temperature range here different from that along 60 degrees north latitude? Why?

The map of annual temperature range shows how much temperatures change from season to season. (See Figure 11–15.) Where are the areas of greatest temperature range? The interiors of continents are generally hot in summer and cold in winter. They are said to have **continental** climates. **Marine** climates have small temperature variations

Figure 11–15 Map of annual temperature ranges. Values indicate the difference in average temperature from warmest to coldest month (°C). Observe effects of land masses. Compare values for Norway and Siberia.

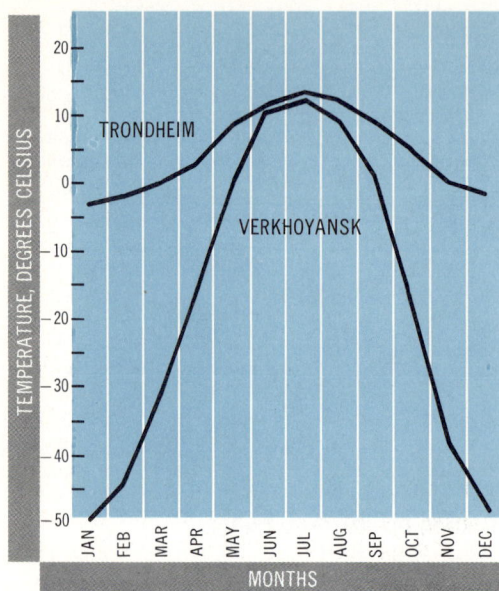

Figure 11–16 *Average monthly temperatures at Trondheim, Norway, and Verkhoyansk, U.S.S.R. Their latitudes are nearly the same.*

from winter to summer. The difference between continental and marine climates is seen graphically in Figure 11–16. Trondheim, Norway, has an annual temperature range of 17°C, whereas Verkhoyansk, at about the same latitude in Siberia, has a range almost four times as great (66°C). Similar comparisons can be made in North America and to some extent in Australia and Africa.

Two major moisture zones are broken by continents and oceans. One is the subtropical desert zone of 25 to 30 degrees latitude, north and south. The other is the high rainfall zone at 40 to 50 degrees latitude. (See Figure 11–12.) The region of heavy rainfall near the equator makes an almost continuous belt around the world; the sun is nearly always overhead, producing low pressure and convergence. The desert zone and polar front rainy zone are broken.

Why don't the deserts extend all the way across the continents to the eastern shore? The reason is seen in Figure 7–17, the air circulation map for July. On

the North American continent, notice the flow of air from the Atlantic Ocean across the southeastern United States. These warm, moist, and unstable air masses of summer bring abundant moisture and oppressive heat to central and eastern United States. At the same latitude on the western side of the continent lies the Great American Desert. The same situation exists in the summertime in southeast Asia so that the Sahara-Arabian desert does not reach the eastern coast of Asia. Similarly, the subtropical deserts fail to reach across the continents of the Southern Hemisphere at the same latitude.

The zone of polar front rainfall at 40 to 50 degrees latitude is also concentrated on the western side of continents. You can probably explain this if you recall the direction in which cyclones move along the front. Air masses forming over the Gulf of Alaska carry moisture inland to western Canada and the United States. In summer these air masses are relatively cool, and in winter relatively warm, but they are always moist. Therefore, the coastal areas of the western United States have high humidity and abundant rainfall. Similar conditions exist in northwest Europe.

As the cyclones move eastward across the continent, they drop most of their moisture before reaching the interior. Along the same latitude inland, the climate becomes continually drier as the cyclone continues to lose moisture. In the deep interior of the continent, far from ocean sources of moisture, there is little precipitation and little evapotranspiration. The air remains dry and the skies clear. The effects of these conditions are reflected on both the precipitation map and the moisture deficit map (figures 11–12 and 11–13) and help to explain the existence of such places as

Figure 11–17
Polar front cyclones bring almost 80 cm of moisture to the coast of France (right), while the Gobi Desert (far right), at the same latitude, receives less than 10 cm.

the Gobi Desert in Central Asia. (See Figure 11–17.)

Obviously the size of the continent has a good deal to do with both the moisture and the temperature range in the interior. The larger the continent, especially in middle latitudes, the greater the tem-

Figure 11–18 *Asian monsoons. Which diagram shows summer? winter? (Below) Conditions in India during the two seasons. Match photos and diagrams.*

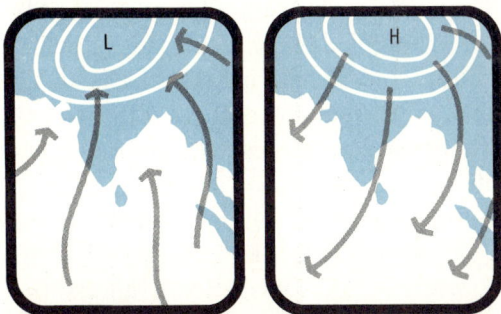

perature range and the greater the tendency for strong monsoons to develop. (See Section 7–11.) During the winter months over Asia, for example, the loss of energy from the land results in cold, dense air and high pressure. At this time the cold dry air flows off the continents. In summer, the flow of air is reversed and maritime air flows into areas of lower pressure over the continent. (See Figure 11–18.)

Ocean currents can also have an important influence on the temperature and moisture of land areas nearby. In the oceans, energy received during the summer is stored and released slowly. Warm water currents carry this energy poleward along the western sides of ocean basins. An air mass moving over the warm Gulf Stream, for example, will be warmed at the base, become unstable, and bring cloudiness to nearby land. By contrast, cold ocean currents flow equatorward near the west coasts of continents. An air mass moving toward the coast of southern California will be cooled at the base, become stable, and tend to resist vertical movement. Fog may result from condensation at the surface, but rain is unlikely.

Now you are in a position to summarize the basic pattern of moisture deficit areas of the world. You will find it very

Figure 11–19 *Transition from dry to wet regions in Africa. Is it a gradual or sharp transition?*

useful to become familiar with this pattern because it provides a simple framework around which the whole structure of world climates is arranged. The basic pattern of dry climates is repeated from continent to continent. This is why the imaginary continent is a suitable model.

Look first at the Northern Hemisphere in Figure 11–13. The desert regions on the western sides of the continents at 25 to 30 degrees latitude are caused by descending and diverging air of the subtropical high pressure. They do not extend to the eastern side because of the onshore summer flow of unstable air. Instead, the deserts extend poleward into the continental interiors. These interior deserts are caused simply by the great distance from ocean sources of moisture.

Keep in mind that the boundaries between moisture surplus and deficit regions are generally not sharp. They are transition zones where moist conditions gradually give way to dry ones. On the wet side, precipitation for the year is greater than potential evapotranspiration. On the dry side, it is less. A line may be drawn where the two values are equal. This line will shift back and forth somewhat from year to year. What you see on the map in Figure 11–13 is the long-term average condition. Figure

11–19 shows the gradual transition from dry to wet regions across Africa from north to south.

Transitions from dry to wet regions are generally gradual. However, certain topographic features like highlands and mountains can produce sharp boundaries between different climatic areas.

11–6 Mountains further modify the pattern.

Mountain barriers have marked effects on large-scale circulation patterns. They channel air movements and modify fronts and cyclones. During most of the winter, cold air moving out of Canada is forced to remain east of the Rocky Mountains as it penetrates into lower latitudes. Turn ahead to the color map of the world and you will see why this is so. (See pages 296–7.) The polar air of winter may sweep down across the central plains of North America as far south as the Gulf states, sometimes freezing citrus crops of Florida. The Rockies, however, usually prevent such bursts of continental air masses from damaging the citrus crops of California.

Mountains lying near the shores of an ocean also prevent marine air from penetrating far inland along the Pacific coast of North and South America and in other places in the world. What effect do you suppose the great Himalaya Mountains have on the cold dry air blowing out of the winter anticyclone over Asia? Do you think this helps to keep Indian winters mild? Northern China and Korea do not have such protection from cold winter winds off the continent.

Highlands also influence the amount and distribution of moisture. In mountain regions most of the precipitation will fall on the windward slopes of the topographic barriers. Little rain will fall on the leeward side of the mountains, and the drying effects of the downslope winds will increase the water deficit. This is shown in Figure 11–20. A dry area on the leeward side of a mountain barrier is said to lie in the **rain shadow** of the mountain. Can you see why the Mojave desert is so dry? Can you see why the dry region of interior North America crowds so close to the Pacific Ocean in contrast to that of Eurasia in the latitude of 40 to 50 degrees north?

Not only do mountains channel air flow and create rain shadows, but they also have a climate different from the surrounding regions. Have you ever gone skiing in the mountains? If so, you will recall how temperature changes with altitude. Places at higher elevations have lower average temperatures than places near sea level.

High mountains near the equator may have warm wet climates at low elevations. As you climb upward through the rain forest toward the mountain top, you will pass through a zone of temperate climates before reaching a zone that is

Figure 11–21 *Kilimanjaro, a snow-capped mountain (5970 meters) in equatorial Africa.*

always cold. Here, only a few miles above sea level, air temperatures are as low as they are in polar zones. (See Figure 11–21.) However, there is a considerable difference between a cold high-altitude climate in the tropics and a polar climate. In the tropics there is little change in the amount of energy received from the sun from one season to another but a great deal of change from day to night. In polar regions the greatest change in energy received is from season to season.

A person standing in the sunlight in a mountain location will sunburn easily and feel warm. However, when night falls or when he moves into a shady area he will feel cool. This is because greater amounts of insolation reach the earth's surface in mountain regions and long-wave earth radiation passes more easily out of the atmosphere at high altitudes. The atmosphere at these elevations contains few clouds and a small amount of water vapor, and there is only a thin layer of air above a person in the mountains. Thus, the rapid burning of the skin is caused by the large proportion of

Figure 11–20 *Cross section of Coast Ranges and the Sierra Nevada mountains in California shows a distinct variation in the amount of precipitation that the east and west slopes receive.*

| PACIFIC OCEAN | COASTAL RANGES | SAN JOAQUIN VALLEY | SIERRA NEVADA | WHITE MOUNTAINS | AMERICAN DESERT |

| SAN LUIS OBISPO 558.8mm | PARKFIELD 381.0mm | COALINGA 177.8mm | VISALIA 279.4mm | GIANT FOREST 1168.4mm | INDEPENDENCE 127.0mm | GREENLAND RANCH 50.8mm |

ultraviolet energy received from the sun. Much of the energy of these wavelengths is normally filtered out in the lower atmosphere.

In mountainous and hilly parts of the world there are great differences in the amounts of energy received and absorbed by slopes facing the sun and those that receive slanting rays or that are in the shade all day long. An example of the way these rays might strike the earth is shown in Figure 11–22. The most obvious response to varying insolation conditions in the mountains can be seen in the different growth of vegetation on sunny and shady slopes. The cooler shady slopes generally carry a denser plant cover because of the lower rates of evaporation and transpiration.

Thought and Discussion . . .

1. How do bodies of land and water affect air masses over them?
2. What are the principal characteristics of marine climates? of continental climates?
3. Why do isotherms over North America bend toward the equator in January and toward the Pole in July? (See figures 11–8 and 11–9.)
4. Which continent has the larger annual temperature range, Antarctica or Asia? Explain your answer.
5. Explain how the size of a continent may influence the amount of moisture reaching the interior.
6. Do you think the heating and cooling of land and water by day and by night can cause air flow to change back and forth on a local scale?

Figure 11–22 *The contrast between north and south facing slopes on a mountain. Arrows on the diagram represent the sun's rays.*

World Climatic Patterns

11–7 Return to the imaginary continent.

You made your observations for the Weather Watch at one point, your school. Do you know if the temperature and precipitation values that you recorded were the same as those at the nearest Weather Bureau station? If they were not, how do you account for the difference? How many weather stations would you need in order to observe all of the changes in weather and climate in your state? all of the changes in the entire United States?

Climatologists collect data from all the weather stations that record observations similar to those that you have made in the Weather Watch. These weather stations are located at points scattered over the surface of the earth. Climatologists must make inferences about the kind of climate that exists at points where there are no stations from those points where observations are available. Their inferences are based on temperature and moisture conditions, on an understanding of the processes that produce various kinds of climate, and on the global pattern of those processes. This is just what you will do as you reinvestigate the imaginary continent.

Procedure

Climate has been described as the summary of energy and moisture conditions at various places on earth. Earlier you identified climatic regions on the imaginary continent. In terms of what you have learned in this chapter, repeat the procedure and make a new climate map of the imaginary continent, as follows:

(1)Identify the major latitudinal zones of converging and diverging air masses. In each case, indicate which are the wet zones and which are the dry zones.

(2)Sketch in the boundaries between climatic regions on the imaginary continent. Start by outlining the moisture deficit regions. Label all regions as to both temperature and moisture conditions, such as hot, warm, cold, humid, dry.

(3)Match each climate graph in Figure 11–23, page 264, with a specific region on your imaginary continent. Include the climate graph of your own area.

(4)Match the climate graphs and the climatic regions on your map with the photographs in Figure 11–23.

(5)Explain the temperature and moisture conditions that would exist in each region in terms of the processes operating in the water cycle.

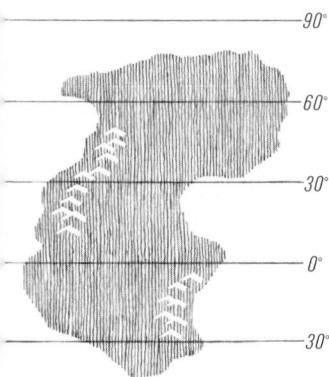

11–8 Investigating climates of the world.

Having investigated the climate of the imaginary continent, you can now apply this model to the earth itself.

Procedure

Each of the climate graphs that you used in Investigation 11–7 represents an actual location on earth. (1) On the world map provided, mark where you think each place might be. (2) Using the imaginary continent as a model, identify climatic zones of the world and draw in their boundaries. Be prepared to justify your work.

(3)Compare two places on the earth for each of the stations represented by the climate graphs 1 through 6 in Figure 11–23 on page 264 and by the climate graph representing your own location. Explain the influence at each place of such climatic controls as air circulation patterns, mountain barriers, ocean currents, and the size and shape of continents.

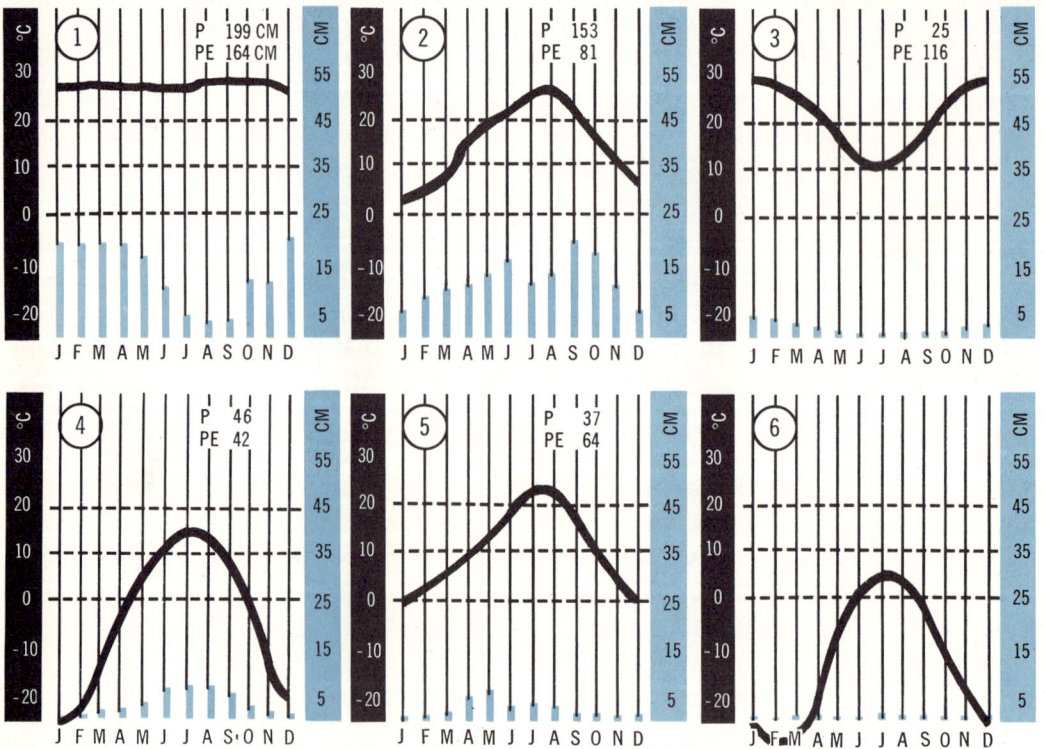

Figure 11–23

Thought and Discussion . . .

1. Which continent has a climatic pattern most like that of the model continent you worked with? Which continent has a completely different pattern? Why is it different?
2. What climatic changes would occur in northwest Europe if the Gulf Stream stopped flowing?
3. Two towns 30 miles apart in a western state recorded overnight lows of 18°C and −3°C. Where might these towns be located?
4. Which factor affects the climate of Kansas most, the shape of the continent or topography?

Unsolved Problems Scientists have been somewhat successful in causing precipitation to form in an area by cloud seeding. In this operation billions of very small crystals are released into the atmosphere from planes or from machines on the ground. These tiny crystals act as nuclei on which raindrops form. The resulting precipitation may be quite welcome to the people living in the area. What of the people in nearby areas? Would this moisture have precipitated on their fields and lawns if their neighbors in the adjacent county had not seeded the atmosphere? If men are successful in modifying the weather in one area, what effects will these changes have on other areas? If a hurricane is diverted to prevent damage in large cities, it may do increased damage to crops in another area. Is it possible to modify climate in one place without producing unfavorable changes in another location?

Can the climate of a place change? Reasonably reliable temperature and precipitation records of climate go back only about 100 years. Over this short period of earth history, these records indicate that the average values change and reveal trends to slightly higher or lower values. For example, the mean annual temperature at Philadelphia has increased about 1°C over the past 50 years. Over the same period in Iceland, the average temperature has increased about 5°C.

The forward margin of mountain glaciers through time provides us with another historical record of climatic change. The amount of ice stored in a glacier represents a temporary balance between precipitation income and availability of energy for melting ice. Records for the past 500 years from Alpine areas of Europe indicate clearly that the forward margins of glaciers have varied considerably in position. This suggests that energy and moisture income have varied at least slightly over the years to produce the changes in the amount of ice stored in the mountain glaciers.

Still another record provides indirect evidence that climates at particular places must have been much different at various times in the distant past than at present. This evidence comes primarily from fossil plants and animals buried in the rocks and from the texture and composition of the rock materials themselves. It suggests that there were times in the past when the polar regions supported animals and plants similar to those now found in the middle latitudes. What could have caused such astounding changes in climate?

A glaciologist examines a gaping crevasse in an alpine glacier. Notice the annual layering in the wall of the crevasse. Can you suggest the cause of the layering?

CHAPTER REVIEW

Summary

Climate can be thought of as the summary of weather history. Whereas weather is an actual occurrence, climate is only statistical—a generalization from weather records over a long period of time. Energy and moisture are the principal elements of climate and of the water cycle. Climatic regions result from the interaction of energy and moisture patterns of the water cycle.

The global pattern of climates is basically latitudinal because the angle of incidence and length of day are the two principal factors in determining energy receipt at places on the surface of the earth. Energy determines air motion. Together energy and air motion regulate the amount of moisture in the air and determine where it goes. Consequently, the moisture pattern is basically latitudinal and is associated with rising or sinking air. In the equatorial belt where the trade winds converge, the air rises, producing heavy precipitation. At about 25 to 30 degrees latitude the air sinks and diverges, resulting in low rainfall and a moisture deficit. At 40 to 50 degrees latitude, warm subtropical air meets cold air at the polar front. Warm air rising along the polar front produces precipitation. Cold air sinking at the polar zone is very dry and yields little precipitation.

The latitudinal pattern of climate is modified mainly by the influence of continents and oceans. The different rates of absorption of energy by land and water cause variations in temperature. For this reason continental climates have a wider range of temperature than marine climates. Continents tend to divert air flow and also interrupt the moisture patterns. The low rainfall zone at 25 to 30 degrees latitude and the high rainfall zone at 40 to 50 degrees latitude are restricted to the western sides of continents. The resulting pattern of climates is quite consistent from one continent to another. Hence, a model continent can serve as a useful tool to describe a basic regional pattern of climate. This pattern is further modified to some extent by the presence of mountain barriers.

The conditions of the atmosphere are constantly changing in time and space. However, the processes that operate to promote change in the atmosphere from place to place operate more or less uniformly from year to year. Hence, the dry and the wet places on the earth remain essentially in the same position from year to year. Thus, it is possible to establish core areas of desert climates, of wet tropical climates, and of other types of climates. Away from the core areas one climatic zone merges into the next. The transition zones are generally broad unless a mountain barrier separates one climatic area from another.

Questions and Problems

A

1. How does the length of day affect the amount of energy received at any point on the surface of the earth?
2. Explain the meaning of the term *angle of incidence*.
3. In what parts of the earth is potential evapotranspiration the greatest? the least? Explain the location of each.
4. How would you define a humid climate?
5. How do mountains affect rainfall?
6. How do mountains affect the movement of air masses?
7. What is meant by the idea that tropical areas have daily climates?

B

1. Why do climatologists make use of the natural vegetation as a significant factor in drawing the boundaries of the climates of the world?
2. What happens to the pressure and wind systems of the world as the path of the sun shifts north and south across the equator during the years?
3. How would you determine which parts of the earth have a dry climate?

4. What would you say the factors are that determine the climate of a region?

5. Do you think that the boundaries of climatic regions over the oceans can be defined with any degree of precision? Why or why not?

6. Are regions in the belt of the westerlies that lie to the west of mountain barriers likely to be cloudier or sunnier than regions to the east? Why?

7. What is meant by the term *rain shadow?* Why do such areas exist?

8. Why do not trees grow in polar regions and on the tops of high mountains?

C

1. What is a monsoon? In what regions do they commonly occur, and what causes them?

2. In which climatic regions are the greatest seasonal contrasts in precipitation found? the smallest? Explain why this is the case.

3. In which climatic regions are the greatest seasonal ranges in temperature found? the smallest? Explain why this is so in terms of what happens to solar energy reaching the surface.

4. In what way are the climates of a high mountain region similar to those of a polar region? In what way are mountain and polar climates dissimilar?

Suggested Readings

BOOKS

Ault, Philip. *This is the Desert.* Dodd, Mead & Co., New York, 1959.

Forrester, Frank H. *1001 Questions Answered About the Weather.* Dodd, Mead & Co., New York, 1957.

Frank, Ross, Jr. *Ice Island: The Story of Antarctica,* Thomas Y. Crowell Company, New York, 1957.

Schneider, Herman. *Everyday Weather and How It Works.* McGraw-Hill Book Company, New York, 1961. Page 133.

Strahler, Arthur N. *Introduction to Physical Geography.* John Wiley & Sons, Inc., New York, 1965. Chapter 7.

PERIODICALS

Hidore, John J. "An Introduction to the Classification of Climates." *The Journal of Geography,* February, 1966.

Kendall, Henry M. "Notes on Climatic Boundaries in the Eastern United States." *Geographical Review,* January, 1935. Pages 117–124.

Maunder, W. J. "A Human Classification of Climates." *Weather,* January, 1962, Pages 3–12.

Opik, Ernst J. "Climate and the Changing Sun." *Scientific American,* June, 1958. (Also Scientific American Offprint #835, W. H. Freeman & Co., Publishers, San Francisco.)

Plass, Gilbert N. "Carbon Dioxide and Climate." *Scientific American,* July, 1959. (Also Scientific American Offprint #823.)

Wexler, Harry. "Volcanoes and World Climate." *Scientific American,* April, 1952.

Went, Frits W. "Climate and Agriculture." *Scientific American,* June, 1957. (Also Scientific American Offprint #852.)

The development of a cloud seeded with silver iodide crystals over the Caribbean Sea in August, 1963. The series of photos was taken in 38 minutes from the time of seeding at the left to the cloud at the right.

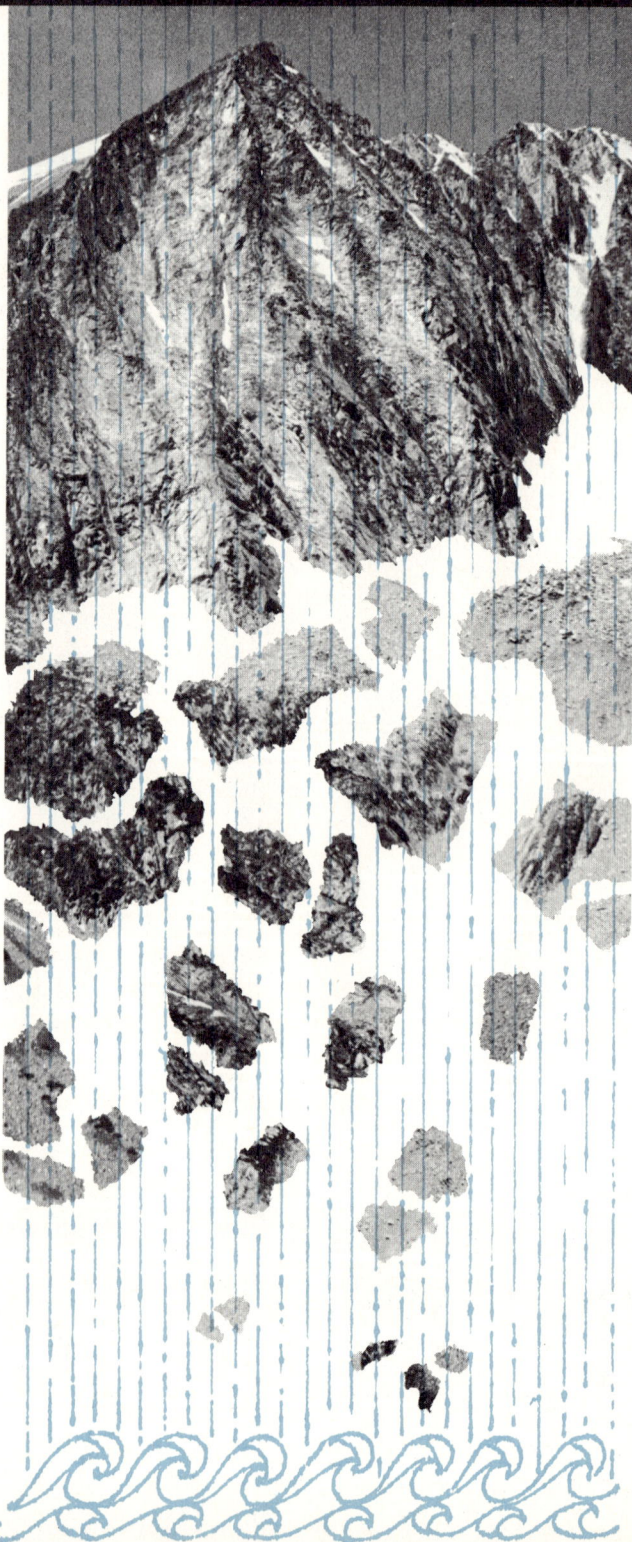

Chapter 12
The Land Wears Away

A summer storm darkens the bright blue sky. Lightning flashes and thunder rolls. Rain, perhaps mixed with hail, begins to fall, sounding like a thousand pebbles rattling and clattering against the ground. You can watch a normal quiet stream become a raging torrent of dirty swirling water overflowing its banks and cutting a new channel. When you see this, you are witnessing a dramatic way in which the land's surface is worn down. The land is also worn down in ways that you are not likely to notice. You seldom observe the slow movement of a glacier carving a mountain valley or the gradual movement of sand grains down a mountain stream.

In the high mountains of the world, when the temperature falls below freezing at night, the clatter of falling rocks can be heard. The rock pieces come to rest at the base of a mountain cliff. How long will they remain there? Will the force of gravity cause this material to move to still lower elevations?

Away from the cliff the slope is more gentle. Broken rock materials may remain there for a long time. Soil may also be found supporting trees and other plants. Where did this soil cover come from? Why hasn't it washed away? The changes involved in the wearing away of the land take place where rocks are exposed to the atmosphere and hydrosphere. Since you live at this interface, you can see evidence of these changes.

Large fragments of rock can be found near a rock exposure or in nearby stream beds. Smaller particles of rock muddy the waters of these streams and are sometimes carried many kilometers from the rock exposure. Stream waters also contain materials dissolved from the exposed rock. The finer materials and the dissolved ions in the water will eventually reach the sea. A calcium ion from a rock high on a mountain may become part of a growing coral reef in the ocean. What processes cause large rocks to be reduced to small particles and ions that can be transported for thousands of kilometers?

Weathering—The Response of Rocks to a New Environment

12–1 Weathering brings about changes.

Most rocks form at depth in environments very different from those that exist at the earth's surface. Temperature and pressure increase with depth in the earth's crust. When rocks formed under these conditions become uncovered and exposed to the hydrosphere and the atmosphere, they must adjust to their new environment. The adjustments that take place are called **weathering.**

When you examine the rock fragments, sand, and mud that result from weathering, it might seem as though weathering should be called a destructive process. It is true that rocks are destroyed by weathering, but the materials of which they are made are certainly not. Indeed, as you will discover, new minerals can be formed in a weathering environment.

Weathering occurs not only at the earth's surface but also at any depth penetrated by air and water. Geologists recognize two main types of weathering processes, physical and chemical. Physical processes work on rocks to make little ones out of big ones without changing

the composition of the rock. (See Figure 12–1.) Chemical processes work slowly but continuously to decompose rocks by chemically altering the minerals of which they are made.

Although physical and chemical weathering operate together, we can for convenience focus attention on one or the other individually. Expansion of water as it freezes in the cracks of rocks is an example of a physical process by which rocks are broken apart. Water in rocks freezes almost every night at high elevations in the mountains such as those shown in the introductory photograph. The water may thaw again the

Figure 12–1 *This rock was uplifted and eroded, reducing the pressure of overlying rock. The bedrock moved and expanded, producing cracks and breaks. Will these cracks affect further weathering?*

Figure 12–2 *Tree roots grow into cracks in rocks. As they grow larger, they exert tremendous pressure and further break down the rock.*

Chemical weathering processes attack certain minerals in a rock more readily than others. The loss of the more easily weathered minerals results in the formation of pits and cracks in rocks. In time, the remaining material may become little more than a skeleton of the original rocks. Such rocks can easily be broken apart. Since chemical weathering occurs on mineral surfaces, it is aided by physical weathering that reduces the size of rock fragments and increases the amount of surface area. Physical and chemical weathering processes almost always work together to break down rocks, the first stage in wearing down the land.

12–2 Water aids weathering.

In Section 2–5 you learned how the dipolar nature of the water molecule accounts for its solvent or dissolving power. The way in which molecules of water aid in *solution*, one type of chemical weathering, is illustrated in Figure 2–16. Solution results in the removal of ions from minerals in rocks and thus causes their chemical breakdown. A compound like sodium chloride (halite) dissolves readily in water. Most earth materials do not dissolve as easily as halite, however, so chemical weathering works slowly.

Water alone is a powerful solvent, but the addition of other natural chemical

next day. How does repeated freezing and thawing help break the rocks? The rocks in Figure 12–2 have been wedged and broken by the growing tree roots. Is this physical or chemical weathering?

The breaking of large rocks into smaller rocks exposes new surfaces and speeds up chemical weathering. How much will the surface area increase if a cube one centimeter on each edge is cut into two equal parts and then into eight equal parts as shown in Figure 12–3? By what natural processes could a piece of rock be broken up to produce an increase in surface area that is as large as that shown in Figure 12–4?

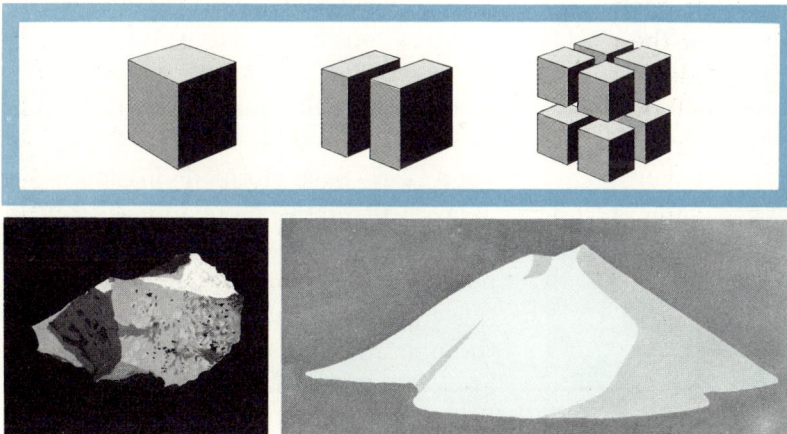

Figure 12–3 *By dividing the cube (top), more surface area is exposed.*

Figure 12–4 *When a cube of rock is weathered to clay-sized particles (below), the total surface area may be increased up to 10,000 times.*

agents such as oxygen and carbon dioxide make water even more effective as a weathering agent. Oxygen from the air dissolves easily in the film of water that surrounds rock particles. The most familiar product of the combination of oxygen with an element during weathering is iron oxide or rust. For example, iron atoms released in the weathering of olivine might combine with oxygen in water to form iron oxide. This iron oxide might then exist as a coating or stain on mineral grains in the weathering zone. Iron staining is one of the most common causes of color in rock exposures. If much oxygen is available, iron stains are yellow or red; if oxygen is not plentiful in the environment, the stains are blue-gray in color. (See photos on page 278.)

ACTIVITY *Moisten some steel wool and wrap it in a piece of plastic or place it in a closed container so it will not dry out. Observe the steel wool for several days. What has been formed? How? Is the "weathered" steel wool easier to break into pieces than the original steel wool? If so, why?*

Figure 12–6 *Plants like lichen and mosses are the first to grow on exposed rocks when weathering begins. They can exist with very little moisture for years at a time.*

Whenever you breathe, you bring about a change in the composition of the air. When oxygen is used by your body and by the living cells of all plants and animals, carbon dioxide is given off. You know that carbon dioxide can be dissolved in water since it is present in every carbonated drink. Warm water holds less carbon dioxide than cold water, so a bottle of warm pop usually bubbles over when opened as the carbon dioxide escapes. Why? The fact that carbonic acid is formed when carbon dioxide dissolves in water is of great importance to the weathering process. (See Figure 12–5.) Hydrogen ions released by carbonic acid (H_2CO_3) have a stronger positive charge than dipolar water molecules. A faster removal or replacement of the mineral atoms results. Large caverns like the one shown on page 278 have formed in limestone as a result of the more intense solvent action of water that contained acid. Removal of the more soluble materials in this manner by water percolating through rocks is called **leaching**. The loss of materials from a weathering zone may contribute to the formation of new

Figure 12–5 *Plant roots give off carbon dioxide that dissolves in the film of water covering both roots and mineral particles. The carbonic acid releases hydrogen ions and increases the rate of chemical weathering.*

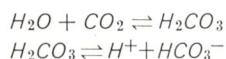

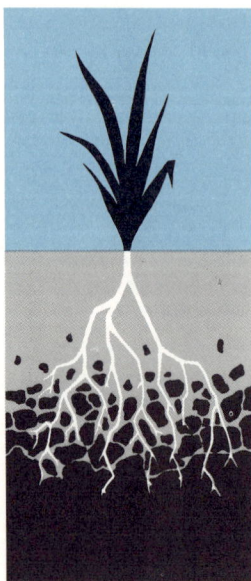

$$H_2O + CO_2 \rightleftharpoons H_2CO_3$$
$$H_2CO_3 \rightleftharpoons H^+ + HCO_3^-$$

Figure 12–7 *What weathering processes produced the results shown in these photographs? Do any of these involve both physical and chemical processes?*

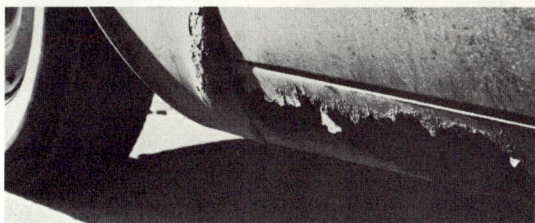

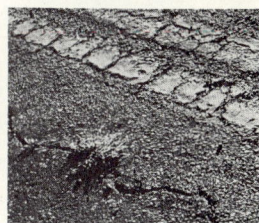

minerals at another location. Where might the dissolved limestone materials go? What might they form?

Some carbon dioxide is dissolved from the air as rain falls. A greater source is the carbon dioxide given off by the respiration (breathing) of plants and animals. Plant leaves use carbon dioxide and give off oxygen during photosynthesis. The roots of plants do not carry on photosynthesis. They are always respiring, however, so that they release a continuous and abundant supply of carbon dioxide into the soil.

Plant roots are in contact with rock and mineral fragments, as shown in Figure 12–5. Both roots and rock particles are usually coated with a very thin film of water molecules. When carbon dioxide produced by plant respiration combines with this water, the hydrogen ions from the resulting carbonic acid trade places with ions in minerals like calcium and potassium. The calcium and potassium ions that are released in this process may then be absorbed by roots and used for plant growth.

The lichen (LY-ken) growing on exposed rock in Figure 12–6 carry on both photosynthesis and respiration. Lichen release carbon dioxide on the rock surface, which aids weathering and allows the lichen to grow where other plants cannot survive. As weathering continues, weathered debris and organic matter accumulate and support other types of vegetation.

The remains of dead plants and animals may be decomposed by microscopic organisms like bacteria. These microorganisms also respire and contribute carbon dioxide to the weathering environment. The dead plant and animal debris is eventually reduced to very fine particles that adhere to the surfaces of mineral grains. For this reason the uppermost layer in a weathering environment may become dark-colored when sufficient organic matter has accumulated. Generally, only a small percent of organic matter is needed to color soil black or brown. (See photos, page 278.)

Examples of the role of water in weathering are everywhere. Can you give the causes of weathering for each object in Figure 12–7? Name some other examples of weathering that you can observe going on around you.

12–3 Investigating products of weathering.

Weathering of granite results in the products shown in Figure 12–8. Granite is a useful example because much of the soil material on the land comes from granitic rocks. What are the common minerals in granite? (Review Section 2–2.)

Figure 12–8 (Right) The products of weathered granite. Minerals weather at different rates. The least resistant minerals form colloids and ions.

Figure 12–9 A soil formed from the weathering of fine-grained limestone (below) and soil formed from granite (bottom).

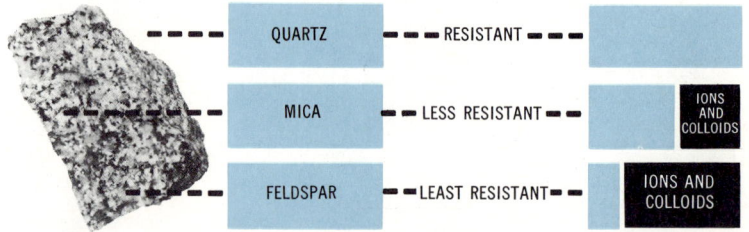

Different minerals weather at different rates in the same environment. Those minerals that weather most slowly remain as fragments whereas the ones that weather more rapidly form colloids and ions. **Colloids** are particles small enough to remain suspended in water for long periods of time. If the products of weathering remain in place, a soil develops. (See Figure 12–9.) Minerals that weather easily produce materials that are washed away, leaving the resistant minerals behind.

Sometimes these remaining resistant minerals accumulate as weathered soil material is moved to lower levels in streams and rivers. Quartz, which is a very common mineral, is resistant to weathering in all climates. Where would you expect to find an accumulation of quartz particles? Where could these particles have come from?

Aluminum, silicon, and iron may be released from minerals during weathering as oxides that do not dissolve in water. These oxides may exist in the soil as colloidal particles. Frequently aluminum, silicon, and oxygen of the parent material recombine to form a group of silicates called clay minerals. Clay minerals have a strong tendency to pick up potassium ions released during weathering. Clay minerals are frequently colloidal in size. The formation of clay minerals in a soil is one of the reasons for not referring to weathering as a wholly destructive process. The weathering process is like wrecking a building and using the pieces to make a different structure. In this investigation you will examine the products that accumulate when weathering occurs in place and only ions and colloids are transported.

Procedure

Examine the granite and the two soil layers provided for you. (1)How are they similar and how are they different?

(2) Can you identify a mineral that exists in the granite and the two soil layers?

Put a half teaspoonful of each material in a test tube with water. Shake the test tubes and let the materials settle. Discuss the results.

The soil layers you received were formed on granite. (3) Which of the two soil samples that you have examined was taken from the top layer?

Thought and Discussion . . .

1. Why do rocks weather?
2. How does physical weathering aid in chemical weathering?
3. How is carbonic acid produced and how does it affect weathering?
4. Why are many earth materials red in color? What element commonly produces color in earth materials?
5. In what ways do soils differ from the rocks from which they formed?

Mature Soils—A Further Response to Environment

12–4 How do mature soils evolve?

When weathering and soil formation begin, there is only one type of material, the unweathered rock, represented by part A of Figure 12–10. Soils represented by parts B and C are immature soils. What layer is found in mature soils, part D, that is missing in immature soils? How does this layer form?

You have just seen that the layer of loose weathered material increases in thickness as soils are subjected to longer periods of weathering. In Chapter 9 you learned that some of the water that falls on the land enters the soil and moves downward to the underground water reservoir. This water leaches away the more soluble materials as ions in solution. As weathering continues, the colloid content of the soil increases and produces some important changes. Some of the colloidal particles are carried downward

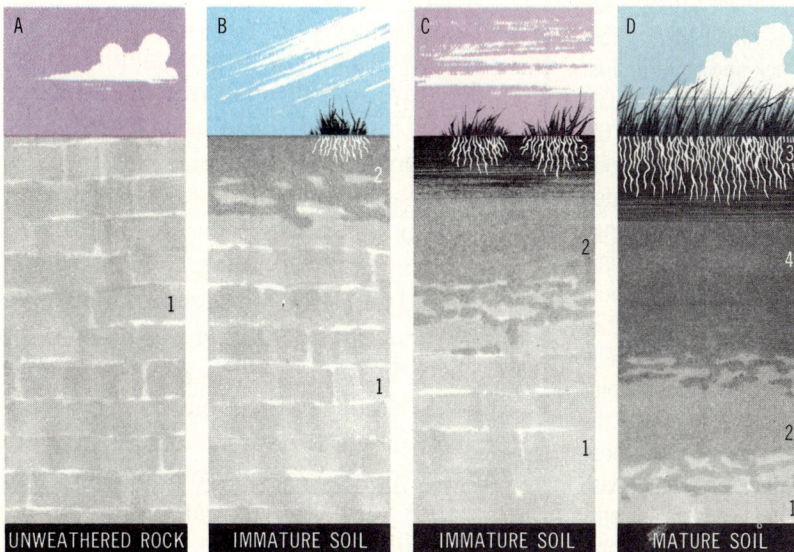

UNWEATHERED ROCK   IMMATURE SOIL   IMMATURE SOIL   MATURE SOIL

Figure 12–10
*Stages in the development of mature soils from rocks.
(1) Unweathered rock, (2) weathered rock, (3) topsoil, (4) accumulation of clay and soluble minerals. What factors would affect the time it takes to develop a mature soil?*

Eugene W. Hilgard

The productivity of American agriculture is in large part due to the rapid development of soil science during the nineteenth century. This development took place under the leadership of men like Eugene W. Hilgard (1833–1916). Hilgard established one of the nation's first agricultural experiment stations, at the University of California, where he went as a professor in 1874. He appears to have been the first scientist to recognize soil as an independent natural body divided into distinctive layers rather than simply broken pieces of rock and plant debris.

His book, Soils, is still valuable today. Hilgard was among the first to suggest that the kind of soil profile that developed in a region reflected the climate and vegetation. He related rainfall and temperature to processes that change parent material into soil, control leaching, influence plant growth, cause clay formation, and affect the accumulation of organic matter. Recognizing the relationship of soil and climate, Hilgard concluded that many ancient peoples lived along the margins of deserts because the soils there were so rich. He believed that these ancient peoples found irrigation of the otherwise fertile desert easier than supplying plant nutrients to the less fertile soils of the humid regions.

by the water as it moves through the topsoil. Because they are not dissolved, the colloidal particles are caught in very small pores or cracks as they are carried downward. Differences in acidity and other chemical factors in the topsoil and the layer underneath may cause colloidal particles to clump together. These clumps are easily trapped as they move downward. A colloid-enriched layer called the **subsoil** forms underneath the topsoil. When this subsoil layer is well developed, the soil profile is said to be mature. What effect will the continued accumulation of colloids in the subsoil have on permeability?

The amount of time required for rocks to weather and for a mature soil to form depends on the kind of rock and the environment. Where would you expect granite to weather faster, in a desert or a humid area? Why? Where would a soil form faster, on the surface of a solid granite mountain or on a pile of weathered granite? Why?

12–5 Mature soils reflect the climate in which they form.

Eugene Hilgard considered climate the dominant factor in the formation of soils. This American soil specialist found that in a given climatic region similar kinds of mature soils develop from a variety of parent materials. He recognized that differences in rainfall and temperature affect soil development. How might they do so?

Chemical weathering processes are speeded up as the temperature increases. The amount of water available for weathering and the amount of water that moves through the soil carrying dissolved material depends on the climate of a region. Water also influences the amount of colloidal material and ions that will be moved out of the topsoil.

Leaching removes soluble plant nutrients from the soil. Why does leaching cause the soil in humid regions to become less fertile?

Thus, climate directly influences soil formation through moisture and temperature. It also has an indirect influence through vegetation. Vegetation is such an important factor in soil-forming processes that soil types are often referred to by the type of plant cover. In the United States, for example, the soils could be grouped into three main types — forest, grassland, and desert — reflecting the three climatic categories, humid, subhumid, and arid. Figure 12–11 shows the distribution of these three soil types in 48 states. It also shows the relationship of these soils to vegetation and depth of leaching and weathering.

In humid regions the natural vegetation over most of the land is forest. A closeup view of a forest soil profile is shown at the lower right in Figure 12–11. Forest soil profiles usually have thin topsoils where organic matter has accumulated. The depth of the topsoil represents the depth to which earthworms and other agents have incorporated the leaves and wood that fell onto the top of the soil. Downward-moving water carries colloids and oxides containing iron, aluminum, and silicon to the subsoil. The iron oxides impart a red color to the subsoil. The aluminum and silicon are usually combined with potassium and water in the form of clay minerals that have a sheet structure like mica. Left behind just under the topsoil is a light-colored layer of resistant minerals. What mineral would be dominant there? Why is the layer light in color?

In subhumid regions the vegetation commonly consists of grass and shrubs. Where grass roots are abundant, they add large amounts of organic matter to

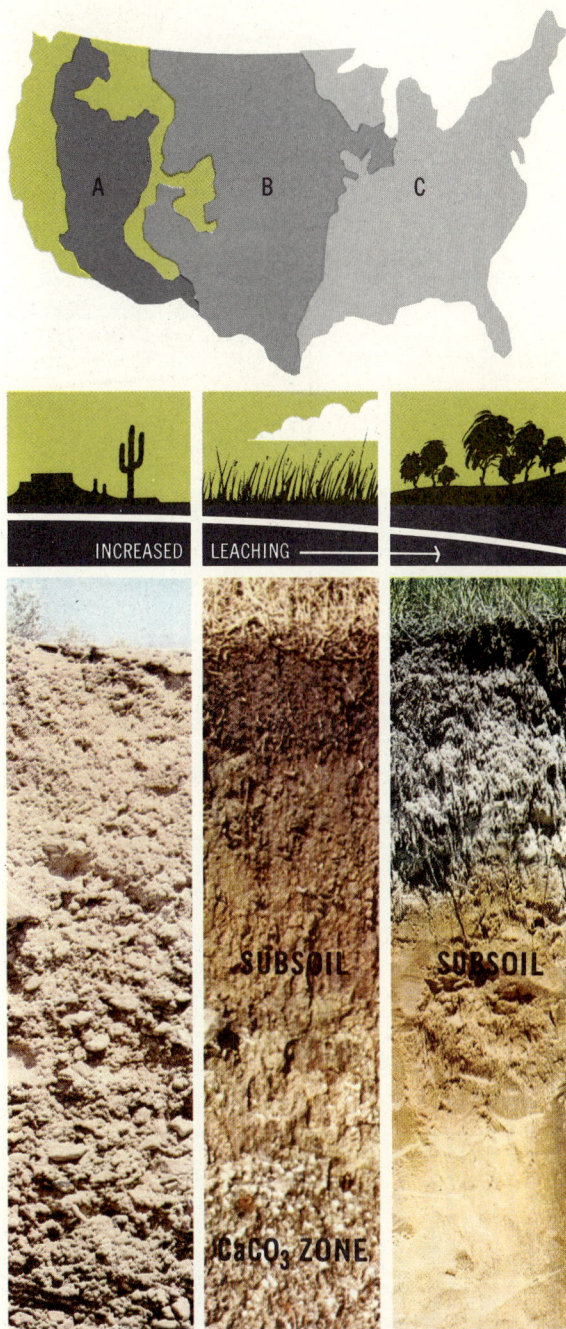

INCREASED LEACHING →

SUBSOIL

SUBSOIL

CaCO₃ ZONE

Figure 12–11 (Above) The distribution of the three main soil types in the United States and their relationship to the vegetation and depth of leaching. Colored areas on the map indicate complex mountain soils. Which soil is found in your part of the country? (Below) Sample profiles of the three main soil types. Can you explain their differences?

(*Above*) *What type of soil profile would you expect to find in each of the three areas?*
(*Below*) *Relate what you see in each photograph to a physical or chemical weathering process.*

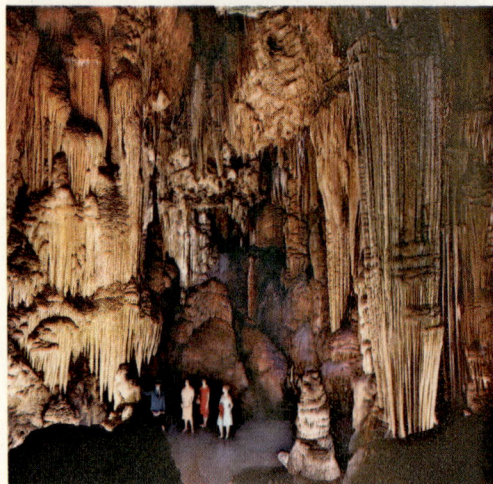

the soil to a depth of about half a meter. This results in thick, dark-colored topsoils as shown in the soil profile at the lower center in Figure 12–11. Grassland soils have subsoils that have been enriched with colloids just as have forest soils. Would you expect them to have as great a clay mineral content as forest soils? In subhumid regions, grassland soils usually have an additional accumulation zone in or underneath the subsoil. Soluble material leached from the upper layers is deposited in this zone because the precipitation is seldom great enough to carry it to lower depths. The soluble material is carried downward and deposited at the depth of water penetration at the wettest time of the year. The light color of this zone is derived from calcium carbonate accumulations. Can you suggest why this zone does not appear in the forest soil?

Because the plant nutrients are not leached out of the soil profile, grassland soils developed in subhumid regions are more fertile for agriculture than the forest soils of the humid regions. Recognizing this relationship between soil and climate, Hilgard concluded that many ancient peoples lived near the margins of deserts because of the richness of soils that were not leached.

Desert soils develop where there is little rainfall and where plant growth is sparse, as shown at the lower left in Figure 12–11. How would the rate of weathering in such areas compare with the rate in humid and subhumid regions? How would the content of organic matter, degree and depth of leaching, and the movement of colloids in desert soils differ from those in soils formed in the more humid regions? In desert areas the small amount of moisture that gets into the soil moves *upward* by capillary action rather than downward. Therefore soluble minerals often accumulate at or near the surface of desert soils.

Weathering and soil formation are the major processes that prepare the materials on the earth's surface for wearing away. In the next section you will learn the ways that products of weathering are transported to lower elevations.

Thought and Discussion . . .

1. How does subsoil differ from topsoil?
2. What is the difference between a mature and an immature soil?
3. Once a mature soil profile is fully developed, will any further noticeable changes take place?

Figure 12–12 *Which of the above streams would carry the most sediment?*

Erosion—A Response of Weathering Products to Gravity

12–6 Investigating factors in stream erosion.

How are the streams in Figure 12–12 different? Which one contains the most water? Which one has the greatest slope? When you begin investigating erosion it is important to understand the significance of the two variables, stream slope and stream volume. In this investigation you will test the effect that each of these variables has on erosion.

Procedure

Examine Figure 12–13. Using the equipment as shown, put 50 ml of gravelly sand in the trough. "Erode" the material from the trough with running water. Answer the following questions:

(1)What was the relationship between stream slope and rate of erosion? (2)What was the relationship between stream volume and rate of erosion? (3)How did the different sizes and shapes of the rock and mineral particles affect the way they were transported in the stream? (4)How could stream volume change in nature? stream slope?

Figure 12–13 *Investigating erosion.*

12–7 Investigating stream action.

The action of water when it falls on land is a major factor in shaping landscapes. Streams play an important role in erosion, since they are the channels for transporting material swept into them from valley slopes. In this investigation, you will observe the way streams behave and what effects they have as they flow over loose material.

Figure 12–14

Procedure

Set up the stream table as shown in Figure 12–14 with the soil arranged as indicated. Allow a stream of water to flow across the soil into the "pond" at the bottom. Observe the changes that take place on the land surface. Also observe the changes in the pond and any changes in the stream itself. Try to relate what you see to processes in nature.

12–8 Gravity drives erosion.

Suppose the products of weathering had accumulated where they developed for the billions of years since the earth formed. How would the appearance of the earth's surface differ from what you see around you? What evidence is there in Figure 12–15 that loose weathered material has been removed?

The process by which rock and soil particles are removed and transported to another place is called **erosion.** If you were asked what *causes* erosion, your answer would probably be water, ice, and wind. Yet if you think about it, you would realize that erosion might take place without the direct action of water, ice, or wind. In Figure 12–16 you see a boulder on a pinnacle. Suppose you pushed the boulder and dislodged it. It would roll down the slope. According to the definition, is this erosion? If so, what caused the erosion in this case— you or some other agent?

Earlier you learned that every object on earth is affected by the force of gravity. The boulder rolled down the hill because of its response to the earth's

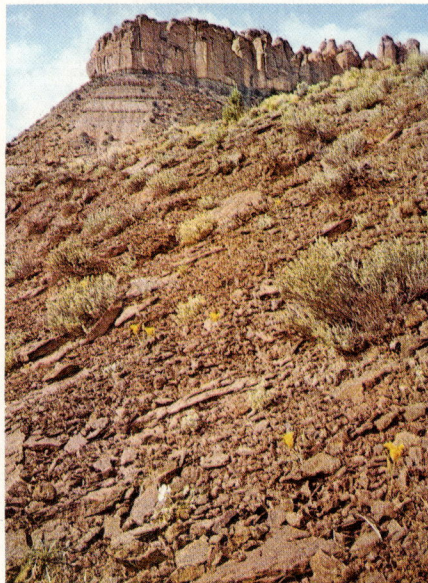

Figure 12–15 *Can you explain the influence of weathering and erosion in each of the photographs? How is gravity aiding erosion in each case? What causes the pinnacles in the two photos at the far right? In the upper photo the pinnacles are many meters high; in the lower photo, only 3 centimeters.*

Figure 12–16 (*Left*) The large boulder could roll down the valley. What energy change would occur if you started it rolling?

Figure 12–17 (*Top*) A landslide in Montana in 1959 dammed the Madison River and caused a lake to form.

Figure 12–18 (*Bottom*) Moist soil moves slowly downhill.

gravitational field. Therefore, gravity caused the erosion. You were simply an agent of the force of gravity. Water, ice, and wind are the natural agents of gravity that sculpture the earth's surface.

Gravity's role in erosion can be understood better by considering the example of the boulder more carefully. When the boulder is perched on the hillside, it has a certain amount of potential energy. As it rolls down the slope, it possesses kinetic energy. (See Section 6–3.) Where will the boulder stop rolling? When it stops, will it still have potential

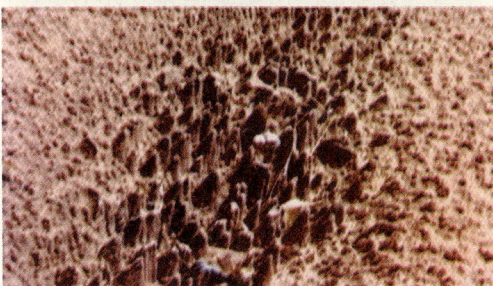

energy? Where would the boulder have to be to possess no potential energy?

Because of gravity, all objects on the earth's surface have a certain amount of potential energy. This potential energy gives all particles of loose material a tendency to move downward. In going from higher to lower places, materials reduce their potential energy. Since the boulder was unable to roll from its perch down the slope and all the way into the sea, it will still have a great deal of potential energy after it comes to rest. It may weather further and gradually be broken down so that its weathering products are eventually transported to lower elevations by the agents of erosion— water, ice, and wind.

A landslide such as the one shown in Figure 12–17 demonstrates the rapid movement of loose material under the influence of gravity. An example of a much slower shifting of weathered materials is shown in Figure 12–18. Gradual downward movement of the soil material results from the lubrication of soil particles by water and the pull of gravity. Freezing and thawing also help in this gradual downward movement.

In addition to the large-scale downslope movement of material by falling boulders, land slides, and creep, a tremendous amount of movement takes place on a much smaller scale. Billions of individual sand and soil particles respond to the pull of gravity and shift downslope each day. Very little of this type of movement is accomplished without assistance by water and ice.

When you look at a stream valley, you may assume that erosion is occurring primarily in the stream channel. However, if you understand the role of gravity, you can see that most of the erosion is taking place on the valley slopes. The stream is really a sort of conveyor belt that carries away the material from the walls of the valley. (See Figure 12–19.)

Streams that transport material away from the weathering environment are also controlled by gravity. Since water is a fluid, it moves easily in response to gravity. After being carried to high places on the earth's surface by the atmosphere, water flows down over the slopes into stream channels. Water moves to levels of lower potential energy in response to gravity. In doing so, it modifies the surface of the land over which it flows.

Gravity also controls the other agents of erosion, ice and wind. Can you explain how gravity does this?

12–9 Water, ice, and wind wear down the land.

It is through the action of water, wind, and ice in response to gravity that erosion occurs. These agents relentlessly wear down the land and transport loose material from the land to the sea. The journey for most mineral and rock particles is long and winding. A particle might come to rest in a given place for thousands of years before it is picked up again and moved along. This process may be repeated many times before ma-

Figure 12–19 *Movement of materials in response to gravity and running water feed material to streams for transportation toward sea level. The stream acts as a conveyor belt.*

terial loosened from a mountain cliff eventually reaches the sea.

Soil may be considered as a temporary depository of weathered material. Soil may form on solid rock or it may be formed on sediments that are deposited on their way to the sea. The amount of soil now on the land is the difference between the amount of soil produced by weathering and the amount of soil that has been removed by erosion. Why are thin, rocky soils commonly found in mountainous regions?

After an intense rainstorm, a field without a cover of vegetation appeared as shown at the bottom left in Figure 12–20. Do the photographs above explain what happened? Erosion is a problem on many farmlands because the land does not have a sufficient vegetative cover to protect the soil. The material removed eventually washes or tumbles into rivers or streams.

The particles of minerals and rocks that enter a stream give it a muddy ap-

Figure 12–20 *Effect of a severe rainstorm (above left) on unprotected soil (left). Note the pinnacles of soil protected by stones. Closeup photos (above) show impact of raindrops.*

pearance. In a large river, this visible load of material may be of tremendous volume. The Mississippi River, for example, carries as much as two million tons of such sediment to the Gulf of Mexico each day. Not all of the material moved by a stream is suspended in the water. Fragments too large for the stream to carry are rolled or bounced along the bottom as shown in Figure 12–21. As they roll or bounce on the stream bed, the fragments strike other particles or perhaps the solid stream bed. When they bounce along, either the particles themselves or other materials in the stream bed may be broken. The newly broken pieces may then be carried farther. The rolling, bouncing particles are like tools, breaking, grinding, and eroding each other and the surfaces of other rocks. Compare the appearance of the rocks in Figure 12–21 with what happened in Investigation 1–4.

A stream's capacity to erode or to deposit material changes from time to time. During flood time a stream can carry more material and larger particles than it can at a normal stage. As flood

Figure 12–21 (*Above*) *Rocks in a stream bed.* (*Left*) *Movement of particles in a stream. Large fragments roll and bounce.* (*Right*) *Enlarged view of stream load. Fine particles are suspended; larger ones settle.*

waters recede and velocity decreases, first pebbles and then smaller particles stop moving. Next, sand settles to the stream bed and is no longer dragged or rolled along the bottom. Finally, only fine silt and clay remain suspended in the water. If the velocity decreases still more, some of these fine particles will be deposited. A stream does not always flow at the same velocity, nor is the velocity the same from one end of the stream to the other. Depending on variations in its velocity, a stream erodes material in some places and deposits it in others.

All streams carry an invisible load of ions in solution. Some streams carry more than others because the volume of this chemical load depends on the kind of rock and soil in the area that feeds the stream. These ions are transported along with suspended particles and eventually reach the sea.

Water in the form of ice can move as a glacier. Glaciers form in areas where the summer melting is less than the precipitation in the form of snow. As a result snow accumulates from year to year. As the snowfields become thicker, the lower layers recrystallize to form non-porous ice. If the ice becomes thick enough, it may begin to flow slowly downhill. Boulders in the ice mass may act like grains in a giant piece of sandpaper, scratching and grooving other rocks. Glacial ice may acquire a load of boulders and pebbles by plucking material from the rocks over which it travels. Rocks falling on its surface may add to the load. This is shown in Figure 12–22. A huge mass of moving ice carrying broken rock debris is a very effective erosional agent.

Wind must have a much greater velocity than water to move particles of the same size. Coarse material like sand may be rolled and bounced along the ground. If there is a large supply of sand, sand dunes are formed where the wind loses energy and drops its load of particles. Sand dunes, which may appear to be entirely stationary, are actually in constant motion because the sand grains roll and bounce over each other on the surface of the dunes.

Figure 12–22 *This glacier in the Alaska Range carries rock debris as it carves and grinds the valley floor* (below). *Which of the valleys* (left) *has been modified by a glacier?*

Fine material like silt and clay-size particles is quite easily lifted by winds. Such wind-blown material may be transported for great distances over the surface of the earth. Because wind usually cannot carry large particles, it is a good agent for sorting small particles from large ones. Pebbles and boulders are left behind and produce a rough, rocky surface, whereas sand grains roll and scatter across the surface. The wind sorts and lifts similar-size particles into the air. How would you recognize wind-deposited sediments? (See Figure 12–23.) Does wind move as much material as water and ice?

12–10 What is the most important leveling agent?

The erosional processes discussed in the preceding section work to level the land. They erode and move materials from high areas and ultimately deposit them in lower regions. You must look at the different leveling processes quantitatively in order to see which is the most important in transporting material.

Glacial ice is a very effective agent of erosion. Today, however, it covers only about 10 percent of the land area of the world, and over 95 percent of this ice is in Antarctica and Greenland. Even during the Ice Ages when the extent of the ice was at a maximum, it covered only about 30 percent of the land. Although glaciers have the capacity to transport tremendous amounts of material, they are today a relatively unimportant leveling agent. Why?

Ocean waves erode the land, but only in a very narrow band along the shores of the continents. Assuming that the strip along the shoreline where waves are active is 200 meters wide, waves acting on the entire coast would affect less than 0.2 percent of the land.

Wind hardly counts as a leveling agent. In some places wind blowing in from the sea actually moves material from the beaches inland, building dunes and thereby returning sediment to the land. Elsewhere in a few arid regions it shifts loose sand around, removing some

Figure 12–23 *The atmosphere transports earth materials. (Top, left) A dust storm in California. (Below, left) Some accumulations of fine material are believed to be wind deposited. (Above, right) Sand dunes in Arabia. (Below, right) An ancient sand dune is now crossbedded sandstone.*

Figure 12–24 Water carried by the atmosphere (A) erodes the land. The Grand Canyon (B) was carved by running water. An aerial view of Dungeon Canyon (C) carved into bedrock (D) by a river. Alluvial fans in Death Valley (E) and in New Zealand (F). A flow-gauging station measures soil being eroded (G).

from stream beds and piling it in dunes, making the land less level than before. Deposits of finer material like silt are common in some areas (figure 12–23).

On some lee shores, as on parts of Cape Cod, sand is blown directly out to sea. This is really the only example of net erosion by wind alone. Although some of the delicate sculpturing of the wind might lead you to believe that wind plays a large part in wearing down the land, it is usually greatly overrated as an agent of erosion. On the land masses, wind acts to continually redistribute fine particles without necessarily transporting them to lower elevations.

If glacial ice, ocean waves, and wind do relatively little to level the land, what leveling process is left? Obviously it is the water that falls on and runs off the land. Even the driest parts of the continents usually show that water from the occasional rains is the dominant factor in shaping their landscapes. The scene in Figure 12–24E is part of Death Valley, where the average rainfall is less than five centimeters a year. In some years there is no rain at all.

The amount of work done by falling and running water is so great that it is difficult to comprehend. The average total precipitation on the land areas of the world each year is estimated to be at least 125,000 cubic kilometers (km^3). Some of it falls gently as snow, but most of it hits hard as raindrops and their impact on loose soil can be seen in almost any climate. Large drops fall at a speed of about 30 kilometers per hour and can splash sand grains 30 centimeters or more into the air. On land unprotected by vegetation, this alone is enough to move particles downslope. Actually, about 75 percent of the total precipitation is returned to the atmosphere by evapotranspiration or is retained in rocks and soil. (See Section 9–1.) This leaves about 30,000 cubic kilometers of water to run off the lands into the oceans each year. The capacity of this torrent in eroding the land is overwhelming when compared with any of the other agents of erosion.

How much land is transported to the sea by rivers each year? In the United States, there are hundreds of stream-gauging stations at which the load of suspended sediment is measured regularly. By allowing for the material carried in solution and dragged along the bed of the stream or river and by measuring the area of the land that the river drains, it is possible to calculate the total amount of land removed. These figures range from less than 40 to over 2000 tons per square kilometer per year. In terms of lowering of the land, this means that the average leveling for the United States is about 6 centimeters per 1000 years. If 700 meters is the average elevation of the land above sea level, this rate of erosion could carry to the sea a volume of material equal to all the land now above sea level in about 12 million years.

Thought and Discussion . . .

1. What is erosion?
2. How are particles picked up by wind? by water?
3. Which can carry larger particles, wind or water? Why?
4. How are particles moved by water?
5. How does erosion by glaciers differ from erosion by streams of water?

Unsolved Problems Our understanding of many earth processes is limited by their enormous magnitude. Further, the rates at which the various processes occur vary greatly and many take place so slowly that they go unnoticed by normal observation. The rate of a process at a particular site may be affected by the extent to which the process has operated. Thus, the thicker a layer of weathered material becomes, the less exposed the unweathered rock below is to the atmosphere and to the effects of plants. Hence, weathering occurs much less rapidly in such rock.

Man is extending his explorations into environments that are different from those on the earth's land surface, such as the sea floor and the moon. Do the processes that operate on the land, like weathering and erosion, also occur under the sea? If so, how do they differ from those that occur on the land? We know that certain kinds of earth movements occur under the sea because transatlantic cables have been broken by underwater mass movements. What kind of rocks and soil occur on the moon? How do rocks weather on the surface of the moon?

CHAPTER REVIEW

Summary

Rock materials at or near the surface of the earth tend to adapt to their new environment through changes that are referred to as weathering. Different minerals weather at different rates in the same environment. Weathering produces an unconsolidated layer of rock materials. If the materials remain in place, soils develop. In time, soils undergo further adjustment to their environment, resulting in mature soils that reflect the climate and vegetation of the area. If the products of weathering are transported, resistant minerals eventually are separated from those that weather easily.

Gravity exerts a constant force to move material to lower elevations. Gravity exerts an influence directly in the movement of material by creep and landslides. Water, ice, and wind are agents that move materials long distances and depend on gravity for their effectiveness. Water is the most effective of these agents.

The route to the sea for most material in the wearing away of the land is long and full of detours. Material may be moved, deposited, picked up again, and deposited many times before it reaches the sea. Weathering, soil formation, and erosion operate continuously. Together, they bring about the wearing away of the land.

Questions and Problems

A

1. What happens to rocks as a result of adjustment to the environment at the earth's surface?
2. Why is water such an important factor in weathering?
3. How does weathering of rocks and minerals contribute to man's well-being?
4. What are the products of the weathering of granite?
5. How does soil differ from rock?
6. What characteristics distinguish topsoil from subsoil?
7. How do mature soils of the subhumid grasslands differ from soils of the humid forest regions?
8. What is the role of gravity in erosion?
9. What kinds of materials does a stream move and how does it move them?
10. Why is water able to transport larger particles than wind? Why can ice transport larger particles than water?

B

1. Why are almost all of the sand particles in the dunes around the Great Lakes or on the beaches of New England composed of quartz?

Compare the land areas shown in the above photos. Which erosional agent was active in each area?

2. Why is the negative charge of colloids important in slowing down the removal of calcium from the soil by percolating water? Why is this important for the growth of vegetation?
3. A limestone contains 10 percent impurities consisting of insoluble clay minerals and other materials. If this limestone weathers at the rate of 30 cm in a thousand years, how many years would be required to form 1.5 meters of soil?
4. Of what importance is the kinetic energy of a stream (velocity) in relation to the amount of dissolved chemicals the stream carries?
5. How would you establish whether the soils in the area where you live were formed from bedrock or sediment?
6. What evidence would you look for to establish the fact that the loose material at a given location was a glacial deposit?
7. How would you be able to detect whether a stream valley in the mountains was formed chiefly by a glacier or by running water?

C

1. A cube with an edge of one centimeter is cut into 1000 cubes of equal size. What is the length of one of the small cubes? How much surface area is exposed by one of the small cubes? What is the total surface area exposed by the 1000 smaller cubes? If this were a cube

of earth material, what effect would the increased surface area have on the rate of weathering?

2. Would the weathering of 1.5 meters of limestone and the weathering of 1.5 meters of sandstone produce soils with the same thickness? Explain.

3. Material on the top of a hill was found to contain 30 percent of limestone fragments. Limestone bedrock exists 30 meters below the surface. The closest limestone deposit is 160 kilometers away. How could you account for the high content of limestone fragments in the soil materials, assuming that the material at the top of the hill had not weathered from the limestone bedrock?

Suggested Readings

BOOKS

Croneis, Carey and William C. Krumbein. *Down to Earth.* Harper & Row, Publishers, New York, 1951.

Emmons, William H. and others. *Geology: Principles and Processes.* McGraw-Hill Book Company, New York, 1960. Chapter 8.

Gilluly, James, A. C. Waters, and A. O. Woodford. *Principles of Geology,* 2nd ed. W. H. Freeman & Co., Publishers, San Francisco, 1959. Chapter 4, "Weathering and Soils," and Chapter 5, "Erosion."

Kellogg, Charles E. *The Soils That Support Us.* The Macmillan Company, New York, 1941.

McGraw-Hill Encyclopedia of Science and Technology. McGraw-Hill Book Company, New York, 1960. Volume 12, "Soil," and Volume 14, "Weathering."

Shimer, John A. *This Sculptured Earth.* Columbia University Press, New York, 1959.

United States Department of Agriculture Yearbooks entitled *Water,* 1955 (see chapter entitled "How Rainfall and Runoff Erode Soil," p. 126 ff.), *Soil,* 1957, and *Land,* 1958. United States Government Printing Office.

PERIODICALS

Field, W. O. "Glaciers." *Scientific American,* September, 1955. (Also Scientific American Offprint #809, W. H. Freeman & Co., Publishers, San Francisco.)

Janssen, R. E. "The History of a River." *Scientific American,* June, 1952.

Kellogg, Charles E. "Soil." *Scientific American,* July, 1950. (Also Scientific American Offprint #821.)

Soil and Water Conservation Activities for Boy Scouts. United States Department of Agriculture Bulletin PA-348, 1964.

See local county Soil Conservation Agent for pamphlets on local soil situations.

Three areas being eroded by running water are shown below. One photo was taken from a satellite, another from an aircraft, and the third by a person standing on the ground. Which is which?

An astronaut's photograph of the Yangtze River
delta in China (above), and the U. S.
Navy's Trieste (below) as it would appear deep in the ocean.

Chapter 13 Sediments in the Sea

Most of the materials that are weathered and eroded from the land eventually reach the sea. There the products of the wearing away of the land are deposited in some part of the world ocean basin. The materials may travel to the sea by the thousands of streams and rivers. They may be borne aloft by winds and then dropped on the sea when the wind energy has diminished. They may be caught up in glacial ice and slowly carried to the sea, where they fall to the sea floor as the ice melts in the ocean waters.

The journey to the sea may be long, with many stops along the way. Some materials remain as deposits in lakes for many years before once again resuming their seaward journey. What happens to these sediments when they reach the sea? Do they simply pile up as huge deposits at the mouths of rivers? (See the photograph of the Yangtze River on the opposite page.) Or do processes act under the sea to shift the sediment? Do any of the materials of the land ever reach the central parts of the oceans?

People have wondered about the topography of the sea floor, the sediments deposited there, and the animals that inhabit the ocean environment. There is some evidence that in the time of Alexander the Great men thought of exploring the depths of the sea in diving bells. An ancient manuscript shows Alexander himself making a descent to the ocean bottom.

To learn more about the sea and the sea floor, man must travel on the surface in ships such as the famous British ship HMS *Challenger* or its modern counterpart, the German R/V *Meteor*. To scientists studying the sea floor, the salty water is merely an annoyance and its motions often cause them discomfort. How do you see the bottom of the ocean? From a ship on the surface it is impossible to see more than a few meters down. To get closer to the sea floor, research submarines have been built like the one designed by Jacques-Yves Cousteau, shown along with the *Meteor* on page 293. However, visibility in seawater is poor and even bright lights allow the undersea traveler to see into the depths no more than a few meters from his vehicle.

Although aided by deep-diving submarines and remote-controlled, underwater television cameras, man has seen only a few hundred square kilometers of the sea floor. The oceans of the world cover 71 percent of the earth's surface, more than twice the area of the land, and 95 percent of the ocean area is greater than 1000 meters deep. Thus 68 percent of the surface is under 1000 meters, or more, of water. Much is left to be learned about the ocean.

Marine Sediments

13–1 Investigating the deposition of sediments.

The violent rush of a stream down a mountain may capture your interest more than the quiet lake into which the stream empties. Even the slow, turbid Mississippi River seems more dynamic than the Gulf of Mexico into which it flows. The reason for this point of view is that you live above the level of the air-water interface. You are familiar with earth processes that take place on the surface of the earth, such as erosion. However, processes that go on day after day, year after year, hidden from your view in the dark solitude of the deep ocean, are just as dramatic as those you see. An example is the deposition on the sea floor of weathered material which has been eroded from the land surface.

Procedure

Set up the equipment as shown in Figure 13–1. Fill the tube with water almost to the top.

Drop small amounts of the different sediment sizes into the column and record the time each particle size takes to reach the bottom. Make three trials for each grain size. Using the average time of the three trials, make a graph of settling time versus grain size.

(1) Does there appear to be a place on your graph where the slope of your curve changes markedly? If so, why do you think this happens?

(2) Make a statement of the relationship between settling time and grain size.

Next drain off enough water so that the column is only half full. Drop in a handful of randomly mixed sediment sizes and observe what happens. Do this several times.

(3) Describe how these mixed sediments become arranged on the bottom of the column.

(4) Where in nature might you find deposits with characteristics like those formed in this investigation?

Figure 13–1 *Column attached to a ring stand for the investigation of sediment deposition.*

13–2 The products of weathering reach the sea.

The products of weathering reach the sea in different ways, but most are brought by rivers. As the material being carried by the river reaches the sea, it enters a new environment. When the flowing river enters the quieter ocean, the speed of the river decreases, as do its energy and capacity to carry sediments. As a result, the coarser particles carried by the river quickly settle out. Sediments that have been on the land surface or in rivers for years and have been carried for thousands of kilometers are abruptly dumped—deposited. The new environment at the river's mouth brakes the movement of the eroded material toward the ocean basins.

Where the river flows directly into a shallow sea, the sediments may form a large deposit called a **delta.** (See Figure 13–2.) This term comes from the shape of the Greek letter delta (Δ). It originates from the triangular shape of the deposits at the mouth of the Nile River. The Mississippi Delta is larger than that of the Nile, has a different shape, and is growing seaward at a more rapid rate. There have been as much as 15 kilometers of growth into the Gulf of Mexico since the Civil War. Here is one place along the coast of the United States where man can see new land added during his lifetime.

You investigated the differences in settling rates of particles in Section 13–1. What can you decide about the size of the material that will be deposited as the speed of the river decreases? What of the fine material? You might think that the very finest, colloidal-sized particles carried by the river would remain in suspension for long periods, to be wafted about by the waves. However, salt water contains more ions in solution than fresh water and, as a result, when the colloids of the river water reach the sea, they are sometimes drawn together into clumps. These clumps may become as large as sand grains. What will happen to them then?

Not all of the material carried to the sea by rivers is deposited near the mouth of the river. Some of the particles pass through to the sea without settling to the bottom. Which particles would you expect these to be? Other particles may eventually reach the sea floor because they are moved along the bottom of the rivers by currents. (See Figure 12–21.) Material passing through the mouths of rivers is moved sideways along the coastline by near-shore currents.

Figure 13–2 *The Nile Delta, Egypt* (top) *photographed from the Gemini spacecraft. (Below left) Jacques-Yves Cousteau's diving saucer to explore the ocean to depths up to 500 meters. The modern research vessel R/V Meteor (below right) operated by West Germany.*

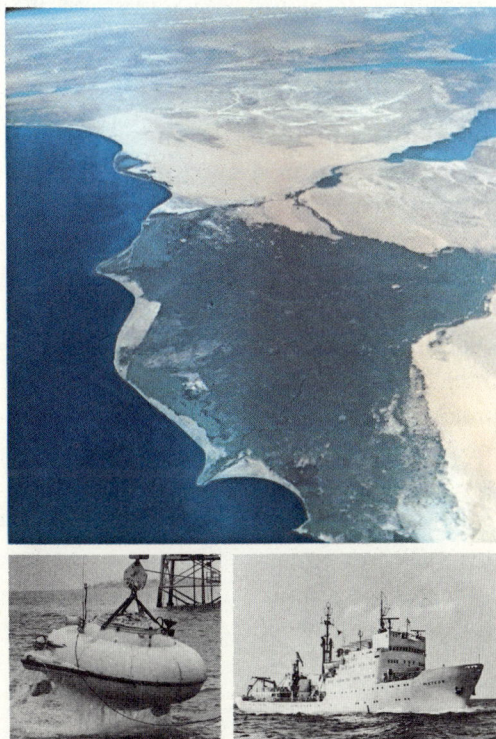

The sand, silt, and colloidal particles that reach the ocean will settle at different rates, determined mainly by their size, shape, and density. This was evident in Investigation 13–1. In the ocean, however, other factors influence the particles. While they are settling, they are carried along by ocean currents. (See Figure 13–3.) How far they travel before reaching the sea floor depends on the settling rate of the particle, the speed and turbulence of the current, and the depth of the water. Look at the settling rate for the finest particle noted in Figure 13–3. Would you expect such particles to be deposited close to, or far from, the river that brought them to the sea? Suppose the colloidal particles were in surface waters where the upward movements of waves were as great as the settling rate of the particles. Would they ever reach the sea floor?

Although most of the products of weathering and erosion are brought to the sea by rivers, in some parts of the world winds carry small fragments and drop them onto the ocean's surface. Such fragments are mainly bits of sand, silt, and volcanic ash. In some areas the wind-borne sediments are so abundant that they make up a large portion of the sediments on the ocean bottom. Where would you suspect such areas to be?

Glaciers entering the sea also supply relatively small amounts of sediment from the land. When pieces of glaciers break off to form icebergs, they may drift for great distances across the ocean. As the icebergs slowly melt, the trapped sediment is released and falls to the bottom of the sea. Particles released from the iceberg may be of any size, from that of colloids to gigantic boulders.

13–3 Basins of deposition form and sediments accumulate.

The products of erosion that pour into the sea settle in the ocean basin. What is this basin like? Is it one huge basin, or more than one? It is clear from Figure 13–4 (pages 296 and 297) that more than one basin exists. The more closely you look at this map of the world, the more basins you will seem to see. A basin of deposition has borders or boundaries of some sort. Perhaps the most obvious of all basins is the Mediterranean Sea, which has one small opening, the Strait of Gibraltar. Another basin that has well-defined boundaries is the Caribbean-Gulf of Mexico basin. Where are the openings for this basin?

A basin of deposition may have borders other than shorelines or ridges. The speed of ocean currents and the turbulence of ocean waters is a type of barrier. Consider particles of various sizes being brought to the oceans. The settling rate of a given particle may be so fast that it and others like it will be deposited before the currents can sweep them into

Figure 13–3 *Particles settling in moving water are carried different distances depending on their settling rates. In this example, the current is flowing at a rate of 10 centimeters per second. Note length of settling time for each size particle.*

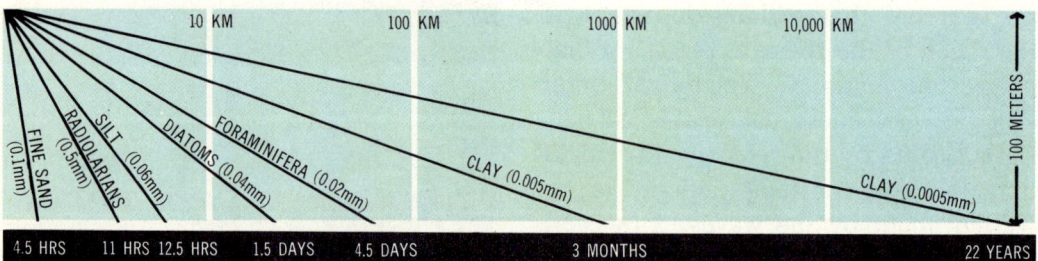

Figure 13–5 *The shelf, slope, and rise of part of the east coast of the United States. The profile below is a cross-section along the bottom of the map.*

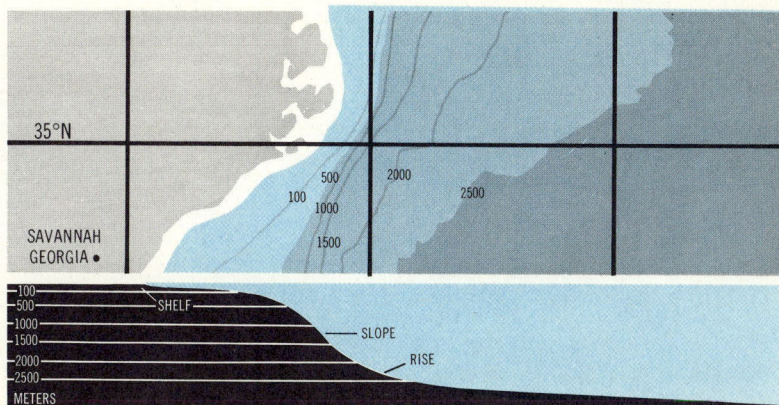

other basins. On the other hand, the particles may have settling rates that are so slow that they will be removed and carried by the currents. All particles of a certain size, such as sand, may be deposited on a particular part of the sea floor, even though there is no visible barrier to stop them. In such cases the sites of deposition are not surrounded by obvious physical borders.

Let us look at the ocean areas near the land masses where processes that move sediment are most active. The submerged parts of the continents bordering the ocean, the **continental shelves,** are merely the edges of the continents covered by the sea. (See Figure 13–5.) On the average, their flat, terrace-like surfaces are as level as a billiard table. The edges of the shelves occur at various depths. Along the east coast of the United States it is between 50 and 150 meters. The more steeply dipping sea floor beyond the continental shelf is called the **continental slope.** Even on this slope, however, the incline is no

steeper than the aisle in a movie theater.

At the base of most of the continental slopes of the world there is an apron of sediments that have slumped down the slope and come to rest in deep water. This is called the **continental rise.** Would these sediments have characteristics of deep- or shallow-water deposits?

Shelves, slopes, and rises border all the continents. Their origins have been debated for many years. However, from a number of recent studies it is clear that the shelves and slopes are shaped by both erosion and deposition. (See Figure 13–6.) In some places, as along the east coast of the United States, the two processes have acted together to form the submerged features. Off other coasts, one or the other process has been the more active. In the Gulf of Mexico, for example, the shelves and slopes have features probably caused by deposition.

Figure 13–6 *The section (below) through the shelf of the east coast of the United States was made perpendicular to the shore, as shown on the left. Note areas of erosion and deposition.*

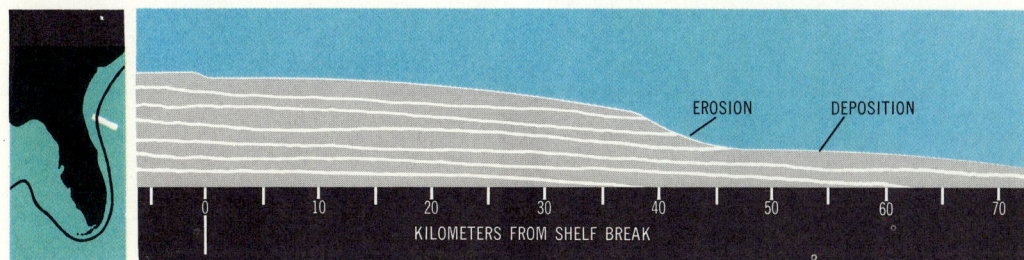

Figure 13-4

ARCTIC

PT. BARROW 140° 60° 40° 20° 0° 20°

ALASKA (U.S.) GREENLAND SPITSBERGEN

60° CANADA

HUDSON BAY ARCTIC CIRCLE NORWAY

ICELAND SWEDEN FINLAND

ROCKY MTS. Trondheim Helsinki

DENMARK Baltic Sea

GREAT BRITAIN BENE-LUX S.W. GERM. POLAND

40° Great Lakes IRELAND London E. GERM. CZECHO. HUNGA.

UNITED STATES Paris SWITZ. AUST. YUGO. RUMA.

MISSISSIPPI R. APPALACHIAN MTS. FRANCE ALPS ITALY ALB. BULG. Bla. Sea

New York PORTUGAL SPAIN GREECE TUR.

Los Angeles A T L A N T I C AZORES Lisbon MEDITERRANEAN SEA SYR. ISRAEL

BAJA CALIFORNIA Rio Grande MOROCCO TUNISIA U.A.R. (EGYPT) JOR.

TROPIC OF CANCER BERMUDA CANARY IS. IFNI ALGERIA LIBYA

MEXICO GULF OF MEXICO SP. SAHARA S A H A R A Nile R.

20° CUBA SANTO DOMINGO MAURITANIA MALI NIGER CHAD SUDAN

HAITI PUERTO RICO SENEGAL Niger R.

CARIBBEAN SEA MARTINIQUE GAMBIA UPPER VOLTA DAHOMEY ETHIOPI

CENTRAL AMERICA PORT. GUINEA GUINEA NIGERIA CENT. AFRICAN REP.

PANAMA CANAL VENEZUELA SIERRA LEONE TOGO UGANDA KEN

COLOMBIA GUYANA SURINAM FR. GUIANA LIBERIA IVORY COAST GHANA CAMEROON

0° GALÁPAGOS IS. ECUADOR EQUATOR SP. EQUAT. GUINEA REP. OF THE CONGO

P A C I F I C Manaus Amazon R. ASCENSION I. GABON CONGO R.

BRAZIL CONGO ZANZIBAR

O C E A N ANGOLA MALAWI

PERU BOLIVIA ZAMBIA

20° ANDES MTS. PARAGUAY Iguasu Falls Rio de Janeiro MID-ATLANTIC BOTSWANA RHOD.

TROPIC OF CAPRICORN ATACAMA DESERT CHILE TRENCH SOUTH-WEST AFRICA

EASTER I. ARGENTINA SWAZILAND LESOTHO MOZ.

ALBATROSS RISE CHILE URUGUAY SOUTH AFRICA CAPE OF GOOD HOPE

O C E A N RIDGE

CHILE RISE CHILE RISE

40° CAPE HORN SOUTH SANDWICH TRENCH

ANTARCTIC CIRCLE

160° 140° 120° 100° 80° 40° 20° 0°

MAP OF THE WORLD

WITH RELIEF IN OBLIQUE PERSPECTIVE

APPROX. SCALE AT EQUATOR

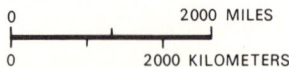

0   2000 MILES

0   2000 KILOMETERS

   Equal Area Projection

OCEAN DEPTHS – IN METERS

☐	0 TO 200 (CONTINENTAL SHELF)
☐	200 TO 3000
☐	3000 TO 5000
☐	5000 AND OVER
—	TRENCHES

297

A marine biologist dives through shallow warm water to study a coral reef near the Florida keys.

No matter where a continental rise exists, it is the result of deposition.

Many deep canyons extend across the continental slopes and into the continental shelves. (See Figure 13–7.) In some ways they resemble canyons in mountainous regions on land. Some are enormous, extending hundreds of kilometers from near shore into the deep-sea basins. In southern California some canyons extend so close to shore that fishermen can drop their lines off piers directly into the deep water of a canyon.

The canyons off the coast of southern California have been studied in great detail. They reach depths of about 500 meters and many appear to be extensions of canyons on land. It was first thought that the canyons were formed by rivers when, during the Ice Ages, sea level was 100 meters lower than it is today. In parts of the world other than southern California, however, canyons extend to depths greater than 3000 meters. The Hudson canyon near New York City is

one example. Do you think such canyons were cut by stream erosion?

Although submarine canyons differ in length, depth, and the rocks through which they cut, they have one feature in common. On the sea floor at the mouth of each canyon is a large, fanlike deposit of sediments. These deposits are like those in Figure 12–24E, showing a fan formed on land, but they are generally much larger and cover great areas of the sea floor. Have these sediments come down the canyon? Are they clues to the origin of canyons? It is not unusual to dredge up shallow-water shells and twigs in the fanlike deposits.

Beyond the continental slope in the sea, at depths greater than 3000 meters, lie wide, slightly undulating plains. Sixty-three percent of the sea floor consists of these flat plains, or nearly one-half of the total area of the earth's surface. (See Figure 13–8.) Deep-sea plains are interrupted by many mountains and deep trenches. In the Atlantic Ocean, the plains extend hundreds of kilometers from the continental slopes to the Mid-Atlantic Ridge. (See Figure 13–4.) In the Pacific Ocean basin, however, they extend from the great island chains instead of from the continental

Figure 13–7 *The arrows (left) suggest the movement of sand and other sedimentary particles into this submarine canyon, from its head near the shore, and down the canyon toward the floor of the deep sea. (Right) A "Sandfall" about 10 meters high in a submarine canyon off Baja California.*

Figure 13–8 *The percentages of the earth's surface that are above and below sea level. The greatest percentage of the surface is at the level of the deep sea.*

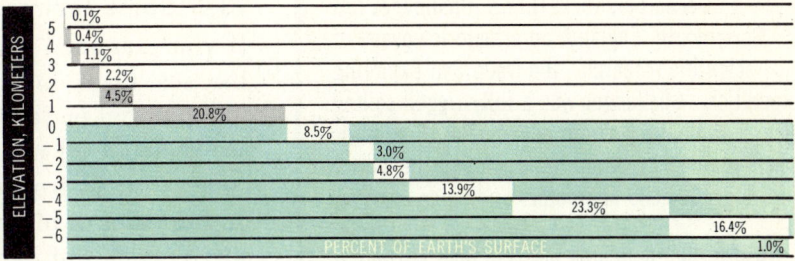

ELEVATION, KILOMETERS

0.1%
0.4%
1.1%
2.2%
4.5%
20.8%
8.5%
3.0%
4.8%
13.9%
23.3%
16.4%
1.0%

PERCENT OF EARTH'S SURFACE

slopes around the borders of this basin. If you carefully examine Figure 13–4, you can see deep trenches between the land and the ocean floor in the Pacific. A good example of such a trench is found along the Chile-Peru coast in South America. Do the trenches influence the formation of deep-sea plains?

Recent surveys indicate that the sedimentary deposits at the mouths of sub-marine canyons blend into the deep-sea plains. The materials of the fans at the canyon mouths and on the plains are similar. In the Atlantic Ocean, the thickness of the deposits decreases away from the continental rise. These sediments are derived from the land. How great a distance did they travel? How could the coarse fragments get so far into the ocean basin?

13–4 Investigating density currents.

You have learned that coarse fragments are found at the mouths of submarine canyons. How did they get there? Could they have flowed like streams of water on land?

So far no one has actually seen a density current in the ocean. You can, however, study density currents by using a laboratory model to see if they might be capable of carrying coarse sediments out to sea.

Procedure

Set up the equipment as shown in Figure 13–9. Mix a slurry of soil and tap water. Predict what will happen when you pour the slurry into the sloping column of water. Test your prediction. Pour four or five more slurries of the same material into the column and let them settle.

(1) Did the results of your investigation differ from what you predicted? If so, in what way?

(2) Describe the speed and motion of the material as it travels down the column.

(3) How do you suppose density currents similar to the ones you produced are caused in nature?

(4) How can density currents carry coarse sediments far out into the ocean?

In Section 13–3 you learned that deep trenches separate the continents from the plains in the ocean basins of the Pacific Ocean. Coarse continental sediments are found throughout the basins in the Atlantic.

(5) Why are they not found in the Pacific basins?

Figure 13–9
Apparatus assembled to study density currents.

In December, 1872, H.M.S. Challenger left Portsmouth, England, on a historic voyage of scientific research—the Deep Sea Exploring Expedition. Challenger was a fully-rigged sailing ship with auxiliary steam power. For three-and-a-half years she roamed the oceans of the world, covering 1,104,000 kilometers and twice crossing the Antarctic Circle.

Aboard the Challenger was Sir John Murray, a famous Canadian biologist and oceanographer whose observations convinced him of the existence of a landmass under the Antarctic Ocean.

The scientists on the Challenger observed sea animal and plant life, dredged the deep sea floor, took samples of water from all depths, and measured temperatures all through the oceans. The men on the Challenger used thick rope up to eight kilometers long to make depth measurements at thousands of points in the Pacific. From this they learned that the sea floor was as varied as the land, with massive mountain ranges, deep valleys, and plains. The deepest measurement, 4475 fathoms, was made in the Mariana Trench off Japan. In the 1950's a depth of 5939.4 fathoms (nearly eight kilometers) was recorded with echoed sound in the Mariana Trench. Challenger was the first ship commissioned solely to investigate the oceans, and from the famous "Challenger Reports" oceanography was born.

13–5 Some sediments form in the sea.

If you examined a sample of mud from the sea floor, much as you examined soil material in Section 12–3, you would see that not all the material it contains comes directly from the land. You would find remains of marine organisms or tiny sharp crystals of minerals that could not possibly have survived a very lengthy land-to-sea journey intact. These materials must have formed in the sea, but how did they originate there?

Rivers bring material to the sea either as particles or as ions dissolved in the water. The shells of organisms and the tiny mineral crystals are formed within the sea from ions carried there by the rivers. Marine plants also depend on a variety of dissolved materials in seawater for growth. (See Section 10–2.) The most familiar marine plants are seaweeds and grasses that grow near the shore. (See Figure 13–10.) However, these do not compare in either number or volume with the large quantities of microscopic plants that live in the open ocean where they are seldom observed. Because plants require light to grow, they can live only in the upper layers of the sea. Seaweeds in shallow water near the shore are attached to the bottom, but in the open ocean tiny plants float in the water in order to remain near the light at the surface.

Wherever tiny plants float in the sea, microscopic animals use them for food. (See Figure 13–11.) Where the plants are numerous, so are the animals. Larger organisms feed on the microorganisms much as cattle graze the fields of the land. The number of animals and plants in the surface water is controlled by the available food, the water temperatures, and the rate at which they are eliminated, either by death or by other organisms. Food is most abundant near

Figure 13–10 (Above) Sea grass growing at the low tide line on a beach in southern Florida. (Below) Kelp harvested on the coast of Ireland.

mouths of rivers and in ocean areas where it is brought from the depths to the surface. (See Section 10–5.)

Upwelling goes on continually along the northern boundary of the great circumpolar current near Antarctica. (See Figure 10–17.) Here the nutrient-rich waters, rising from ocean depths, support an enormous population of microscopic plants called **diatoms.** The sediments on the nearby sea floor are composed mainly of the remains of these microscopic plants.

The remains of animals and plants may be carried many miles from where they died before they reach the sea floor. Turn again to Figure 13–3 and determine how long it will take for a diatom to settle to the bottom in 6000 meters of water. How far will it have traveled in this time?

The most common organic remains in marine sediments are the carbonate skeletons of microscopic animals called **foraminifera.** (See Figure 13–11.) Most marine animals and many plants use calcium carbonate for their shell material. Thousands of species of foraminifera live in all the surface waters of the sea. Most marine sediments contain remains of these species. (See Figure 13–12.)

Ever since the analyses of the sediments collected during the *Challenger* expedition, the mineral phillipsite has been known to be abundant in the deep-sea deposits of the Pacific Ocean. (See Figure 13–13.) Phillipsite is interesting because it is not found in rocks on the continents. The crystals have been recovered only from deep-sea sediments. Phillipsite is found as isolated crystals in

Figure 13–11 Photos at left show typical marine microorganisms. (Above) Diatoms with silica shells; (below) foraminifera with calcium carbonate shells.

Figure 13–12 (Center) Shell remains of microorganisms found in deep-sea sediments.

Figure 13–13 (Right) Well-formed phillipsite crystals from the Challenger reports.

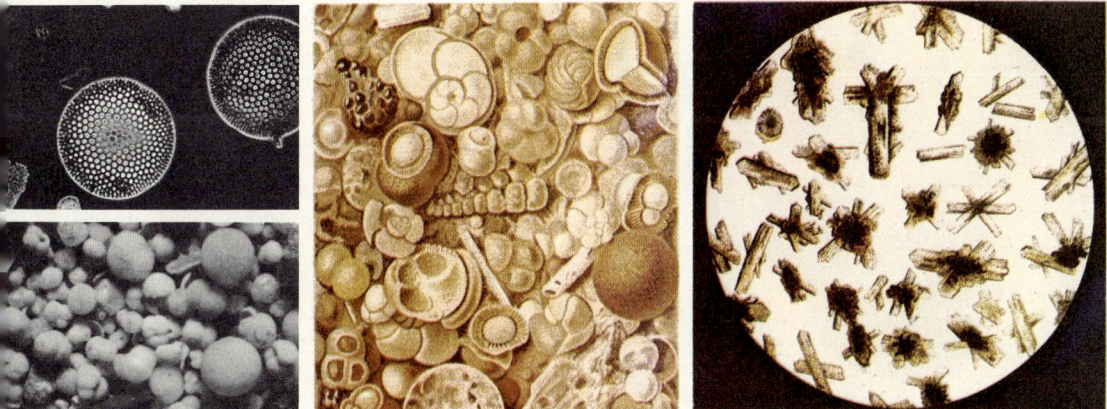

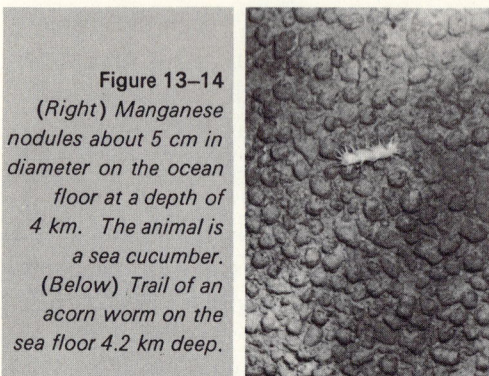

Figure 13–14 (*Right*) *Manganese nodules about 5 cm in diameter on the ocean floor at a depth of 4 km. The animal is a sea cucumber. (Below) Trail of an acorn worm on the sea floor 4.2 km deep.*

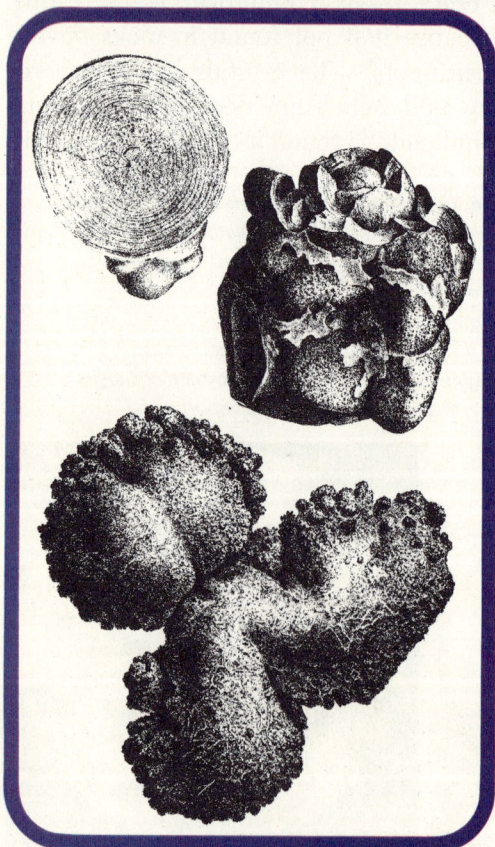

sediment, rarely touching one another, and not clumped together. It seemed clear to the men working with the sediments collected by the *Challenger* that the mineral had crystallized directly from the seawater rather than being carried from the land to the sea.

Many deposits on the sea floor similarly consist of materials that have formed directly by precipitation from seawater. In many places, extensive deposits of manganese nodules formed in this way. (See Figure 13–14.) These, too, were first discovered during the *Challenger* expedition. Their possible economic value was not realized, however, until further exploration during the International Geophysical Year (1957–58). These studies revealed how vast an area the nodules cover on the sea floor, especially in the South Pacific.

The manganese, with small amounts of cobalt and iron, occurs as grains, nodules, slabs, and coating on rocks. (See Figure 13–15.) Most of the nodules are about 5 centimeters in diameter. It is not known how fast the nodules form, but their growth must be slower than the normal rate of deposition of particles and organic debris on most of the deep-sea floor. This means that manganese nodules must form in areas in which there is little deposition of sediment. Otherwise the first tiny grains of manganese formed would be kept from contact with the surrounding water because of a cover of sediment and would not grow any larger.

Not all materials precipitated in the sea form in deep water. Under some conditions materials may be precipitated

Figure 13–15 (*Left*) *Manganese nodules taken from the Pacific Ocean floor, as drawn in the Challenger reports. (Top, right) A typical nodule. (Top, left) A cross section showing concentric rings. (Bottom) The underside of a nodule.*

in shallow water. Calcium carbonate is quite soluble in seawater because of the carbon dioxide that the water contains. The amount of calcium carbonate that can be dissolved depends on the amount of carbon dioxide in the water. Seawater is normally saturated with calcium carbonate. When cold water from deep in the sea rises over a shallow bank, the warming of the water reduces the amount of dissolved carbon dioxide in the water. This is because cold water can hold more carbon dioxide than warm water. What then happens to the solubility of calcium carbonate? On such shallow banks there is usually a great growth of sea plants. The photosynthesis carried on by the plants further reduces the amount of carbon dioxide in the shallow water. This decreases the solubility of calcium carbonate even more. As a result, calcium carbonate is deposited on such banks. (See Figure 13–16.)

Thought and Discussion . . .

1. Do all particles eroded from the land stop at the edge of the sea?
2. The invisible barriers of some ocean basins are related to energy. Explain.
3. Where do the sediments at the mouths of submarine canyons originate?
4. What is the source of the materials that organisms use to make their shells?
5. How do manganese nodules develop?

The Continental Margins

13–6 The shorelines have moved.

The ground immediately beneath where you are sitting was once a beach. Waves washed up and down the sand carrying shells, seaweed, and pebbles. It is even possible that children once played on a beach that has long since disappeared from where you are on the land surface. How can scientists be so sure that such a beach actually existed?

Evidence for this statement comes mainly from the distribution of sedimentary rocks on the continents. These rocks cover about three-fourths of the continents. Most of them contain fossils, indicating that they formed in shallow seas. The absence of sedimentary rocks from certain places on the continents indicates that erosion has occurred and stripped the rocks away. Marine sedimentary rocks, therefore, are evidence that the continents were at some time at the bottom of shallow seas similar to those over the present continental shelves. As the ancient seas moved across the land, either advancing or retreating, their edges were the beaches.

Mastodon teeth have been recovered from the surface of the continental shelf off the east coast of the United States. They were found in water depths of 60 meters with shells of sea animals that

Figure 13–16 *Great Exuma Island in the Bahamas photographed from the Gemini 5 spacecraft. Extensive deposits of calcium carbonate mud can be seen in the shallow waters near the island.*

lived only in the shallow waters of mud flats. Both shells and teeth indicate that sea level was once lower than it is today.

During the Ice Ages vast quantities of water were locked in glaciers that covered much of the land surface in the Northern Hemisphere. Because of the continual advancing and retreating of land glaciers that alternately locked up and released water, the level of the sea varied greatly. The greatest difference in elevation of sea level during the Ice Ages is not exactly known. Many features that must have been formed then, such as beaches, sand dunes, and mud flats, have been changed or removed by the processes of erosion and deposition.

Changes in glacial ice account for some of the geologically recent fluctuations in sea level, and scientists know that the melting of existing glaciers would change all the shorelines of the world. However, glaciation is a comparatively rare feature in the overall history of the earth. Careful measurements over

the last century have shown that shorelines of certain areas sometimes change with respect to sea level while other shorelines do not. These changes could not be caused by glaciation, so there must be other processes that have caused past fluctuations of sea level.

Perhaps you can imagine the entire seashore with its breaking waves, beaches, sand dunes, and gaily-colored umbrellas moving slowly back and forth across the continental shelf. The actual migration of the seashore would take place so slowly that you could not notice the change from day to day or even from year to year. (See Figure 13–17.) Even though the migration could hardly have been noticed by man, by the standards of geologic time it was rapid. Thus, the continental shelf was above sea level during some periods and covered with as much as 200 meters of water during others. Furthermore, as the beaches migrated, erosion and deposition produced the rather level shelf surface of today.

Figure 13–17 *During glacial times (A) mastodons roamed beaches which today are part of the continental shelf. When the continental glaciers melted and sea level rose (B), ancient man hunted along beaches now covered by shallow shelf waters. Today (C) the coastline lies at its highest level since glacial times.*

13–7 Sediments are deposited near the shore.

From investigations 13–1 and 13–4, you better understand that coarser sedimentary material is deposited rapidly and finer fragments are often carried far out to sea. (See Figure 13–18A.) You have learned this too from the distribution of particles within density-current deposits on the deep-sea plains of the Atlantic Ocean. A similar pattern of sediments exists on the continental shelf and slopes off the eastern United States.

Sandy beaches, layers of fine-grained material on the shelves, deposits from density currents on the slopes, and carbonate sediments may all be deposited at the same time on different parts of the continental margin. (Figure 13–19.) You have seen sedimentary rocks formed

Figure 13–18 *(Above) The Mississippi Delta and the Gulf Coast photographed from the Gemini 9 spacecraft. The drawings show how the movement of shorelines can cause coarse sediment to overlie fine sediment.*

● CAIRO, ILLINOIS

| SEDIMENTARY ROCK | SEDIMENTS FROM THE LAND | CARBONATE DEPOSITS |

Figure 13–19 *Areas of deposition of different types of sediment in the Gulf of Mexico. Would there be a sharp interface between these areas?*

from such deposits. You know that these rocks exist in layers or beds. How can a layer of sandstone alternate with a layer of shale when sand and mud are deposited in different environments?

As a delta grows seaward gradually a layer of coarser sand is deposited above a bed of fine clay. The movement of shorelines in the geologic past has produced similar relationships between fine and coarse sediments. Would the finer material be on top of the coarser or beneath it for a shoreline advancing over the continents? for a shoreline retreating (Figure 13–18B)?

Beaches, whether above or below the surface of the sea, are particularly susceptible to erosion. If sea level becomes lower, stream erosion wears away the beach deposits, scattering the fragments into the sea and along the new shore. If sea level rises, waves breaking over the old beach soon destroy it. Ancient beaches are thus rarely found on the continental shelf or within the layers of sediments that make up the shelf. However, the remnants of old beaches, whether pebbles, shells, or sand, are scattered over the new shelf and contribute to the deposits laid down there.

Where the shallow waters on shelves are warm and tropical, and where there is little or no deposition of particles from the land, carbonate sediments form. (See Section 13–5.) Plants, animals, and bacteria flourish in such waters, and their reactions with the warm water bring about the accumulation of calcium carbonate fragments on the sea floor. The carbonate fragments combine with the calcium carbonate remains of the millions of plants and animals to form extensive deposits. (See Figure 13–16.)

What other deposits are laid down on the continental shelf and along the continental slope? Deposition certainly does not occur only on beaches. What of the seaward growth of great deltas as noted in Section 13–2? What of the material that flows down submarine canyons? Do these deposits from deltas and canyons help build the continental shelf?

The delta of the Mississippi River is growing seaward, as it has been for millions of years, since it first began to form at what is now Cairo, Illinois. In a sense, the river has built its own platform for the delta as it has grown into the Gulf of Mexico. Other rivers do the same thing, although not all at the same rapid rate or with the same great volume of sediments as the Mississippi. As deposits form deltas and beaches along the coasts, other sediments move farther seaward.

13–8 Are the continental margins sinking?

Flowing past New Orleans, the Mississippi River carries two million tons of sediment to the Gulf of Mexico each day. Some of the particles are deposited on the delta and in the shallow water along its edges. Some are swept along the

Figure 13–20 *A sequence of events in the history of a continental shelf shows the seaward growth of a delta, (A) the spread of increasingly finer sediments across the shelf and down the slope, and the sinking of the basin of deposition, (B) and (C).*

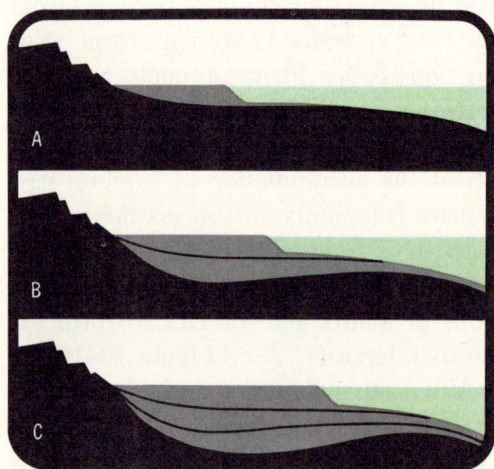

coast and into bays and marshes. Others travel down the slope of the delta into the Gulf of Mexico. (See Figure 13–20.) For tens of millions of years the river has been carrying material to the sea. Where has all of this material gone?

It is apparent that the Gulf of Mexico is gradually filling with sediment contributed by the Mississippi River and the other rivers that enter its basin. The filling has been going on for millions of years. The water in the Gulf of Mexico is not particularly deep, reaching at most about 3800 meters. Little sediment brought to the Gulf escapes through the Florida Straits, so it is surprising that the basin was not filled long ago.

Geologists, in their continual search for oil, have made intensive studies of the sediments in the Mississippi Valley and along the Gulf Coast. From these studies they have learned that the sedimentary layers in the lower Mississippi Valley and along the coast are 15,000 meters thick. These layers have all been deposited by the Mississippi River. Sediments in the deepest part of the Gulf are only a few hundred meters thick. Thus, sedimentary deposits under the Gulf Coast bend down into the earth's crust almost four times as deep as the bottom of the Gulf of Mexico.

Data from deep wells along the east coast of the United States have shown that the sediments there are nearly as thick as those along the Gulf Coast. But what of these thick sediments along the eastern and southern margins of the United States? Perhaps they are thin compared to the sediments in the deep sea. Detailed studies made in many of the ocean basins of the world have shown that sediments in the deep sea are from 0.3 to 0.5 kilometer thick. Compare this with the 15 kilometers of thickness along the Gulf of Mexico. It can be concluded, therefore, that the thick continental margin sediments are unique.

The shelves of the east and Gulf coasts of the United States have been discussed as if they were separate and different structures. You can see from Figure 13–5 that the shelves and their associated coastal plains seem to be continuous from the east coast to the Gulf, with Florida extending the shelf to the south. Thus, the east and Gulf coast shelves appear to be related features.

Because all of the sediments from the shelves seem to have shallow water features, it is reasonable to believe that the area receiving these sediments is sinking. (See Figure 13–20.) As tremendous masses of material spread farther and farther from the shore, continual deposition extends the shelf and slope out into the ocean basin. A great deal of material slides down the continental slope to form the thick layers of the continental rise. The great thickness of sediments deposited in shallow water seems to be ample evidence for a slow, gradual sinking of the continental margin. What is the source of this material?

Weathering and erosion of rocks on the continents have contributed nearly all of the sediments to the continental margins. Therefore, the sedimentary particles, like the continental rock from which they form, are of low density (about 2.7 grams per cubic centimeter).

How can materials of low density push down materials of higher density? Think back to earlier investigations involving density. From measurements, it has been determined that the rocks that underlie the Gulf of Mexico have higher densities than the river sediments that seem to be forcing them down. Because the density of the sediments is less than that of the rocks being pushed down, the sediment load cannot account for all of the sinking. Surely the deposit of great masses of sediment on shelves, as is the case here, results in some subsidence. However, other forces must be active in causing some continental margins to continue sinking.

Not all of the continental margins of the world are sinking during the present geologic period. But the processes that lead to subsidence are as active today as always. (See Figure 13–21.)

Figure 13–21 *White areas bordering continents represent continental shelves. Particularly wide shelves have been discovered off the southeast coast of South America, southeast Asia, and the Siberian coast of Asia.*

Thought and Discussion . . .

1. How would you prove that the shore-lines of the oceans are not stationary?
2. What do great thicknesses of sediment such as those found along the Gulf of Mexico indicate?
3. How do nearshore basins of deposition develop?
4. How do glaciers influence changes in sea level?
5. Explain why the continental shelves are nearly level.
6. How do the deposits along the east coast continental shelf compare with those in the Gulf of Mexico?

Unsolved Problems The greatest unsolved problem of the ocean basins is their origin. It seems that the only approach to the solution or solutions will come from an understanding of the structure of ocean basins.

The lack of great thicknesses of sediments in the deep-sea basins is a problem that may be related to their origin. Thick deposits near the shore are understandable, but according to the measured rates of deposition of sediments in the deep sea at least 3 kilometers of sediments rather than only 0.3 to 0.5 kilometer should have been deposited.

CHAPTER REVIEW

Summary

The oceans of the world are immense. They cover roughly 71 percent of the earth's surface. They are great in depth: 95 percent of the sea floor lies more than 1000 meters beneath the sea's surface. Scientists have only recently mapped the great expanses of sea floor. Much detailed work remains to be done on this little-explored part of the earth. Recent explorations have contributed greatly to man's knowledge of the processes acting on the sea floor.

Coarse-grained sediments are moved into the deep oceans by density currents like those you investigated in Section 13–4. These sediments are spread over great areas of the sea floor and out into the deep-sea plains.

The shelf, slope, and rise of the continental margins of most of the major land areas of the world are probably depositional features. They make up tremendously thick deposits along the borders of the continents and ocean basins. The Atlantic and Gulf coasts of the United States are thought to be depositional areas that are slowly sinking under a heavy load of sediments.

As you read the remainder of this book, especially chapters 14 through 16, you will learn more about what may happen to these thick marginal deposits.

Questions and Problems

A

1. What happens to the settling velocity of a particle of volcanic ash as it descends through the air and crosses the air-sea interface?
2. Some submarine landscape features such as volcanoes and submarine canyons show sharper, more rugged outlines than their counterparts on land. How would you explain this?
3. What determines the rate of production of microorganisms in the ocean and the quantities in which they are deposited on the sea floor?

B

1. How do density currents move and distribute sediment on the sea floor?
2. What are some sediments that originate in the sea and how do they form?
3. How did the Ice Ages affect the level of the oceans? How do you know that glaciers are not the main causes of changes in sea level?

C

1. The average thickness of sedimentary rocks in the earth's crust is about 0.74 kilometer. Assuming an average rate of

deposition of 40 millimeters per 50,000 years, and assuming that this rate has been uniform for millions of years, how long did it take to accumulate the sedimentary rocks of the crust? Does this figure represent the total time elapsed since the deposition of the first sedimentary rocks? Why or why not?

2. It is believed that some submarine canyons may have been carved by rivers that flowed across the continent. How could this happen? What evidence is there to indicate that all these canyons were not produced in this way?

Suggested Readings

BOOKS

Brindze, Ruth. *All About Undersea Exploration.* Random House, Inc., New York, 1960.

Carson, Rachel. *The Sea Around Us,* rev. ed. Oxford University Press, Inc., New York, 1961.

Coker, R. E. *This Great and Wide Sea.* Harper & Row, Publishers (Torchbook), New York, 1962.

Cousteau, Jacques-Yves and F. Dumas. *The Silent World.* Harper & Row, Publishers, New York, 1953.

Cowen, Robert C. *Frontiers of the Sea.* Doubleday & Company, Inc., Garden City, N.Y., 1960.

Darwin, Charles. *The Voyage of the Beagle.* Doubleday & Company, Inc. (Anchor Book), Garden City, N.Y., 1962.

Daugherty, Charles M. *Searchers of the Sea: Pioneers in Oceanography.* The Viking Press, Inc., New York, 1961.

PERIODICALS

Bailey, Herbert S., Jr. "The Voyage of the 'Challenger.'" *Scientific American,* May, 1953. (Also Scientific American Offprint #830, W. H. Freeman & Co., Publishers, San Francisco.)

Dietz, Robert S. "The Sea's Deep Scattering Layers." *Scientific American,* August, 1962. (Also Scientific American Offprint #866.)

Fairbridge, Rhodes W. "The Changing Level of the Sea." *Scientific American,* May, 1960. (Also Scientific American Offprint #805.)

Fisher, Robert L. and Roger Revelle. "The Trenches of the Pacific." *Scientific American,* November, 1955. (Also Scientific American Offprint #814.)

Heezen, Bruce C. "The Origin of Submarine Canyons." *Scientific American,* August, 1956. (Also Scientific American Offprint #807.)

Pequegnat, Willis E. "Whales, Plankton and Man." *Scientific American,* January, 1958. (Also Scientific American Offprint #853.)

Stetson, Henry C. "The Continental Shelf." *Scientific American,* March, 1955. (Also Scientific American Offprint #808.)

Stommel, Henry. "The Anatomy of the Atlantic." *Scientific American,* January, 1955. (Also Scientific American Offprint #810.)

An infrared photo of a tidal swamp on the Colorado River delta resembles a burning tree. Can you tell which way the water flows?

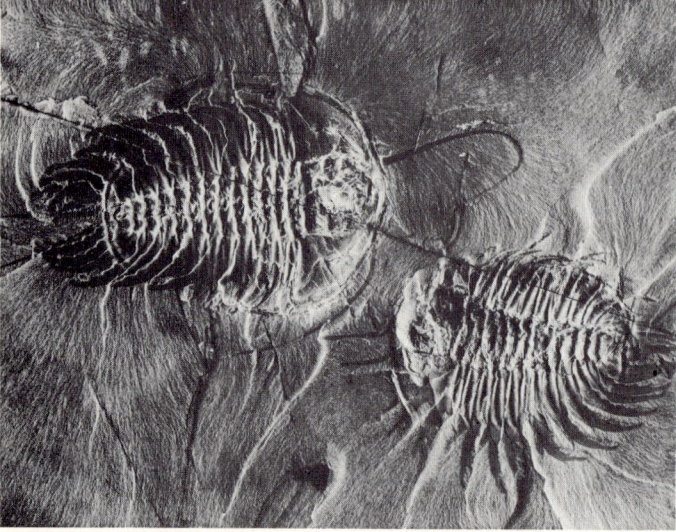

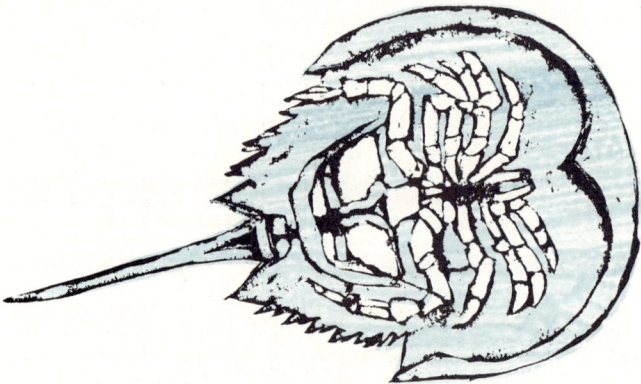

14 Mountains From the Sea

Early in this century an extraordinary fossil discovery was made high in the Canadian Rockies. A geologist's packhorse stepped on a loose slab of black shale and turned it over. There, embedded in the dark rock, were the remains of animals that had once lived in the sea. Even more surprising was the fact that the soft parts of delicate marine organisms like jellyfish and marine worms had been beautifully preserved. This fossil discovery provided important evidence about the origin of the rocks making up the Rocky Mountains.

The fossils were found in rocks that had formed from sediments deposited in waters full of marine organisms. The organisms were buried in the sand and mud of the sea more than 500 million years ago and were then covered and compressed by deposits several kilometers thick.

In examining the photographs (top, left) can you find other evidence that the rocks now found high in the mountains were originally deposited in the sea? What does the rock layering suggest? Could the rocks once have lain beneath an ocean basin? Compare the photograph of the fossils with the drawing of a modern horseshoe crab (below). Why is it significant that the fossils and the living forms are related?

Many rocks now found in the mountains were obviously originally deposited as sediments in the sea. Then how did they come to rise so high above sea level? As yet, no one can answer this question completely.

In the previous chapter you saw what happened to sediments when they finally reached the sea. Now you will explore some of the features of the sea floor and some of the crustal activity occurring both on the margins of continents and in the depths of the sea. From this you can begin to form some idea of how sediments from deep in the ocean can become part of the highest mountains on the surface of the earth.

Evidence for Geosynclines

14–1 Development of an idea—James Hall's field trip.

About 1837, James Hall, a geologist on the staff of the New York State Geological Survey, was puzzled by the great thicknesses of shallow water sediments in western New York State. He was intrigued by rock layers that showed unexplained variations in thickness. Some of the layers were tilted and yet were composed of materials that must have been deposited in horizontal or nearly horizontal layers.

Using the same kind of information from which Hall worked, you will have the opportunity to retrace some of James Hall's field studies. Assemble evidence from the area extending from Buffalo, New York to western Massachusetts, shown in Figure 14–1. Interpret the record from the photographs in Figure 14–2 and see if you can reconstruct past events from the evidence presented.

Procedure

Draw a cross section along the route shown in Figure 14–1. At each station make sure the rock layers are the proper thickness, as shown in Table 14–1. Since all of the sediments were deposited beneath the ocean's surface, those at the top of the basin must be flat. Rock Unit I is above Rock Unit II.

(1) What evidence do you find in the photographs that these are marine sediments?

(2) Describe the general shape of the basin as shown by the cross section.

(3) Explain what the evidence indicates.

(4) How can you explain the rock types at the last stations as compared with those that were found at the first stations?

Figure 14–1 *Map showing the locations of the stations included in this investigation.*

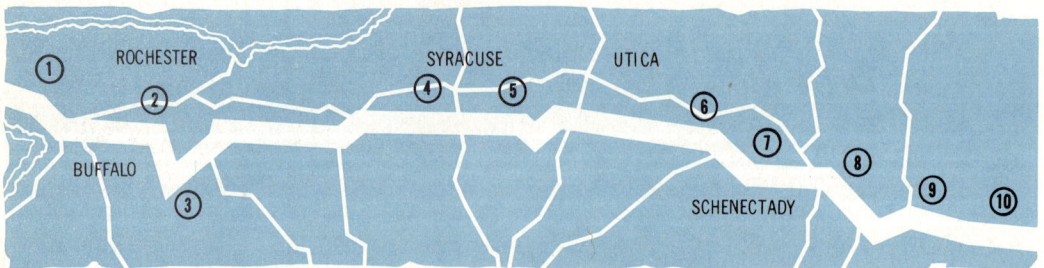

TABLE 14–1 THICKNESS IN METERS OF SEDIMENTARY ROCKS BELOW SURFACE ALONG ROUTE SHOWN IN FIGURE 14–1										
STATIONS	1	2	3	4	5	6	7	8	9	10
ROCK UNIT I	900	1500	1500	1500	1500	2000	2500	0	0	?
ROCK UNIT II	300	350	650	3000	3300	3300	3000	3300	3000	?

Figure 14–2
(*A*) *Niagara River flowing over sedimentary layers* (*station 1*). (*B*) *Flat-lying sedimentary rocks* (*station 2*). (*C*) *Rock layers at station 3.* (*D*) *Station 5: rocks containing fossil coral.* (*E*) *Station 6: Fossils and thin layering are common.* (*F*) *Station 7: Erosion has exposed slightly warped sedimentary layers.* (*G*) *At station 8, rocks are contorted and shattered.* (*H, I, J*) *The rocks at stations 9 and 10 show evidence of igneous activity.*

313

Figure 14–3 (*Left*) *These ripple marks were formed on the bottom of an ancient sea.* (*Right*) *Ripple marks on the beach today indicate wave action. Where else might you find ripple marks?*

14–2 How do geosynclines form?

James Hall's studies of the area covered in his field trips led him to form the concept of a geosyncline. A **geosyncline** is a shallow ocean basin that is sinking and being filled with sediments. Such a basin occurs near the shore of an ocean. Was your answer to Question 2 in Section 14–1 similar to the definition given here?

James Hall's concept of the geosyncline would have been useful even if it had applied only to the area that he was studying. His explanations, however, contributed so directly to the understanding of this geologic process that

they have been used with success in interpreting and identifying many ancient and modern geosynclines.

Suppose that you extended Investigation 14–1 to Pennsylvania and Ohio. You would find that rocks totaling 13,000 to 14,000 meters thick in New York become only one-tenth as thick toward the west. Measurements in many parts of the world show that sedimentary rocks in mountainous areas are often 10,000 to 15,000 meters thick. Rocks representing the same time span are only a fraction as thick in the adjoining plains.

Throughout the areas of greatest thickness there is evidence that the sediments were deposited in shallow water. For example, the rocks contain fossils closely resembling some life forms now living in shallow seas. They also contain ripple marks, the small ridges formed by wave action on sediment in shallow water. (See Figure 14–3.)

How could these great thicknesses of sediment accumulate in shallow water? You might conclude that the sea floor had been sinking or that sea level had been rising at a rate equal to the accumulation of the sediments. In either case the sea would maintain a constant depth as sediments were deposited.

If you accept the second hypothesis, you would expect to find evidence that

Figure 14–4 *Continental regions where some geosynclinal mountains have been developed during geologic history. Notice that mountains occur in each of these regions today.*

sea level had everywhere risen 13,000 to 14,000 meters. The geological record indicates no rise in sea level of this amount or anything close to it. Hence, the sinking of the sea floor seems the more likely explanation for the great thickness of shallow water deposits.

If the explanation that sediments accumulate in a sinking basin near the continent is correct, how can you account for the force that drags the bottom of the basin down? Uplift might result from the release of whatever force was causing the basin to sink. As yet, neither the sinking of the crust nor uplift has been fully explained to everyone's satisfaction.

You can see in Figure 14–4 areas of the earth's surface exhibiting thick accumulations of shallow-water marine sediments that are part of today's mountain chains. Hence, scientists now consider these mountain chains to be the sites of former geosynclines.

ACTIVITY *Where are today's geosynclines? You have learned how sediment from the continents is carried into the ocean basins. Using Figure 13–21 and the relief map of the world (Figure 13–4), list as many localities as you can that may be areas where modern geosynclines are forming.*

14–3 Are geosynclines forming today?

Great thicknesses of sediment have been deposited on the continental shelves, slopes, and rises of the Gulf and east coasts of North America. The Gulf Coast is a great basin of deposition in which some 15,000 meters of sedimentary layers have accumulated. (See Figure 14–5 and Section 13–8.) Compare this with the maximum thickness of sedimentary layers in the state of New York

James Hall

James Hall's life spanned an age of great scientific progress and discovery in the United States. Hall was born in Hingham, Massachusetts in 1816. When he began his analysis of the geology of New York State in 1837 for the newly-formed state geological survey, New York was still largely an unsettled frontier. Hall's report of his field trip quickly established his reputation.

In 1857, Hall advanced what was later called the geosynclinal theory of mountain building. It was based on his observations of a sedimentary rock sequence that decreased from a thickness of 12,000 meters in the Appalachian Mountains to one of only 1200 meters in the central plains near the Rockies.

From its texture and fossil content, Hall knew the rock must have formed from shallow-water sediments. This he explained with the theory that the sediments had been deposited in shallow, slowly sinking ocean basins that had accumulated eroded materials so fast that they never became very deep. These basins, he felt, eventually contained the mass of material from which mountains formed. Hall did not attempt to explain the forces necessary to uplift these sediments into mountain ranges but only to account for the accumulation of such thick deposits. The concept of sinking ocean basins filled with sediments is considered an essential part of modern geology.

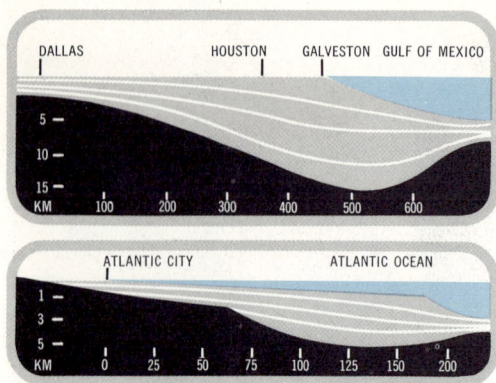

Figure 14–5 *(Top) A cross section through the Gulf Coast of North America. (Bottom) Cross section through the east coast of North America.*

reported by James Hall. When all of the sediments in the Gulf Coast have become sedimentary rocks, would you expect them to maintain their present thickness? The sediments of North America's east coast are nearly as thick as those of the Gulf Coast. (See Figure 14–5.) Do these areas have the characteristics of a geosyncline?

Will modern geosynclines in time take on the characteristics of ancient geosynclinal areas? Can you predict with confidence that there will someday be a range of mountains made up of the thick sediments now accumulating along the coast of the Gulf of Mexico?

There are two types of evidence that suggest that sedimentary rocks in mountains were once part of a geosyncline. They are so important and so useful to geologists that they can be regarded as rules. The first rule is: *The sediments from which layered rocks formed were*

Figure 14–6 *A generalized cross section of part of the Appalachian geosyncline.*

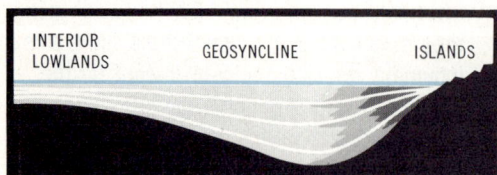

deposited in horizontal or nearly horizontal layers. The second rule is: *Rocks containing remains of sea life (marine fossils) were originally deposited at or below sea level.* You can work with these rules as they are stated here although you may discover that some exceptions to them do exist.

The concept of a geosyncline brings together into a single image a variety of details involving geology and geography. It helps to describe conditions and forms of life that existed at various places in the past. It also enables you to predict where in a geosynclinal area you are likely to find certain types of rocks. (See Figure 14–6.) Where would you expect to find coarse-grained deposits? Where would you expect to find fine-grained deposits? The concept of a geosyncline also provides a frame of reference that helps us to interpret the behavior of portions of the earth's crust. It is useful in deciphering the history of certain mountains.

14–4 Deformation takes place within geosynclines.

As you move across the earth's surface toward the center of a geosyncline, you find not only sedimentary rocks of increasing thickness, but other changes as well. In the field trip from Buffalo to western Massachusetts you saw that the rocks became more and more deformed as you got farther into the geosyncline. You found that the rocks were bent, broken, and squeezed. In fact, these deformational features are so much more obvious than the thickening of the rocks that it is to the credit of James Hall that he was able to determine the overall shape of the geosyncline.

Deformation produces a change in shape, size, or arrangement. Rocks that are bent, broken, squeezed, or stretched

Figure 14–7 *Outcrops of deformed sedimentary rock. (A) Tilted shale and sandstone on the San Francisco peninsula. (B) Folded rocks in the mountains of Colorado. (C) A fault in sedimentary rocks.*

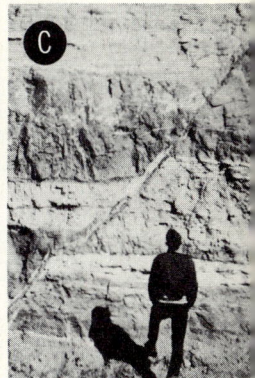

have been deformed. To identify the kind of deformation that has taken place, you must have a good idea of what the rocks looked like before deformation. An inflated basketball on which someone is sitting can be described as slightly flattened because you know what the basketball looked like when no one was sitting on it. It would be absurd, however, to refer to a football as a deformed basketball because the football was not a basketball to start with. In each case you use your knowledge of the object before it was deformed to detect and describe the changes, if any, that have resulted from deformation. (Look back at Figure 1–1.) What caused the various kinds of deformation in the three outcrops of sedimentary rock that are illustrated in Figure 14–7?

Deformation is common in the central regions of geosynclines. This is probably caused in part by the subsidence of the geosyncline. As the central region sinks, the sediments it contains are subjected to forces of compression.

The pattern of deformation can vary considerably. There are examples of layers of rock in many places. (See Figure 14–7.) Large belts of folded rock (Figure 14–7B) occur in some mountain ranges. In these belts, up-folds, or **anticlines,** and down-folds, or **synclines,** alternate like ridges and valleys in a wrinkled tablecloth or rug. Faults also occur in a geosyncline. A **fault** is a fracture along which the rocks have slipped, as shown in Figure 14–7C. Sometimes folds and faults occur together.

Thought and Discussion . . .

1. What does the presence of marine fossils in present-day mountains suggest?
2. How could you distinguish between rocks formed on the continents and rocks formed under the sea?
3. Describe a geosyncline.
4. What evidence in the rock record would indicate that the geosynclinal basin had stopped sinking for a short time between two long periods of sinking?
5. Under what circumstances can layered rocks be deposited so that the layers are not horizontal?
6. How do you determine what a rock looked like before deformation?
7. Are weathering and erosion examples of deformation? Explain.

ACTIVITY *The Activity in Section 3–7 suggested that you draw some earth features to scale. What does a geosyncline look like if drawn to scale? Assume an area 500 kilometers across with 20,000 meters of sediments. This would be a typical geosyncline. Keep this scale drawing in mind when you are considering movements of the earth's crust related to geosynclinal activity.*

Patterns of Crustal Movement

14–5 Investigating earthquakes.

Earthquakes occur in many magnitudes, releasing varied amounts of energy and causing varied amounts of destruction. The Good Friday earthquake of March 27, 1964, centered at Prince William Sound, 150 kilometers from Anchorage, Alaska and caused destruction as far as 175 kilometers away. (See Figure 14–8.) In the Prince William Sound area, 31,000 square kilometers of land were raised as much as 10 meters above sea level. In Kenai Peninsula and Kodiak Island about 57,000 square kilometers of land dropped as much as 1.7 meters. Some other aspects of this earthquake are described in Section 1–7 and Figure 1–10. This was a relatively shallow earthquake. Its focus was estimated to be at most 60 kilometers below Prince William Sound. Yet it released at least twice as much energy as the highly destructive San Francisco earthquake of 1906.

The earthquake of August 17, 1959, at Hebgen Lake, Montana, northwest of Yellowstone National Park, is another spectacular example. (See Figure 14–9.) The shock caused the water in Hebgen Lake to overflow the dam and surge down the narrow canyon of the Madison River. The river in turn was dammed by an earthquake-triggered landslide that moved 80 million tons of rock. Three large faults appeared at the earth's surface, accompanied by land movement that permanently tipped Hebgen Lake like a slightly tilted pan. The patterns of eruption of many of the geysers in Yellowstone Park were altered as a result of this earthquake.

The 1906 earthquake in San Francisco resulted in tremendous destruction because it occurred in a great metropolis

Figure 14–8 (*Below*) *A map showing areas of crustal movement during the Good Friday earthquake.* (*Below, right*) *Destruction on the main street of Anchorage.*

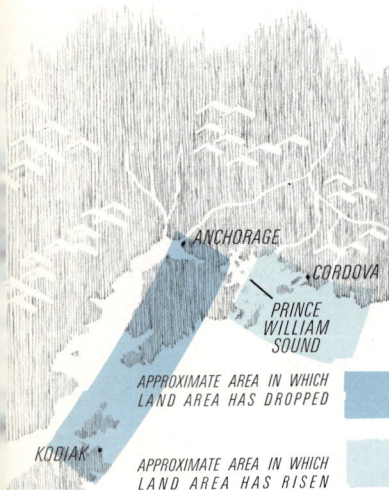

ANCHORAGE
CORDOVA
PRINCE WILLIAM SOUND
APPROXIMATE AREA IN WHICH LAND AREA HAS DROPPED
KODIAK
APPROXIMATE AREA IN WHICH LAND AREA HAS RISEN

LAND ROSE 8 FEET   LAND DROPPED OVER 20 FEET

HEBGEN LAKE   HEBGEN FAULT   RED CANYON FAULT

Figure 14–9 (*Above*) *Cross section showing the effects of an earthquake in the Hebgen Lake area and two of the faults. Dashed line shows former position of lake.* (*Below*) *An aerial view and a ground view of the fault that formed.*

unprepared to cope with such a disaster. The debris from toppling buildings caused many deaths. Fires from overturned stoves and heaters could not be fought because water mains had ruptured. In fact, the cost of fire damage was 20 times that from direct effects of the earthquake itself. Over 490 city blocks were burned out.

Not all earthquake activity is so spectacular. You learned in Chapter 1 that there is much activity going on all the time that is so faint that only seismographs can detect it. Like any flow of energy that can be detected, the activity reveals something about energy sources and the materials through which the energy passes. Hence, this faint earthquake activity has provided much information about the crust. Faint earthquake signals are also important in studying areas where active faults have given rise to large earthquakes.

Since you began your Earthquake Watch in Section 1–7, you have been locating the positions of earthquake epicenters and the depths of earthquake focuses on a world map. You now have some of the data used by scientists to recognize patterns of great belts of activity in the earth's crust. Some of your observations and data will also help you understand processes operating beneath the crust.

Procedure

Examine the map of the earth on which you have been recording the epicenters and depths of earthquakes. (1)What is the general pattern of earthquake distribution? Does it resemble or coincide with any other major patterns of the crust? (See the relief map of the world, Figure 13–4.) If so, how can you relate these features to earthquakes? Must similarly distributed features be either the cause or the effect of each other? (2)Where did the greatest number of earthquakes take place?

You can use the information on depth of earthquake focuses to get some idea about where earthquakes occur within the

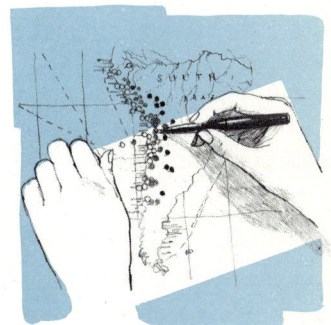

earth. Choose an area from the active belt around the edge of the Pacific Ocean where deep, intermediate, and shallow earthquakes have occurred. Place a sheet of transparent plastic over the area you have selected. Now draw a line from the ocean onto the continent in the area you have picked. Mark the coastline and the location of several shallow-, intermediate-, and deep-focus earthquakes near the line.

Now construct a cross section along the line you have drawn. Using the millimeter scale and graph paper, plot the location of the earthquake focuses to scale at the depth at which they occur. Many points will not be on the line you have drawn, so plot those that are nearest the line. Trace your cross section on a piece of paper.

(3)From your completed drawing, describe the pattern of distribution of earthquake focuses in this area. (4)How would you interpret this pattern? (5)From figures 14–4 and 14–10A, describe the distribution of earthquakes with respect to that of (A) volcanoes and (B) mountains that have been uplifted from former geosynclines.

14–6 Volcanoes, island arcs, and ocean trenches.

As you discovered in Investigation 14–5, volcanoes, faults, and earthquakes seem to be related. They occur on the ocean floor as well as on land. Curved chains of volcanic islands form great arcs around the margins of the Pacific Basin. (See figures 14–10B and 13–4.) The Antilles and East Indies are also a series of island arc structures. Many of the volcanoes in these chains are still active and occasionally spew out masses of lava and other volcanic materials.

Long, deep trenches in the sea floor lie between the island arcs and the flat deep-sea plains. (See Figure 14–10B.) On the eastern border of the Pacific Basin, the trenches are next to the continents, and the volcanic "island" arcs such as the Andes are part of the continental mass. The earthquake and volcanic activities associated with island arcs and trenches show that the earth's crust is in motion in these regions.

There is a close spatial association of earthquake belts, ocean trenches, island arcs, and volcanoes. Are they also in some way connected with geosynclines? Since the cores of geosynclinal mountains contain faulted and folded rocks, it is reasonable to conclude that earthquake activity accompanies deformation in a geosyncline. If the crust has been pulled down and squeezed, the movement could result in deep trenches in the ocean floor. It is possible that the fractures in the deformed layers of a geosyncline act as passageways for the upward flow of volcanic materials.

Recall that there was evidence for volcanic activity associated with the geo-

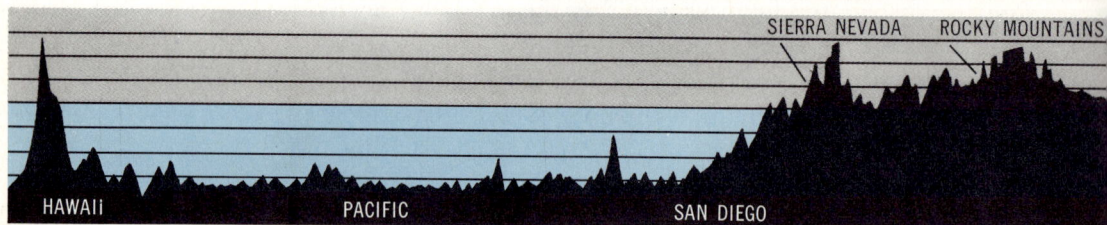

SIERRA NEVADA   ROCKY MOUNTAINS

HAWAII   PACIFIC   SAN DIEGO

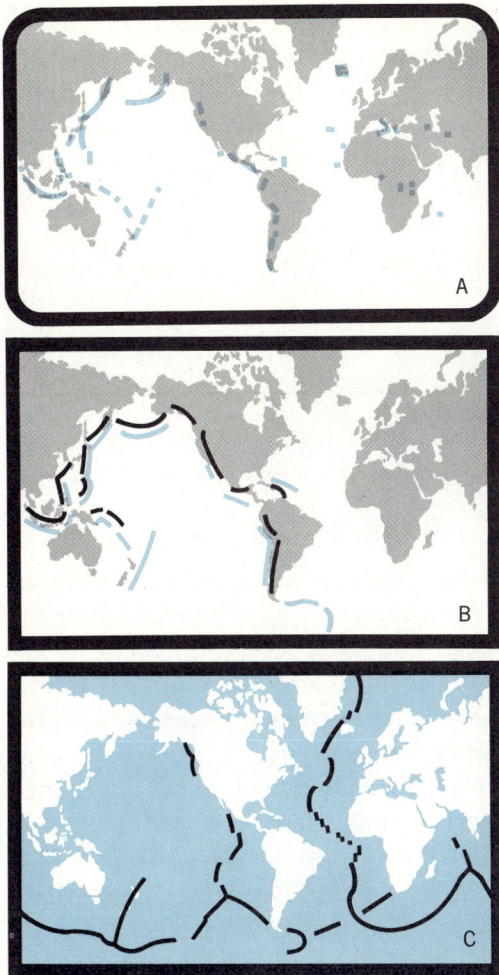

Figure 14–10 *World distribution patterns of (A) active and extinct volcanoes, (B) island arcs and trenches, and (C) oceanic ridges.*

syncline that you studied in Investigation 14–1. Many of today's volcanoes are related to island arc systems.

14–7 Mid-ocean ridges and fault block systems.

In your Earthquake Watch you saw another pattern of crustal activity along the middle of the oceans. These are the **mid-ocean ridges.** Do they seem to be related to geosynclines? Can you tell by comparing figures 14–4 and 14–10C?

The longest and highest mountain ranges on earth are the great submerged ridges that wind across the ocean floor. They follow a path that is in many places roughly midway between the continents. (See figures 14–10C and 13–4.) The mid-ocean ridges are volcanic in composition. Vast volumes of lava have flowed through great cracks, or fractures, and piled up on the sea floor. (See Figure 14–11.) In a few places, such as the Azores and Easter Island, parts of the ridges rise above sea level as islands. Can you find other islands like this on a world map? The crest of a ridge may be 6000 meters above the sea floor, yet still be below sea level.

In 1953 a deep trench was discovered running along the Mid-Atlantic Ridge. Can you find this trench in Figure 14–11? Similar trenches or sets of parallel trenches have since been discovered and mapped elsewhere in the mid-ocean mountain system.

Investigations of the sea floor have shown that mid-ocean ridges exist in the Atlantic, Pacific, and Indian basins. Russian and American scientists working from drifting ice floes, and more recently Americans in nuclear-powered submarines, have also confirmed the existence of a mid-ocean ridge in the Arctic Basin. (See Figure 14–10C.) The ridge in the Pacific Basin is not so distinct as those in the Indian and Atlantic basins. Oceanographers have learned that all of

Figure 14–11 *Profile of the sea floor from Hawaii to Gibraltar, and of the continental United States. Compare the heights of various features.*

these mid-ocean ridges make up a single mountain system 46,000 kilometers long. (See Figure 14–10C.) Detailed mapping of the ridge in some areas shows that where its direction changes sharply, it is not really bent. Instead it is sliced by a series of parallel faults that make it look like a crude stairway viewed from the side. (See Figure 14–12.) Why is the ridge broken and not bent?

You know from plotting earthquake epicenters that the mid-ocean ridges are also regions of frequent earthquake and volcanic activity. The eruption of Surtsey is evidence of such crustal unrest today. (See Figure 14–13.)

The mid-ocean ridges are quite unlike geosynclinal mountains and island arcs although all three features clearly indicate deformation of the crust. Some scientists have suggested that the mid-ocean ridges and their trenches are evidence of a stretching or **tension** in the earth's crust while geosynclinal mountains are evidence of squeezing or **compression** in the earth's crust.

Why do the mid-ocean ridges tend to lie along the centers of the ocean basins? This puzzling relationship has a still more puzzling exception. If you trace the mid-ocean ridge northward through the Pacific Ocean, it appears to enter

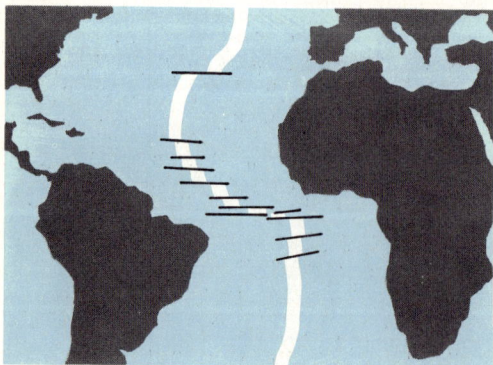

Figure 14–13 (*Left*) Surtling, a small volcanic island forms near Surtsey.
Figure 14–14 (*Right*) The west face of the Wasatch Mountains is an eroded fault block.
Figure 14–15 (*Far right*) This dome near Sinclair, Wyoming was produced by upwarping of an area of the earth's crust.

North America through Baja California and coincide with the California mountains. Are these mountains a part of the mid-ocean ridge? (See map, page 296.)

In other regions the earth's crust has given way and large blocks have moved up or down along fault lines. Two of the most famous down-dropped blocks of which you may have heard are Death Valley and the Dead Sea. Both have dropped so low that their surfaces are below sea level. The rift valleys of eastern Africa and the Rhine River valley in Europe are other examples of down-dropped blocks. In the western United States the whole region between the Wasatch Mountains and the Sierra Nevada is a fault block system and is made up of alternating up-thrown and down-dropped blocks. (See Figure 14–14.)

Are these features the result of tension or compression? Could they be related to geosynclines? In the case of eastern Africa they are not, because this is not a region of geosynclinal mountains. (See Figure 14–4.) What happened in the area between the Wasatch Mountains and the Sierra Nevada? Could the blocks there be related to stages in the uplift of geosynclines?

Figure 14–12 *The pattern formed by faults cutting the Mid-Atlantic Ridge.*

14–8 Other evidence for crustal movement.

Geosynclinal mountains, volcanic island arcs, and mid-ocean ridges are not the only irregularities or signs of unrest in the earth's crust. There are domes, like the area shown in Figure 14–15, and sags, like the Michigan and Paris basins, that provide evidence of gentle bending or warping of the earth's crust. These features are many times the size of the typical anticlines and synclines associated with geosynclinal belts. They may be as wide as they are long. They have been found in continental areas separate from geosynclinal belts. Domes and basins have developed under conditions involving much less mobility of the crust than the areas where geosynclinal mountains developed.

In observing features of the earth's crust that relate to deformation, we cannot ignore the vast expanse of the crust that lies under the oceans. In the ocean basins there are volcanic peaks that are not part of either island arcs or mid-ocean ridges. The Hawaiian Islands are part of a small chain that appears to be isolated from the belt of volcanic features circling the Pacific. Since these islands are also heavy loads on the crust, they provide information on how the crust supports such loads.

Much has been learned about features of the ocean floor through the use of new and ingenious tools. The echo-sounder bounces sound waves off the sea bottom and translates them into a record of the profile of the ocean floor. (See Figure 14–16.) Another method

Figure 14–16 (*Far left*) *A scientist aboard ship watches a graph of sea floor depth variations being drawn by a precision depth recorder.* (*Left*) *A rift valley in East Africa.*

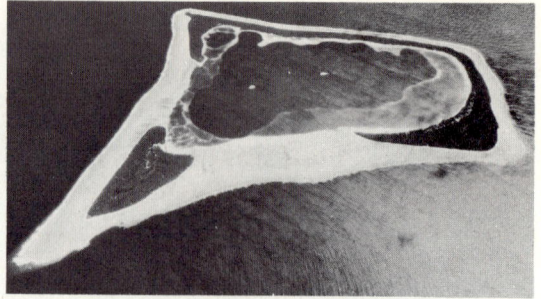

Figure 14–17 *(Above) Can you explain flat-topped seamounts so far below the ocean surface?*
Figure 14–18 *(Right, above) Ifalik Atoll in the Pacific, a typical coral reef formation. (Right, below) A marine geologist gathers a coral sample.*

provides information on the materials beneath the ocean floor by analyzing how they transmit waves generated by underwater explosions.

Scattered across the deep-sea floor, either isolated or in groups, are thousands of volcanic mountains or **seamounts.** Some have sharp or pointed peaks and others have flat tops. (See Figure 14–17.) Seamounts with flat tops are thought to have once been at sea level where they were eroded by ocean waves. How can they be several hundred meters below the sea surface today? This depth is too great to be explained by the lowered sea level during the Ice Ages. Nevertheless, if flat-topped seamounts were eroded by waves they must have once reached sea level. If sea level were never as low as the flat tops of seamounts today, how did the erosion take

place? A clue comes from a series of pointed and flat-topped seamounts near the Aleutian Trench.

Before the development of the Aleutian Trench some of the volcanic seamounts must have reached the sea surface. As the trench formed, the sea floor sank, not only in the trench but also some distance out from it. This sinking of the sea floor lowered the volcanic peaks in the area. This lowering was greatest near the trench and gradually decreased away from it. The locations of the pointed and flat-topped seamounts in relation to the Aleutian Trench agree

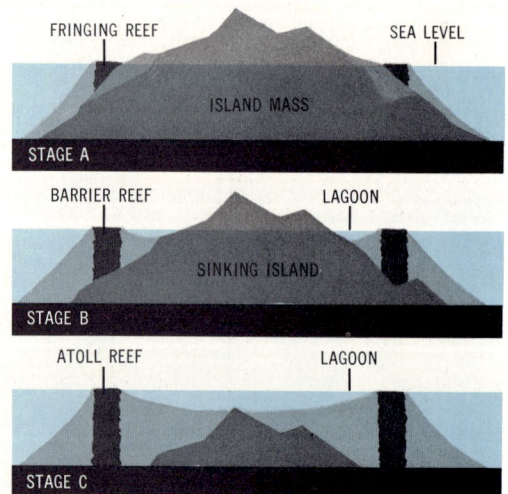

Figure 14–19 *Stages (A, B, and C) in the development of a coral atoll, based on the theory proposed by Charles Darwin in 1842.*

with the idea that crustal sinking accounts for the present depths of the tops. (See Figure 14–17.)

Are there other indications of vertical movement of the ocean crust? Coral reefs are among the most interesting deposits in the sea. (See Figure 14–18.) Recent studies of cores from drill holes through coral reefs down to 1400 meters reveal the structure of these deposits. These particular cores were taken from a circular reef, or *atoll*, called Eniwetok (en-i-WEE-tok) Atoll, in the west Pacific. Corals were found throughout the entire Eniwetok core. Since reef-building corals live only in shallow warm waters the depth of the core and the presence of coral indicated that conditions in the surface waters of the tropical seas in this area had not changed for the past 60 million years.

How do we know this? How is it possible to explain 1400 meters of coral rock when such rock forms only in shallow water? Charles Darwin, who visited coral atolls as a young man of 22, first proposed that the sea floor and the islands had slowly subsided. The corals grew upward, keeping pace with the lowering of the sea floor. Darwin identified three types of coral reefs, which he interpreted as three stages of development. (See Figure 14–19 A, B, and C.) These stages were (A) reefs growing along the shores of volcanic islands, (B) reefs with a patch of water (a lagoon) between them and the shore, and (C) atolls. Darwin believed that atolls had originally been shoreline reefs that had not reached the last stages of sinking.

A hundred years of argument followed the publication of Darwin's ideas on atolls in 1842. The borings on Eniwetok in the 1950's reached volcanic rock after passing through 1400 meters of coral. These results agree with Darwin's ideas

Charles Darwin

In 1831, Charles Darwin (1809–1882) became ship's naturalist of the H.M.S. Beagle, which had been commissioned to survey the southern seas and the lands of Patagonia and Tierra del Fuego at the tip of South America. On the Beagle's historic five-year voyage, Darwin's careful observations of nature led him to the theory of evolution. He also made a contribution to earth science—a theory of the origin of coral atolls.

Coral atolls had long been a mystery to travelers in the South Pacific. Where had they come from? The accepted theory was that the coral had grown up from the rims of volcanic craters deep in the sea. Darwin doubted this theory.

On the voyage, Darwin saw some atolls over 80 kilometers in diameter, far larger than any volcanic crater he knew. Since Darwin knew that corals only lived within 20 to 30 fathoms of the surface, he reasoned that they could not have built up from great depth.

Darwin theorized that mountains once high above sea level had slowly sunk below the surface as the sea floor lowered. Coral animals had attached themselves about the edges of the mountain top near sea level and had continued to grow as the mountain sank. "We see in each atoll a monument over an island now lost," wrote Darwin. Eventually, borings from Eniwetok Atoll confirmed his predictions.

concerning the development of atolls. Judging from Figure 14–18, in what stage do you think Darwin would have considered Ifalik Atoll to be?

14–9 Stable and mobile regions.

Do geosynclines develop everywhere on the earth's surface? Compare figures 14–4 and 13–4. Observe the pattern that exists between plains and mountain chains. You learned that present mobile belts are located on the edges of continents. In addition to this modern evidence, the composition and thickness of rocks in ancient geosynclines indicate that they also formed near the margins of continents. Features today that might be modern geosynclines also border continents. It is clear, then, that these belts of crustal mobility are somehow boundary zones between the continents and ocean basins. Possibly they indicate a weakness in the crust where the continental mass meets the oceanic area. What could cause this weakness?

It has been discovered that the materials making up the continental and oceanic crusts are fundamentally different from each other. The oceanic crust is made up of dark, iron-rich, relatively dense materials—**basaltic rocks.** The continental crust is made of light-colored, potassium- and sodium-rich, lower density materials—**granitic rocks.** The continental crust is five to six times thicker than the oceanic crust. It is likely that there is some movement at the interface between the two types of crustal material. Scientists cannot determine whether this interface is sharp

or gradual with the evidence about the crust now available to them.

There does seem to be a fairly consistent pattern relating geosynclinal mountains and more stable regions in the interiors of continents. This pattern is depicted in Figure 14–20. Every continent has a region of ancient rocks that are the worn-down remains of belts of deformation. Figure 20–5 shows such an area in central Canada. These areas have undergone little deformation for long periods of time. Lying nearly horizontal in the interior lowland are beds of sedimentary rocks that overlap onto the stable interior regions. These beds extend seaward toward the mountains and thicken, as you saw in the James Hall field trip, becoming greatly deformed in the belt of the geosynclinal mountains. (See Figure 14–21.) Beyond the mountains are more flat-lying sedimentary rocks that continue outward beneath the sea. Just off the shore of the continent is the continental shelf. In some cases the shelf may be a modern geosyncline in the stage of accumulating sediments.

All of these units need not appear on every continent. Some appear only here and there within a continent. When these units do appear, however, they are generally in the same position in relation to each other.

Ancient mountain systems may be so eroded that they appear as nearly flat land. The eroded remains of highly deformed mountain systems are really the inner part of a former mobile belt now

Figure 14–20 *Cross section of a model continent showing the major units.*

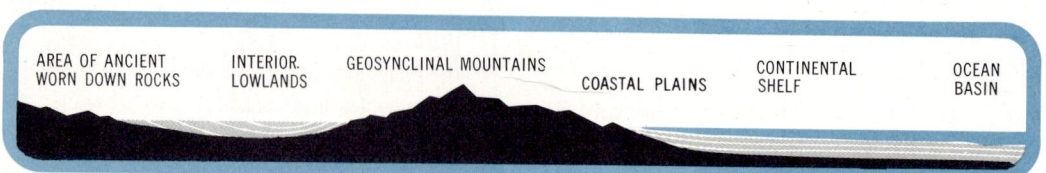

AREA OF ANCIENT WORN DOWN ROCKS   INTERIOR. LOWLANDS   GEOSYNCLINAL MOUNTAINS   COASTAL PLAINS   CONTINENTAL SHELF   OCEAN BASIN

Figure 14–21 (*Above*) *A radar photo of the Appalachian Plateau and Mountains in West Virginia. (*Below*) Evidence of folding can be seen in the area near Harrisburg, Pennsylvania.*

essentially inactive. The rock types found in the interiors of mountain ranges bring up many new problems about the earth's surface. How do such rocks form? Is there any place where such rocks are forming today? How do these problems relate to the rock cycle?

In the next chapter you will have an opportunity to study the deeper parts of mountains. You will gain a better idea of what kinds of rocks are being formed and what types of activity are going on in the mobile belts and deep within the earth's crust. You will be looking at a part of the rock cycle in which dramatic changes take place deep beneath the surface of the earth in places like the active zone around the Pacific and in the Antilles of the Caribbean.

Thought and Discussion . . .

1. If the Gulf Coast area is geosynclinal, where would you expect volcanic islands to develop?
2. Describe the island arc pattern at the western border of the Pacific Ocean.
3. How can you explain the presence, side by side, of flat-topped and pointed seamounts of the same height?
4. Do thick rocks, features of deformation, and geosynclinal mountains always occur together? Why?

Unsolved Problems Although James Hall's concept of the geosyncline is over a century old, it is not yet possible to identify a clearly defined family of geosynclines. Each unit identified as a geosyncline, except for Hall's original Appalachian geosyncline, seems to be lacking one or more important features. This is especially true for so-called modern geosynclines. The uncertainties involved in identifying modern geosynclines indicate the need for better understanding of geosynclinal processes. Many questions remained unanswered.

What are the sources of sediments in geosynclines? If the Gulf Coast area is a modern geosyncline, it is difficult even there to trace sediments back to their sources. Consider how much more difficult this is in the case of ancient geosynclines. Still more difficult is the problem of describing sediment sources from now vanished land masses on the seaward sides of ancient geosynclines, such as Hall's original Appalachian geosyncline. The sedimentary record clearly indicates that high land areas must have been present during the development of some ancient geosynclines. Where were these high areas and what did they look like? Might some of them now lie beneath coastal plain deposits?

Why do geosynclinal mountain ranges tend to be uplifted at the margins of continents? Is this in some way related to the differences in density between the continental and oceanic crusts? What is the connection, if any, between island arcs and their trenches on the one hand, and geosynclines and geosynclinal mountains on the other hand? Why do the island arcs and the trenches associated with them lie along the margins of the ocean basins?

CHAPTER REVIEW

Summary

The geosyncline concept, introduced over a century ago by James Hall, pulls together knowledge of ancient environments that is important in both physical and biological history. It enables us to predict the kinds of rocks to be found in various parts of a geosynclinal area and provides ideas about how the crust has been deformed there.

A geosyncline is a shallow, nearshore basin on the sea floor that is sinking and being filled with sediments. The sinking of the crust in geosynclinal areas requires a downward pull in addition to the loading caused by the deposition of sediments. The exact nature of this force is not yet known.

As sinking continues, the geosynclinal deposits are deformed and other changes in the rocks can take place. Sinking can be followed by uplift when sea-floor deposits are raised to the height of mountains. These are the stages of development that account for the great belts of geosynclinal mountains found near the margins of continents.

There are areas at the margins of the oceans today that may have at least some geosynclinal characteristics. Development of geosynclines can stop at any stage. Volcanic activity and earthquakes have been associated with geosynclinal evolution.

The mid-ocean ridges are also great belts of deformation in the earth's crust. However, the mid-ocean ridges seem to indicate tension in the crust while geosynclinal belts seem to indicate compression. Other features of deformation in the earth's crust within the continents and ocean basins indicate gentle warping and yielding in large blocks bounded by faults.

The major features of crustal deformation described in this chapter appear in a generally orderly pattern with respect to continents and ocean basins.

Questions and Problems

A

1. Describe some of the puzzling features of rock formations that led James Hall to the geosyncline theory.

2. What evidence suggests that geosynclinal sediments have been deposited in shallow water?

3. What features does the Gulf of Mexico Basin have that lead some scientists to believe that it is an active geosyncline?

4. State the rules that govern the reasoning behind the geosyncline theory.

5. How do you know that rocks have been deformed?

6. With what principles must you be familiar in order to recognize and interpret rock deformation?

7. Describe the features of a folded mountain range.

8. What is a fault? Describe the various motions that may be associated with the formation of a fault.

9. Where on the continents are geosynclinal mountains generally located? Where in the oceans are island arcs generally located?

10. Where is a mid-ocean ridge not a mid-ocean ridge?

11. How can coral reefs be used to indicate vertical movement of the ocean crust?

12. Why would you expect to find active geosynclines today? Where might some of these be located?

B

1. Explain the location of limestones in geosynclinal deposits.
2. In a geosynclinal basin, where does most of the rock deformation take place? Describe the conditions and the changes caused by these conditions.
3. Where does the energy that causes earthquakes come from?
4. What evidence indicates that island arcs may be a middle stage in the formation of geosynclinal mountains? What evidence rules against this idea?
5. What should happen to the crust of the earth in an area in which volcanic islands are growing?
6. Give a possible explanation for the development of mid-ocean ridges and trenches.
7. Why are the mid-ocean ridges *not* believed to be the result of compression?
8. How did the tops of seamounts become eroded if their present level is far below the lowest possible level of the oceans?
9. How is it possible to find corals at a depth of 1400 meters when coral does not form below a depth of 80 meters?
10. Describe the difference between materials comprising the continental and oceanic crusts. How do we know about this difference?
11. How do the water cycle and the rock cycle work together?

C

1. Sediments moved from high areas into geosynclinal basins lose potential energy, as does the water that moves them. What is the source of the potential energy of the sediments and what is the source of potential energy of the water?
2. Under what conditions would the remains of animals that had lived on land be found in sea floor deposits?
3. Why is the deposition of sediments on the ocean floor considered to be not

sufficient to cause the sinking of a geosyncline? What other force probably aids in the subsidence?
4. What finally causes the uplift of these deep geosynclinal rocks?
5. Under what conditions might thick sediments accumulate in a geosyncline without finally undergoing uplift?
6. Describe the processes that could someday make the East Indies and Japan a part of the Asian mainland.

Suggested Readings

BOOKS

Bates, Robert L. and Walter C. Sweet. *Geology, an Introduction.* D. C. Heath & Company, Boston, 1966. Chapters 14 and 16.

Darwin, Charles. *The Voyage of the Beagle* (Edition of 1860). Doubleday & Company, Inc. (Anchor Books), Garden City, N.Y., 1962. Paperback.

Fenton, Carroll L. and Mildred A. Fenton. *Mountains.* Doubleday & Company, Inc., Garden City, N.Y., 1942.

Fenton, Carroll L. *Our Amazing Earth.* Doubleday & Company, Inc., Garden City, N.Y., 1938.

Milne, Lorus J. and Margery Milne and the Editors of *Life. Mountains.* Time, Inc. (Life Nature Library), New York, 1962.

PERIODICALS

Bucher, Walter H. "The Crust of the Earth." *Scientific American,* May, 1950.

Graves, William P. E. and Maynard M. Miller. "Alaskan Earthquakes." *National Geographic Magazine,* July, 1964.

Kay, Marshall. "The Origin of Continents." *Scientific American,* September, 1955. (Also Scientific American Offprint #816, W. H. Freeman & Co., Publishers, San Francisco.)

Matthews, Samuel W. "The Night the Mountains Moved." *National Geographic Magazine,* March, 1960.

PAMPHLET

Geology. Boy Scouts of America, Boy Scout Merit Badge Series, New Brunswick, N.J., 1953.

Chapter 15 Rocks Within Mountains

You have seen the effects of weathering on rocks that become exposed to the hydrosphere and the atmosphere. In adjusting to the environment at the earth's surface, rocks break down and provide materials that become sediments. Because sediments and the rocks that form from them cover about three-fourths of the earth's land masses, most people are familiar with them. However, this covering is quite thin in comparison with the entire thickness of the earth's crust. What relationship does this sedimentary covering have to the rocks that lie beneath it?

You may have heard about plans to drill holes deep into the earth's crust and to drill down through the crust under the Pacific Ocean. In spirit these projects have the same purpose as space exploration—to satisfy man's curiosity about a formerly unreachable part of his environment. Mystery and challenge have always driven man to search the unknown.

Even if projects to drill through the earth's crust are successful, they will shed only a glimmer of light on the interior of the earth. Is drilling the only way

The massive, granitic walls of Wyoming's Tetons rise over 4000 meters. What evidence do they give of the rock environment beneath the crust?

to find out about the hidden materials and conditions at great depth? You realize by now that there are many ways of learning about things that are hidden from view. In what other ways besides drilling can scientists explore the earth's interior?

In this chapter you will be asked to adopt a spirit of exploration and to make a mental excursion deep into the crust of the earth. In venturing into this unfamiliar territory, you must realize that your experiences with materials on the earth's surface may not help you to fully understand the entire crust.

Rocks in the crust are always being exposed to new kinds of environments and as a result they continually change. The response of rocks to changing environments is part of the rock cycle. How do deep environments differ from surface environments? What effects do they have on rocks? The only direct evidence to help you understand processes deep in the crust is contained in rocks that have been uplifted from the depths by mountain-building processes and then exposed by erosion.

Changes in Solid Rock

15–1 Investigating rocks from the cores of mountains.

In mountain ranges such as the Appalachians, Rockies, Sierra Nevada, or Adirondacks, you will see rocks different from sedimentary and volcanic rocks. Such rocks are also found in large areas where there are no mountains but where mountains may have existed long ago, as in northeastern North America. In this investigation you will examine several kinds of rocks from mountainous areas and try to determine how they might have formed.

Procedure

Examine the rock specimens provided. Separate the specimens into groups that have something in common. Find as many different ways as you can of arranging them into distinct groups.

(1) For each different grouping you suggest, record the common properties you found that led you to make this particular grouping.

(2) Try to pick out the rocks that formed deep within the crust. Which ones would you pick? Explain which features of the rocks prompted you to decide.

15–2 How does metamorphism change rocks?

Changes that occur in rocks deep below the surface are very different from the changes caused by weathering. Weathering destroys rocks and minerals. In contrast to weathering, processes that affect rocks and minerals deep in the earth commonly cause minerals to grow larger. These processes also cause rocks to become more dense, and they cause new minerals to form.

Metamorphic rocks, as you will recall from Section 2–1, are defined as rocks that have been changed into new forms as a result of high temperature and pressure. Geologists use the term **metamorphic** to describe the processes that occur deep in the earth at temperatures and pressures that are higher than those on

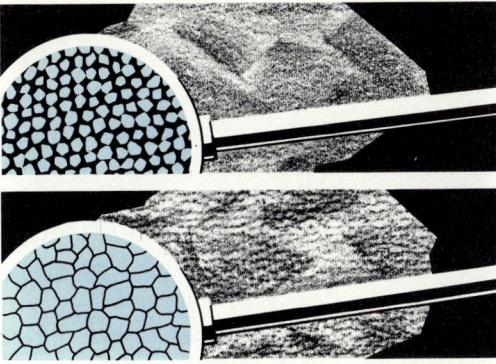

Figure 15-1 *Which of the rocks that are shown above is the metamorphic rock?*

the surface, but still are not high enough to cause the rocks to melt.

Examine the two rocks sketched in Figure 15–1. Both sketches represent rocks made up entirely of quartz. One is a sedimentary rock called sandstone. The other is a metamorphic rock called quartzite. What differences can you detect between the two rocks shown? Which sketch represents the metamorphic rock and which the sedimentary rock? What features of the rocks influenced your choice? The kind of change shown in this figure is involved in almost all metamorphic processes.

Another kind of change is shown in Figure 15–2. Which of these sketches represents the sedimentary rock and which the metamorphic? What kinds of changes have occurred? Have new minerals been formed? How do these examples differ from the rocks in Figure 15–1?

In order to investigate this problem experimentally, you could put a piece of quartz sandstone similar to that in Figure 15–1 into a hot laboratory oven. If

the oven were hot enough, the sample would melt. If you heated the sandstone to a temperature just below its melting point, changes would begin to occur. The changes would take place slowly, however. If you cooled the sample after a short time, you would see little or no change. Probably you would have to leave the sandstone in the oven for many months or even years to notice a change. A better way to cause the changes would be to seal the sandstone in an airtight container and squeeze it intensely on all sides at the same time that you heated it. If there were a small amount of water in the sealed container, it would be even easier to cause the type of change shown in the illustrations. On the basis of such experimental evidence, what sort of physical conditions do you think would be necessary to change the sedimentary rocks of figures 15–1 and 15–2 into the metamorphic rocks shown beside them?

How hot is it inside the earth? The graph in Figure 6–13 shows the limit of present-day measurements. The temperatures shown on this graph are averages of measurements made in deep drill holes. According to this graph, what is the temperature increase per kilometer?

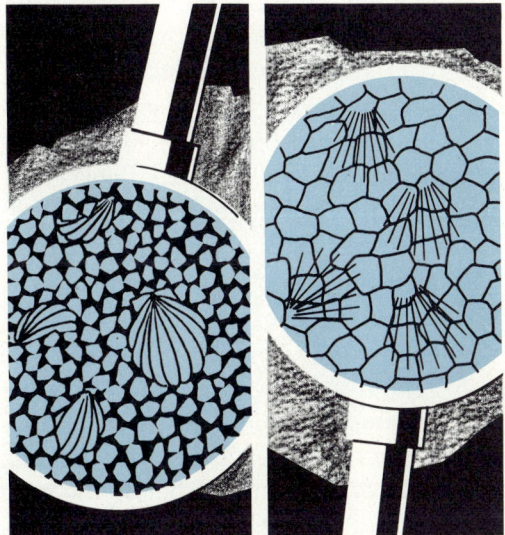

Figure 15-2 *The rock sketched at the near right consists of quartz grains (SiO_2) and shells of scallops ($CaCO_3$). The rock at the far right consists of wollastonite ($CaSiO_3$) and quartz (SiO_2). Which is metamorphic? sedimentary?*

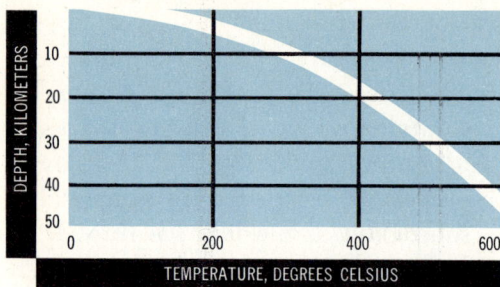

Figure 15-3 *The probable relationships between temperature and depth below the level of the deepest drill holes. The curve represents the probable temperature at a given depth.*

If this curve remained the same at greater depths, what would the temperature be at a depth of 30 kilometers? at the earth's center? (See Section 6–8.)

Indirect evidence suggests that the line shown in Figure 6–13 must begin to curve downward beyond 10 kilometers. The curve in Figure 15–3 gives a probable prediction of the temperature at greater depths. What would be the temperature at a depth of 50 kilometers according to this curve?

If you ever go into a deep mine, you may see mine timbers that appear to have been bent and rocks that seem to be bulged out. What do you think caused this? Imagine yourself down several kilometers in a mine shaft. How many *tons* of rock do you think might be over your head? Besides the thickness of the rock above you, what else would you need to know in order to calculate the pressure of the overlying rock (measured in kilograms per square meter or pounds per square inch)? If you put a rock specimen under very great pressure on all surfaces at once, how could the rock change in order to occupy less space?

Although high temperature and pressure are important in causing metamorphism, some rocks have apparently been buried several kilometers below the surface without being changed. Think back to the imaginary experiment with the piece of sandstone. You were told that changes occur more easily when there is water in the rock. How does water help metamorphism to occur?

You learned in Section 2–4 that minerals are made up of atoms. During metamorphism some ions break loose from the minerals to which they have been attached. For ions to move about very far in the solid rock, small amounts of water or other fluids must be present. Ions do not move very easily in rocks that contain little or no water. Therefore, rocks that have been deeply buried for long periods of time but contain little or no water would undergo less metamorphism than if water were present.

The rearrangement of ions during metamorphism makes the total number of ions in the rock occupy less space than before. Therefore, the rock becomes more dense. You saw evidence in Figure 15–2 that some of the silicon ions joined with calcium (Ca) and carbonate (CO_3) ions to form a new mineral, wollastonite ($CaSiO_3$). Wollastonite is more dense than the original calcite ($CaCO_3$). A sandstone containing shells ($CaCO_3$) may undergo a similar change and become more dense. The change involves the disappearance of one mineral, calcite, and the appearance of another, wollastonite.

A **parent rock** is the material from which a metamorphic rock forms. The two sandstones shown in figures 15–1 and 15–2 are the parent rocks of the two quartzites. Each kind of sedimentary or igneous rock may become a metamorphic rock. The chemical elements that are present in a parent rock have an important effect on the kinds of metamorphic rocks that can form from it.

The major reason for the many different kinds of metamorphic rocks is the many different kinds of metamorphic conditions. Each different combination of heat and pressure can produce a different kind of metamorphic rock. The most important factors in rock-forming environments are temperature, pressure, amount of water, and ions free to move about in the rock. A single kind of rock can change into many different forms depending on the particular rock environment in which the change occurs.

15–3 Metamorphism varies with rock environments.

Can metamorphism take place at the earth's surface? Imagine a red-hot stream of lava spilling out of a volcano. As lava flows over the top of other rocks, it can bake them. Baking of this type is called **contact metamorphism** because it occurs when molten rock comes in contact with another rock. Contact metamorphism occurs when molten rock comes in contact with cooler rock and causes its minerals to change in composition and structure. Zones of contact metamorphism can be quite small, as shown in Figure 15–4.

Some bodies of molten rock material exist deep below the earth's surface. The great heat from this deep material also causes contact metamorphism. The intensity of changes in the solid rock near

Figure 15–4 *Contact metamorphism, the light zones in the photograph, was caused by intrusion of the darker basaltic rock (top) at high temperature.*

a molten mass of rock material or a lava flow depends on how hot the molten material is. Even more important, the intensity of changes depends on how long the hot, molten material is in contact with the solid rocks around it.

A lava flow on the earth's surface cools rapidly and does not have time to do much baking. On the other hand, the great heat from a deeply buried body of molten rock material cannot escape to the air. This heat can only escape through the rocks surrounding the molten material. It may take such molten rock thousands or hundreds of thousands of years to cool. In such long periods of time many metamorphic changes may occur in the surrounding rocks.

When metamorphism occurs over a large area, it is called **regional metamorphism.** Rocks that have been metamorphosed regionally may cover thousands of square kilometers. Regional and contact metamorphism seem to accompany the building of mountains.

You examined evidence in Chapter 14 that suggested the existence of subsiding areas in the earth's crust called geosynclines. Geosynclines are thought to sink deeper and deeper into the crust. A thick pile of sediment accumulates as the area sinks and sediments in the lower part are slowly carried into deeper and deeper rock environments. Temperature and pressure continue to increase. What would happen to a layer of clay in the bottom of the geosyncline as it sank deeper and deeper? The changes that would affect this layer of clay in the various rock environments are shown in Figure 15–5. Describe the characteristics that each rock type would have if it formed in the different environments that are represented in the figure. How would rocks found on the surface reflect the environment in which they formed?

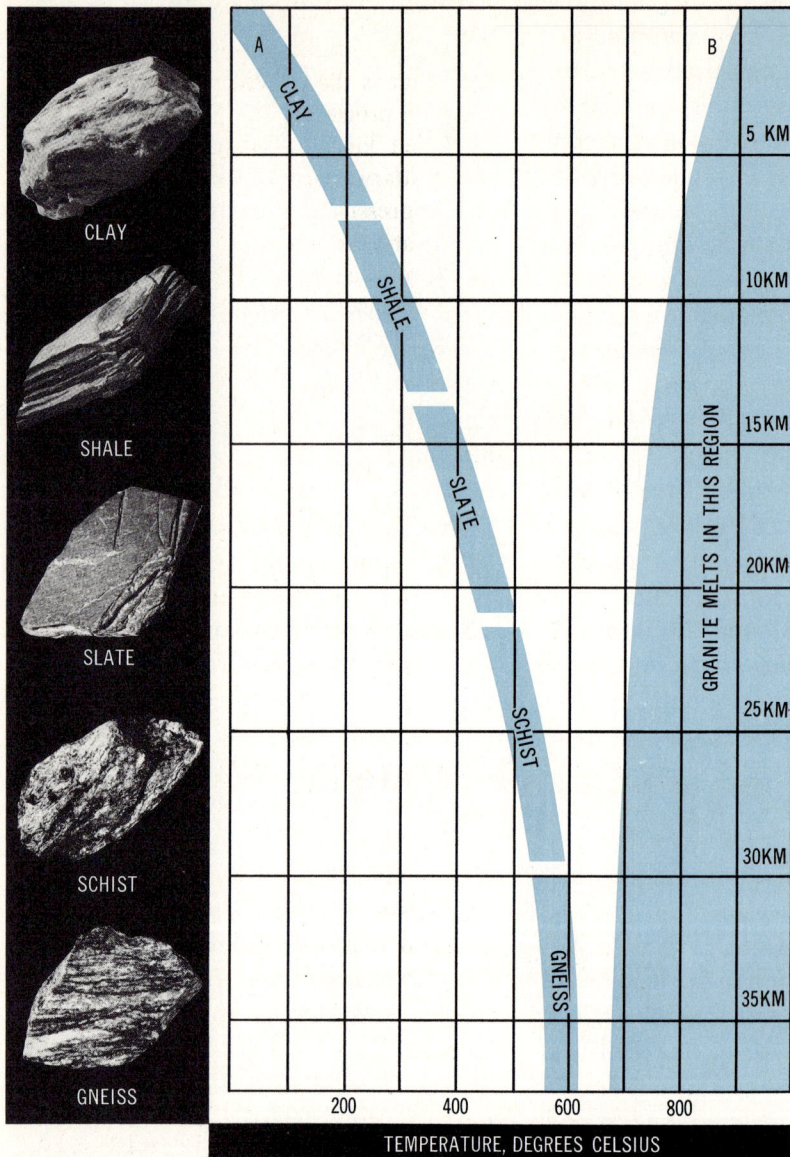

CLAY

SHALE

SLATE

SCHIST

GNEISS

A

CLAY

SHALE

SLATE

SCHIST

GNEISS

B

5 KM

10 KM

15 KM

20 KM

25 KM

30 KM

35 KM

GRANITE MELTS IN THIS REGION

200   400   600   800

TEMPERATURE, DEGREES CELSIUS

Figure 15–5 *Curve A shows the approximate zones beneath the crust at which different rocks are metamorphosed. Granitic rocks melt at the temperature and depth conditions to the right of curve B.*

According to the diagram, what might happen to the rock if it were pushed down much below 35 kilometers? What would happen if the temperature at a depth of 25 or 30 kilometers were 50 or 100 degrees hotter than the temperatures shown by curve A?

Rocks become more dense as the rock environment becomes hotter and as squeezing becomes more intense. (See Figure 15–5.) The minerals that make up the rock also change as the rock

environment changes. You have seen in Figure 15–2 that calcite shells and quartz changed into wollastonite and quartz. In rock environments where schist and gneiss form, very dense minerals such as garnet begin to grow. If you checked the density of the various rock types shown, you would find that the density of the rocks increases from clay through shale, slate, schist, and gneiss. On the basis of Figure 15–5 and the information provided in the last few paragraphs, see if you can make a general statement about changes that take place in rocks that are subjected to greater and greater heat and pressure.

The temperatures and pressures shown in Figure 15–5 for the formation of various kinds of metamorphic rocks are based on laboratory experiments. If the conditions of the experiment approximate the conditions in nature, it should be possible to look at a metamorphic rock and gain some idea of the environment in which it formed. For all rock environments to the right of curve B in Figure 15–5, rocks of the types that make up most of the crust can no longer exist in a solid state. They begin to melt. Once rock material has melted completely, it may later solidify to form different kinds of igneous rocks.

Thought and Discussion . . .

1. What is meant by rock environment?
2. What is the role of water in metamorphic processes?
3. What kinds of changes occur in sedimentary rocks as they are subjected to progressively higher pressures and temperatures?
4. Compare changes that take place in the grain size of rocks during weathering with changes in grain size that take place during metamorphism.
5. What effect does the parent rock have on the kind of metamorphic rock that will form in a given temperature and pressure range?
6. Suppose that a piece of clay is slowly buried to a depth of 28 kilometers and at the same time heated to a temperature of 800°C. Describe the changes that would probably occur in the clay.

Rocks That Form from Molten Material

15–4 Investigating igneous rocks.

You saw evidence in the preceding section that solid rocks melt when they are placed in certain environments. (See Figure 15–5.) The molten material may later cool to form igneous rocks. The purpose of this investigation is to examine some different kinds of igneous rocks. Reread Section 2–1 to review what you have learned about igneous rocks.

Procedure

Examine the rocks provided. Divide them into groups that have something in common. Be prepared to discuss the following questions:

(1)What is the basis for your grouping? (2)Which rocks do you think might have formed at or near the surface? Why? (3)Which rocks do you think might have formed deep below the surface? Why?

After you have grouped your rocks, use the chart in Figure 15–6 to answer the following questions:

(4)What characteristics of a rock specimen must you observe to use this chart? (5)According to this chart, what minerals should a granitic rock contain? (6)Compare a granite with a rhyolite. (7)Why are the differences between various rock types not always distinct to an observer?

Mt. Shasta, a 4300-meter, snowcapped, extinct volcano, rises above spruce forest in northern California.

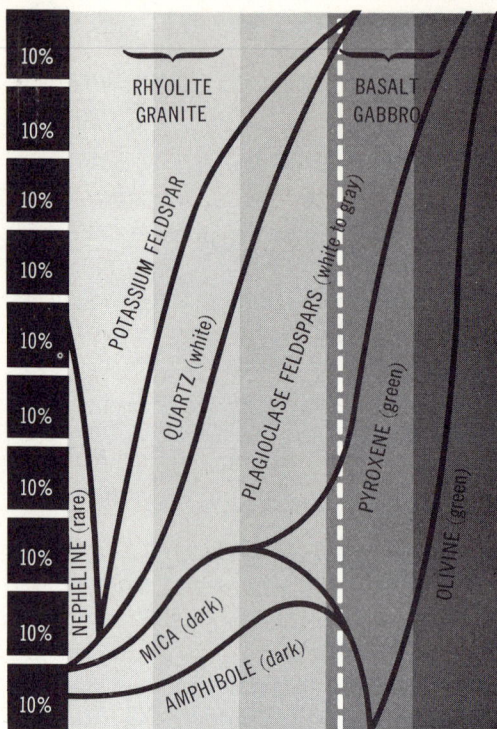

Figure 15–6 *This chart relates the percentages of minerals in igneous rocks. Rhyolite and granite are equivalent in mineral composition but different in texture. This is also true of basalt and gabbro. A rock with a composition represented by the dashed line contains plagioclase feldspar (58 percent), pyroxene (20 percent), and amphibole (15 percent). What minerals make up the remaining 7 percent of the rock? Igneous rock types are shown below chart.*

15–5 Solid rock from molten rock.

Molten rock material at great depths is called **magma.** So far no one has ever examined magma. The molten rock material observed in lava flows cannot be quite the same as magma. When magma rises from the depths to the surface, pressure decreases. Water vapor and other gases move nearer the surface and eventually escape into the air. Before magma rises from the depths, pressure holds in dissolved gases just as pressure in a tightly capped bottle keeps dissolved carbon dioxide in soda pop.

Suppose you melted a piece of granite. What would happen? The graph in Figure 15–7 shows the experimental results you would observe as the temperature and pressure increased. At what temperature would granite begin to melt at the earth's surface? At what temperature would it begin to melt at a depth of 12 kilometers? What general statement can you make about the melting temperature of a piece of granite containing no water as it is buried deeper and deeper? According to the graph, does all of the granite melt at exactly the same temperature? What do you think might be a reason for this?

The results of melting granite mixed with a little water are also shown in Figure 15–7. How do the curves in this graph differ from the curves without any water? Make a general statement about the melting temperature of granite mixed with water as it is buried deeper and deeper. Probably small amounts of water are present everywhere in the crust. If this is true, is deep magma likely to remain melted at lower temperatures than surface lava?

Many igneous rocks are present in and on the earth's crust. What caused them to cool and harden? How did their various textures form? Lava changes from the liquid to the solid state mainly because it loses heat to the air. Magma deep below the surface becomes solid by losing heat to the surrounding rocks. Would a deep body of magma cool as rapidly as lava cools? Why?

Suppose that a granitic magma at a depth of 12 kilometers and a temperature of 850 or 900°C is suddenly squeezed up to the earth's surface. What would happen to the molten material? Refer to Figure 15–7. Changes in temperature, pressure, or gas content of a magma can cause it to solidify. Such changes in rock environment can occur when volcanoes erupt or when folding in the earth's crust causes bodies of magma to move.

You may have watched ice crystals forming in cold water. The same kinds of things happen when molten rock material cools. Igneous rock can be thought of as frozen magma or lava. It freezes at 800°C to 1200°C instead of at 0°C. When molten rock material cools very rapidly, as in some lava flows, the silicon tetrahedrons do not have time to become very well organized. Silicon tetrahedrons do not become linked into the orderly arrangements found in minerals. Under these conditions volcanic glass

forms. X-ray photographs indicate that glass contains silicon-oxygen tetrahedrons arranged in a haphazard pattern. Therefore, glass is really more like a liquid than a solid.

When magma or lava cools more slowly, the silicon-oxygen tetrahedrons become better organized. Depending on the temperature and chemical composition of the magma, these tetrahedrons make single-tetrahedron structures or share oxygen ions to form the chain, sheet, or framework structures you studied in sections 2–7 and 2–8. Review the models of these structures.

When cooling is fairly rapid, tiny crystals form in many places at once. As a result the magma is changed into a solid mass of crystals before large crystals have a chance to form. When cooling is slow, only a few small crystals begin to grow. These crystals continue to grow slowly as the magma cools.

Figure 15–7 *The graphs show the temperatures at which granite containing water (far right) and granite containing no water (right) remain solid (A), melt partially (B), and melt totally (C). (Left) A lava flow over sedimentary rocks and the flow of plate glass at high temperature over rollers as it cools.*

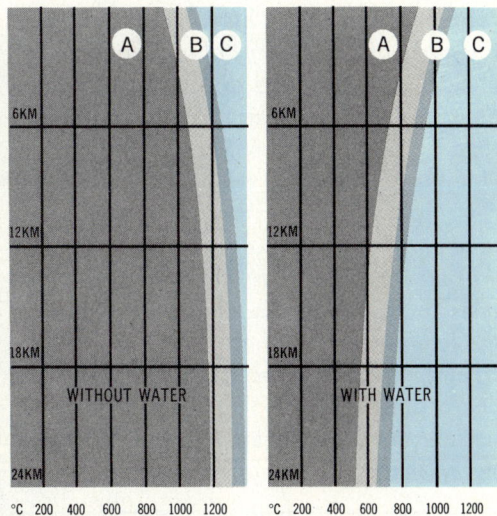

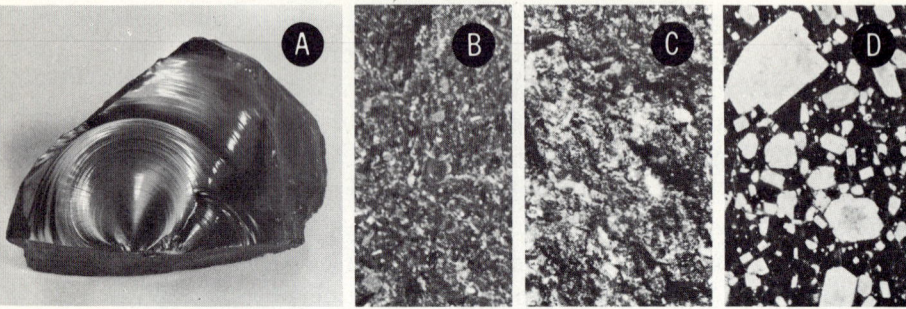

Figure 15–8 *Under what conditions might these various igneous rocks have formed? A is obsidian, B a fine-grained basalt, C a coarse gabbro, and D is a porphyry.*

Which rock specimen in Figure 15–8 cooled quickly from a lava? Which specimen cooled somewhat more slowly but might still have come from a lava? Which cooled very slowly and at great depths? Can you explain your choices? How might a texture such as the one in Figure 15–8D have formed? What does the texture of this rock suggest about the cooling history of the rock?

ACTIVITY *Pour a thin layer of salol (phenyl salicylate) into a small glass petri dish. Cover the dish and melt the chemical. (Use a hot plate or a Bunsen burner on low heat.) As soon as the salol has melted, turn off the heat. Let the dish cool so that it feels warm to the touch but not hot, and place it under a microscope. Drop a small piece of a salol crystal into the melt and watch what happens. Describe what you see and make several sketches.*

Remelt the salol. This time crush a small fragment of a salol crystal and sprinkle the powder into a cooling dish. Describe what happens. Does it take a longer or shorter time for the liquid to become crystalline? How do you explain what you have seen?

(1) Melt a small amount of salol in a test tube and (2) plunge the warm test tube into a beaker of ice water. Describe what happens to the salol. Examine the texture of the solid salol that forms. How does it differ from the texture of the salol observed at the end of steps 1 and 2?

How is the behavior of salol similar to the formation of igneous rocks?

15–6 Why are there many types of igneous rocks?

Has it ever seemed strange to you that substances as different as milk, cream, cottage cheese, and butter all come from a single source—cow's milk? Similarly there are many types of igneous rocks. Does each type of igneous rock originate from its own special type of magma? Or do you think that many different kinds of rock can somehow come from one kind of magma, just as many different products come from milk?

According to one theory, most different kinds of igneous rocks come from a single parent magma. This magma is thought to be similar to melted basalt with water added to it. Many scientists think that similar materials make up the lower part of the earth's crust and the upper part of the mantle. If the temperature increases in these deep rocks, they may melt and form magma.

Cracks deep in the crust may form during the sinking of geosynclines. Magma can be squeezed through these cracks to the earth's surface and flow out as lava. Basaltic rocks like those shown in Figure 15–8B are formed when the lava cools. Such rocks are widespread over the earth's surface, both on land and on the sea floor. In some places such as eastern Oregon and Washington, layers of basalt flows more than a thousand meters thick cover large regions of thousands of square kilometers. (See Figure 15–9.)

How could rocks of other types form from a parent magma that has a composition similar to basalt? A possible explanation is diagrammed in Figure 15–10. If magma A cools quickly, a basaltic rock containing iron and magnesium will form. If magma A cools slowly, the first crystals that form have time to sink to the bottom, as shown in Figure 15–10B. Most of these early-formed crystals are olivine and chain silicates. (See Figure 2–23.) Because olivine and chain silicates are rich in iron and magnesium, they remove most of the iron and magnesium from the magma.

What is the composition of the liquid shown in Figure 15–10C? How does this differ from the composition of the liquid in Figure 15–10A? If the liquid part of Figure 15–10C were now squeezed to the surface and cooled suddenly, *it could no longer form basalt*. If this final liquid were now erupted from a volcano, it would form rhyolite, a fine-grained granitic rock. If it cooled slowly deep below the ground, it would form coarse-grained granite. The process shown in Figure 15–10 is one way in which different kinds of igneous rocks can form from a single parent magma. The crystals that form early during cooling settle out. As a result, the *relative* amounts of silicon (Si) and potassium (K) increase in the melt. Meanwhile, the relative amounts of iron (Fe) and magnesium (Mg) decrease in the melt.

Do all igneous rocks come from basaltic magma? Most geologists now agree that the process just described probably accounts for some of the compositional differences in igneous rocks. However, many differences cannot be explained in this manner. It seems likely that there are many different kinds of parent magma instead of a single basaltic one. Each different magma might go through processes like that shown in Figure 15–10. Melting of all kinds of rocks probably occurs below the surface and each newly formed body of magma can cool to form particular kinds of rocks.

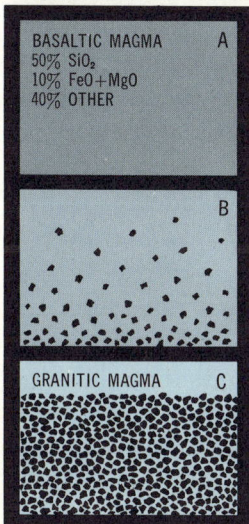

BASALTIC MAGMA   A
50% SiO_2
10% FeO+MgO
40% OTHER

     B

GRANITIC MAGMA   C

Figure 15–9 (*Above*) A dark basalt flow crosses the Snake River Plain in the Pacific Northwest.
Figure 15–10 (*Left*) Inferred stages (*A, B, and C*) in the evolution of magma by crystal settling. Early-formed crystals remove iron and magnesium from the magma. Remaining magma in C contains 70% SiO_2, 2% FeO + MgO, 28% other.

15–7 How does granite form?

Masses of granite covering thousands of square kilometers occur in the exposed cores of both young and old mountain ranges. (See Figure 15–11.) Where has all of this granite come from? Many geologists have suggested that most of the granite formed from basaltic parent magma as a result of crystal settling and other such processes. If this were true, what percentage of granite would you expect to separate out of a mass of basaltic magma? (See Figure 15–10.) Suppose that most large masses of granite had been separated out of an original

Figure 15–11 *View of Tenaya Canyon in Yosemite National Park, Northern California. The Sierra Nevada feature vast outcrops of granitic rocks. At the right is Halfdome.*

basaltic liquid. What kind of rocks would you expect to find nearby?

Most large granite bodies are surrounded by various kinds of sedimentary and metamorphic rocks rather than basaltic rocks rich in iron and magnesium. This makes it unlikely that large granite bodies came from basalt. The chemical composition of granite is very much like that of a sandy shale, even though the two rock types look very different side by side.

Note that sedimentary rocks become progressively more metamorphosed as they sink into the crust. If rocks are exposed to an environment like that represented to the right of curve B in Figure 15–5, they will melt. Shale deep in a geosyncline would melt to form a magma with the composition of granite.

Figure 15–12 *The igneous rock (near the center) forced its way up through sedimentary rocks.*

It is likely that most granitic magma comes from the metamorphism and melting of sedimentary rocks deep in the roots of mountain chains. Once the magma has formed, it may be squeezed up to higher levels, where it cools and solidifies. Other bodies of granitic magma may remain where they are formed and cool slowly in place.

Are all rocks that look like igneous rocks really igneous? This is a question that has been asked by many geologists. When the boundary of a granite body cuts sharply across the rocks around it, most geologists agree that it was probably squeezed in as a magma. (See Figure 15–12.) But many large granite bodies merge gradually into intensely metamorphosed sedimentary rocks and their interface is difficult to define.

Suppose that a group of sedimentary rocks sinks deeper into a geosyncline. Temperature and pressure gradually increase and the amount of metamorphism of the rocks also increases. As the two curves shown in Figure 15–5 get closer together, the minerals that form by metamorphism of the sedimentary rock are the same minerals that would form if a granitic magma began to solidify at only slightly higher temperatures. Ions of various elements move about easily in the small amounts of water vapor and gas present in the metamorphosed sedimentary rock. So it has been proposed that some granite forms by very intense metamorphism just short of melting.

The texture and mineral content of the rock may be just like the texture and mineral content of a granite formed by igneous processes. Therefore, it is not always possible to determine whether a rock that formed deep below the surface is igneous or metamorphic.

When you are given a piece of granite, you cannot automatically assume that it is an igneous rock. You cannot say immediately whether it formed from magma or whether it formed by metamorphism of sedimentary rocks. You must investigate the exact makeup of the granite and determine its relationship to other rocks in the area from which it was taken before you can make reasonable hypotheses about its origin.

It is important to distinguish between what you actually see in rocks and what you infer about their origin. Two geologists can study the same body of granite, observe the same relationships, and still disagree on whether the granite formed when a melt solidified or whether it formed by intense metamorphism.

Thought and Discussion . . .

1. What is the difference between lava and magma?
2. What is the difference between granite and basalt?
3. What kinds of evidence can give us an idea of what magma is like and how it behaves?
4. What conditions affect the texture of a rock that has solidified from a melt?
5. How could a rock with a composition like granite form from basaltic magma?
6. Explain why it is believed that some granite might have formed during intense metamorphism.

Born in Kingston, Ontario, in 1887, Norman L. Bowen entered Queen's University there at age 16. He received a degree in mineralogy and geology in 1909 as well as a scholarship to continue his studies at the Massachusetts Institute of Technology in Cambridge, Massachusetts. The following year Bowen went to the newly established Geophysical Laboratory of the Carnegie Institute of Washington to study the problems of rock and mineral composition and origin. This work gained him a Ph.D. from MIT in 1912. After a series of different academic positions, Bowen finally returned to the Geophysical Laboratory in 1947 and remained there until his death in 1956.

Bowen saw the importance of geologic field observations and spent many of his summers on field trips in Canada, the United States, Norway, and Africa. He also strongly believed in the need for laboratory studies in order to provide a chemical basis for hypotheses of rock and mineral origin made from field observations.

By the age of 28, Bowen had established his reputation as an outstanding scientist. In 1928 he published an influential work, The Evolution of Igneous Rocks, which emphasized the importance of the principles of physical chemistry as a foundation for geologic processes.

Norman L. Bowen

Completion of the Rock Cycle

15–8 The rock cycle follows many paths.

What might happen to a single atom or ion caught up in the rock cycle, such as a calcium ion dissolved in sea water? Many things could happen to this ion. Suppose that it is taken up by a clam as the clam filters out microscopic plants that form its food. Clams use calcium for their shells. The calcium ion may combine with ions of carbon and oxygen to form calcite ($CaCO_3$) in the clam's shell. After the clam dies, its shell is moved about by bottom currents and finally carried up onto the beach by waves. On the beach the shell is rolled around by the waves and broken and crushed. The fragment of shell containing the calcium ion is covered over by sand and mud.

Suppose that a geosyncline develops in this area and the land gradually begins to sink. The sea moves up onto the land and the shell fragment becomes more and more deeply buried by sand, clay, and other sediments. The pressure of the overlying rocks becomes so great that the loose sediment containing the shell fragment becomes cemented and squeezed together to form solid rock.

As the geosyncline continues to sink, the rock environment changes. Gradually metamorphism begins. At a certain pressure and temperature the calcium ion is so tightly squeezed that it becomes separated from the carbon and oxygen in the calcite. Loose calcium ions are charged particles, however, and cannot remain free for long. At this point the ion might combine with silicon and oxygen to form wollastonite ($CaSiO_3$), a mineral which is able to exist in this particular rock environment. (See Figure 15–2.)

If downward sinking continues, the quartzite containing wollastonite may ultimately come into an environment where melting occurs. Perhaps the rock will melt and the calcium ion will again be released. The ion will remain loose in the melt until cooling begins. It might then combine with silicon, oxygen, and aluminum in a newly forming crystal of feldspar ($CaAl_2Si_2O_8$). The melted rock material may thus solidify into granite or some other deep igneous rock. Or it may be squeezed to the surface to form part of a lava flow.

If the geosyncline becomes unstable, the rocks within it will undergo folding and uplift. Millions of years might pass before the feldspar crystal containing the calcium ion is exposed at the surface. This would have required the erosion of many kilometers of overlying rocks.

When the granite reaches the surface, it is in a rock environment much different from the one in which it formed. At the surface, free oxygen, water, and

other weathering agents will attack the rock. (See Chapter 12.) The feldspar crystal may break loose from the surrounding grains. As physical and chemical weathering continue, the individual ions in the crystal may be broken free, dissolved in water, and eventually carried to the sea. The calcium ion thus returns to the sea and continues its journey through the rock cycle.

This story describes only one of a number of paths that the calcium ion could have taken. Go back over the story. How many different side roads can you think of that this ion could have taken during the journey described?

The processes of rock formation—including erosion, deposition, burial, metamorphism, melting, and solidification—are all interconnected. But what causes the down-bowing of the geosynclines and their ultimate uplift into mountain chains? From where does the energy come that perpetually drives the cycle of deposition, downsinking, rock formation, mountain uplift, and erosion?

Additional Investigation

15–9 Field trips through the mountains.

Information from a variety of sources must be combined to interpret the life cycle of mountains. Looking at the rocks on the surface is one of the first things that must be done. In order to determine what conditions exist beneath the surface, data must be used from devices that measure small changes in the gravity and magnetic fields and in the heat that flows from the surface.

By means of a series of slides, your teacher will introduce you to a field trip through the mountains. You will first view the area as it would appear if you were driving across it in an automobile. Be alert to clues about the structure and history of the region. Note the vegetation and cultural features to get a better idea of the climate and the way people are adapting to this particular environment.

After you have looked at the slides, additional information will be provided so that you can gain deeper insight into the nature of mountains. Try to become more aware of the continuous changes that must have taken place throughout geologic time. The observations you have made from slides and photographs can be applied in your own locality.

Scenes from the California field trip (below, opposite page) and the Colorado field trip (below, this page).

Unsolved Problems One of the reasons for attempting to drill a hole through the earth's crust is to examine samples of rock material deep in the crust and in the upper mantle. However, any such hole will only be a few centimeters in diameter. Will it be safe to make very many interpretations or predictions about deep rocks in other parts of the crust and upper mantle on the basis of one small hole?

Where do the enormous amounts of basalt on the continents and in the ocean basins come from, and how do such enormous volumes of basalt get to the surface? The evidence strongly indicates that the source of basaltic magma probably is at the bottom of the crust and top of the mantle. This means that great amounts of magma must be able to rise through 30 kilometers or more of crust. How does this happen? The problem is even more difficult to solve if the extremely large bodies of granite that we find really do form from still larger bodies of basaltic magma as a result of crystal settling. (See Figure 15–10.)

Ore deposits are especially likely to occur near bodies of granite. This connection has led to the idea that water and other fluids in magma are the sources of these mineral deposits. Yet some ore deposits with similar minerals occur in regions where there are no known bodies of igneous rocks. How do such deposits form?

CHAPTER REVIEW

Summary

The materials of the earth's upper crust are exposed in mountains and the roots of former mountains. The upper crust has a relatively thin layer of soil and sedimentary and volcanic rock.

Metamorphic rocks have formed from preexisting rocks without melting and at high temperatures and pressures. The degree of metamorphism of a rock reflects the temperature and pressure to which the rock was subjected.

Igneous rocks are believed to form from magma. Magma is molten rock material containing small amounts of water vapor and other gases. These gaseous substances are kept in a magma at depth by the pressure of the rocks above. When magma reaches the surface as lava, these gases escape. Much water vapor and gas have been transferred to the earth's atmosphere and hydrosphere in this way since the birth of the planet.

Igneous rocks can probably originate in at least three ways. Some have evolved from a single basaltic parent magma by crystal settling. Others have crystallized from magma formed during melting of sedimentary rocks. Rocks that appear to be igneous may also form during mountain building by a kind of extreme metamorphic process.

Rocks of the crust are involved in a rock cycle that has many subcycles. The parts of the rock cycle occurring beneath the surface must be driven by energy from some source within the earth.

Questions and Problems

A

1. Why is it thought that the environmental conditions within the crust are entirely different from those on the surface of the earth?
2. Why are some igneous rocks fine-grained and some coarse-grained?
3. What is likely to happen to sandy clay sediment buried for a long time at a depth of 20 kilometers? How and in

what ways might such rock be changed into a granite?

B

1. Estimate the difference between the approximate temperature when rocks begin to melt and the average crustal temperature at a depth of 20 kilometers. Assume the rock composition is that of granite. (Refer to Figure 15–5.) What is the significance of this temperature difference?
2. Is granite always an igneous rock? Suggest ways in which granite may form.
3. Suggest paths in the rock cycle that the material in a piece of granite might follow.
4. Show how mountains, oceans, geosynclines, metamorphism, and igneous activity may be related.

C

1. By melting granite in an open container, early investigators tried to discover the lowest temperature at which a magma of this composition could exist. How meaningful were such experiments? What other factors should be controlled to make such experiments more meaningful? Explain.
2. Certain ancient rocks exposed in mountains are called volcanic rocks. Since their formation was not seen, how do you think it can be determined that they are volcanic?
3. Suppose that the earth had no atmosphere. Would this have any effect on the amounts and kinds of rocks that compose the crust? Explain.

Suggested Readings

BOOKS

Coleman, Satis N. *Volcanoes New and Old.* The John Day Company, Inc., New York, 1946.

Beiser, Arthur. *The Earth.* Time, Inc. (Life Nature Library), New York, 1963.

Geology. Boy Scouts of America (Boy Scout Merit Badge Series), New Brunswick, N.J., 1962.

Harland, W. B. *The Earth: Rocks, Minerals, and Fossils.* Franklin Watts, Inc., New York, 1960.

Editors of *Life. A Guide to the Natural World: An Index to the Life Nature Library.* Time, Inc. (Life Nature Library), New York, 1965.

Milne, Lorus, Margery Milne, and the Editors of *Life. The Mountains.* Time, Inc. (Life Nature Library), New York, 1962.

Pough, Frederick H. *Field Guide to Rocks and Minerals.* Houghton Mifflin Company, Boston, 1953.

Zim, Herbert S. and P. R. Shaffer. *Rocks and Minerals.* Golden Press, Inc., New York, 1957.

PERIODICALS

Bucher, W. H. "The Crust of the Earth." *Scientific American,* May, 1950.

Tuttle, O. F. "The Origin of Granite." *Scientific American,* April, 1955. (Also Scientific American Offprint #819, W. H. Freeman & Co., Publishers, San Francisco.)

Williams, Howel. "Volcanoes." *Scientific American,* November, 1951. (Also Scientific American Offprint #822.)

An opening appeared in a plowed field on Feb. 20, 1943, near Paricutín, Mexico. A volcanic cone about half a kilometer high was formed here in less than four years.

Chapter 16 Interior of the Earth

So far you have learned about processes and forces that operate at or near the earth's surface. Most atmospheric circulation, for example, occurs below the stratosphere, and crustal movements and metamorphism both take place in the upper 50 kilometers or so of the earth. You have looked at only the very outermost skin of the earth. What can you learn about the earth's interior?

For centuries man has speculated about the interior of the earth. Over one hundred years ago Jules Verne's fictional Professor Von Hardwigg made an imaginary journey to the center of the earth and back. So far man himself has not made this journey. In spite of being unable to travel deep into the interior of the earth, we have found out a great deal by indirect methods. You already know that knowledge was obtained about the temperature and composition of the sun by studying the quality and quantity of its radiation. What methods have been devised to gather information about the conditions and forces in the earth's interior? Will knowledge about conditions at depth help explain the surface features of the earth?

The evidence gathered strongly suggests that mountain building forces originate deep below the earth's surface. When James Hall first began to realize the nature of the structure he later named a geosyncline, many hundreds of people had already concluded that some rocks were formed in the sea and later uplifted. Marine fossils high in the mountains, bent and broken rocks, and rocks formed at high temperature and pressure that have come to the surface are only part of the evidence of movements of the crust.

The evidence has excited scientists and led them to attempt to determine the causes of these movements. If the down-bowing of the crust in depositional basins cannot be caused by the weight of the sediments alone, then what *does* cause the downward movement?

To gather evidence that may aid in answering this question, scientists have studied a great variety of materials at all scales. They have used electron microscopes that can "see" molecular structure and a 200-inch telescope that can "see" the structure of galaxies. The distribution and composition of microfossils and meteorites have been analyzed. Earth's rotation and earthquake waves have provided information about crustal movement.

Many kinds of information are needed because man cannot venture into the interior of our planet. Since observable surface processes cannot account for mountain building, we probe the interior by indirect means. Conclusions must be based on limited observations as we search for the forces that drive the solid-earth portion of the rock cycle.

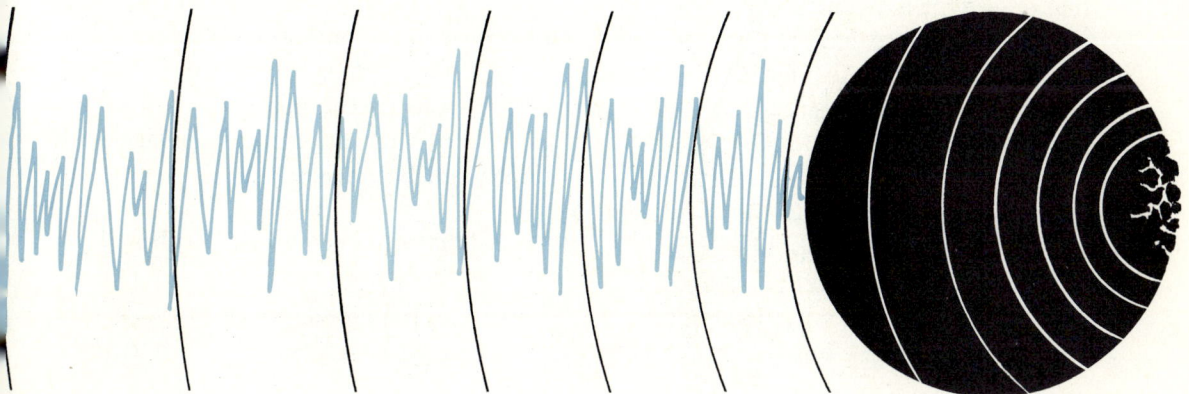

Studying the Earth's Interior

16–1 Investigating the inside of a sphere.

The hidden interior of an object can be studied without seeing or sampling it. The two spheres that have been given to you by your teacher seem to be the same. But are they? Experiment with them and see. Make whatever observations or measurements you think are necessary and record any similarities and differences that you detect.

16–2 How is the earth's mass distributed?

Among the things we would like to know about the earth's interior is whether its density is the same throughout or whether it varies with depth and, if so, how. In other words, we would like to know about density distribution. Since density is mass per unit volume, this is essentially the same as mass distribution.

Mass distribution affects the way an object rotates, whether the object is a top or a celestial body. Does the earth's rotation offer any clues about the distribution of mass in the earth? The earth's mass, radius, and period of rotation are known. If the composition of the earth is assumed to be homogeneous, its kinectic energy of rotation can be calculated. The answer turns out to be 260 units. Now if we knew the earth's actual energy of rotation, it could be compared with the calculated energy and we would have some idea of the mass distribution. Fortunately there is an astronomical method of determining the actual energy of rotation. It involves measuring a slow movement of the earth's axis like the wobbling of a top's axis. Calculations based on this method show that the earth's actual energy of rotation is only 214 units. This is con-

siderably less than the 260 units a homogeneous earth would have. Can you think of a way to account for this difference? It means that the mass must be concentrated near the center. In other words, density increases with depth. Knowing the difference between the actual and calculated energy of rotation does not tell us the exact pattern of density increase. It does set up limits to which any model of the earth must conform if the model is to be acceptable.

Perhaps the most significant information about the earth's density distribution is the result you obtained when you calculated the density of a pebble in Investigation P-2. The value for this was probably near the average for all rocks of the crust, about 2.8 grams per cubic centimeter. You learned in Section 3–8 that the density of the entire earth is 5.5 grams per cubic centimeter, almost twice that of average crustal materials. When this information is combined with evidence from earthquake waves, a better picture of the variation of density with depth can be developed.

16–3 Earthquake waves reach the interior.

Late in the nineteenth century, it was discovered that some of the energy released by earthquakes takes the form of waves called **seismic waves.** These waves may travel downward into the interior. Eventually some return to the earth's surface at locations far away from the site of the original quake. When the waves return to the surface, they can be detected and certain of their characteristics measured by seismographs. Among the useful measurements seismographs make are: (1) type of wave, (2) arrival time, and (3) intensity or strength. The locations of seismographs are known. When wave data from many stations are compared and analyzed, a great deal can be learned about the material of the interior through which the waves passed.

Before this information can be understood, however, you must know something about the waves themselves. Different types of seismic waves are generated. One type is similar to the familiar sound waves of everyday experience. These waves are called **compressional** or primary (P) waves. The behavior of the individual particles in a substance as a compressional wave passes is shown in Figure 16–1. When compressional waves pass, they vibrate in the same direction

Figure 16–2 *Waves that come to the surface at greater distances have traveled deeper into the earth and increased in speed.*

Figure 16–1 *Particles of a material vibrate as a wave passes. The particles are imagined to be equally spaced (top). A compressional wave squeezes and stretches the material (center). A shear wave causes layers of particles to slide past one another (bottom).*

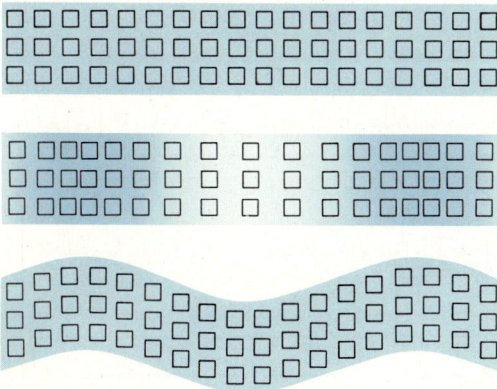

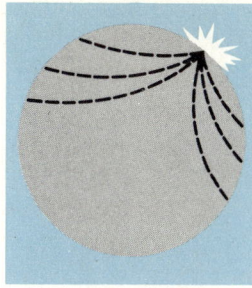

as the waves are traveling. *Compressional waves can travel through solids, liquids, or gases.*

Another type of wave is known as a shear wave or secondary (S) wave. (See Figure 16–1.) In **shear waves,** the individual particles vibrate back and forth at right angles to the direction of motion of the wave. A consequence of this difference is that *shear waves cannot travel through liquids or gases.*

The speed of travel of seismic waves is determined by measuring the time it takes them to move between two points. It turns out that their speeds depend in part on the density of the material through which they pass. Thus, once the speed is determined, certain inferences can be drawn about density. For example, it has been found that in general the farther a seismograph is from the source of a wave, the greater the wave's average measured speed. Since greater distance means that the wave penetrated deeper into the earth, this indicates that the average wave speed increases with depth. (See Figure 16–2.) When density is computed on the basis of these speeds, it turns out that density also increases with depth. How does this compare with your earlier conclusion about density distribution?

In 1909, a Yugoslavian seismologist named Andrija Mohorovičić (Moh-hoh-roh-VEECH-ich) discovered a fundamental interface in the material of the earth's interior by analyzing P-wave

Beno Gutenberg

Beno Gutenberg, born in 1889 in Darmstadt, Germany, became interested in studying the earth's internal structure at the University of Göttingen. Gutenburg became a world authority on the manner in which earthquake waves travel through the earth. In 1914, he located the boundary of the earth's core at 2900 kilometers below the surface. From this determination he found the thickness of the mantle and postulated a central core 3470 kilometers below the earth's surface. Gutenberg made extensive studies of the earth's interior. He became convinced that major geologic changes were caused by the spreading of continents. He believed that the continents were gradually growing as material came up through rifts in the sea bottom from deep within the earth. Gutenberg thought that this process of growth caused the continents to move. Later discoveries of mid-ocean ridges supported his ideas. Gutenberg later identified a low-velocity zone, about 150 kilometers below the earth's surface, which seemed to slow down seismic waves. Gutenberg compiled his lifelong research into a book entitled Physics of the Earth's Interior, which was published in 1959, the year before he died. It has since become a standard reference for geophysicists throughout the world.

arrival times. Mohorovičić studied records of relatively nearby earthquakes. He noticed two distinct P-wave arrivals. When the records from increasingly distant stations were examined, the arrival times came closer together until finally they were identical. At even more distant stations, the second kind of P wave always arrived before the first kind. (See Figure 16–3.)

The situation can be demonstrated as follows: Suppose you live in city A and want to get to city B. You can drive either by a relatively slow older road directly between the two cities on which you can average 40 kilometers per hour, or you can drive out to a new interstate highway on which you can average 80 kilometers per hour. Obviously, although the distance may be greater on the interstate highway, the trip would take less time. What generalization can you make about the relative merits of the two routes for traveling short and long distances?

On the basis of the arrival-time data, Mohorovičić reasoned that the first P wave traveled a relatively slow route through materials within about 20 km of the surface. The second wave traveled at greater depths and entered a deeper zone where the velocity abruptly increased. (See Figure 16–3.) The boundary between the two zones was subsequently named the *Moho discontinuity* in honor of its discoverer. The term **discontinuity** is applied to an interface where the physical properties of materials change markedly.

ACTIVITY *Go outside and place your ear against the building. Listen to the sound made by another student who hits the wall with a board. Describe what you hear. Do sound waves travel faster through the building or through the air?*

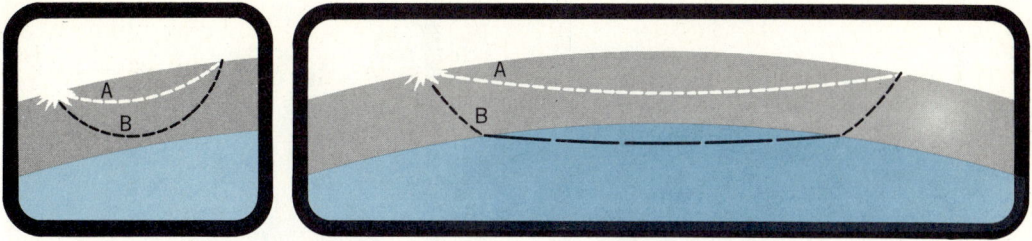

It has been found that the Moho varies in depth, averaging about 30 km beneath the continents but dipping to about 50 km beneath mountain chains. Under the ocean basins its average depth is about 5 km below the sea floor. The earth's crust is most accurately defined as the part above the Moho discontinuity.

Another property of earthquake or any other waves is that they are **refracted**, that is, their direction of motion is changed, when they pass from material in which they have a certain speed into material in which they have a different speed. Figure 16–4 illustrates what happens to the direction of motion when a wave enters a material in which it has a greater speed. In the earth, wave speed generally increases with depth,

Figure 16–3 (Left) Two types of P waves arrive at a nearby station. (Right) The wave that travels deeper increases its speed and arrives at distant stations before the shallow wave.

and the direction of refraction is toward the surface as shown in Figure 16–5.

About the turn of the century, however, people studying earthquake waves noticed an unusual fact. If a seismographic station was between 105 and 140 degrees distant from a wave source, no P waves were received. This area is called the **shadow zone**. (See Figure 16–6.) Stations closer than 105 degrees recorded the arrival of the P waves at the expected time. Stations farther away than about 140 degrees also recorded the arrival, but about four minutes later than expected with a continuous increase of speed with depth.

In 1906, R. D. Oldham, a British scientist, explained this pattern by saying that the earth has a central core in which the P-wave speed is lower. Wave A in Figure 16–6 just misses the core. Most of the travel time of Wave A occurs in the zone between the core and the crust, where it moves at relatively high speed and arrives at a point 100 degrees from the source in about 14 minutes.

Wave B, on the other hand, penetrates slightly deeper, hits the core, and is refracted into it. It continues on and spends a good portion of its travel time in the core where its speed is relatively low. Wave B reaches the surface about 180° from the earthquake's source, more than 22 minutes after it occurred.

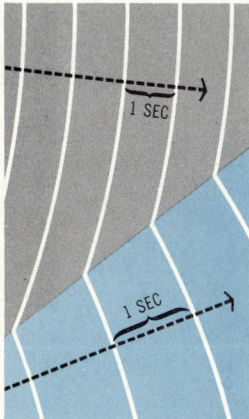

Figure 16–4 This wave travels more slowly in the material at the top. Arrows indicate the direction of the wave path in the two materials.

Figure 16–5 (Below) Because wave speed increases with depth, earthquake waves are refracted toward the surface.

1 SEC

1 SEC

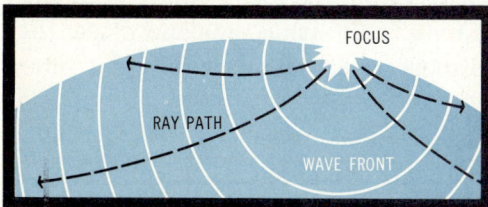

FOCUS

RAY PATH

WAVE FRONT

Figure 16–6 *The existence of a shadow zone where no S or P waves come to the surface is interpreted as evidence for a core.*

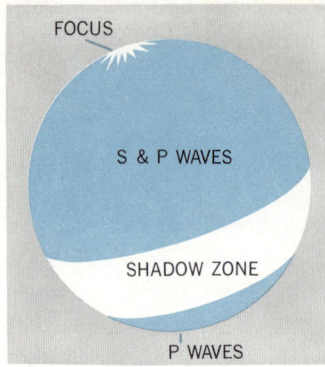

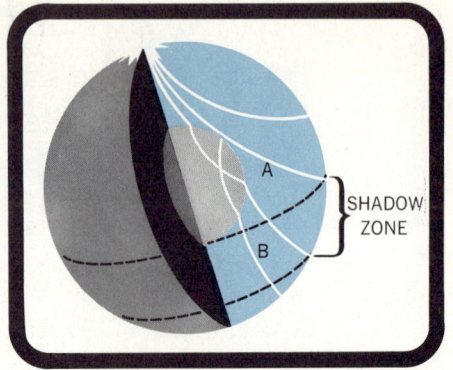

The S wave, however, does not appear again beyond 105 degrees from its source. Because the S wave seems to disappear after it is refracted into the core, scientists have concluded that the core is in part liquid. Since S or shear waves cannot travel through liquids, the core can be thought of as a trap in which they disappear. Careful analysis of waves beyond the 105-degree line has led other seismologists to propose a solid inner core at great depth. Certain curious relationships in P-wave pattern provided the evidence for this conclusion. The curve in Figure 16–7 summarizes what scientists have discovered by measuring P-wave speeds. The zone between the crust and the outer core is called the **mantle.** By relating these wave speeds to density, a pattern of density change within the earth can be graphed. (See Figure 16–8.)

Figure 16–7 *(Left) Wave speeds vary with depth due to variation in composition and rigidity.*

Figure 16–8 *(Right) Variation of density as interpreted from variations in wave speed.*

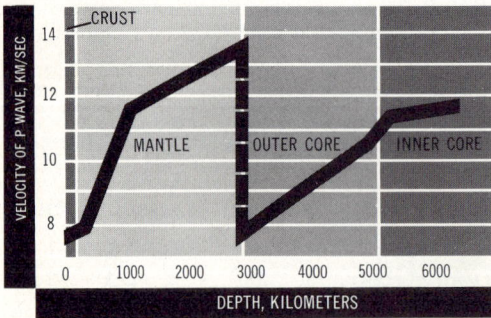

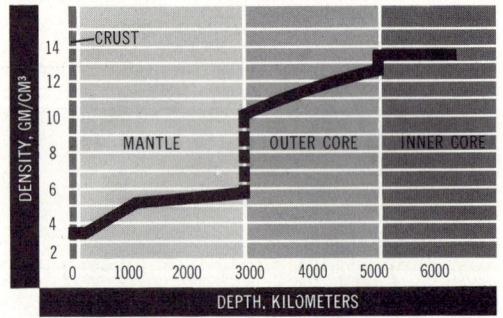

16–4 Locating the epicenter of an earthquake.

One of the important tools of a seismologist is a travel-time graph. It is used to locate the epicenter of an earthquake.

The P and S waves that are generated by an earthquake travel at different velocities from the focus through the inner earth. Since they originate at the same time and place, they arrive at a distant seismographic station at different times.

Procedure

Suppose that a mild earthquake occurred near Washington, D.C. at 8:00:00 Greenwich Mean Time (the time in Greenwich, England). The shock was registered on seismograms in different cities at the times shown in Table 16–1.

Plot a graph showing travel-time versus distance for both the P and the S waves.

Now that you have constructed a travel-time graph, answer the following questions by using your graph.

(1)How long does it take for a P wave to travel from an earthquake to a seismographic station 2000 kilometers away?

(2)What is the travel time for an S wave to go a distance of 2000 kilometers?

(3)What is the difference in arrival time between P and S waves for an earthquake that is 5000 km away from the station? 8000 km from the station?

(4)What relationship exists between the difference in arrival time of the waves and the distance of a seismographic station to the earthquake?

Using your travel-time graph and a globe, locate the epicenter of the earthquake that produced the energy shown on the seismogram tracings in Figure 16–9 on the next page. The figures you are using are tracings made from actual seismograms. Time marks appear on each of the seismograms to provide common reference points.

TABLE 16–1   ARRIVAL TIMES OF WASHINGTON, D.C., EARTHQUAKE WAVES

CITY	DISTANCE IN KILOMETERS	P-WAVE ARRIVAL TIME (GREENWICH MEAN TIME)	S-WAVE ARRIVAL TIME (GREENWICH MEAN TIME)
BUENOS AIRES, ARGENTINA	8640	8:11:50	8:21:42
CAIRO, EGYPT	9590	8:12:37	8:23:12
BOGOTA, COLOMBIA	4840	8:08:05	8:14:25
CHICAGO, ILLINOIS	988	8:01:54	8:03:32
LONDON, ENGLAND	6060	8:09:27	8:17:06
LOS ANGELES, CALIFORNIA	3810	8:06:42	8:12:11
MEXICO CITY, MEXICO	3120	8:05:48	8:10:32
HOUSTON, TEXAS	2010	8:04:08	8:07:28
MOSCOW, U.S.S.R.	8040	8:11:20	8:20:41
NEW YORK, NEW YORK	339	8:00:38	8:01:18
SAN FRANCISCO, CALIFORNIA	4040	8:07:00	8:12:40
STOCKHOLM, SWEDEN	6800	8:10:12	8:18:31

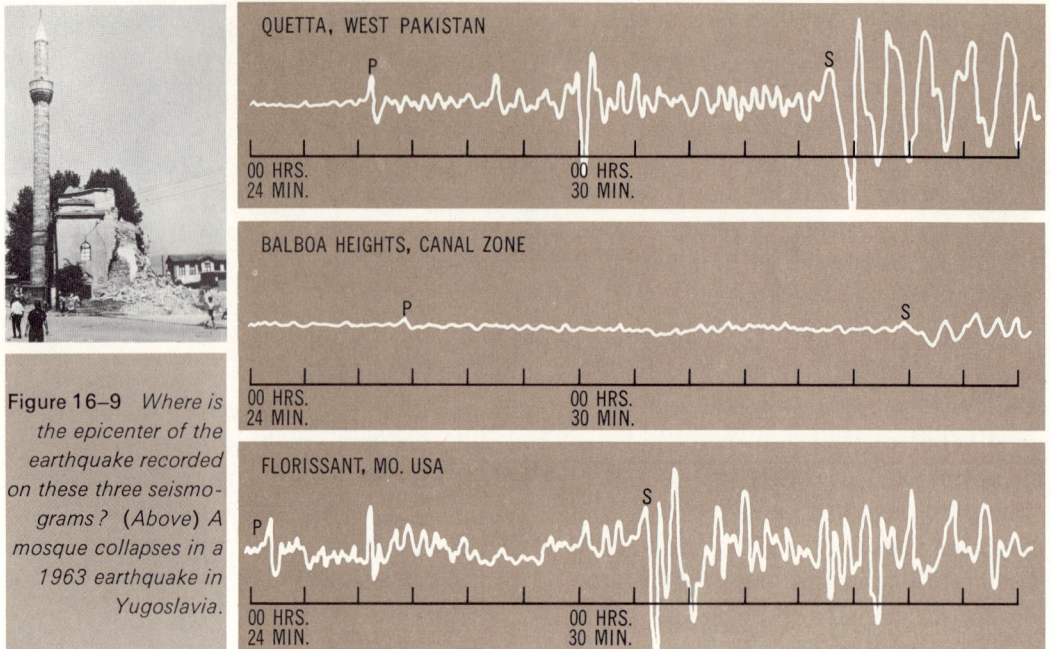

QUETTA, WEST PAKISTAN

P   S

00 HRS.   00 HRS.
24 MIN.   30 MIN.

BALBOA HEIGHTS, CANAL ZONE

P   S

00 HRS.   00 HRS.
24 MIN.   30 MIN.

FLORISSANT, MO. USA

P   S

00 HRS.   00 HRS.
24 MIN.   30 MIN.

Figure 16–9 *Where is the epicenter of the earthquake recorded on these three seismograms? (Above) A mosque collapses in a 1963 earthquake in Yugoslavia.*

16–5 Of what is the interior made?

Has anyone ever examined a piece of material from the earth's interior? Some scientists believe that chunks of the earth's mantle are included in volcanic bodies and lava flows. Others have suggested that the mid-ocean ridges may be partly composed of mantle material exposed in these zones of weakness in the crust. Some investigators argue that stony meteorites represent material that is very similar to the mantle in composition. But no one is yet positive of their ideas, so the answer to the question remains uncertain.

Can we guess the kind of material within the mantle? If you were asked to make an intelligent guess about the composition of a portion of the interior at great depth, what facts and principles would you use as guides?

First, the material you choose must have physical properties that account for the transmission of seismic waves in the manner described in Section 16–3. For example, the speed of seismic waves must agree with observed values. Then, the material must account for the increased density in the interior of the earth. Further, the interior must have a chemical composition that agrees with observed facts. It would not be reasonable to suggest that the mantle contains gold. This might explain the high density, but gold is not common in our solar system. It is not found in meteorites and these are believed to be pieces of the material from which planets are made.

Finally, the material of the interior must behave in a way that agrees with observations. For example, let us say that seismic measurements indicate the material in a given interior zone to be a solid. You would be foolish to suggest that the zone is composed of mickeymousite if someone else had shown in the laboratory that mickeymousite would be molten under the temperature and pressure expected in this zone.

This kind of approach has led to the conclusion that the mantle is a mixture of iron-magnesium silicates, much of which is probably olivine, $(Mg,Fe)_2SiO_4$. Laboratory studies suggest that a material with this composition can be expected to have the required seismic wave speed when it is subjected to the temperatures and pressures thought to exist in the mantle. Stony meteorites have a similar composition. Furthermore, these minerals can undergo changes under pressure that account for observed variations in density.

The discussion of the common rock-forming silicates in Section 2–8 applied only to the composition of the earth's crust. The effect of the high pressures that are present in the mantle did not have to be considered. Laboratory studies prove that the common rock-forming silicate minerals may be changed to new minerals under high pressures. The SiO_4 tetrahedron, common to all of the silicates that have been discussed, may not exist under pressures much higher than those in the crust. Instead the silicon atom may have six oxygen atoms packed around it, giving SiO_6 clusters and a different, more dense, crystalline form. The distances between atoms, such as magnesium and oxygen, may be shortened under pressure so that a mineral takes up less space (volume) per unit of mass. Therefore, the mineral has greater density.

The most likely composition of the earth's core is thought to be iron with minor amounts of other materials. Iron was chosen because it is a common element in the solar system and it has a density close to the value required by our model of the earth. Metallic meteorites are made of iron with some nickel. The presence of iron in the sun is revealed by the sun's spectrum. Investigators have subjected iron to extreme pressures for short times in the laboratory. The results of these experiments have given us no reason to believe that iron could not be the main element in the core. The evidence is indirect and difficult to evaluate. Not all earth scientists agree that the core is made of iron, but many of them do. Another hypothesis is that the core is chemically the same as the mantle but the material has a high density and behaves like a metal because of the enormous pressure.

16–6 How hot is the interior?

Ever since man began to think about the interior of the earth, he assumed that it must be very hot. His observation of volcanic activity and hot springs led to this assumption. Another line of evidence mentioned earlier is the general increase in temperature with depth beneath the surface. As you learned earlier, measurements of temperatures in wells and mine shafts all over the world

(Below) A stony meteorite weighing 8.3 kilograms (18 pounds), which fell near Richardton, South Dakota, on July 21, 1918. (Bottom) One nickel-iron meteorite found at Cape York, Greenland, by Admiral Peary in 1895 is 3.5 meters long, 1.5 meters wide, 2 meters high, and weighs 34 tons.

Steaming hot springs issue from openings in the earth's crust at Yellowstone National Park. From such features men have long considered the inside of the earth to be very hot.

show that temperature increases with depth at an average rate of more than 30°C per kilometer. This increase continues as deep as 8 kilometers, which is as far as measurements have been made.

Theoretical studies also indicate that the earth's interior must be hot. Compression by overlying materials could heat the interior even if the earth had formed by the accumulation of cold particles. A second source of heat would be the original heat remaining from the time of the earth's formation. Some of this original heat might still be preserved even after nearly five billion years of cooling. This heat would remain because rocks are very poor conductors of heat and tend to retain the heat. A third factor that must be considered is radioactive heat. Although the percentage of radioactive materials in the earth's crust is small, it has been shown that their decay would have generated a large quantity of heat during the time since the planet formed. (See Section 6–8.)

How hot is it at the center of the earth? Certain factors place limits on any estimates of interior temperatures. The seismic evidence, for example, strongly suggests that the earth is solid at least down to the core. The fact that shear waves cannot penetrate the core indicates that the core is probably liquid. Most investigators feel that the temperature at the center lies within the range of 3000° to 6000°C. One estimate of the variation of temperature with depth is shown in Figure 16–10.

The reason that scientists are so interested in interior temperatures is related both to the origin and evolution of the earth and the origin and evolution of mountains. Although molten rock in the form of lava suggests that, even relatively near the surface, temperatures are high enough to melt some rocks, this evidence may be misleading. Pressure as well as temperature increases with depth. This affects the environment of material in the interior. The increased pressure also raises the melting point of these materials. The question is which increases faster, temperature or melting point. Since the data about composition, temperature increase, and the rise in melting point with greater pressures are incomplete, no definite conclusions about whether interior materials are solids or liquids have been reached.

16–7 How do solids and liquids differ?
At first glance, differences between solids and liquids may seem to be obvious. For one thing liquids flow and solids do not. Is this true under all conditions? Do

Figure 16–10 *Inferred variation of temperature with depth. Refer also to Section 6–8.*

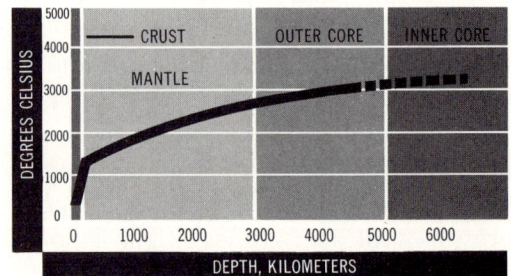

liquids ever take on the characteristics of a solid or vice versa? You ordinarily think of glass as a solid. Yet in Section 15–5 you learned that volcanic glass is more like a liquid than a solid because of the arrangement of the silicon-oxygen tetrahedrons. Perhaps the distinction between liquids and solids is not so obvious as you think.

Consider ice for a moment. Below 0°C ice is a crystalline solid so it does not flow. Yet glaciers flow and they are composed of great masses of ice. The ice in these glaciers is below the freezing point and yet it flows. Is ice a liquid or a solid?

Common table salt is another crystalline solid. If you hit a lump of it with a hammer, it will shatter into thousands of small fragments. On the other hand, in the Gulf Coast region of the United States there are large accumulations of salt that were once buried beneath thousands of feet of sediment. Because of its low density, the salt flowed into great masses and then was squeezed upward through the overlying sediments. This is similar to the way warm air masses are forced upward through denser overlying cold air. Some of these salt domes are currently being mined. Along the walls of the mine shafts flow structures can be seen which clearly show that the salt has flowed more or less like a thick liquid. (See Figure 16–11.) Is salt a liquid or a solid?

As you may know, quartzite is a fairly common rock that is made up of tightly connected grains of crystalline quartz. Quartzite is an extremely hard, brittle material that breaks into sharp fragments when struck with a hammer. At Baraboo in southern Wisconsin there are places where beds of quartzite have been twisted into tight folds. Here quartzite has behaved more like a flexible clay than like the hard brittle material it seems to be. (See Figure 16–11.) Yet there is no evidence that the quartzite was ever heated to anywhere near its melting point of over 1700°C. Is quartzite a solid?

What properties do solids have that liquids do not have? The only general difference between the two is that solids tend to retain their shape when subjected to deforming forces whereas liquids do not. A cube of granite is rather strong and will retain its shape under a fairly large crushing force. A cube of water, on the other hand, cannot even keep its shape under the deforming force of its own weight. This ability of solids to withstand deforming forces up to certain limits is generally called *strength*.

However, the strength of a material may not be maintained when the deforming forces are applied for great periods of time. Evidence is accumulating which suggests that if very small forces are applied to solids for very long periods of time, slow but more or less continuous deformation will take place. Is it possible that all solids behave in this way when subjected to deforming forces?

Figure 16–11 *Flow lines in salt (right). This pattern was photographed in a Texas salt dome. An outcrop of Baraboo quartzite (far right).*

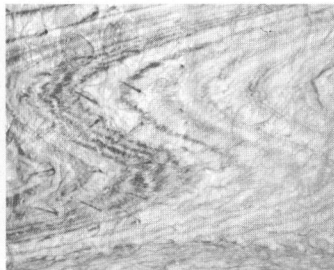

What about the steel beams that hold up tall buildings and bridges, and the stone blocks in the Egyptian pyramids? Are they deforming continuously under their loads? Is there some lower limit of force below which deformation will not occur?

A great deal of experimental work remains to be done before such questions can ever be answered completely. One of the difficulties is that these experiments require long periods of time before deformation can be measured. Often the time required exceeds the lifetime of an individual and it may even exceed the time that has passed since man began scientific investigations.

16–8 Is the earth's interior solid or liquid?

Much of the earth's interior reacts as a very strong, elastic solid to the short-term deforming forces of earthquake waves. Part of the earth's outer core does not transmit shear waves and is therefore thought to be a liquid, as you saw in Section 16–3.

The earth is also deformed by the gravitational attraction of the moon. An earth tide occurs in the crust and mantle, similar to the ocean tide in water, which causes the surface of the earth to rise and fall once every 12 hours. It may be hard to believe, but the Empire State Building rises and falls about 30 centimeters twice a day. This earth tide is very close to that predicted for an elastic earth. It is concluded that, for deforming forces acting over short time spans, the earth reacts as an elastic solid.

Additional evidence on the state of the interior is provided by our knowledge of crustal movements. You know from your study of geosynclines that the crust undergoes extensive downward movements. This downward movement cannot occur unless material in the

The gravitational attraction of the moon "lifts" the Empire State Building 30 cm twice a day.

mantle moves out from underneath the sinking crust. Neither can large areas of the crust be uplifted unless mantle material forces it upward. Consequently, study of vertical crustal movements may tell us something about the mantle.

Large areas of Norway, Sweden, and Finland were covered by a thick sheet of ice during the Ice Age. Ever since the ice sheet began melting away, this area has been undergoing uplift. Measurements relative to sea level indicate that the present rate in some places is as high as 40 centimeters per century. Evidence exists indicating that the center of the region has been raised a total

of more than 500 meters. It is almost as though Scandinavia were a raft floating in a thick liquid. When the immense load of ice (over 3 kilometers thick) accumulated, the raft sank into the mantle. Once the ice was removed, the raft began to rise slowly and is still rising. In this instance, where the mantle has been subjected to a long-term force, it seems to have reacted somewhat like a thick liquid.

The disappearance of S waves seems to indicate that the outer part of the core is liquid. Surprisingly enough the presence of the earth's magnetic field provides an additional line of evidence on this subject. In Section 5–9 you saw that the magnetic field resembles one that would result if there were a bar magnet near the earth's center, although no scientist believes that such a magnet really exists down there. Motions in the core seem to offer the best explanation for the existence of the magnetic field. The theory says that the earth's magnetic field originates from the interaction of electric currents and magnetic forces deep within the earth because of fluid motions in the core. This explanation is called the **dynamo theory,** because the principle is the same as that on which a dynamo, or electric generator, works.

When an electric current flows through a conductor, a magnetic field is created in the space around the conductor. An explanation for the main features of the earth's magnetic field could be the flowing of electricity in loops around the magnetic axis. The most likely place for these currents is in the core because the metal of which it is apparently made may be a good electrical conductor. Fluid motions play the same role as the rotating part of a power-station generator. They may furnish the energy to keep the electric currents going in the earth's core.

In the dynamo theory, the main fluid motion is the turning of the fluid core inside the mantle around an axis that almost coincides with the earth's axis of rotation. This motion produces a part of the field that looks like the field of a bar magnet. It may be that convection currents operate inside the core along with this general rotation. If so, the recorded departures of the observed field from a simple stationary pattern can be explained.

The dynamo theory has not been proved. One thing in its favor is that it offers a reasonable explanation of the slow changes in the earth's magnetic field at the surface. (See Section 5–10.) You can imagine that the fluid motions in the core may change slowly with time. If these motions cause the field, the field could be expected to change slowly. Observed magnetic field variations support the dynamo theory.

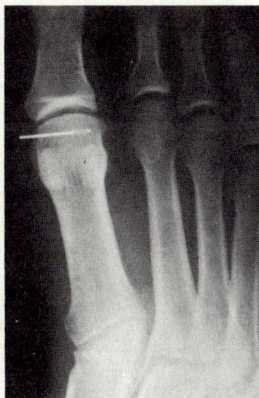

Would the weight of pyramids (left) cause crustal movement? (Right) What type of energy was used to detect this needle? What type of energy is used to "see" inside the earth?

Thought and Discussion . . .

1. Some people think the earth is hollow. How would you prove or disprove this?
2. What shape would the earth be if the moon always remained directly over one place on the earth's surface?
3. Could the mantle be more dense than the core? Explain your answer.

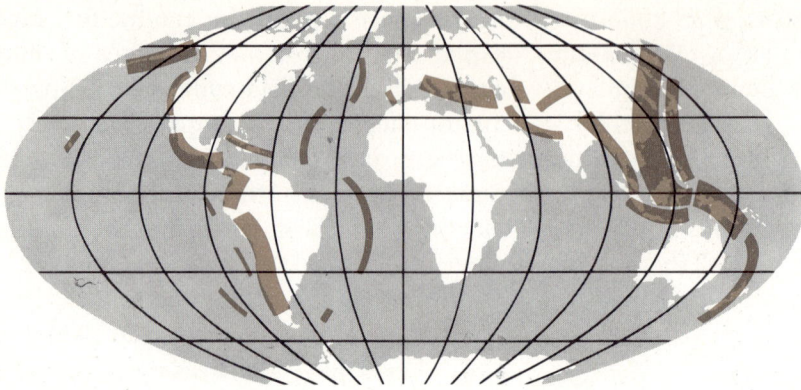

Figure 16–12 (Left) Earthquakes occur along the mobile belts of the earth's crust.
Figure 16–13 (Right) Horizontal movement along a fault has occurred since the orchard was planted.

Mountain Building Theories

16–9 What must a theory of mountain building explain?

Before considering theories that have been developed to explain the topography of the earth and mountain building, it may be useful to review features and conditions that must be explained. To be acceptable, any theory that is proposed must explain the observed conditions. Foremost among these features is the worldwide pattern of mobile belts as shown in Figure 16–12 and the Earthquake Watch. Questions related to this pattern are: Why are there so few of these belts and how does it happen that one of them borders the Pacific Ocean so closely? Why don't mobile belts border all the continents? These are questions that any reasonable theory should be able to answer.

A related problem concerns the pattern of mid-ocean ridges shown in Figure 14–10C. The trough found along the crest of the mid-ocean ridge could be the result of tensional (pulling apart) forces. The presence of relatively thin and recent deep ocean sediments must also be explained. If present rates of deep-sea sedimentation are used, an estimate can be made of how thick the sediments should be. The expected thicknesses turn out to be on the order of 3 kilometers, whereas the actual thicknesses average something like one-half kilometer. The sedimentary and volcanic rocks found within ocean basins are relatively young when compared with the age of the basin. Most of the sediments and volcanic rocks are younger than 100 million years, whereas some of the basins containing them are thought to be as much as 30 times that age.

The relationship between an active continental margin, the continent itself, and oceanic crust must also be explained. The fact that an active zone of weakness extends to a depth of about 700 kilometers beneath the continental crust suggests that continental structure extends as deep as this also.

Equally puzzling is the existence of tremendous faults along which movement is predominantly horizontal, such as the San Andreas Fault in California. (See Figure 16–13.) The accumulated movement along some of these faults during geologic time amounts to hundreds of kilometers. The predominant effect of mountain building in most cases seems to be a reduction in area of the continental crust because of folding and crustal overriding, where one block of

crust is pushed over another. Estimates of the amount of horizontal folding and compressional faulting produced in some mountain chains range up to hundreds of kilometers.

The most obvious thing that must be accounted for is the subsidence of geosynclines and deep ocean trenches. As pointed out in Chapter 13, sediment load alone cannot account for the sinking, so some other mechanism must be brought into play. Equally important, the force causing subsidence must be relaxed or altered at some later time so that uplift can occur.

Perhaps it is clear why no general theory of mountain building has been widely accepted. A great many things must be explained and the data are incomplete. Also it must be remembered that man has thus far been confined to a single planet for an extremely brief period of its long and complex history. It is as if we were trying to generalize about the human race on the basis of studying one person for an extremely short period of his lifetime.

16–10 Is the earth cooling and contracting?

One of the theories that has been developed to explain the apparent compressional features of the earth's crust is referred to as the **contraction theory.**

Compressional features and the fact that the earth is continually losing heat lead some scientists to believe that the earth is cooling from an originally molten state. As it cools, it shrinks, producing compressional forces that deform the crust.

Although it is a simple hypothesis that explains many aspects of mountain building, the contraction theory has several shortcomings. The belief that the earth is cooling is unproved. Calculations based on estimates of the interior's content of radioactive elements suggest that the earth may actually be heating up rather than cooling off. If this is the case, the thermal contraction theory must be abandoned.

However, some scientists have proposed another version of the contraction theory that does not depend on loss of heat. Instead, contraction is thought to result from the movement of high density materials toward the center of the earth. The concentration of mass toward the center could cause some crystal structures of minerals to be modified to more dense forms in order to take up less space. This would result in a loss in volume that produces contraction.

One of the difficulties with both versions of the contraction theory is that neither accounts for the fact that most earthquakes result from horizontal movements along faults. The well-known San Andreas Fault in California is an example. Some scientists believe that if contraction were causing the movement along these faults, the movement would be largely vertical. Whether or not contraction could explain the observed distribution of mobile belts and mountain ranges is still a major question. As is the case with all theories discussed in this chapter, contraction is only a partial explanation for the movement that takes place in the earth's crust.

16–11 Are there convection currents in the mantle?

You are familiar with convection currents in the atmosphere and hydrosphere where higher density materials "fall through" lower density material and force the lower density material upward. Density differences in the atmosphere are caused by temperature differences. Can temperature differences cause similar convection in the mantle?

If you are wondering about how convection can occur in a solid, recall Section 16–7 and the fact that solids sometimes react to long-term forces by yielding more or less like liquids. The fact that large areas of the earth's crust have been uplifted and others have subsided indicates that the mantle does respond to forces that are applied over a long period of time. In view of this, does it seem possible that the material in the mantle of the earth would respond to density differences by developing convection currents?

If there are such currents, they may account for many of the earth's major surface features. Geosynclinal subsidence and later uplift are no longer problems because downward pull between two currents, as shown in Figure 16–14, could account for the necessary downward force. If the currents later stopped or reversed, uplift would occur as the low density materials were forced upward by the higher density mantle.

Some scientists suggest that the mid-ocean ridges lie between two sets of upwelling convection currents. This upwelling would account for the elevations of the ridges above the sea floor and the

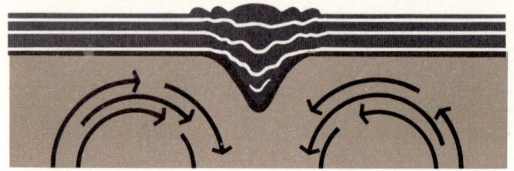

Figure 16–14 *One theory relates geosynclinal subsidence to convection currents below the crust. Convective movement would be very gradual.*

observed tensional features. Furthermore, the ridges contain volcanic rocks that are extremely rich in minerals that are thought to be characteristic of the upper mantle zone.

The greatest weakness in the convection theory is the lack of any convincing proof that such currents actually do exist in the mantle. Some scientists believe that the strength of the mantle is too high to allow such circulation. Interpretations of seismic evidence suggest several possible density differences within

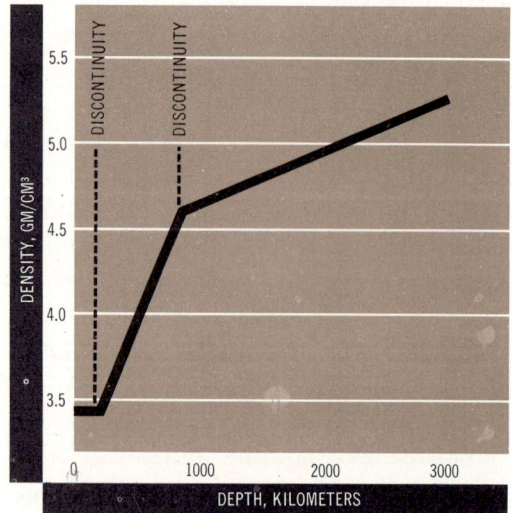

Figure 16–15 (*Above*) *Seismic evidence indicates that the mantle is not the same density throughout.*
Figure 16–16 (*Below*) *The similarity of continental outlines has aroused the curiosity of scientists.*

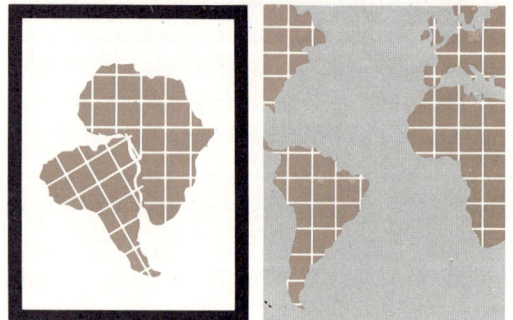

the mantle itself. (See Figure 16–15.) These density layers would slow down the formation of density currents. Convection also does not account for the distribution of mobile belts.

16–12 Are the continents drifting?

Look at shapes of the eastern coastline of North and South America and the western coastline of Europe and Africa. (See Figure 16–16.) The similarity of the continental outlines has excited the curiosity of scentists ever since the time of Francis Bacon (1561–1626). Were these two continents joined together at one time?

The theory of continental drift suggests that the low-density continents are floating about on the higher density mantle. North and South America are supposed to have gradually drifted westward during the past 200 million years. In the course of this movement, the leading edges of the two continents tended to lag behind. This caused them to be folded and buckled upward into the Andes Mountains and the numerous ranges of western North America. According to this theory, the continent of Antarctica must have drifted to the south and Australia to the south and east.

The basis for the theory of continental drift is not shape and distribution alone. The close matching of belts of crustal activity and similarities in rock and fossil types on opposite sides of the Atlantic are also significant. Evidence can be obtained from ancient lavas regarding the direction of magnetic north at the time of cooling from a liquid to a solid. Such paleomagnetic measurements suggest past movement of continents with respect to each other and thus support the drift theory. Drifting explains the thinness and youth of the sea floor sediments and the shape of the Mid-Atlantic Ridge, some scientists believe.

The greatest weakness of the theory is the lack of any known force sufficient to move the continents. Another difficulty is the fact that continental crust is no stronger than oceanic crust, so that the continents could not reasonably be expected to float more or less freely through the oceanic crust. Recent data also suggest that continental structure may extend to a depth of about 700 kilometers. This would require that the continents behave as a unit to this great depth. Furthermore, recent investigations of the distribution of fossils indicate that the continents have been in their same positions relative to the north and south poles for many millions of years.

16–13 How will mountain building theories be tested?

All of the major theories of mountain building are only as good as their relationship to the observable evidence. If they do not meet the needs of the data, they are not acceptable. All theories will be tested severely as new information is gained from many sources. Much evidence is now being gathered that suggests that some mountains may form from the slipping downward of great quantities of materials near the surface in response to gravity. Other theories have been proposed that explain mountain building on the basis of either the expansion or the contraction of the earth.

Undoubtedly men will continue to gather information about this important phase of the rock cycle. Satellites and space probes are providing more information about the earth as well as the other planets. When scientists are able to compare the earth with the moon, Mars, and other planets, they will gain deeper insight into the behavior of the rock cycle. It is likely that mountain-forming processes can be evaluated with more certainty on the basis of such comparisons. If material is obtained somehow from the mantle, then much should be learned about the environment where many of the changes relating to crustal movement seem to originate. More information about the composition, temperature, and pressure conditions within the interior will also aid in proving or disproving present theories that attempt to explain mountain building.

16–14 How are earth processes related?

You have seen evidence for slow vertical movements of portions of the earth's crust. An area that sinks and receives sediment from higher land masses during an interval of geologic time later becomes elevated to supply sediment to other sinking areas. You have investigated processes that act to wear away the land and transport earth materials from higher to lower elevations. Most of these

Figure 16–17 *The concepts of the water cycle and the rock cycle relate surface and internal processes. Using this generalized drawing, review the relationships of climate, weathering, erosion, sedimentation, and mountain building processes.*

processes involve the materials of the hydrosphere or the atmosphere. The hydrosphere and the atmosphere, then, react with the lithosphere to level the earth's surface. You might have concluded that in time the earth's surface would become smooth and these surface processes would cease. Further observations prevented you from accepting such a conclusion. Mountains containing marine fossils, volcanoes, and coral reefs were evidence of internal forces acting to lift portions of the crust.

Most of the wearing down of the surface is carried on by water being pumped from the oceans back to the land by the sun's energy. Hence, we can point to the sun as the energy source for surface processes that tend to level the land. What is the source of energy for the internal forces that raise and lower areas of the earth's crust? When we relate these internal forces to processes such as convection currents or contraction, we must account for a source of energy needed to drive such a process.

The concepts of the water cycle and the rock cycle relate surface processes and internal processes. (See Figure

(Far left) Entrance to a cave west of Denver which contains a 21-meter quartz rod (center) used to detect earth movements as small as 1 mm in 16km. A Colorado School of Mines scientist checks the instruments (left).

16–17.) Although you have seen evidence to substantiate the idea of a rock cycle, little has been said about how much time is involved in such a cycle. If you could actually follow an atom through a complete cycle from a mountain top to a geosyncline and back to another mountain top, how much time would be involved? To attempt to answer this question, you must relate geologic events to some sort of time scale.

Thought and Discussion . . .

1. Describe the contraction theory and discuss its strong and weak points.
2. How do density differences provide the driving force for supposed convection currents in the mantle?
3. Describe the convection theory and list its strong and weak points.
4. What would you look for on Mars that could give you an insight into mountain building on the earth?

Unsolved Problems   Man has a better understanding of what goes on in the interior of stars than what is happening in the interior of the earth. Almost everything about the earth's interior and its effect on the surface is still a mystery. Perhaps the greatest need for research at the moment is gaining a better understanding of how materials behave under the immense pressures found in the interior. For example, what effects do high pressures have on the melting point and crystal structure of solids and the speed of seismic waves?

Another area where additional work is needed is in the reactions of earth materials to long-continued stresses. Many geologic facts indicate that crystalline solids react to long-continued forces by flowing like liquids. As yet the theory of such flow, the details of how it takes place, and the factors that control it are imperfectly understood. One of the difficulties is that such experimentation requires the passage of periods of time that often exceed the lifetime of an individual experimenter.

A third area of investigation where more data are needed involves the amount of heat flowing to the surface of the earth and its geographic distribution. Such information has direct bearing on theories of mountain building and the thermal conditions in the interior. Until such conditions are better understood, it will be difficult to discover which of the theories of mountain building is most nearly correct.

CHAPTER REVIEW

Summary

There are many good reasons for studying the earth's interior. As you have seen in preceding chapters, certain things about the surface simply cannot be explained by surface and near-surface processes. In an attempt to answer some of these questions scientists have gathered a great deal of indirect evidence about the interior.

It is thought that the earth is more dense toward the center. The density increase seems not to be uniform, for the core is thought to be composed chiefly of iron, whereas the mantle is composed of silicates rich in iron and magnesium. The outer crust is variable in composition. The mantle has the greatest effect on the features of the crust. It seems to be primarily solid but reacts to long-continued forces by deforming like a liquid.

Convection currents in the mantle may explain some of the puzzling effects seen at the surface, such as the subsidence and later uplift of geosynclines to produce mountain ranges. Other theories have also been suggested such as continental drift and contraction. None of these hypotheses, including convection, is entirely satisfactory. Much remains to be learned before any fully acceptable theory can be devised. This is one of the reasons why man is turning with the space program to the study of the moon and other planets. It is hoped that investigation of different planets will lead to greater understanding of the planet earth.

Questions and Problems

A

1. How do we know that density increases toward the center of the earth?
2. What explanation is given for the fact that S waves do not pass through the earth's core?
3. How many seismographic stations must record arrival times so that an epicenter location can be determined?
4. What single fact would you have to know to determine the distance to the epicenter of an earthquake with a travel-time graph?
5. Of what is the mantle generally thought to be composed?
6. What fraction of the distance from the surface to the center of the earth has been reached by drilling?
7. What part of the earth's total volume can be currently examined directly?
8. What simple relationship led to the idea of continental drift?

B

1. What is the difference between compressional and shear waves?
2. Use a diagram to describe in detail how the Moho was discovered.
3. What evidence do scientists have about the composition of the earth's core?
4. The radius of the earth is 6370 kilometers. The location of the core-mantle interface is at a depth of 2900 kilometers. What percentage of the earth's volume is occupied by the core? What percentage is occupied by the mantle? (Neglect the volume of the crust.)
5. Name two lines of evidence that suggest the earth's interior is very hot.
6. What evidence suggests that some lavas originate in the mantle?
7. In what characteristics do solids and liquids differ?
8. What evidence is there that some solids can flow?
9. What bearing do the age and thickness of deep-ocean sediments have on theories of mountain building?
10. Describe three different theories that attempt to explain the gross features of the earth's crust.

C

1. Why are waves refracted as they pass from one material to another?

2. Construct a diagram that will explain why there is a P-wave shadow zone on the opposite side of the earth from an earthquake.
3. What evidence do scientists have that suggests something about the composition of the mantle?
4. You could explain the average density of the earth by a dense mantle over a less dense core. Why is the explanation not acceptable?
5. What evidence is there that the mantle reacts to long-continued forces by flowing like a liquid?
6. What evidence is there to answer the question of whether the earth's interior is liquid or solid?

Suggested Readings

BOOKS

Bates, D. R. *The Earth and Its Atmosphere*. Basic Books, Inc., Publishers, New York, 1957. Chapters 3 and 6.

Gilluly, James, A. C. Waters, and A. O. Woodford. *Principles of Geology*. W. H. Freeman & Co., Publishers, San Francisco, 1959. Chapter 19.

Hodgson, James H. *Earthquakes and Earth Structure*. Prentice-Hall, Inc., Englewood Cliffs, N.J., 1964. Chapter 3.

Iacopi, Robert. *Earthquake Country*. Lane Magazine & Book Co., (Sunset Book), Menlo Park, Calif., 1964.

Verne, Jules. *Journey to the Center of the Earth*. Available in several hardbound and paperback editions.

PERIODICALS

Anderson, Don L. "The Plastic Layer of the Earth's Mantle." *Scientific American*, May, 1958. (Also Scientific American Offprint #855, W. H. Freeman & Co., Publishers, San Francisco.)

Bullen, K. E. "The Interior of the Earth." *Scientific American*, September, 1955. (Also Scientific American Offprint #804.)

Edson, Lee. "Journey to the Center of the Earth." *Petroleum Today*, Spring, 1966.

Wilson, J. Tuzo. "Continental Drift." *Scientific American*, April, 1963. (Also Scientific American Offprint #868.)

(Right, above) Why are heavy timbers used in mines? (Below) High pressure equipment used in tests of rock deformation. (Far right) In Jules Verne's fantastic Journey to the Center of the Earth the men rafting on a sea inside the earth are startled by a spouting geyser.

UNIT III   *Earth's Biography*

When the Spaniards invaded Central and South America in the sixteenth century, they came upon groups of people who remained from a once mighty civilization, skilled in art, architecture, and certain aspects of science. In 1521, when Cortez' men stormed the Aztec capital (near modern Mexico City), they found a great and delicately carved stone disk 4 meters across and weighing 18 metric tons. This was the Aztec calendar (photograph, opposite page), sculptured in 1502. It depicts information on the organization of the whole universe and the laws that governed the actions of men and gods.

The supreme god of the Aztecs was Tezcatlipoca (above, center). He was considered the giver of life. A second god, Quetzalcoatl, was god of the sun, the air, and of wisdom (above, left). He had a light complexion and a long beard. After reigning for a period of peace and plenty he was taken away by Tezcatlipoca, saying he would someday return. When Cortez landed on the shore of Mexico, the Aztecs believed the god had returned. They bowed down to him, offering little opposition to his invasion.

Among the many legends in early America, some of the most prominent deal with earth's biography. In the Mayan tradition in Guatemala, for example, Hurakan (Mayan

for Tezcatlipoca) and Gukamatz (or Quetzalcoatl) gave a series of commands. Mountains rose out of the sea and rivers and vegetation came forth, followed by various animals and, finally, by man. The creation of maize (corn) was an important part of this development. Hurakan was also the god of wind. He would rush along at night with extraordinary speed and violence. Winds bearing his name still wreak havoc in the Caribbean.

An interesting tradition of both Aztecs and Mayans is the legend of the four suns. It seems there were four periods of history prior to our own. Each period ended in disaster. The four periods are represented by the four rectangles near the center of the calendar. One legend tells how the first period ended when the earth's inhabitants were devoured by tigers. At the close of the second period, mankind was swept away by terrible winds and survivors turned into monkeys in order to hang on. At the close of the third period, men changed into birds to avoid a fearful shower of fire and lava. A great flood ending the fourth period caused men to turn into fish. The fifth period, in which we live, will be destroyed by earthquakes.

The divine calendar regulated every aspect of life. It was divided into 18 months of 20 days each (ring of 20 figures outside of rectangles), plus a final five-day unlucky period. Each month brought an elaborate fiesta, with the most impressive fiesta coming at the end of the 52-year "century," when it was feared the world might come to an end. Perhaps time will take on new meaning for you as you relate these ancient legends of earth history to the modern biography of the earth in this Unit III.

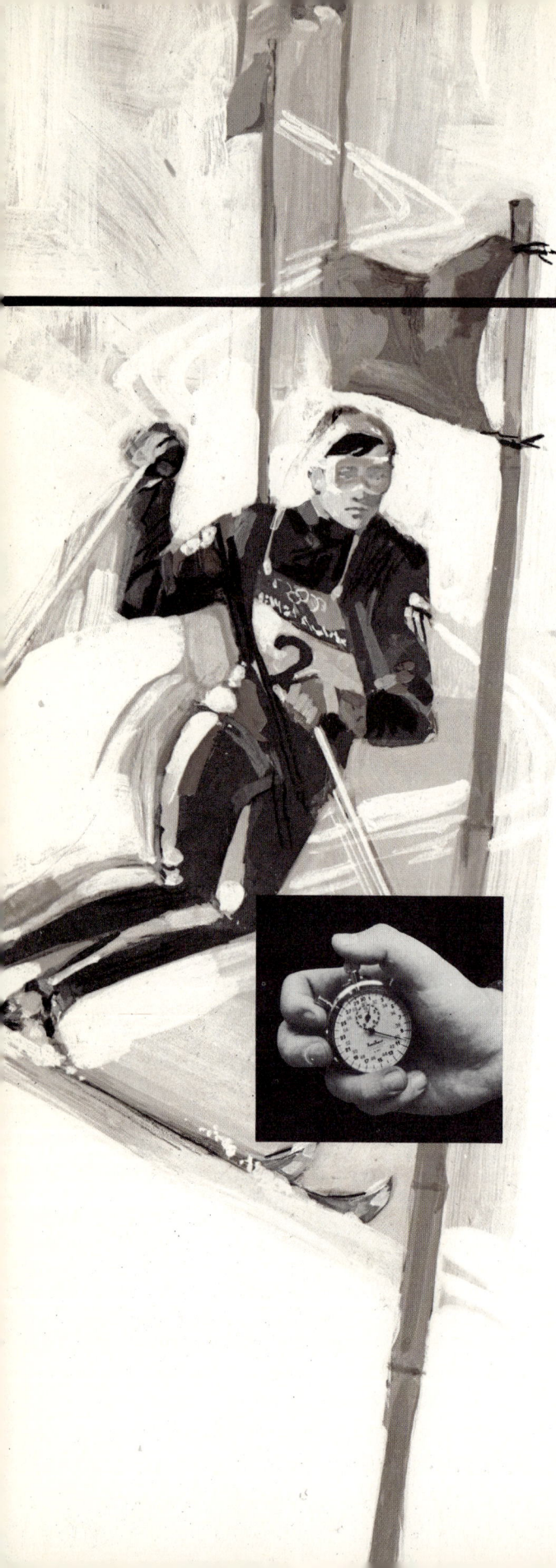

Chapter 17 Time and Its Measurement

Seven, six, five, four, three, two, one, lift off. This expression is becoming familiar to most of us today. The period of time immediately preceding the launching of a mighty rocket is one of the most critical periods of time that man measures. Because this time period is so critical, extremely accurate clocks are used to measure time in the control center at the launching site. A one-second delay in launch time can cause a launching to be cancelled. Is the launching of a giant rocket the only event that is so dependent on the accurate measurement of time and on accurate clocks? Of course not. You can think of many other events and happenings that are equally dependent on accurate measurement of time. Have you ever missed a bus or part of a television program simply because you were a few minutes late? If you have, you know that you did not allow yourself enough time or that perhaps your watch was not running properly.

Everything you do is related to time. Stop for a minute and make a mental list of the things you do each day that depend on the measurement of time. You get up in the morning at a particular time in order to get to school on time. At school you attend classes that begin and end at a given time. Then after school you probably participate in various activities which are also scheduled to start and end at specified times.

We are living in an age in which time and time measurement are extremely important. But time is not just a feature or phenomenon of the present. Time has been flowing since the beginning and will continue to flow long after present generations have gone from the earth. If this is so, shouldn't we be just as interested in the past and the future as we are in the present?

It has been said that to know the present, one must know and understand the past. For many centuries learned men speculated about the age of the earth and whether or not the earth was formed at the same time as the universe. Only recently, however, have scientists been able to obtain some answers to these and other time-related questions about the history of the earth.

Are earth scientists as interested in the future as they are in present and past time? The answer is of course, yes. They are constantly searching for clues that will indicate what kinds of climatic changes might occur in the future and when, how long the sun will continue to give off just the "right amount" of radiant energy to sustain life here on earth, and when the next serious earthquake will occur. Knowledge already gained through research makes it possible for earth scientists to make some predictions about the future. You will read about some of these predictions in the chapters that follow this one.

Figure 17–1
Sedimentary rocks in Monument Valley, Arizona. Match the rock layers in the pinnacle on the right with the rock layers in the foreground.

How Is Time Measured?

17–1 What is time?

Have you ever tried to describe or define time? If you have, you know it is not an easy task. Why is this?

ACTIVITY *Cover all clocks and watches in the room. After this select a student to be a "timekeeper." He will place a mark on the blackboard when you are to start to "measure" a five-minute period of time. Use any method or technique you can think of to determine the duration of the five-minute period. When you think five minutes have passed, signal the timekeeper. The timekeeper will make a mark each time someone signals. Did everyone's hand go up at the same time? How did you decide when five minutes had passed? How did your classmates decide? What do the marks on the blackboard tell you? What is time?*

It is change that makes us aware of time and that provides a basis for the measurement of time. Change may involve the emergence or coming into existence of something new, the alteration of something that exists, or the disappearance or loss of something. Can you give examples of each of these from the natural environment? If all change were suddenly to cease, would time exist?

You can mark the passage of time by relating it to a series of events. What events did you use in the Activity? In order to construct a history of past events you must determine how much time elapsed between the events and how long it took for the events to occur.

17–2 Relative time differs from measured time.

ACTIVITY *List four events of your past life in the order that they happened.*

Now add to your list the four events one of your classmates listed. Place all eight events in order of occurrence.

Did you have difficulty in deciding whether a certain event occurred before or after other events? How long did it take for each of these events to occur? Was the time span between events the same?

Time is marked by events. When you list events in the order in which they took place, you have only established what happened before or after something else. Does this tell you "how long before" or "how long after"? In Figure 17–1 you see a series of sedimentary rock layers. Which layer is the oldest? Which layer is the youngest? What evidence did you use in reasoning out your answers to these questions?

When you are able to list events in the order that they occurred, you have established a sequence with respect to time. Such an ordering establishes a relative time scale. A **relative time scale** is a "before or after" scale based on a sequence of events. Using such a scale, you can only say that an event occurred before or after some other event.

Look again at Figure 17–1. These sedimentary layers have not been overturned so you can be sure that the top layer is younger than the bottom layer. But how *much* younger? What information would you need to answer this question? If you knew exactly how long it took for each of the layers to form, could you tell the difference in age of the oldest and youngest layers?

Compare the sedimentary rock layers with the events that you listed in the Activity in this section. If you knew how long it took for each of these events to take place and the length of time between the events, you could determine how much time passed between the first and the last events.

In the case of the rock layers, you must know not only how long it took for each layer to form, but also how much time elapsed between the formation of layers. Suppose that each layer required a million years to be deposited and that five million years passed between the formation of each layer. Now you can calculate how much older the bottom layer is than the top layer.

What does that tell you? Did the youngest layer form yesterday or a million years ago? You are able to say that the second layer is five million years older than the first, but you cannot determine when the top layer formed. You can determine "how long" but not "how long ago."

In order to decide "how long ago" you would have to measure backward from our point of reference in time. Our point of reference is *now*. When you can relate these ages to now, you have established a **measured time scale**. A measured time scale tells you in certain units "how long ago" an event took place.

17–3 Change, clocks, and calendars measure time.

To illustrate how important change is in measuring the passage of time, imagine what it would be like to live for two or three years in a totally dark, soundproof room without any kind of time-measuring device. Do you think that you would be able to tell when a day, a month, or a year had passed? What is it that makes us aware of time?

Measurement of time is accomplished with two kinds of clocks—mechanical clocks and natural clocks. In addition, we keep records of events and changes that have occurred with the passage of time. Your wristwatch is a mechanical clock. Can you think of any natural events that occur with such regularity that they could be used as clocks? Could

GET ME THE SPOOK!

HOW LONG HAVE YOU BEEN IMPRISONED HERE?

I CAN ANSWER THAT, IF YOU CAN TELL ME THE LIFE SPAN OF A RAT.

the "natural clocks" you have thought of be used for measuring short as well as very long spans of time such as the age of the earth? Is a calendar a clock?

Determination of relative time and relative ages is of importance in working out geologic history, but it does not provide earth scientists with the kind of information that enables them to say how long ago an event occurred.

Ideally, events in history, whether human history or earth history, should be dated in relation to the present in addition to being arranged in a relative sequence. For example, to know that dinosaurs became extinct before man appeared on earth is not as useful in constructing the history of life as it is to know that the dinosaurs became extinct approximately 70 million years ago. This can be related to the earliest record of man, which dates back to approximately two million years before the present. Now you can say how many years separated man from the dinosaurs.

To refer events to the present, we use various kinds of calendars and clocks. With these calendars and clocks we keep track of years, months, days, hours, minutes, and seconds. The lengths of two of these units, the year and the day, are based on the period of rotation of the earth and the period of the earth's orbit around the sun. These motions were considered in sections 4–4 and 4–5. The other units we use to keep track of time are arbitrary units established by man. An hour is $1/24$ of a day, a minute is $1/60$ of an hour, and a second is $1/60$ of a minute or $1/86,400$ of a day. Is there any reason why the second could not be twice or three times as long as it is?

Clocks and calendars enable us to assign specific times to events that are taking place now, but what about events that took place 1×10^4 years ago or 1×10^9 years ago? Is there any way to determine how much time certain earth changes required or how long ago they took place?

Since man-made clocks have been in existence for only a very short time, scientists must rely on natural clocks for a record of events that occurred in early historic and prehistoric time.

You know from the evidence presented in sections 4–4 and 4–5 that the day and the year are natural units of time resulting from motions of the earth. These same motions combined with the orientation of the earth with respect to the sun cause seasonal changes. It is reasonable to assume that the earth has been rotating on its axis and revolving around the sun since the solar system was formed. Therefore, it would seem that evidences of seasonal change might be recorded in the rock and fossil records. Does such evidence exist?

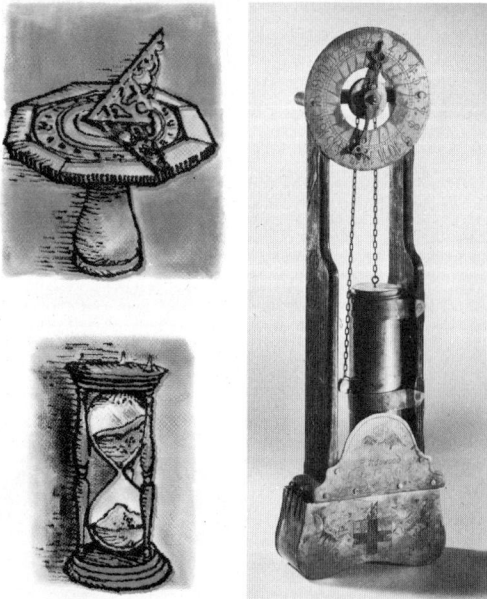

Man has devised many ways to measure the passage of time. The sundial (upper left) and the hourglass (lower left) are familiar examples. The timepiece shown in the photograph is a water clock made in 1682.

Before looking at the rock and fossil records, however, it might be useful to look for evidence of seasonal change being recorded at the present time. By doing so, you should be able to narrow your search in the record of the past. What type of evidence should you look for? Can you think of any organic or inorganic matter in which seasonal change is being recorded at the present time? Is it possible that variation in growth rates of organisms show evidence of seasonal changes?

ACTIVITY

1. *Figure 17–2A is a magnified view of tree rings. Which wood cells represent spring growth and which ones represent summer growth?*
2. *Did the two trees shown in Figure 17–2B live at the same time during any part of their lives?*
3. *What evidence is there for seasonal changes in the shell growth and the sedimentary layers in Figure 17–2C and D?*
5. *What could cause each of these features?*

In the preceding Activity you examined naturally occurring materials that have recorded annual changes at various times in the past. These clocks provide information about climatic conditions for short spans of time during the past but their recording period is too short to be used in establishing earth events of millions of years ago.

Thought and Discussion . . .

1. Durations of time can be compared or they can be measured with clocks. When you considered durations of time in your classroom, which way did you consider time? What word is used to describe this kind of time?
2. In a time-ordered sequence of events, event A preceded event B, which in turn preceded event C. Event D, however, preceded event B but followed event A. Can you represent these events in the proper order, placing the earliest event at the bottom of your list?
3. Change is said to be a feature of events. Can you think of any events that do not involve change?
4. Why is it important to earth scientists that they be able to determine relative and measured geologic time?
5. How would you define time?

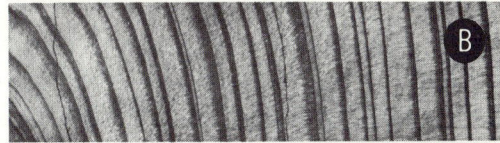

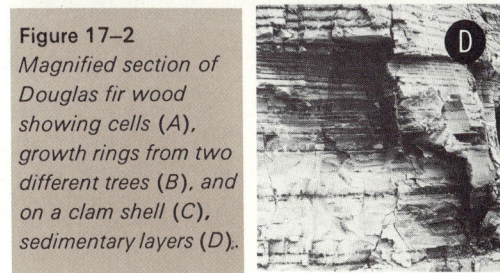

Figure 17–2
Magnified section of Douglas fir wood showing cells (A), growth rings from two different trees (B), and on a clam shell (C), sedimentary layers (D).

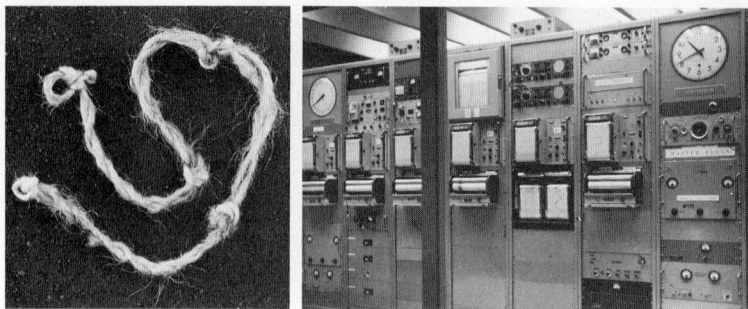

The ancient Chinese burned a dampened rope to measure time (far left). The atomic clock of the Naval Observatory (left) is regulated by the vibrations of cesium atoms.

Geologic Clocks

17–4 Creating a model of radioactive decay.

Physicists have developed a model of the nucleus of an atom that portrays a nucleus as a dynamic bundle of shifting energy patterns. The positively charged protons of the nucleus repel each other, and the neutrons, which are chargeless, add mass to the nucleus. The forces that bind the nucleus together are not clearly understood. The equilibrium or balance between the repulsion of the protons and the binding forces in the nucleus is often disturbed, resulting in the emission of a charged particle from the nucleus. This process is called **radioactive decay.**

Some of the minerals found in the earth's crust contain radioactive elements. These elements decay to more stable elements at a known rate and can be used to date events in the earth's past. Half of the atomic nuclei of a radioactive isotope in a sample decay in a period of time known as the half-life of the isotope. The reason why all of the nuclei do not decay at one time is that the behavior of nuclei follows probability, as illustrated by the model of radioactive decay in this investigation. The dynamic behavior of a nucleus is such that it is not able to remain stable indefinitely. It is impossible to tell how long a particular single nucleus resists radioactive decay. Since a sample contains millions of atoms of a radioactive isotope, the average rate of decay can be determined. Once this average rate is established by measurements, calculations can be made to determine how long it would take for 50 percent of the atoms in a given sample to decay. This time is called the half-life of the isotope. Different radioactive isotopes have different half-lives.

To illustrate the role of probability in radioactive decay you will use a model of the process.

Procedure

Place the markers in a square or rectangular box with one side marked. Then shake the box vigorously. Remove the

markers that point to the marked side and assume that these markers have "decayed." Record the number of "undecayed" markers remaining in the box and label this "turn-A." For "turn-B" repeat the shaking with the "undecayed" markers that were left in the box. Repeat with as many more turns as needed until the box is empty.

Plot the number of "undecayed" markers against the letter for each turn. Follow this procedure again with two sides of the box marked and again with three sides marked. Assume that each shake represents 1000 years. After constructing a graph for each procedure, answer these questions.

(1)What was the "half-life" of each of your models?

(2)How did you change the "half-life" of the models?

(3)What difference would it make in your results if a classmate added or subtracted some of the markers from the box during your investigation?

17–5 Atomic clocks measure geologic time.

Although many earth scientists who were living in the eighteenth and nineteenth centuries were convinced that the earth was very old, they lacked evidence with which to prove it. As a result, they were in constant conflict with other scientists of their time, particularly physicists. This conflict resulted from the fact that the physicists were supposedly able to show mathematically that the earth could not be much more than 20 to 40 million years old.

The figures proposed by the physicists for the age of the earth were based on the assumption that the earth had cooled from an originally molten state. To obtain the age of the earth, they determined the temperature of rocks of the earth's crust and an approximate rate of cooling for the earth. Using these figures, they then calculated the age. As additional support for their conclusion, they pointed out that there was no known source of energy that could keep the sun hot for more than 20 million years and that it was not logical to assume the earth to be older than the sun.

Decades passed and the earth scientists and physicists were still at odds on the question of the age of the earth. It began to appear that the problem had no solution. But, as often happens in scientific studies, a chance discovery was made that opened the way for solving the problem. In 1896, Henri Becquerel (On REE Beh-KREL), a French physicist, placed an unexposed photographic plate next to a piece of uranium compound in his darkroom. Later, when he wanted to use the photographic plate, he found that it had been partially exposed. But how had this happened? The plate had been carefully protected from light in the darkroom. Figure 17–3 shows what Becquerel's photographic plate might have looked like after it had been exposed. He experimented further and

Figure 17–3 *This picture was made by placing a key between a film and a radioactive substance.*

finally concluded that certain natural substances, such as uranium, give off energy. This discovery led others, like Marie and Pierre Curie, to do additional research on this mysterious property. Eventually their studies led to an understanding of the property that is now called radioactivity.

°**Radioactivity** can be defined as the natural decay or breakdown of nuclei of unstable isotopes. (See Section 2–4.) In the decay process electromagnetic energy and charged particles are given off. When isotopes decay, eventually more stable isotopes are produced.

ACTIVITY *You used a cloud chamber in Section 6–8 to observe the emission of particles from a radioactive source. Obtain a small amount of uranium ore or a specimen of uranium-bearing mineral from your teacher and place it in the cloud chamber. Observe the emission of particles from your specimen. Next place the uranium specimen in a drawer next to an unexposed piece of cut film or roll of film. Be sure that the film is still tightly wrapped and light-tight. After the radioactive substance and the film have been next to each other for a couple of days, have the film developed.*

Discovery of the property of radioactivity soon led to other discoveries about radioactive substances, including rates of decay, the type of energy generated, and the products of decay. In 1907 the American chemist and physicist, B. B. Boltwood, discovered that uranium undergoes radioactive decay, forming lead as the final product. Knowing this, he reasoned that it would be possible to find out how long ago a particular mineral formed, if the amount of the parent material (uranium) remaining in the mineral and the amount of the decay product (lead) could be measured.

In addition, the rate of decay of the parent material would have to be determined. Careful study and theoretical observations have shown that both these measurements can be made.

As you learned in Section 17–4, the rate of decay of a radioactive substance is expressed in terms of its half-life. **Half-life** can be defined as the length of time required for half of the atomic nuclei in any given quantity of the material to decay or break down. The half-life of radioactive substances varies from a fraction of a second to billions of years. With the exception of carbon-14, each of the radioactive isotopes used to date rocks has a very long half-life.

The radioactive dating method that has been used most widely up to now depends on the disintegration of an isotope of the element uranium, called uranium-238 (U^{238}). This disintegrates through a series of 14 steps, finally producing lead-206 (Pb^{206}), a stable isotope that undergoes no further change. As the disintegration from uranium to lead progresses, the amount of uranium decreases and the amount of lead increases. The rates of decay of U^{238} and other unstable isotopes used for dating have been precisely determined. On the basis of

Figure 17–4 (Left) Equipment used in radiocarbon dating of objects not more than 50,000 years old. The Dead Sea scrolls shown at right were discovered by archaeologists in a cave in Jordan. Radioactive dating methods indicated that they are about 2000 years old.

extensive investigations, these rates of decay are believed to have been constant throughout geologic time.

When a mineral forms and traps uranium atoms, the products of uranium decay begin to accumulate in the mineral. The age of the mineral is calculated by determining the ratio of the parent material (U^{238}) to the end product (Pb^{206}). Elaborate analytical equipment must be used for determining U^{238}/Pb^{206} ratios. In applying this method, it is assumed that none of the Pb^{206} escapes from the mineral, that no outside lead is added, and that no lead from a nonradioactive source was present to begin with. If any of these conditions have affected the sample being tested, the results obtained will not be accurate. Can you suggest how the ages obtained in dating three samples might be affected if each of the samples were altered in one of the ways indicated above?

The half-life of U^{238} is incredibly long, 4510 million years (4.51×10^9 years). Thus, this isotope can be used to date very old rocks in the earth's crust. Some intrusive igneous rocks from Canada and Africa dated by this method are around 3.3×10^9 years old. These are the oldest reliable rock dates obtained so far. Could these ancient rocks be part of the original crust of the earth?

In order to date events that have occurred during the last 50,000 years or so, a radioactive isotope having a much shorter half-life must be used. (See Figure 17–4.) One isotope that has been widely used in dating events of relatively recent times is carbon-14. Carbon-14 was first discovered in nature by the American chemist, Willard F. Libby.

Radiocarbon (C^{14}) is formed continuously in the earth's upper atmosphere by the bombardment of nitrogen atoms (N^{14}) with high energy **cosmic rays,** the nuclei of atoms that reach the earth from space. Once the carbon-14 atoms are formed, they unite readily with oxygen to form carbon dioxide. The formula for carbon-14 carbon dioxide is written as $C^{14}O_2$ instead of CO_2 to indicate that it was formed from radiocarbon. This reaction, which is part of the carbon cycle, is shown in Figure 17–5.

The radiocarbon dating method has been used to date thousands of relatively recent specimens including wood, bones, flesh, hair, shells, peat, and even old

Figure 17–5 *The simplified drawing shows how nitrogen (N^{14}) in the atmosphere is converted to radiocarbon (C^{14}) by cosmic radiation from the sun.*

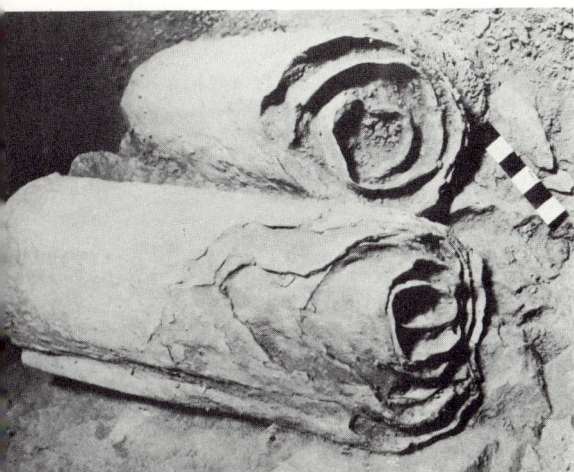

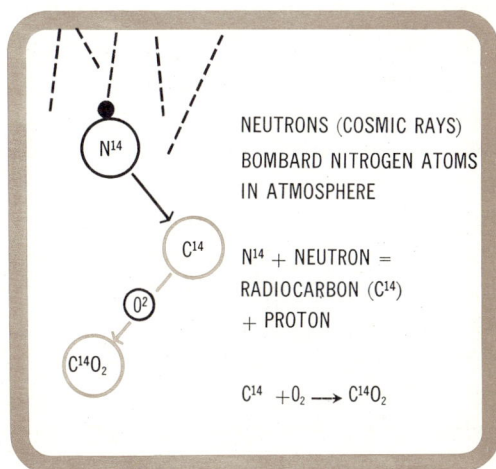

NEUTRONS (COSMIC RAYS) BOMBARD NITROGEN ATOMS IN ATMOSPHERE

N^{14} + NEUTRON = RADIOCARBON (C^{14}) + PROTON

$C^{14} + O_2 \longrightarrow C^{14}O_2$

N^{14}

C^{14}

O^2

$C^{14}O_2$

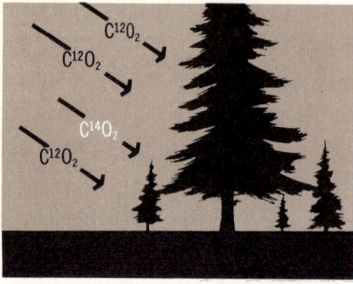

Figure 17–6 $C^{14}O_2$ enters a tree. When the tree dies, the amount of C^{14} in the wood begins to decrease as it decays. Thus the ratio of C^{14} to normal carbon C^{12} changes with time.

violins. (See Figure 17–6.) The method has been checked by comparing the dates obtained with events in recorded history and found to be very reliable.

The two radioactive dating methods discussed in this section are not the only methods scientists use to determine the ages of rocks. Some of the other methods that have been developed can be used even more widely than the U^{238}/Pb^{206} method and the C^{14} method. The reason for this is that the isotopes on which they are based are more abun-dant in most rocks than are U^{238} and C^{14}. However the U^{238}/Pb^{206} and C^{14} methods are good illustrations of the general nature of radioactive dating methods.

Thought and Discussion . . .

1. What information besides chronologic sequence can be obtained through the study of tree rings?
2. Can you define the term half-life? Do all radioactive isotopes have the same half-life?
3. What effect does the radioactive decay of unstable isotopes in the earth's crust have on the rocks surrounding them?
4. Which method of radioactive dating is used for relatively recent events? Why?

The Geologic Time Scale

17–6 Early attempts to organize the record.

The present day Geologic Time Scale has been developed over a period of more than 200 years. This scale is an attempt to relate rock units to one another and to establish their relationship in time. Early attempts to organize the rock record into units related to time were restricted to local areas. It was not until about 1833 that a time scale was developed that could be applied with some certainty throughout most of the world. One of the first efforts to work out such a scale was made by Johann Lehmann (1719–1767). He developed a relative time scale on the basis of rocks exposed in central Europe where he lived. Lehmann's classification can be briefly described as follows:

Youngest: Loosely consolidated sands and gravels.

Intermediate: Secondary rocks, which were layered rocks containing the preserved remains of plants and animals and particles eroded from older rocks.

Oldest: Unlayered rocks, which did not contain the remains of plants and animals and believed to be of chemical origin prior to the beginning of life.

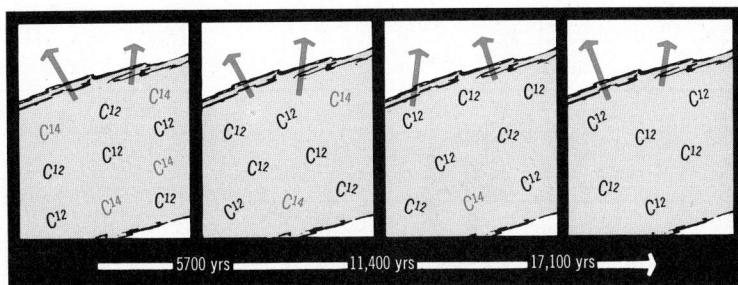

In the decades that followed the publication of Lehmann's classification, several other systems of classification were proposed by earth scientists and others. Real progress in organizing the rock record was not made until late in the eighteenth century, however, when three basic ideas pertaining to relative dating of rocks were proposed. These basic ideas were superposition, uniformity of process, and fossil correlation.

Nicolaus Steno originally proposed the first of these ideas in 1699, but it was not clearly stated or applied until much later. James Hutton, a Scottish physician and student of nature, examined sediments accumulating along the seashore. He recognized that in a sequence of layers of sediments, the layers deposited first are covered by layers deposited later. This relationship of the oldest bed being on the bottom in a sequence of rock layers is called the **principle of superposition.** It is a basic concept which has been widely used by geologists in working out sequences of rock layers in all parts of the world.

The principle of superposition seems so elementary and obvious to us now that we sometimes wonder why it was not thought of and applied earlier in history. As often happens, an idea that seems obvious as we look back required a long time to be recognized.

In addition to stating the principle of superposition, Hutton proposed another principle that has proved basic to our understanding of earth history. In his studies he observed that many of the features of sedimentary rocks were duplicated in sediments being deposited at the time. Hutton's observations led him to the conclusion that the processes affecting the earth today also affected the earth in the past and that the *present can be used as a key to the past.* This is often referred to as the **principle of uniformity of process.**

The other fundamental idea discovered in the latter part of the eighteenth century was that fossils differed from rock layer to rock layer in a sequence of sedimentary rocks and that different layers could be identified by the fossils they contained. This idea, which is called **fossil correlation,** was first recognized by William Smith, an English engineer, who was primarily concerned with how he could use this knowledge in building roads and canals. Fossils are the remains or evidence of prehistoric life preserved in rocks of the earth's crust.

The work of Hutton, Smith, and other European scientists during the late 1700's and the early 1800's eventually led to a general understanding of the relative ages of most rocks exposed on the earth's surface. This was accomplished by first working out the relative age sequence of old, older, and oldest in a large number of local areas. The sequences obtained locally were then matched, or *correlated,* with sequences in other areas.

After the principles of uniformity of

TABLE 17–1 GEOLOGIC TIME SCALES, 1833 AND 1905

	1883		1905
	RECENT PERIOD		PRESENT PLEISTOCENE
TERTIARY PERIOD	NEWER PLIOCENE	CENOZOIC ERA	PLIOCENE
	OLDER PLIOCENE		MIOCENE
	MIOCENE		OLIGOCENE
	EOCENE		EOCENE
SECONDARY PERIOD	CRETACEOUS	MESOZOIC ERA	CRETACEOUS
	WEALDEN		COMANCHEAN
	JURA LIMESTONE		JURASSIC
	LIAS		TRIASSIC
	NEW RED SANDSTONE		PERMIAN
	COAL MEASURES	PALEOZOIC ERA	COAL MEASURES
PRIMARY PERIOD			SUBCARBONIFEROUS
	MOUNTAIN LIMESTONE		DEVONIAN
	OLD RED SANDSTONE		SILURIAN
	TRANSITION LIMESTONE		ORDOVICIAN
		PRECAMBRIAN	CAMBRIAN

TABLE 17–2 THE GEOLOGIC TIME SCALE AS IT IS NOW USED IN NORTH AMERICA

ERAS	PERIODS	EPOCHS
CENOZOIC	QUATERNARY	RECENT
		PLEISTOCENE
	TERTIARY	PLIOCENE
		MIOCENE
		OLIGOCENE
		EOCENE
		PALEOCENE
MESOZOIC	CRETACEOUS	
	JURASSIC	
	TRIASSIC	
PALEOZOIC	PERMIAN	
	PENNSYLVANIAN	
	MISSISSIPPIAN	
	DEVONIAN	
	SILURIAN	
	ORDOVICIAN	
	CAMBRIAN	
PRECAMBRIAN / PROTEROZOIC		
ARCHEOZOIC		

process and superposition and the technique of fossil correlation were established, several versions of the Geologic Time Scale were produced. Two of these time scales, one published in 1833, the other in 1905, are illustrated in Table 17–1. Compare these with Lehmann's classification given at the beginning of this section and with the Geologic Time Scale used at the present time. (See Table 17–2.) Notice that some of the names used in 1833 are still used today.

17–7 Investigating the Geologic Time Scale.

As a clock face is a reference scale for a 24-hour day, so the Geologic Time Scale is a reference scale for earth history. The Geologic Time Scale broadly subdivides geologic history into workable units. In the Time Scale, the earth's history is divided into major units, somewhat like the chapters and sections of this book. The chief difference is that the units are units of time instead of units of pages. (See Table 19–1.)

Scientists have established this table for convenience in discussing the rock and fossil record in a time sequence. The dividing lines between the time units of eras, periods, and epochs are based on changes of some kind such as changes in life forms or mountain building. Two examples are the extinction of dinosaurs, which divides the Mesozoic Era from the Cenozoic Era, and the uplift of the Appalachian Geosyncline, which ends the Paleozoic Era. In no case is the dividing line a sharp one. It is more a zone of transition, an interface in time.

In comparison with the age of the earth, the span of man's existence is like the blink of an eye. It is difficult to visualize the vastness of geologic time when a man's life span may be only 70 years. How long is a billion years? A graphical model will help you to appreciate the great age of the earth.

Procedure

Examine the list of events given below and decide how to represent these in a time-ordered sequence. A roll of paper tape will be provided on which to plot your graphical model.

Ages of Events in Years Before Present

1. Oldest known rocks, 3.3 billion years ago.
2. First known plants (algae), 3.2 billion years ago.
3. First known animal (jellyfish), 1.2 billion years ago.
4. Beginning of the Cambrian and first abundant fossils, 600 million years ago.
5. Beginning of the Ordovician, 500 million years ago.
6. Beginning of the Silurian, 440 million years ago.
7. Beginning of the Devonian, 400 million years ago.
8. Beginning of the Mississippian, 350 million years ago.
9. Beginning of the Pennsylvanian, 305 million years ago.
10. First reptiles, 290 million years ago.
11. Beginning of the Permian, 270 million years ago.
12. Beginning of the Triassic, 225 million years ago.
13. First mammals, 200 million years ago.
14. Beginning of the Jurassic, 180 million years ago.
15. First birds, 160 million years ago.
16. Beginning of the Cretaceous, 135 million years ago.
17. Beginning of the Paleocene, 70 million years ago.
18. Beginning of the Eocene, 60 million years ago.
19. Beginning of the Oligocene, 40 million years ago.
20. Beginning of the Miocene, 25 million years ago.
21. Beginning of the Pliocene, 11 million years ago.
22. First man-like animals, 2 million years ago.
23. Beginning of the Pleistocene, 1 million years ago.
24. Last Ice Age, 10,000 years ago.

Convert the following to years before the present:

25. Mount Vesuvius eruption destroys Pompeii, A.D. 79.
26. First U.S. satellite orbited, 1958.

James Hutton, born in Scotland in 1726, was one of the most important figures in geology. His observations about the earth can be compared with observations made by Copernicus and other scientists of the past and present. Hutton had an inquiring mind and was a keen observer of nature. He became interested in the physical and biological aspects of his environment, first as a physician, then as a farmer, and finally as a geologist.

For over thirty years Hutton traveled, observed, and studied the surface of the earth, always in search of evidence to support his theory that it had changed in time. Finally in 1795 he summarized his findings in a work entitled Theory of the Earth. This work, containing many brilliant ideas and deductions, including the principle of uniformity, marked a turning point in our understanding of the earth, its materials, and its processes. However, the book had relatively little influence on scientific thought in the years immediately following its publication. Perhaps the most important reason for this was Hutton's difficult and involved style of writing. Fortunately, after Hutton's death in 1797 one of his friends, John Playfair, decided to present the ideas contained in Theory of the Earth in a more readable form. Playfair's volume, entitled Illustrations of the Huttonian Theory of the Earth, was published five years after Hutton's death and has become one of the classics of geology.

17–8 Calibrating the Geologic Time Scale.

Prior to Boltwood's discovery of uranium dating in 1907, it was only possible to discuss events in early history in reference to a before and after time sequence (relative time). Specific events could not be dated so it was not possible to tell how many years before the present they had occurred. Natural radioactive clocks make it possible to assign ages to many events in geologic history and to establish a time-measured scale.

Using the methods you have learned, as well as several other methods, earth scientists have been able to determine actual ages of rocks ranging from a few thousand years of age to 3.3×10^9 years. Thousands of rocks have been dated and many more will be dated in the years ahead. With the passing of each year, earth scientists gain a better understanding of the actual age relationships of the events represented on the Geologic Time Scale. The dates that are now generally accepted for the major units of geologic time are the same as those on your tape from Investigation 17–7.

To see how earth scientists calibrate the time scale, let us examine a simplified version of a technique they use. In Figure 17–7 you can tell on the basis of relative age relationships that the granite is younger than rock unit X, which it intruded, and older than unit Y, which contains weathered pieces of granite. You also know that the granite is older than unit Z, but you cannot tell how long ago the events took place unless some actual age determinations are available for you to use. Assume that age determinations obtained from the minerals in these rocks indicate that the granite is 1.5×10^8 years old and unit Z is 1.3×10^8 years old. Now what can you determine with respect to the age

Figure 17–7 *How is the principle of uniformity of process applied in determining the relative ages of the three rock units labeled X, Y, and Z?*

relationships of the rock units X, Y, and Z represented in the diagram?

The oldest rocks thus far dated are granitic rocks from Canada and Africa. These rocks, which were intruded into still older rocks, are around 3.3×10^9 years old. What does this imply about the earth's age? Additional evidence supporting the view that the earth is very old has been obtained from meteorites, some of which have contained radioactive isotopes. Some of the meteorites that have been dated are as much as 4.5×10^9 years old. How does this age compare with that of the oldest rocks found in the earth's crust?

Thought and Discussion . . .

1. Was Lehmann's method of classification of geologic time relative or measured? Why did he use this method?

2. Explain how the correlation of fossil species is related to the development of a Geologic Time Scale.

3. How would you go about developing a Geologic Time Scale for your local area if one were not available?

Unsolved Problems How old is the earth? Will we ever know exactly? Radioactive age determinations of some meteorites indicate that the meteorites are about 4.5×10^9 years old. Is this the age of the earth, which presumably originated at the same time as the other planets? How long did it take for the earth's crust to form?

How old are the ocean basins? Will the oldest sediments in the ocean basins ever be found? And if they are, will it be possible to date them by radioactive methods? By dating events more accurately, man will be able to better determine the rates of geologic processes such as uplift and erosion. Were these rates the same in the past or were they slower or faster? Knowledge of rates of processes in the past will give man a clearer picture of the development of the earth as we now know it.

Are the oldest rocks in each continent about the same age or are they of different ages? If so, which continent is the oldest? the youngest?

CHAPTER REVIEW

Summary

Time is measured by events. It can be considered in a relative sense—old, older, oldest—or it can be considered as a measure of duration (how long) or age (how long ago). Earth scientists consider time in all these ways. Long before the discovery of radioactivity in 1896, earth scientists were able to develop a Geologic Time Scale that was workable on a worldwide basis. The Time Scale was worked out on the basis of relative ages. Three basic ideas, the principle of uniformity of process, the principle

Time-lapse photography enables scientists to "speed up" events that occur too slowly to observe visually. These photographs show a geranium blooming on the first, third, and seventh day of the flowering process.

of superposition, and correlation by fossils were used in establishing the relative ages of rocks of the earth's crust.

With the discovery of the property known as radioactivity, it was possible to date events that occurred at various times in the distant past. Some minerals that occur in the rocks of the earth's crust contain unstable isotopes whose atomic nuclei start to decay as soon as they are formed. In the process of decay, energy is released from the nuclei of unstable isotopes, and in the process they are gradually transformed into stable isotopes.

Several radioactive dating methods including the uranium-lead ratio method and the carbon-14 method are widely used in determining the ages of rocks of the earth's crust. Carbon-14, which has a half-life of 5700 years, can be used to date very young rocks and objects of historic time. Other methods are used for dating much older rocks, some as old as 3.3×10^9 years. Based on the ages of these rocks and on other evidence, earth scientists now believe the earth to be at least 4.5×10^9 years old. Geologic time is incredibly long, especially in comparison to the short span of man's existence.

Questions and Problems

A

1. If the earth's rate of rotation is slowing down as a result of the moon's gravitational attraction, as scientists believe, what effect will this change have on the length of a day? the length of a year?

2. Why is carbon-14 not used for dating rocks of Paleozoic age?
3. Why is carbon-14 more useful in dating certain earth materials than other dating methods?
4. How old are the oldest rocks dated thus far? Do these rocks represent the original crust of the earth?

B

1. Why were earth scientists unable to prove before the year 1907 that the earth was more than 20 to 40 million years old?
2. Why were many of the early age determinations obtained by the uranium-lead dating method inaccurate?
3. Why is it necessary to study carefully both the rocks and the geology of an area from which a sample for radioactive dating is obtained?
4. You know that William Smith was able to correlate rock layers from one locality to another through the use of fossils. If rocks in other continents contain the fossil remains of large dinosaurs, would they be approximately the same age as rocks in the United States containing similar fossil remains?

C

1. Some charcoal and charred, broken bones of deer and rabbits were dug from beneath several feet of sand and gravel along the shore of a river. Analysis of the charcoal in a laboratory showed that one-eighth of the C^{14} remained in the charcoal. (a) How old is

the charcoal? (b) Reconstruct the sequence of events that may have taken place at the site of this find.

Suggested Readings

BOOKS

Dunbar, Carl Owen. *Historical Geology*, 2nd ed. John Wiley & Sons, Inc., New York, 1960.

Heller, Robert L., ed. *Geology and Earth Science Sourcebook*, Holt, Rinehart & Winston, Inc., New York, 1962. Chapter 16.

Gould, R. T. *John Harrison and his Timekeepers*. National Maritime Museum, Greenwich, England, 1958.

Hurley, Patrick M. *How Old is the Earth?* Doubleday & Company, Inc., New York, 1959.

Hood, Peter. *How Time is Measured.* Oxford University Press, 1955.

Poole, Lynn and Gray Poole. *Carbon 14 and Other Science Methods That Date the Past.* McGraw-Hill Book Company, New York, 1961. Chapter 2.

Stokes, W. L. *Essentials of Earth History: An Introduction to Historical Geology,* 2nd ed. Prentice-Hall, Inc., Englewood Cliffs, N.J., 1966.

Strahler, Arthur N. *The Earth Sciences.* Harper & Row, Publishers, New York, 1963. Chapter 24.

PERIODICALS

Briggs, Lyman and Kenneth Weaver. "How Old Is It?" *National Geographic Magazine,* August, 1958.

Curtis, Garniss H. "A Clock for the Ages: Potassium-Argon." *National Geographic Magazine,* October, 1961.

Deevey, E. S. "Radiocarbon Dating." *Scientific American,* February, 1952. (Also Scientific American Offprint #811, W. H. Freeman & Co., Publishers, San Francisco.)

Libby, Willard F. "Radiocarbon Dating." *Science,* March 3, 1961.

Lyons, Harold. "Atomic Clocks." *Scientific American,* February, 1957, p. 71. (Also Scientific American Offprint #225.)

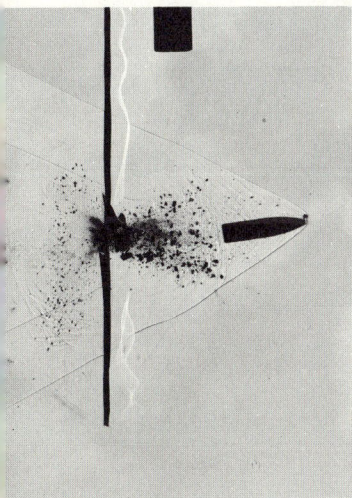

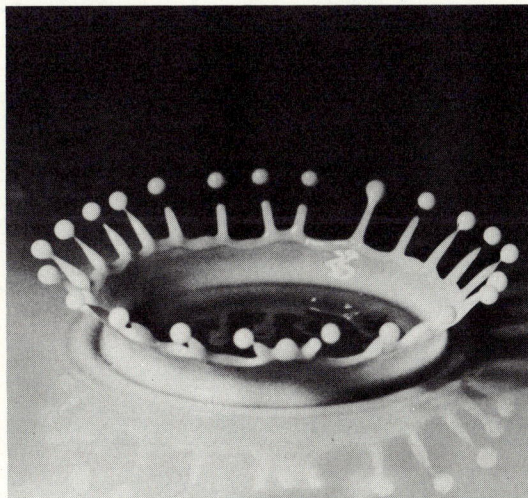

High-speed photos. (*Far left*) A bullet passing through a sheet of plexiglass. (*Left*) The impact of a milkdrop on a surface of milk.

Chapter 18 The Record in the Rocks

In 1893 the master of the sailing ship *Jason* set foot on an Antarctic Island largely covered by ice. To his surprise he found what looked like petrified ferns, snails, and trees in the rocks exposed there. Other unexpected discoveries were made by members of Admiral Richard E. Byrd's expedition to the Antarctic in 1935. They found fossil tree trunks about a half meter in diameter and beds of coal separated by layers of shale and limestone.

Coal has also been found at the other end of the world, on the Arctic island of Spitsbergen. On the same island fossil corals occur in rocks made of sediments similar to those now being deposited in shallow marine environments. Modern relatives of the plants and animals found in these rocks can exist only in tropical and subtropical climates. How could these organisms have existed in such cold places? Is it possible that climatic conditions were different at the time when these organisms lived?

You may have read that in relatively recent time streams have cut great gashes like the Grand Canyon in the earth's surface, or that millions of years ago seas covered the Grand Canyon area and deposited great thicknesses of sediments that are now visible in the walls of the canyon. How can you test the truth of such statements?

You may also have read that cone-shaped mountains such as Mount Shasta in California and Mount Hood in Oregon are extinct volcanoes, and that the Columbia Plateau in Washington and Oregon consists of ancient lava flows. Yet no one has ever seen molten lava flowing from Mount Shasta or Mount Hood or seen thick sheets of lava spreading across Oregon and Washington. How is it known that these features are the result of volcanic activity? What kind of evidence leads to this conclusion?

A geologist's only clues about the history of an area are contained in the rocks themselves. As you study this chapter, see if you can put yourself in the place of a geologist. Try to read the complete record in the rocks by putting together all the separate pieces of evidence you can find.

From this present-day photo of barren Antarctic wastes it is difficult to imagine that areas like this one were probably once semitropical coal swamps.

Figure 18–1

Looking at Rocks

18–1 How do you read a rock?

Imagine yourself standing in front of a rock outcrop somewhere in the foothills of the Rocky Mountains. (See Figure 18–1A.) Stand back so that you can get an overall view. Describe what you see.

In order to tell a story so that it makes sense, you must start at the beginning. Where does the story begin in a pile of layered rocks, at the top or at the bottom? Which is the oldest layer in Figure 18–1A? Are the layers horizontal or tilted? What does this mean about the history of the rocks in this outcrop?

Suppose you go up to this outcrop and examine it closely. You discover that it looks like the photograph in Figure 18–1B. If you examine the rock even more closely, you will see a texture like that shown in Figure 18–1C. How do the fragments that make up the rock seem to fit together? What does this kind of texture indicate about the origin of the rock?

Other kinds of rocks are shown in Figure 18–2. Describe the features of these specimens. What is the probable origin of each rock? On what specific evidence do you base your statements?

18–2 What do layers show about past events?

The most common feature in sedimentary rocks is layering. Examine Figure 18–3, which shows two sedimentary rock outcrops. Describe the layers. What causes their layering to show up? Is it a difference in the color, size, or kind of grains that make up the rock? Are the layers regular and continuous or are they irregular and broken?

Figure 18–4A shows how particles settle in water with no current. Describe the shape of the layers. Suppose that the particles halfway up the small humps are loose and roll easily. What do you think will happen to them?

You know that there is a current of some kind in lakes and oceans. Most sedimentary particles settle under conditions shown in Figure 18–4B, C, and D. Compare the potential energy of particles that settle on top of the small humps with that of the particles that settle in the small basins. On the basis of these

Figure 18–2 *Can you determine the probable origin of each of the rocks shown below?*

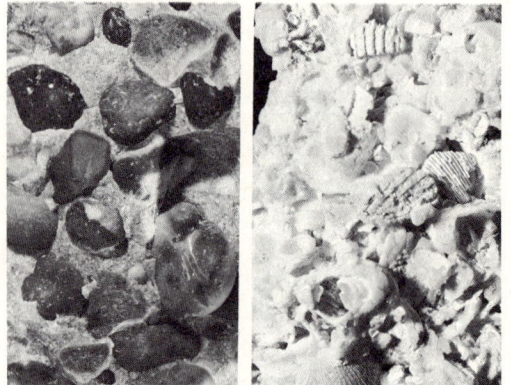

diagrams, would you expect most sedimentary layers to be roughly horizontal or tilted steeply at the time of their formation? Look back at Figure 18–1. What do you think might have happened to these layers since the time when they were first deposited?

As you have probably noticed in the samples of sedimentary rocks available in your classroom, interfaces between individual layers of sediment may be sharp or gradual. Observations of sediments now being formed show that interfaces between layers form when there is a change in the conditions of deposition. What kinds of changes would you expect to find in a sediment if the velocity of a depositing current were suddenly increased or reduced? (Review Section 13–1, Investigating the deposition of sediments.)

Suppose that a stream bringing large amounts of sand into a basin of deposition dries up. Suppose that after the first stream dries up, a stream from another source area begins to flow into the basin, bringing sand with different characteristics. The result would probably be a new layer quite different in appearance from the first sand layer on which it is deposited.

A single layer of sediment that covers several square kilometers may also vary in appearance from one place to an-

Figure 18–3 *What causes the layering to show up in these outcrops of sedimentary rocks?*

other. In one place a single layer may be sandy and in other places gravelly or clayey. In Figure 18–5, for example, sand close to shore grades into clay away from shore. How can you explain the fact that there are fingers of clay extending into several layers of sand? Refer to Figure 13–18B on page 305.

Many sediments are deposited under water in streams, lakes, and oceans. You can see grains of sand being moved about by water in a stream or in the ocean. When you observe seashells preserved in sedimentary rocks of central Kansas or on the top of a mountain in New England or California, you can be quite certain that such rocks formed from sediments deposited in water.

Other sedimentary rocks appear to have been deposited on land. If you find

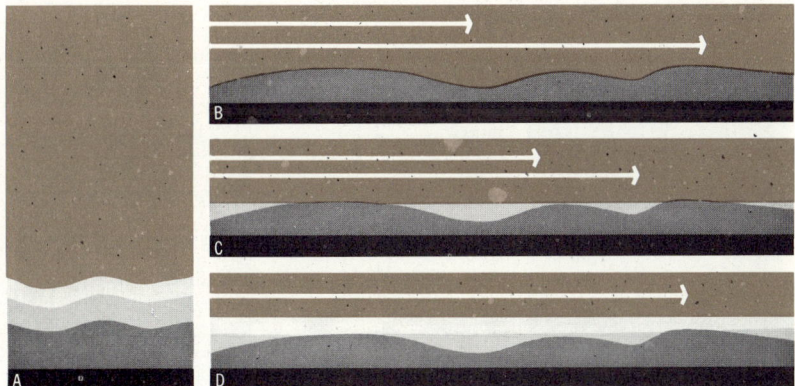

Figure 18–4 *Compare the settling of sedimentary particles in water in which there is no current (A), and in water that is in motion (B, C, and D).*

Figure 18–5 *Horizontal variation in marine sediments. How are the sand and clay related?*

fossil horse remains in a sedimentary rock, it is likely that the rock formed on the land. The soil under your feet could be converted into rock if the particles were cemented together. Layers of desert sand can also be cemented together to form rock. Where does the cement come from? Ground water that flows through the pores of rocks contains ions of calcium, silicon, and iron. These ions can combine with oxygen and other elements in the water to form a cement of calcite ($CaCO_3$), quartz (SiO_2), or various iron minerals.

However, not all layered rocks are sedimentary. There are thick piles of ancient layered lava flows on the Columbia Plateau. (See Figure 18–6.) Layers also form on volcanic cones when flows of lava pour down the sides and harden, and when ash and dust from the volcano settle on the cone. What differences in the rocks would help you to distinguish these volcanic layers from sediments deposited in water?

A single volcanic flow may include different colored layers all wrinkled like an untidy tablecloth. (See Figure 18–7.) In what direction did the lava flow in the two examples in Figure 18–7? How can you tell? Some rocks formed from lava flows contain long crystals that are oriented roughly in the direction of flow. Crystals floating in lava behave in much the same way as logs floating in a river. The next time you look at a river or stream, notice the way that sticks are oriented as they float with the current. Do they line up parallel to the direction of flow or perpendicular to it? Could the orientation of crystals in a lava flow be used to determine the location of the source of the lava?

Some metamorphic rocks also exhibit layering. In some places layered metamorphic rocks resemble sedimentary rocks. The layering in these rocks could be remnants of layers that were present

Figure 18–6 *(Left) A thick sequence of lava flows on the Columbia Plateau.*

Figure 18–7 *In what direction did the lava flow in each of the examples shown on the right?*

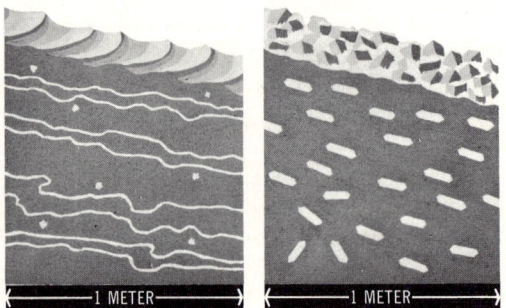

in an original sedimentary or volcanic rock, or it could be the result of metamorphic processes. (See Section 15–2.)

18–3 Why are cross-beds and ripple marks important?

Before you can determine the history of layered rocks, you must be able to distinguish the bottoms of the layers from the tops. Suppose the layers were tilted or even turned upside down by folding processes you studied in Chapter 14. What features could you use to reconstruct what happened?

You examined the way that particles of different sizes settle out of a column of water in Section 13–1. How were these layers arranged? Examine the series of layers of sediment in Figure 18–8.

Some sedimentary layers contain cross-beds. **Cross-beds** are thin layers within a larger layer. As shown in Figure 18–9, they lie at an angle to the larger layer that contains them. One way in which cross-beds form in sediments deposited by water is shown in Figure 18–10. Describe the series of events represented in this diagram. From the shapes of cross-beds shown in the diagram, how could you use the cross-beds to tell the top layer from the bottom? How could you use cross-beds to determine the direction the current must have been flowing at the time of deposition?

Ripple marks are another feature found in sedimentary rocks that can help you understand the rock record. You have probably seen ripple marks formed by currents in the shallow waters of a lake or ocean. You can also see ripple marks on sand dunes, on the sandy bottoms of streams, on snowdrifts, or even

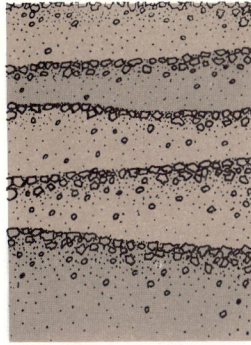

Figure 18–8 *Layers of sediment show gradation in size of particles. Is the sketch right side up or upside down?*

in gutters after a rainstorm. Ripple marks formed by currents moving in one direction are usually asymmetrical (not symmetrical). The steep side of ripple marks formed by currents is the down-current side. Look at the asymmetrical ripple marks in Figure 18–11. In which direction do you think the current must

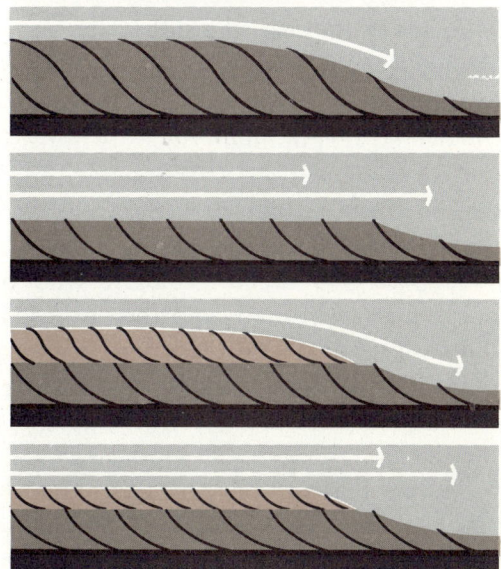

Figure 18–9 (*Right, above*) *Cross-bedded layers of sandstone. Compare with Figure 18–10.*
Figure 18–10 *Cross-bedded sediments form in alternating stages of deposition and erosion.*

Figure 18–11 *Asymmetrical ripple marks. In which direction did the current flow?*

Figure 18–12 *Symmetrical ripple marks. How can you tell if either of the examples is upside down?*

side down. Which way do the crests of symmetrical ripple marks point if a layer is right side up? (See Figure 18–12.) Can a symmetrical ripple mark be used to tell anything about current direction? Can asymmetrical ripple marks be used to tell whether a layer is right side up? It will be easier to answer these questions if you draw cross sections of the various kinds of ripple mark patterns.

ACTIVITY   *Place a small tray of wet mud beside a radiator or in a sunny window for several days. Examine the cracks that form on the surface. Imagine similar cracks on a mud layer that has been changed to rock. How could you use these cracks to recognize the top of the layer?*

---

have flowed? Why? Ripple marks are not always asymmetrical. Symmetrical ripple marks form when the water is moving back and forth as on a beach. These ripple marks can be used to tell whether a layer is right side up or up-

Fossils in rocks can also be used to determine whether a layer is upside down. Have you ever noticed the way clam shells come to rest on a beach? Waves or currents usually turn them over so that the hollow or concave side is down. Do the fossils shown in Figure 18–12 enable you to find the tops of the layers? Can you tell by studying fossils which layers are oldest?

18–4 Investigating an ancient stream channel.

During the late 1940's and early 1950's extensive prospecting for uranium took place on the Colorado Plateau. Geologists discovered rich uranium deposits in fossil logs that had been buried in ancient stream channels. In order to locate such deposits, prospectors went through the same steps you will use in this investigation.

Suppose you are a geologist who has found a ripple-marked, cross-bedded sandstone exposed at the surface. On the basis of available evidence, you suspect that the sandstone was deposited by an ancient stream. How can you trace the channel of the former stream?

Procedure

Assume that you have already done the fieldwork for this problem. The map you have shows the locations at which the thicknesses of the rocks beneath the surface have been measured by means of drillholes. (See Figure 18–13.) To the left of each location marker, a small number in parentheses gives the thickness in meters of the sandstone body that looks as though it might have been formed in an ancient stream. Note that at many locations no sandstone was found. The small arrows represent the direction of the current indicated by cross-beds and ripple marks. Put a piece of tracing paper over the map and use a soft pencil to draw the shape of the ancient stream channel.

Be prepared to discuss the following questions:

(1) What types of evidence can be used to determine the position of the buried stream channel?

(2) How do you know exactly where to draw the lines showing where the stream must have been?

(3) Did the ancient stream meander (make loop-like bends), or was it straight?

(4) Did the stream have any tributaries? Can you be certain from the data? Why?

(5) Make a sketch showing what this stream-type sandstone would look like if you could dig a north-south trench five meters deep along one of the white lines in Figure 18–13.

(6) Where do brush piles and debris from plants (logs, twigs, branches) accumulate along the banks of present-day winding streams? Why?

(7) If you were looking for fossil logs containing uranium minerals along this ancient stream channel, where would you begin drilling or digging?

Figure 18–13 *The data for investigating an ancient stream channel.*

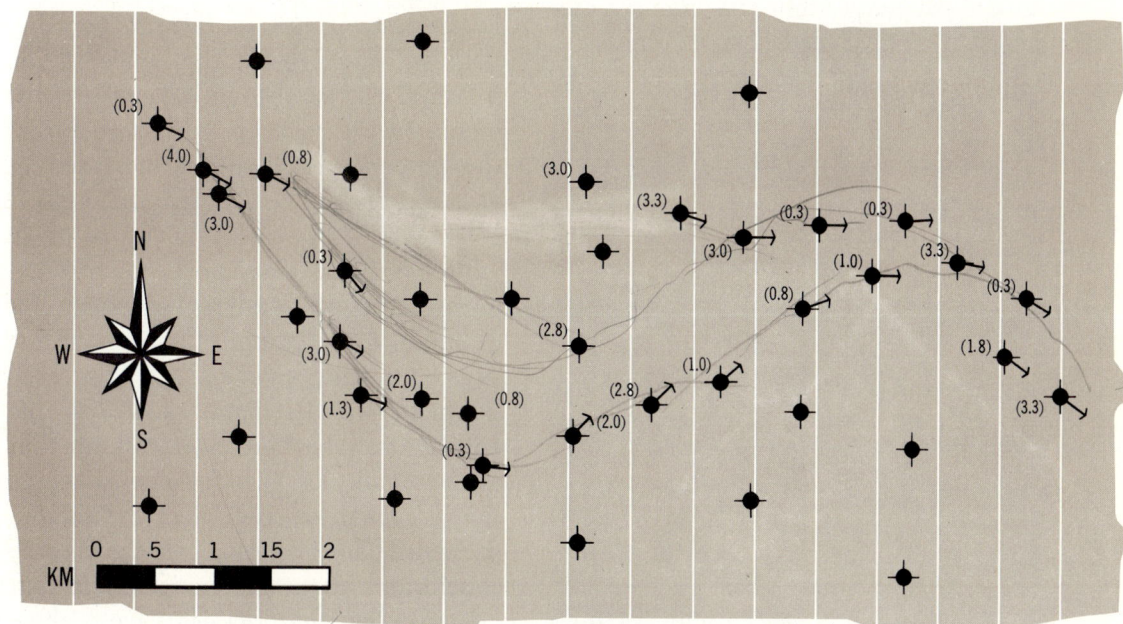

18–5 Texture and mineral content indicate origin of rocks.

Almost all sedimentary rocks are composed of fragments of other rocks. The size of sedimentary grains may be a clue to the velocity of the depositing current, as you learned in Chapter 13. What can you say about the origin of a sedimentary rock that contains both large and small angular rock fragments?

The shape of sedimentary particles also indicates something about their past. What could you infer by comparing a sedimentary rock composed mainly of rounded particles with one composed mainly of angular particles?

Some kinds of minerals that occur in sediments provide clues about the location of the area from which the sediment was eroded. Although such special minerals usually occur in small quantities, they can be used to help interpret rock origin. For example, if garnet grains are observed in a sandstone and the only other garnets in the area occur in an exposure of metamorphic rock 50 kilometers to the north, it is likely that the metamorphic rock was the source of at least some of the sediment. This hypothesis would be strengthened if you followed the sandstone bed toward the metamorphic rock and discovered that the percentage of garnet increased as you approached the metamorphic rock.

Some sedimentary layers may be made entirely of the broken shells of organisms. Ancient coral reef deposits, for example, are built almost entirely of fossils. Sedimentary layers may also consist of fossilized remains of microscopic animals or plants. If you assume that these organisms lived in environments similar to those occupied by related present-day forms, you can draw some conclusions about the environment that existed when the organisms were alive.

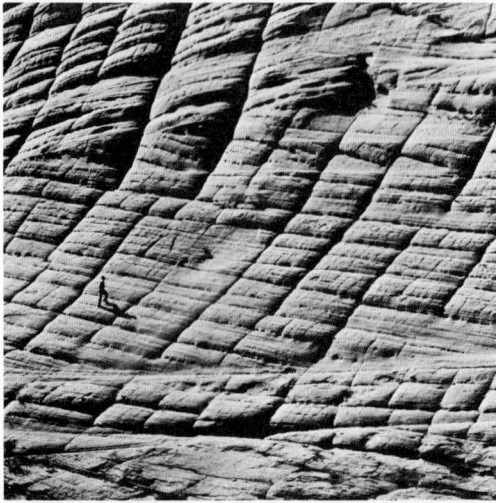

From top to bottom: Large-scale cross-bedding in Zion National Park, Utah. Shells washed up on a beach by waves. Sandstone beds in the Great Smoky Mountains. Twisted rope lava in Craters of the Moon National Monument, Idaho.

You learned in Section 15–5 that the texture of a volcanic rock shows something about how it cooled. A very fine-grained crystalline or glassy texture usually means that the lava cooled rapidly. Would you expect the center of a thick lava flow to be fine-grained or coarse-grained? What does the texture of a coarse-grained crystalline rock such as granite suggest about its rate of cooling?

Metamorphic rocks also contain clues about their origin. For example, most metamorphic rocks have been subjected to high pressure. As a result, flaky crystalline textures such as those observed in schists develop. Furthermore, the presence of certain minerals in metamorphic rocks can tell you something about how deeply the rock must have been buried at one time. (See sections 15–2 and 15–3.) The minerals in a metamorphic rock may also provide evidence about the rock before metamorphism took place.

Thought and Discussion . . .

1. How do the characteristics of sedimentary rocks help you determine the environmental conditions under which they formed? Give specific examples.
2. Discuss the statement: All layered rocks are sedimentary, and all sedimentary rocks are layered.
3. Describe several ways of determining which is the upper surface of a sedimentary layer.
4. Where would you expect to find the most coarse-grained texture in an igneous intrusion? Why?

Putting the Pieces Together

18–6 Investigating the puzzle.

The situation in this investigation is similar to reconstructing a picture on a jig-saw puzzle when most pieces of the puzzle are missing. Often earth scientists have only a limited amount of evidence to use in putting together the geologic history of a particular area. You will examine pieces of a geologic puzzle in the form of rock fragments and fossils. See how much information you can get from these pieces and how useful the information would be in determining the geologic history of rock outcrops in a given area.

Procedure

In different parts of the classroom you will find a series of numbered boxes containing fragments of rocks and fossils or models of fossils. You will be allowed a limited amount of time in which to study and describe the contents of each box. Record your observations in your notebook. Which of the boxes would you group together and why?

18–7 How are rock layers correlated?

In Investigation 18–6 you attempted to correlate a number of boxes containing rocks and fossils. **Correlation** is the process of showing a relationship between two things. In geology correlation usually means finding out which parts of the rock record were laid down at the same time or as part of the same layer.

In some places correlation is simple and obvious. Look at Figure 18–14, a view of the Grand Canyon. Identify the different layers that make up the canyon wall on the left-hand side of the

William Smith

William Smith was born in Oxfordshire, England, in 1769. At the age of eighteen he became a surveyor's assistant. In surveying routes and supervising the building of canals to transport coal, Smith traveled 16,000 kilometers a year on horseback or by carriage. From observing rocks exposed along the banks of these canals, he soon discovered that certain rocks seemed to lie in layers, "like pieces of bread and butter." He noticed that each rock layer contained special fossils that could be used to match layers kilometers apart. "The same strata" he said, "were found always in the same order and contained the same peculiar fossils."

Smith made this important discovery when he was only twenty-two years old. A famous story is told of Smith's visit to the Reverend Benjamin Richardson, who collected fossils as a hobby. Smith astonished the minister by telling him exactly where and in what formation specimen after specimen had been found. Smith then predicted correctly the rock layers and fossils in a distant hill.

William Smith's work made possible the first geologic map of England and Wales in 1815. In 1831 the Geologic Society of London gave him a gold medal for his pioneering work in the study of stratified or layered rocks and geologic mapping.

photograph and correlate them with layers on the right-hand side. Suppose the middle part of the photograph were missing. Is there any evidence that the layers on the right are the same as the layers on the left? Trace several distinct layers across the picture. Would this be more difficult to do if you were standing in the canyon?

Sedimentary rock layers that have a distinctive color, texture, or composition, or contain a distinctive set of fossils, can be traced fairly easily over short distances even if not exposed continuously. The farther apart the outcrops are, however, the harder it is to correlate them on the basis of physical characteristics alone. Nearly two hundred years ago William Smith discovered that physical characteristics and the fossil content of rocks could be used to correlate rock layers that were many kilometers apart. Smith's discovery was one of the kilometerstones in the development of our understanding of earth history.

An example of a problem in correlation is shown in Figure 18–15, which represents outcrops in four places. A geologist looking at these outcrops recognizes several different rock layers and wants to know how the rocks at location A are related to the rocks at location D, nine kilometers away. He observes that the white, fossil-containing limestone in locations B, C, and D is overlain by conglomerate. Because the sequence of layers is the same, he can correlate the conglomerate layers in the three sections. Further, he notices that basalt in locations A and C is overlain by green sandstone. From this evidence he ties column A in with column C. Since column C has already been correlated with column D, he can tell how columns A and D are related to each other *even though they have no layers in common*. What

Figure 18–14 *A view of sedimentary layers exposed in the Grand Canyon of the Colorado.*

other difficulties in correlation would he have had if the conglomerate in location A had been overlain by basalt instead of by gray sandstone? From his observations the geologist concludes that the red sandstone in location D gradually thins out and does not extend into location B. Is this a reasonable conclusion? Why? What other evidence could the geologist have looked for to help him?

In places where rock layers were once continuous, correlation of various layers is relatively easy. However, the correlation of rock layers in widely separated areas, such as on different continents, is much more difficult.

At any one time in the past, conditions in different areas varied just as they do now. Deposition was going on in some places, erosion in others. For this reason no rock layers span the entire earth or, for that matter, even an entire continent. How, then, can earth scientists correlate rocks from two different continents? One way to correlate rocks from one continent to another and from one locality to another is by using fossils.

Figure 18–15 *The rocks in both outcrops A and D can be correlated even though these outcrops do not have any rock layers in common.*

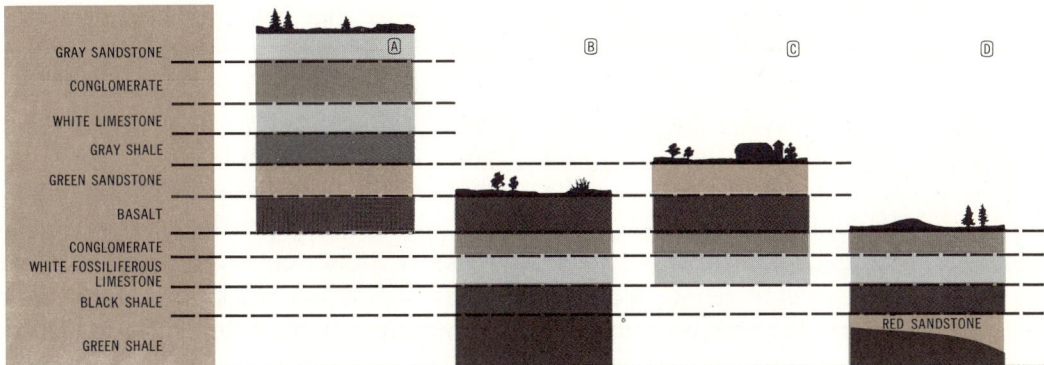

18–8 Interpreting the history of a model.

If you examine a rock outcrop carefully, you will find that you can piece together the sequence of events that formed the outcrop. In this investigation your teacher will ask several members of your class to make geological models of various areas out of some modeling material. They will keep lists showing the exact sequence of the steps that they took to make the models. Once the models have been completed, other students in the class will be asked to examine them. They should attempt to determine the sequence of steps that were necessary to construct the models.

Procedure

In class your group will receive one of the models prepared earlier. By examining the model your group should be able to answer the following questions:

(1) Which layer is the oldest? How do you know?

(2) Which layer is the next oldest and so on down to the youngest layer?

(3) If your model contains folded layers, when did folding occur? Can you determine from the shape of the folds how they were formed?

(4) Is there any evidence that erosion occurred in any of the layers? How do you recognize a former erosion surface?

(5) How would you explain a layer of one color cutting through layers of other colors?

(6) Have any layers been disrupted by faults?

If you have difficulty answering any of these questions, how could you obtain additional information that would aid your interpretation of the model?

18–9 Outcrops reveal a sequence of events.

Sedimentary layers are usually horizontal when deposited. If layers of sedimentary rock are deformed by folding or faulting, the deformation must have occurred after the layers were deposited. Missing layers are important in reconstructing geologic history. Suppose you conclude from fossils in two horizontal layers of rock that Cretaceous rocks lie directly on top of Cambrian rocks. How can you account for the missing layers? Refer to the Geologic Time Scale in Table 19–1 (page 425). How many millions of years are missing from the record?

This situation would be similar to discovering that the middle 100 pages of a detective novel had been clipped out. What would you do to learn the full story? You could probably reconstruct the events that occurred in the middle of the book and, if you had read enough detective novels, you might work them out fairly accurately. In studying rocks you might not be able to tell the story from a single outcrop. By correlating the rocks in the puzzling outcrop with rocks in other outcrops you might be able to figure out what events took place during the period of time represented by the missing layers.

Where certain rock layers are missing from a sequence of layers, the upper surface of the older rocks may represent an old erosion surface. Such buried erosion surfaces are called **unconformities** because a noticeable gap in the record exists between the layers. Unconformities are easy to identify when folded rocks have been eroded and flat-lying rocks deposited on top of them.

How can you determine the relationship between igneous rocks and sedimentary rocks that you find together in the same outcrop? An igneous rock that cuts across layers in sedimentary, metamorphic, or other igneous rocks is usually thought to be younger than the rocks it cuts through. An igneous rock that has baked the rocks around it or that has torn fragments from these rocks and carried the fragments along with it is probably younger than the surrounding rock.

Suppose that you found a layer of igneous rock in the middle of a thick pile of sedimentary rocks. Such igneous rock could be a lava flow that was buried by sediments. It might also be an intru-

Figure 18–16 *Which diagram represents an intrusion and which a buried lava flow?*

sion squeezed in between the layers of sedimentary rocks already deposited. Examine Figure 18–16 carefully. From the evidence in these diagrams and the information in the previous paragraph, which diagram represents a buried lava flow and which represents an intrusion? List three types of evidence to support your answer. What are the relative ages of the basalt and the uppermost rock layer in each of the sketches?

18–10 Rocks reveal ancient climates.
Rocks contain evidence that climates have changed radically during the geologic past. Fossils are among the most important indicators of ancient climates. If you found fossil corals in the Antarctic where coral could not live now, what could you conclude about the climate at the time the corals lived there?

Living organisms, especially plants, have climatic preferences. Palm trees do not grow in Alaska, nor does reindeer moss grow in the tropics. Plants and animals now fossilized probably had the same climatic preferences as closely related forms that are living today. The presence of fossils of subtropical plants such as magnolias in rocks on the Arctic island of Spitsbergen suggests the climate there was once much warmer than it is now.

Several other pieces of evidence indicate that different climatic conditions existed in the past. Some fossil plants have features that suggest they grew in a warm climate. Among these features are large cells or a lack of annual rings. Dinosaurs were reptiles and presumably were cold-blooded, as modern reptiles are. During the Mesozoic Era large dinosaurs lived in what is now the northern United States and southern Canada. It is reasonable to assume that the climate there was mild during the Mesozoic

Figure 18–17 *Interpretation of geologic history from evidence found in cross sections. Describe the sequence of events that occurred in each case. See Table 17–2 for time terms.*

SANDSTONE
SHALE
LIMESTONE
CONGLOMERATE
GRANITE
BASALT
METAMORPHOSED

because reptiles must hibernate when the temperature approaches freezing. Obviously a dinosaur 20 meters long and weighing several tons would have had trouble finding a cave large enough to crawl into for the winter.

ACTIVITY *A series of additional geologic cross sections is given in Figure 18–17. Examine each of these cross sections and describe the sequence of events that occurred in each area. Begin with the oldest and end with the most recent event.*

The number and variety of fossils may also be a clue to an ancient climate. Today the number of plant species is far greater in the tropics than it is in northern latitudes. The situation was probably the same in the past. Hence, finding a large number of fossil plants of a variety of species is good evidence that a given area once had a tropical climate.

If you study the worldwide distribution of certain fossils of a single geologic period of the Cenozoic Era, you may discover that each species is restricted to a latitudinal zone. This indicates that it adapted to conditions in a particular ancient climatic zone. The maps in Figure 18–18 describe possible climatic zones from several different periods. The subtropical zone in the map on the left, for example, outlines areas where Cenozoic rocks contain fossils whose

Figure 18–18 *Climatic zones in North and Central America have changed since early Cenozoic time, as shown in these maps.*

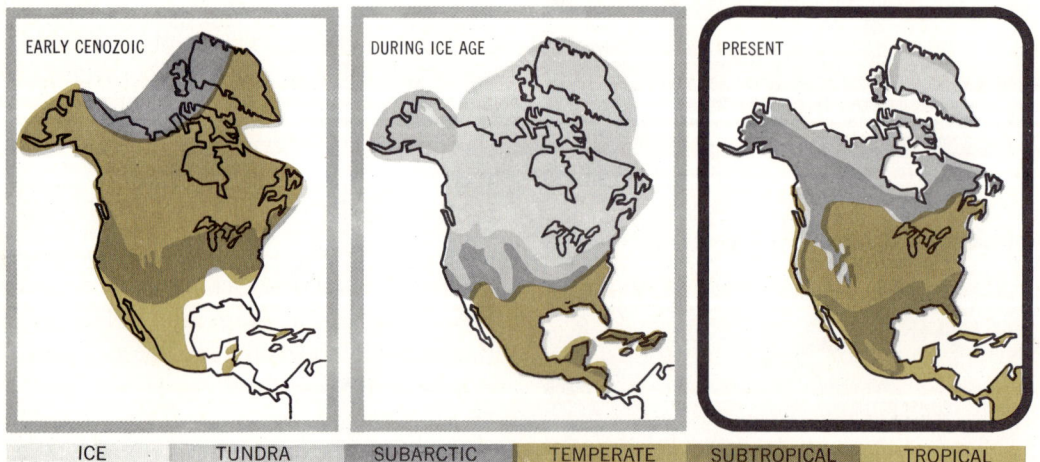

EARLY CENOZOIC   DURING ICE AGE   PRESENT

ICE   TUNDRA   SUBARCTIC   TEMPERATE   SUBTROPICAL   TROPICAL

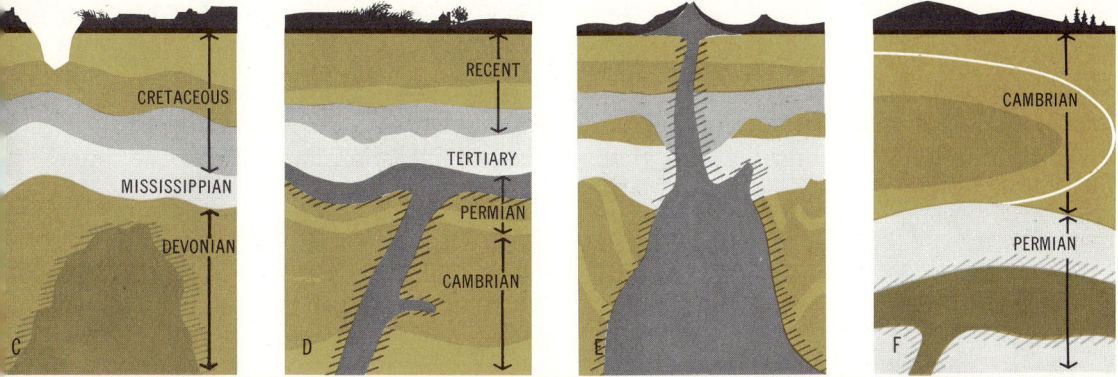

modern relatives live in subtropical areas. Do you think that maps of this type apply to periods of time more than a few millions of years ago? Why? Can you be sure that the distant ancestor of a modern warmwater animal or plant also was strictly a warmwater organism?

Reef-building corals also help to identify ancient environmental conditions. Present-day varieties require a warmwater environment in order to digest their food and carry on other life processes. Most of them live only in salt water between 25 and 29°C and in a zone between the surface of the ocean and a depth of about 75 meters. Certain other types of organisms require fresh water and would cease to exist if seawater invaded their habitat.

Minerals can also be indicators of ancient climates. Gypsum ($CaSO_4 \cdot 2H_2O$) and rock salt ($NaCl$) are good examples. When water evaporates from lakes or bays or from the soil in regions where evaporation is greater than precipitation, salts crystallize and form layers. Paleozoic salt is being mined in Michigan, Kansas, Germany, and elsewhere. What would you conclude about the climate in these areas at the time the salt was forming? Did it differ from the present climate in these same regions?

Imagine that you have been transported several million years into the future. What might you find in the rock record representing the 1960's in the area where you now live?

Thought and Discussion . . .

1. What might a buried erosion surface look like?
2. How could you tell whether an igneous rock was a lava flow or an intrusion?
3. What types of evidence found in rocks can be used to find out something about ancient climates?
4. How are fossils used in correlating rock units separated by great distances?

Unsolved Problems Many parts of the earth's surface have not been thoroughly examined. Some parts have not been studied at all. As a result, our knowledge of earth history is far from complete. Even areas that have been thought of as well known yield important additional information when new techniques of observation are used. The geologic history of the area in which you live probably has great gaps in it. Some of these gaps may never be filled. Find out what you can about the geology of your own area and determine the amount of missing information. Is there any possibility of filling these gaps in the record?

One of the problems geologists are most interested in is the environment where sedimentary deposition occurs. Geologists are using skin-diving equipment, drilling through coral reefs, and doing experimental work in laboratories in an attempt to examine features that are forming in modern sediments. In the area where you live, what kinds of processes are going on that you could study in order to learn more about the processes that form sedimentary, igneous, and metamorphic rocks? How could you study them?

CHAPTER REVIEW

Summary

Rocks reveal many things about past events on the earth. The layering in sedimentary rocks can show the conditions under which the rocks formed and the types of sediment contributed. The kind of fossil remains tell whether sedimentary rocks originated in the ocean or on the land. Layering in igneous and metamorphic rocks also provides clues to the conditions under which these rocks formed.

Cross-beds and ripple marks in sedimentary rocks can help geologists determine the top and bottom of sedimentary layers, as well as the direction of the current during their formation. The position of fossils right side up or upside down in rock layers also shows how the layers have changed position since their formation.

Texture and mineral content are important clues to the origin of rocks. Rounded or coarse particles, shell fragments, and uncommon minerals in sedimentary rocks all suggest how the rocks originated. Fine- or coarse-grained texture in igneous rocks reveals how fast they cooled. Crystal size in metamorphic rocks depends on the temperature and pressure at the time of formation. Since chemical changes also accompany rock formation under pressure, the presence of certain minerals is a clue to the conditions under which rocks were produced.

Identifying rocks in different outcrops that formed at the same time is called correlation. Both the type of rock and the fossil content can reveal related rocks. Correlation helps geologists fill in missing parts of the rock record. Certain layers missing from the sequence at one location may exist at another. Often unconformities, or buried erosion surfaces, can account for missing layers. The relative ages of two different types of rocks that cut across each other can also be pieced together. Igneous rocks, for example, that have baked surrounding sedimentary rock and contain sedimentary fragments must be younger intrusions.

Fossils contained in rocks are particularly useful in revealing ancient climates. Fossils of tropical plants and animals in areas that are today arctic or subarctic show that the climate there was once much warmer. Similarly, deposits of minerals such as salt or gypsum, abundant in some temperate areas of the world today, probably formed at a time when these areas had different climates.

Questions and Problems

A

1. Besides the examples of horizontal variation that are given in Section 18–2, describe some other situations in which horizontal variation might occur within a body of rock.
2. How would you explain a situation in which a graded bed shows the large grains on top and the smaller grains on the bottom?
3. How could a sandstone that is composed almost entirely of well-rounded sand grains form?
4. What features in sedimentary rocks help to differentiate them from igneous and metamorphic rocks?
5. Suppose that you find two sedimentary rocks. One of these, composed of rounded fragments of calcite, is relatively soft. The other rock, composed of fairly angular fragments of quartz, is

relatively hard. What can you say about the distance the calcite grains have been transported as compared to the distance the quartz grains have been transported?

B

1. Propose several situations in which sediments might not be horizontal at the time of deposition.
2. Are the interfaces between sedimentary layers always distinct and abrupt? Explain your answer.
3. Would you expect to find horizontal variation in igneous and metamorphic rocks? If so, what kinds of variation can you think of?
4. Quartz is probably the most common mineral in sandstones throughout the world. Yet on many beaches in Florida most sand grains are composed of calcite. Suggest reasons for this situation.
5. Some rocks consist entirely of volcanic ash and fragments of rock that have fallen into a pile at the foot of a volcano. Would rock formed from this material be sedimentary or igneous? Why?

C

1. Suggest a way that cross-beds might form from ripples in sand on the bottom of a sedimentary basin.
2. Suppose you find a rock composed of 50 percent fragments and 50 percent crystalline cement. Would you call it fragmental or crystalline? How can you

make up a classification that involves complete, continuous variation from one rock type to another?

Suggested Readings

BOOKS

Barnett, Lincoln and the editors of *Life*. *The World We Live In*. Time, Inc., New York, 1955. Especially pages 58 and 59.

Beiser, Arthur and the editors of *Life*. *The Earth*. Time, Inc. (Life Nature Library), New York, 1962. Chapter 6, The Record of the Rocks.

Clemons, Elizabeth. *Rocks and the World Around You*. Coward-McCann, Inc., New York, 1960.

Fenton, Carroll L. *Our Amazing Earth*. Doubleday & Company, Inc., Garden City, N.Y., 1945.

Harland, Walter Brian and Paxton Chadwick. *The Earth*. Franklin Watts, Inc., New York, 1960.

Pearl, Richard M. *Wonders of Rocks and Minerals*. Dodd, Mead & Co., New York, 1961.

Stokes, William L. *Essentials of Earth History: An Introduction to Historical Geology*, 2nd ed. Prentice-Hall, Inc., Englewood Cliffs, N.J., 1966.

PAMPHLET

Page, L. W. *The Earth and Its Story*. American Education Publications, Education Center, Columbus, Ohio, 1961.

A pine tree growing in volcanic rock in Craters of the Moon National Monument, Idaho.

The year was 1900. A Russian hunter slowly worked his way along the Bere-zovka River in Siberia. He was tracking a wounded deer, but he found some-thing quite different. Imagine the hunter's astonishment when he discovered what appeared to be the head of a full-grown elephant lodged in the frozen ground. (See photo above.) The discovery of this well-preserved beast, 100 kilometers inside the Arctic Circle and more than 3250 kilometers north of the normal range of present-day elephants, created great excitement.

News of the extraordinary find eventually reached scientific authorities in Leningrad and an expedition was sent to collect the unusual specimen. Al-though part of the flesh had been eaten by wild animals and the body was in an advanced state of decay, it soon became apparent that this was no ordinary elephant. The creature had long, curved tusks and its body was covered with thick, coarse hair with a protective undercoat of woolly fur. Further study re-vealed that the hunter had found the frozen carcass of a woolly mammoth, a type of elephant now extinct that inhabited Eurasia and North America thousands of years ago.

Chapter 19 Life—Present and Past

Since the discovery of the Berezovka mammoth other frozen mammoths have been found in Siberia and Alaska. We know, of course, that elephants do not presently inhabit Siberia and Alaska. How did the carcasses of these elephant-like creatures get to areas where present-day elephants could not exist? These well-preserved prehistoric specimens are an unusual kind of fossil, reminders of a time when the Arctic region supported types of life entirely different from those in that area today.

Fossils like the Berezovka mammoth are evidence that the geographic distribution of life on earth has not always been what it is now. You have already learned that fossils are clues to the nature of ancient climates in the areas in which they are found. More important, fossils provide valuable information about living things of the past. But the earth scientist is interested in more than the life of the past. He is also interested in the interaction between the world of living things, the atmosphere, hydrosphere, and lithosphere in various earth processes. In this chapter you will not only learn more about fossils, but you will also see how the kingdom of life is related to the nonliving realm.

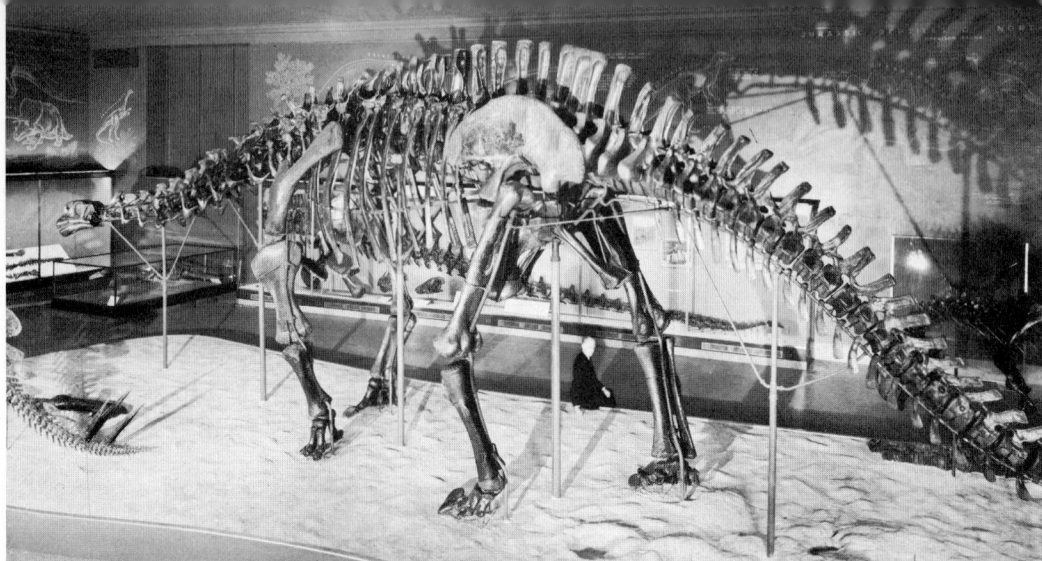

Life Today

19–1 What is life and where is it found?

Untold billions of organisms inhabit the earth. They dwell on the land and in the waters. Microscopic organisms even fill the air that you breathe. Organisms exist not only in great abundance, but also in an almost unbelievable variety of forms. They range in size from microscopic plants and animals to the giant sequoia trees of California and the great whales of the oceans. There is hardly a place on earth where life in some form does not exist. But what is life and how does it differ from nonliving material?

ACTIVITY *Consider a lizard, a rock, and a plant. (See Figure 19–1.)*

1. What differences between the lizard and the rock would determine which is alive?

2. How are the plant and the lizard similar? How are they different?

3. What are the similarities and differences between the plant and the rock?

4. Was the rock ever alive?

Growth, reproduction, and response to outside stimulation are some of the basic characteristics that distinguish living from nonliving objects. Another distinguishing feature is their chemical composition. The members of the **biosphere** or world of living things are composed mostly of *organic* compounds. These are compounds containing carbon atoms that share electrons with one another and with other kinds of atoms. The abundance of carbon in living things might lead you to believe that it is one of the more common elements in the earth's crust. Yet you know from Table 2–1 that oxygen and silicon are the most abundant elements by weight. Carbon makes up only 0.032 percent by weight of crustal rocks and ranks seventeenth in order of abundance. A few nonliving or *inorganic* compounds such as calcite ($CaCO_3$) and silica (SiO_2) may be produced by organisms. However, most inorganic substances are produced by processes that are not associated with living things.

Scientists have catalogued more than 1×10^6 different species of animals. A **species** is the smallest group of related organisms that can interbreed. About 130,000 of these species are now no longer in existence. The variety of present life is great, but the number of different organisms that have inhabited the earth since the beginning of life is even more impressive. Scientists estimate that perhaps four billion species of plants and animals have existed since life began. The combined volume of all creatures that ever lived during the past 600 million years is about the same volume as the earth itself. However, the total mass of the biosphere at any given time is very small. It is only about ⅟₃₀₀ of the mass of the atmosphere and ⅟₇₀,₀₀₀ of the mass of the hydrosphere.

Life can adapt to almost any environment on earth. Bacteria have been found in the upper regions of the atmosphere some 20 kilometers above the earth's surface. They have also been found in water taken from oil wells almost two kilometers beneath it. Countless microscopic plants and animals live in the surface waters of the oceans and specialized organisms dwell in the deepest ocean trenches 10 kilometers below sea level. Certain organisms are active at −4°C in polar oceans, while others live at 85°C in hot springs. Organisms are known to thrive in deserts, in the acid water of peat bogs, and in freshwater streams as well as in salt-saturated lakes.

Interfaces are common environments for organisms. The plant-soil zone that grades downward from living plants into soils is a typical interface environment for life. Although there are few regions on earth that do not support some form of life, the greatest concentration of organisms is found in the 200-meter-deep zone that lies immediately beneath the surface of the oceans. This is the zone penetrated by sunlight, the energy source necessary for plant growth. Here, too, live most of the world's animals. The majority of these plants and animals are microscopic in size and consist of single cells.

The ocean-sea floor interface is especially heavily populated by animals if it lies in the 200-meter zone. Many of these creatures crawl about on or burrow into the sediments on the sea bottom. Others are attached to the ocean floor. Many sea bottom-dwelling animals, such as clams, snails, barnacles, corals, and crabs, have heavy skeletons. Their body forms normally represent adaptations that enable the animal to survive in this sea-bottom environment.

19–2 Life and energy cannot be separated.

Life functions all require activity, and activity requires energy. Where do organisms get this necessary energy? Life on earth, now and in the past, depends on energy from the sun. This energy reaches the earth in the form of light of different wavelengths. How do organisms convert sunlight into usable energy? Animals cannot get energy directly from light, but green plants can and do capture light energy. They do this by

Figure 19–1 *How do we distinguish living things from nonliving things?*

$$6CO_2 + 12H_2O + \frac{\text{light energy}}{\text{chlorophyll}} \longrightarrow C_6H_{12}O_6 + 6H_2O + 6O_2\uparrow$$

$\begin{pmatrix} \text{carbon} \\ \text{dioxide} \end{pmatrix}$ + (water) + $\begin{pmatrix} \text{light energy} \\ \text{in presence of} \\ \text{chlorophyll} \end{pmatrix}$ $\begin{array}{c} \text{react} \\ \text{to form} \end{array}$ (carbohydrate) + (water) + (oxygen)

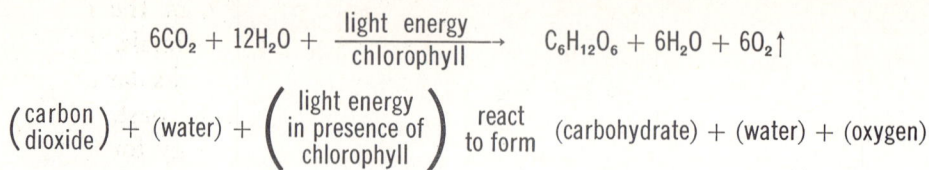

a process called **photosynthesis,** producing new chemical compounds by using light energy with chlorophyll present.

The term photosynthesis literally means "combining by means of light." It involves combining water and carbon dioxide to form carbohydrates. **Carbohydrates** are organic compounds of carbon, hydrogen, and oxygen such as sugars, starches, and cellulose. The chemical reaction involved in photosynthesis can be represented by the formula in the box at the top of the page.

What happens to the light energy in this chemical reaction? It is changed into chemical energy and stored in the carbohydrate molecule. It remains in storage until it is used by plant and animal cells to provide the energy necessary for life functions. In the process of converting light energy to the chemical energy of food, photosynthesis changes

As this wheat grows, it is storing energy by using sunlight to convert carbon dioxide and water into organic compounds. Where will this energy go?

light energy into a form that can be used by other living things.

Because plants alone can convert light energy from the sun to the chemical energy of food, animals directly or indirectly depend on plants for their existence. Thus, plants form the beginning of a food chain. A **food chain** starts with a plant, and then involves a series of organisms that depend upon one another for food. Food chains are ideal energy pathways and effectively transfer energy from one part of the biosphere to another.

Consider a typical green plant such as grass as the beginning of a food chain. During photosynthesis the grass converts the light energy of the sun into the chemical energy of food. When the grass is eaten by an animal, like a deer, its energy is then transferred to the deer. Suppose the deer is killed and eaten by a mountain lion. The energy obtained by the deer from the grass is then transferred to the mountain lion. The lion, however, will probably not consume all of the deer's body. Some of it will remain on the ground where it will provide food and energy for a special group of organisms called *decomposers.* The decomposers break down the remains of the deer (and eventually the mountain lion) into a form usable by plants.

19–3 Organisms and chemical cycles continuously interact.

As time passes, chemical elements move through a cycle from nonliving to living objects and back again. An example of such a cycle is the **carbon cycle.** While living, organisms discard carbon-bearing wastes that are returned to the lithosphere, atmosphere, and hydrosphere. As these organisms die, they leave an accumulation of carbon compounds in their bodies. The remains of each dead plant or animal furnish food for decomposers, which release carbon to the atmosphere as carbon dioxide. They thus make materials available for reuse by plants. Most decomposers are microscopic in size, but some, like the toadstool, are large enough to be easily seen with the naked eye.

The main pathway in the carbon cycle is from the atmosphere into living things and then back again. (See Figure 19–2.) In some instances carbon may deviate from this path, as when certain organisms take carbon into their shells as $CaCO_3$. When such an animal dies, the shell is not broken down by decomposers but may be deposited as sediment. Large masses of carbon compounds have also accumulated in the earth where they have been converted to coal or petroleum. These are commonly referred to as *fossil fuels* since

they are derived from the remains of ancient plants and animals. Fossil fuels represent a stockpile of solar energy that was produced in the past. How does man release this energy for his benefit?

ACTIVITY *In Section 15–8, you followed a calcium ion through a cycle involving the hydrosphere, biosphere, and lithosphere. Although a calcium ion was used to illustrate the rock cycle, it also illustrated the calcium cycle. Diagram the calcium cycle.*

The water cycle is also basic to all life. Without the continuous return of fresh water to the land in the form of rain and snow, the land would soon become a lifeless desert. Water is a part of all living things. Organisms that live on the land may pick up water at a number of points in the water cycle. However, land plants normally absorb water from the soil and land animals drink it. The amount of water present in different organisms may vary considerably. Our own bodies, for example, normally consist of about 66 percent water. Yet a jellyfish may be more that 95 percent water. Moisture

Figure 19–2 *The carbon cycle. Carbon exists in the atmosphere and hydrosphere as carbon dioxide. (See also Figure 12–5.) Life processes convert this carbon dioxide to carbohydrates and other organic compounds.*

absorbed by plants is quickly carried to their leaves, where it changes to vapor and escapes to the atmosphere through leaf openings by transpiration. Animals commonly return moisture to the atmosphere through respiration, perspiration, and discharge of waste products.

Thought and Discussion . . .

1. Where do organisms get their energy?
2. Construct your own definition of life.
3. Can you explain the statement: Coal is "petrified sunshine"?
4. Explain how the idea of cycles is useful in relating natural processes.

Life of the Past

19–4 Fossils are evidence of prehistoric organisms.

In Chapter 18 you saw that the history of the earth may be unraveled by means of evidence found in the rocks. What kinds of rocks are most likely to contain such evidence and where might such rocks be found? How is it known, for example, that dinosaurs once lived in Utah and that great swampy forests formerly covered parts of Pennsylvania and Illinois? **Paleontologists,** scientists who study fossils, have inferred this from the study of fossils found in the rocks in these areas. Ancient fossil remains can be used to piece together both the history of life as well as the geologic past. Thus, dinosaur bones in Utah and fossils of swamp-dwelling plants in Pennsylvania indicate the past conditions in these areas.

Paleontology is related to biology. To understand animals that disappeared from the earth hundreds of millions of years ago, the paleontologist needs to know as much as possible about living organisms. The environment of extinct organisms is not always clear. However, when the members of a fossil group closely resemble the members of a living group, it can usually be assumed that the fossil group lived under conditions similar to those of the living group. Thus, the principle of uniformity of process is again applied to interpreting the past.

Although paleontologists have discovered many fossils, pieces in the puzzle of life history are missing. Why, for example, are not more fossils found in Precambrian rocks? Equally puzzling is the fact that once-numerous animals such as dinosaurs have become extinct. Finally there is the question of whether the

Figure 19–3 *Fossils weathering from rock.*
Figure 19–4 *Paleontologists use microscopes to study microfossils.*
Figure 19–5 *These rocks were formed from the remains of trees that lived 200 million years ago.*
Figure 19–6 *Plant microfossils called diatoms.*

rocks contain clues to the greatest mystery of all: How and when did life originate on earth? In his attempt to solve such problems, the paleontologist must carefully examine the record of life from the rocks of the earth's crust.

The term "fossil" is derived from the Latin word *fossilis,* meaning "dug up." Most fossils, however, are actually freed from exposed rock by the processes of weathering and erosion. (See Figure 19–3.) Like living organisms, fossil plants and animals are numerous and varied. Animal fossils range in size from a dinosaur bone two meters long and weighing several hundred kilograms to fossils so tiny that 100 of them could fit on the head of a pin! These smaller forms are called **microfossils** because they must be studied with a microscope. (See Figure 19–4.)

The great stone trees that lie scattered about Petrified Forest National Park in Arizona, shown in Figure 19–5, are spectacular examples of plant fossils. The Petrified Forest provides much information about the geologic history of this part of Arizona. Leaves, seeds, and even fruit have in some places been preserved.

Plant microfossils are also quite abundant in certain types of rocks. For example, thousands of tiny one-celled plants may be found in a single teaspoonful of some crushed marine sedimentary rock. (See Figure 19–6.) Plant fossils are not nearly so common as animal fossils, however, because plant remains are normally delicate and decay easily.

Fossil remains of animals have proved most valuable in interpreting earth history. These include the remains of animals with backbones (*vertebrates*) and animals without backbones (*invertebrates*). Figure 19–7 shows some typical invertebrates and Figure 19–8 shows a variety of vertebrates.

Figure 19–7 (*Top*) *Typical invertebrates.*
Figure 19–8 (*Below*) *Typical vertebrates. One animal in each figure is a reconstruction of an ancient life form from fossil evidence. Which ones ?*

Fossils may consist of the actual remains of plants and animals such as fossilized bones, teeth, leaves, and shells. They may consist simply of evidence of ancient organisms such as tracks of worms, the imprints of leaves, and the tracks of dinosaurs. (See Figure 19–9.)

Figure 19–9   *Evidence of ancient life. (Top left) Imprints of ancient fern leaves, (right) footprints, and (bottom left) worm tracks.*

19–5 Investigating a footprint puzzle.

Suppose that you had discovered a set of fossilized tracks like those diagrammed in Figure 19–10 and that you wanted to reconstruct what had occurred. Your problem would be similar to a detective's investigation in that you would have to determine past events from limited evidence. Here your only clues would be the footprints preserved in stone.

Procedure

Carefully study Figure 19–10. The diagram represents a group of fossilized footprints. Tracks such as these are common in certain parts of New England and in the southwestern United States. Using the evidence provided by the fossil tracks, see if you can interpret what may have taken place. Can you tell anything about the size or nature of the animals from their footprints?

Figure 19–10

19–6 How are fossils formed?

Because dead plants and animals decay quite rapidly, usually only hard parts such as teeth, shell, or woody tissue are fossilized. However, under exceptionally favorable circumstances organisms composed completely of soft parts, such as jellyfish, have been wholly preserved. (See Figure 19–11.)

Even an organism with hard parts will not necessarily be fossilized. You know that you rarely see the complete

Figure 19–11   *Remains of soft organisms like jellyfish may be preserved if buried in fine sediment.*

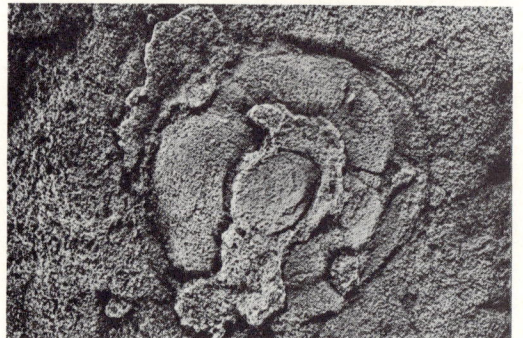

skeleton of a dead animal. You may also know how hard it is to find a seashell on the beach that is not broken or worn down. This is to be expected, for there are many ways in which the remains of organisms may be destroyed. When an animal dies, its flesh is immediately attacked by a variety of organisms ranging from vultures and coyotes to maggots and bacteria. The flesh soon disappears, leaving behind only the animal's bones, teeth, or shell. These too may soon be destroyed. Shells can be crushed by overlying sediments and bones may be eroded as they tumble along the bed of a stream.

What factors affect fossilization? Of the many factors involved, there are two that are of particular importance. Hard body parts will greatly increase the chances of fossilization, and the composition of these parts may affect the type of fossilization that occurs. Second, the plant or animal remains must be covered by some type of protective material shortly after death. The type of material that buries the remains, which normally depends on where the organism lived, also affects the type of fossilization. For example, the remains of marine animals are commonly preserved because they fall to the ocean floor shortly after death and are buried by soft mud and sands. Figure 19–12 shows how such fossilization takes place and how fossils form in layers of sediments.

In general, the finer the sediment covering the organisms, the more likely that the remains will be preserved as fossils.

Although fossils are not usually found associated with igneous rocks, windblown volcanic products are sometimes suitable covering materials in which fossils are formed and preserved.

In Yellowstone National Park, Wyoming, hundreds of trees were covered by volcanic ash and dust from volcanoes that erupted during Early Tertiary time. At one place in the Park as many as 27 fossil forests are found one on top of the other.

The Yellowstone fossil forests are exceptionally unique because the trees are so well preserved. Many of them are still upright, standing where they grew millions of years ago. Although the Early Tertiary forests of Wyoming must have been the home of many different animals, no animal fossils have yet been found there. Can you suggest some reasons for this scarcity of fossilized animal remains?

Although most organisms undergo changes during fossilization, original remains are sometimes preserved unchanged. The soft parts of some animals, such as the Berezovka mammoth, have been preserved by freezing. Soft parts have also been fossilized by drying, a process that may produce a natural mummy. Insects and spiders have been preserved in amber, a type of fossil resin

Figure 19–12 *Stages in the fossilization of a fish. The fish dies and is buried in sediments. In time its bones may be completely replaced by mineral matter dissolved in the water.*

that flowed from certain cone-bearing trees. (See Figure 19–13.)

Hundreds of thousands of practically unchanged bones have been removed from the La Brea tar pits at Los Angeles, California. (See Figure 19–14.) These tar pools, which formed on the earth's surface many thousands of years ago, are famous for their well-preserved fossils. Does the presence of these bones embedded in tar suggest why so many animals might have died here?

Although the preservation of unchanged soft and hard parts of organisms has resulted in some rather spectacular fossils, most organic remains have undergone considerable chemical and physical change. Normally an animal's soft parts will be destroyed in a relatively short time even if the whole animal is quickly buried in soft sediment. Shells may be slowly changed by chemical agents in the sediments. Mineral-bearing water passing through the sediments may gradually dissolve calcium carbonate from the shell and replace it with silica or some other mineral that precipitates from solution. In this manner the shell, which was originally composed of calcite (calcium carbonate), may be completely replaced by a new compound—silica.

Under other conditions the replacing solution may be rich in compounds of iron, magnesium, or calcium. In fossils that have been formed by replacement, microscopic details of the original hard parts may be beautifully and accurately preserved. (Refer to Figure 19–15.)

Some excellent fossils are also formed through the slow decay of organic material after burial. While slowly decomposing, the organic material leaves behind a thin film of carbon, which shows a detailed outline of the organisms. (See Figure 19–16.) In this type of fossilization some trace or impression of the plant or animal provides information about it.

Many fossils occur in the form of *molds* and *casts*. To see how these are formed, consider a seashell buried in ocean sediments. After the sediments have hardened under pressure, ground water may slowly dissolve the shell, leaving a cavity in its place. This cavity becomes a mold that preserves markings of the shell. How would a ridge on a shell be represented on this mold? Many molds are later filled by mineral matter from ground water. By this process, casts of the original shells are created. (See Figure 19–17.)

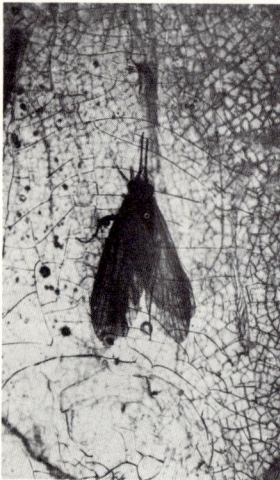

Figure 19–13 (Far left) Insect preserved in amber.
Figure 19–14 (Left) Bones preserved in the La Brea tar pits.
Figure 19–15 (Right, above) Wood cells preserved by mineral replacement.
Figure 19–16 (Right, below) Carbonized fossil of a fish.

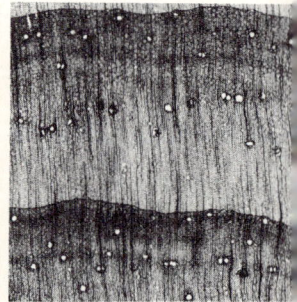

19–7 Investigating casts and molds.

Many sedimentary rocks contain fossils. Some early scientists doubted that these had once been living creatures. They suggested that such objects were put there by magic or were merely freaks of nature. Now, after more than 200 years of careful study and observation, nearly everyone accepts the idea that fossils are the preserved remains and traces of ancient plants and animals. Often only part of the organisms are preserved and their environment and life processes have to be inferred from very little evidence. Yet a great deal can be learned about ancient life by studying fossils. In this investigation you will be given the opportunity to interpret evidence that gives you clues about "organisms."

Procedure

Prepare both plaster molds and casts of various objects. Then exchange your plaster blocks containing your "fossils" with other members of the class. (1)Try to identify the objects that were used to make the molds or casts. (2)What does the evidence tell you about the "organism"?

19–8 Fossils are clues to earth history.

One of the most important uses of fossils is correlating rocks in one area with those in another. (See Section 18–7.) Some fossils represent plants and animals that survived only a short time in geologic history but were widely distributed. Some of these fossils are so characteristic of certain geologic times that they have been called **guide** or **index** fossils. Such fossils are especially useful in identifying the rock layers that contain them. It is known, for example, that dinosaurs lived only during the Mesozoic Era. Thus, when dinosaur remains are found, it is usually safe to assume that the rocks containing them are Mesozoic in age. In general, however, the paleontologist prefers to correlate rocks by means of a group of fossils representative of that part of geologic time rather than through a single kind of fossil.

The presence of fossil reindeer in Arkansas suggests that this area had, at some time in the geologic past, a climate quite different from what it has today. The positions of ancient lands and seas can also be inferred from the character of the rocks and the distribution of marine and nonmarine fossils. Using this information, maps can be drawn showing where the margins of continents and oceans have been at various times during geologic history.

Fossils serve as clues to geologic formations that may contain valuable deposits of ore, coal, or petroleum. Certain

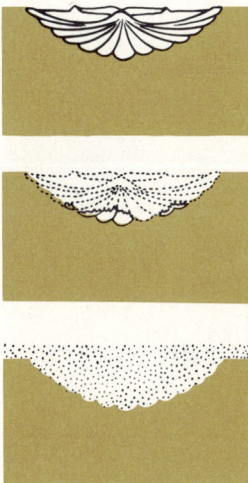

Figure 19–17 (Top) A shell is buried in fine sediment. If the shell is removed or dissolved, it leaves a mold (center) that may then be filled by some other material, creating a cast of the shell (below). Did you do something similar to this in Investigation 19–7?

kinds of microfossils are especially useful to the oil geologist. These fossils are so small that many of them are not broken by the bits used to drill oil wells. They can thus be brought to the surface almost undamaged and used as markers to guide the geologist.

Paleontology has provided much support for the idea that living organisms have gradually changed or evolved into their present forms. Fossils can be used to trace the development of plants and animals from the Precambrian Archaezoic Era to the present.

Thought and Discussion . . .

1. Why are soft-bodied animals such as jellyfish seldom preserved?
2. Name some materials that may replace organic matter.
3. How are fossils useful to man?

Evolution—Changing Life

19–9 Plants and animals have changed through time.

In 1859, Charles Darwin, an English naturalist, published a book titled *On the Origin of Species by Means of Natural Selection.* It contained a theory about the evolution of plants and animals. Darwin's work, based on many years of extensive study of living and fossil organisms, started a controversy that has not yet ended.

What application does the theory of evolution have to a study of earth history? First, it assumes that living things may change over long periods of time and that plants and animals now inhabiting the earth are different species from the first organisms on earth. Second, it means that many species that were once abundant no longer exist. They have become extinct and are known only by their fossilized remains.

When a plant or animal species changes, the new generations differ from their ancestors. Darwin called these natural changes **variations,** and this concept of change provided the basis for his theory of organic evolution.

Even the members within a single species vary. Do all dogs look alike? Some people can run faster than others.

The child of a fast-running person may run faster or slower than the parent could run at the same age. Yet differences within species do not necessarily prove that they evolve. Evolution occurs when a consistent trend over a series of generations produces an animal or plant that is recognizably different from its ancestors. Darwin's work suggested that such a trend existed, and that it depended on what he termed natural selection. By **natural selection** Darwin meant that the individuals best suited to their environment are most likely to survive and pass favorable characteristics on to their offspring. Through this adaptation or adjustment over a series of genera-

A well-preserved skeleton of the earliest known bird found in a limestone in Germany. Notice the imprint of feathers. (See also Figure 19–24.)

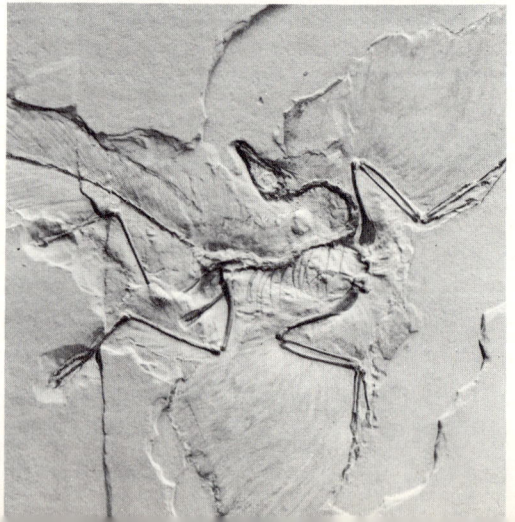

Figure 19–18 *The beaks of the finches indicate the type of food they consume. Which of the finches could crack hard seeds or nuts?*

tions, the descendants of the original organisms would be better fitted to survive in their environment.

In his travels around the world Darwin saw many examples of plants and animals that seemed to prove his theory of adaptation through natural selection. But it was in the Galápagos, a bleak chain of volcanic islands 960 km off the west coast of South America, that Darwin found a natural laboratory for a study of evolution. These islands contained a great variety of unusual plants and animals. Of particular interest to Darwin were the birds, especially the large numbers of finches. Closer study of these outwardly similar finches revealed remarkable differences in the shapes and sizes of their beaks. Darwin noted that these birds had beaks especially adapted for the type of food they ate. You can see some of the different beaks of the Galápagos finches in Figure 19–18. Which of these birds had a beak that would have been well suited for cracking hard seeds? Which ones had a beak that would have been useful for picking up small insects? Is a finch illustrated that might have been able to extract insects from deep, narrow openings in the bark of trees?

When Darwin had completed his study of finches, he concluded that adaptation through natural selection had, over a period of a million years, produced several species of finches.

19–10 Investigating variation and evolution.

Do the two fossils shown in Figure 19–19 represent an evolutionary trend? How could you find out? These same questions concerned paleontologists a century ago. The studies and interpretations of Charles Darwin and Alfred Wallace helped provide the answers. In this investigation you have reproductions of two slabs of rock containing fossils. You will have the opportunity to try to determine for yourself what evolutionary trends might have occurred.

Procedure

(1) Examine the slabs of rock and decide how you could describe the fossils to determine similarities and differences. Discuss with the class the characteristics that can be used.

(2) Using length and width, describe each member of the population preserved on the slabs.

(3) For each slab make a graph of the length or width of the populations.

(4) How do the individual fossils on each slab vary?

(5) What similarities are apparent in each population? What differences exist?

(6) What evolutionary trends might be exhibited?

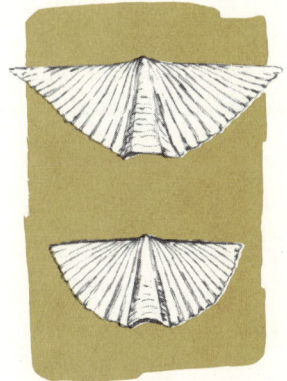

Figure 19–19

Alfred Russel Wallace was born in 1823, 14 years after his countryman Charles Darwin. On his travels in South America and the East Indies between 1848 and 1862, Wallace was struck by the many different animal species, which he noticed were restricted in habitat and range. Earlier he had read Lyell's theory of physical evolution and an essay by the English clergyman Malthus that stated that population always increases faster than food supply. Wallace reasoned that dwindling food supply would allow only the strongest animals to survive, and that in this way new species would eventually evolve. Combining what he had seen with his application of Lyell and Malthus, Wallace developed a theory of evolution much like Darwin's.

Wallace sent Darwin his manuscript on evolution in 1858, and the theory was jointly presented before the Linnaean Society.

In 1868 Wallace published The Malay Archipelago, containing his research on evolution. Wallace was also interested in the geographic distribution of animals. He applied the theory of evolution to a world classification of animal species. He also divided Australian and Asiatic regions according to animal species. This boundary is still called Wallace's Line. His studies on animal species also added to the evidence that the continents were once connected.

PALEARCTIC

ORIENTAL

NEOTROPICAL

AUSTRALIAN

Alfred Russel Wallace

19–11 Certain changes have been carefully traced.

In looking for evidence to support his theory of evolution, Darwin studied many fossils. He noticed that fossils collected from older to younger rocks showed gradual changes. Was it possible that the older fossils could be ancestors of the later forms? As Darwin carefully examined the fossil record, he found more and more evidence to suggest that this was so.

Modern paleontologists study fossils in much the same way. By examining fossils from an undisturbed sequence of layered rocks, paleontologists can sample many generations. This often makes it possible to establish the evolutionary line of a species.

Probably the best known evolutionary series is that of the horse. (See Figure 19–20.) Its development has been traced back to Eocene time, about 60 million years ago. The first horses were leaf-eating forest dwellers about the size of a fox, probably living on the North American continent. The ancestral Eocene horse had four toes on each front foot and three toes on each hind foot. Each toe bore a small hoof. This construction made the animal well suited for traveling on the soft, sometimes spongy forest floor. The animal had short, low-crowned teeth with small irregularities on the grinding surface. Teeth of this sort are well suited for crushing soft foods like forest leaves.

Near the end of the Tertiary Period the climate of North America grew cooler and the forests gave way to open, grass-covered plains. As the environment changed, horses adapted to it. Through a series of gradual changes over almost 60 million years the horse developed hard, hoofed, single toes for running over the harder surface of the

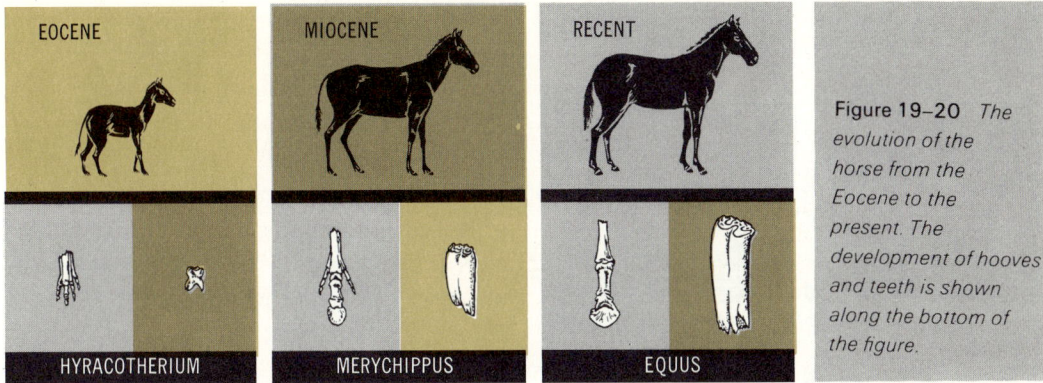

EOCENE

MIOCENE

RECENT

HYRACOTHERIUM

MERYCHIPPUS

EQUUS

Figure 19–20 *The evolution of the horse from the Eocene to the present. The development of hooves and teeth is shown along the bottom of the figure.*

plains. This change was accompanied by the development of rather complicated, high-crowned teeth, a suitable adaptation for feeding on the coarse, dry grasses of the prairie. Each change as it occurred was very slight and resulted from natural selection. Yet the accumulation of these changes produced differences that can be detected in the series of fossil horses.

What can you learn from studying fossils selected from ten million generations of horses? First, you can see that horses gradually changed over a long period of time. Second, these changes were orderly and resulted in variations that seem to have enabled the horse to adapt to new environments. Here once more is evidence to support Darwin's theory of natural selection. The evolutionary sequence of the horse is not unique in geologic history. Similar lines have been established for elephants, camels, and many invertebrate animals.

Charles Darwin was not the only scientist who noticed variation among plants and animals. In 1858, just a year before he published *The Origin of Species*, Darwin received a letter from Alfred Russel Wallace, a young Welsh naturalist. Wallace enclosed a manuscript announcing a theory of evolution that was almost identical to Darwin's.

Thought and Discussion . . .

1. How does the theory of evolution relate to paleontology?
2. How did Darwin explain the process of natural selection?
3. By what varied means did the finches of Galápagos Islands adapt to their environment?

The Parade of Life

19–12 Paleozoic time was the age of invertebrates.

No one knows when or where life first appeared on earth. But it is known that life was present more than three billion years ago, for simple bacteria-like organisms have been found in Precambrian rocks. (See Figure 19–21.)

Complex Cambrian fossils provide additional evidence that life was evolving during Precambrian time. Yet during the Precambrian organisms left very little record of their presence.

Whatever the reason for the scarcity of Precambrian fossils, evidence of life is abundant from the beginning of the Cambrian Period to the present. This rather clearly defined record stretches 600 million years back into time and provides a record of the evolution of life.

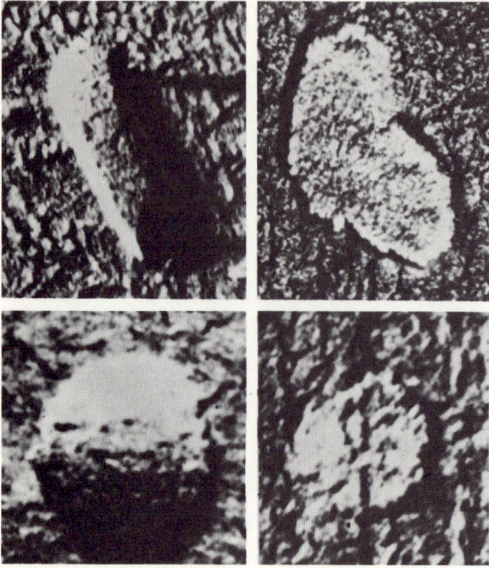

Figure 19–21 *These fossils of bacteria were found in rocks more than three billion years old. They are less than 1×10^{-4} centimeters in diameter.*

You have already learned that plants and animals have undergone continuous change. The earth has also changed. Seas invaded the land, mountains were lifted up and eroded away, and ice sheets appeared and vanished. Meanwhile, countless numbers of organisms have lived, multiplied, and then disappeared. Luckily, however, not all of these ancient plants and animals vanished without leaving a trace.

Figure 19–22 (*Top*) *Well preserved trilobite fossils from Devonian rocks in the Canadian Rockies. (Below) Reconstruction of an early Paleozoic sea. A trilobite crawls in the mud and a large arthropod swims through the weeds.*

How can we use fossil remains to reconstruct the parade of life on earth? Let us start by climbing one of the peaks in the Rocky Mountains of Canada. As you look closely at the rocks beneath your feet, you can see the unmistakable outline of an animal quite unlike any living organism. It is a **trilobite**, an extinct, distant relative of the horseshoe crabs, shrimps, and lobsters. Scientists have studied thousands of trilobite fossils that usually occur in marine sedimentary rocks. Features of trilobite shells suggest, moreover, that they spent most of their time crawling through the mud on the ocean floor. (See Figure 19–22.) How did this trilobite fossil, once buried in the mud of an ocean floor, come to be in the Canadian Rockies?

With the discovery of the trilobite you have begun to read the record of life. The fossil record of Paleozoic time shows the successive development of many new forms of invertebrates. During the early part of this era, in the Ordovician Period, the first vertebrates also appeared. They were probably primitive, fish-like creatures that originated about 500 million years ago.

During the Cambrian and Ordovician periods life apparently was confined to the sea. Evidence in the rock record, however, shows that in Silurian time both plants and animals became established on land. The first land plants must have been simple, rootless forms, and the first land animals were probably scorpion-like invertebrates.

Near the middle of the Devonian Period, about 375 million years ago, there appeared a specialized group of fishes capable of spending brief periods out of water. These unusual fishes, called the "lobe-fins," eventually evolved into the amphibians. The earliest amphibians must have looked—and

TABLE 19–1 CALIBRATED GEOLOGIC TIME SCALE

ERA	PERIOD	EPOCH	EVENTS IN THE HISTORY OF LIFE	OTHER IMPORTANT EVENTS
CENOZOIC	Quaternary	Recent (10,000)	Earliest man	Modern horse evolves in North America, then dies out — Ice Ages — Grand Canyon carved — Pacific Coast Ranges formed
CENOZOIC	Quaternary	Pleistocene (1,000,000 to 2,000,000)	Earliest man	
CENOZOIC	Tertiary	Pliocene (11,000,000)		
CENOZOIC	Tertiary	Miocene (25,000,000)	Rapid spread and evolution of grazing mammals	
CENOZOIC	Tertiary	Oligocene (40,000,000)	Earliest elephants	
CENOZOIC	Tertiary	Eocene (60,000,000)	First primitive horses, rhinoceroses, and camels	
CENOZOIC	Tertiary	Paleocene (70,000,000)	First primates	
MESOZOIC	Cretaceous (135,000,000)		Extinction of dinosaurs Great evolution and spread of flowering plants	Uplift and folding of Western Geosyncline — Half of North America covered by seas — Uplift of Sierra Nevada
MESOZOIC	Jurassic (180,000,000)		First birds and mammals Dinosaurs at their peak	Dinosaurs
MESOZOIC	Triassic (225,000,000)			Arid climates in much of western North America
PALEOZOIC	Permian (270,000,000)		Mammal-like reptiles	Ice Ages in Southern Hemisphere World climate much like today Deserts in western United States
PALEOZOIC	Pennsylvanian (305,000,000)		First reptiles	Large insects	Widespread swamps, coal source Tropical climate in United States
PALEOZOIC	Mississippian (350,000,000)			Uplift and folding of Appalachian Geosyncline — Widespread flooding of North America, limestone deposited
PALEOZOIC	Devonian (400,000,000)		First amphibians First forests	Sharks abundant	Trilobites
PALEOZOIC	Silurian (440,000,000)		First air-breathing animals (scorpions) First land plants	Filling of Appalachian Geosyncline and Western Geosyncline — Deserts in eastern and central U.S.
PALEOZOIC	Ordovician (500,000,000)		Trilobites at peak First vertebrates (fish)	Widespread flooding of North America by seas
PALEOZOIC	Cambrian (600,000,000)		Marine shelled invertebrates common First abundant animal fossils	
PRECAMBRIAN PROTEROZOIC	(2,500,000,000)		Marine invertebrates probably common; few with shells (1,200,000,000)	Glaciation-possibly worldwide — Many geosynclines filled, uplifted, and eroded
PRECAMBRIAN ARCHEOZOIC	(4,500,000,000)		Earliest plants (marine algae) (3,200,000,000)	

NUMBERS REFER TO TIME IN YEARS B.P. (BEFORE PRESENT) SINCE THE BEGINNING OF THE ERA, PERIOD, OR EPOCH

behaved—much like fishes. However, the fins had evolved into flipper-like legs. Gills could no longer be used for respiration. Instead, the primitive lung of the lobe-finned fish passed oxygen from the atmosphere into the blood. In what ways are amphibians different from fish?

Even though the amphibians were restricted to areas near water, they were the dominant land animals until the Pennsylvanian Period, when the first reptiles appeared. Reptiles do not need to return to the water, for their outer skin allows them to live even in very dry places. With their protective outer skin and ability to lay eggs that could develop on land, the reptiles were well adapted to life out of water.

Although fishes, amphibians, and reptiles became common in Paleozoic time, this era was really the time of marine invertebrates. The trilobites were especially numerous on the bottoms of Early Paleozoic seas. But near the end of the Paleozoic Era their numbers began to decline. Finally, at the end of the Permian Period the trilobites became extinct. What might be some reasons for the extinction of this once highly successful group of animals?

Brachiopods, animals with shells somewhat like clam shells, were among the most abundant creatures on earth during the middle part of the Paleozoic Era. Sedimentary rocks in which their fossils are found show that most of these animals lived in shallow seawater. Throughout the ages certain varieties of brachiopods seem to have been able to adapt to various kinds of marine environments—muddy and sandy bottoms, shallow and deep water, and the areas near coral reefs. Perhaps this adaptability is one reason why brachiopods are still found in shallow seas today—nearly 600 million years after the first brachiopod shells were buried and preserved in the mud of a Cambrian sea. How much longer will man have to inhabit the earth before he equals this record?

In the last part of the Paleozoic Era, erosion so lowered the level of great areas of the continents that numerous large swamps formed. The partly decayed swamp vegetation slowly accumulated on the swamp bottom and was gradually converted to peat. Centuries later, after the peat was buried and compressed beneath sediments, it slowly changed into coal. These great deposits of Paleozoic coal make up one of the largest concentrations of carbon on earth and certainly one of the greatest sources

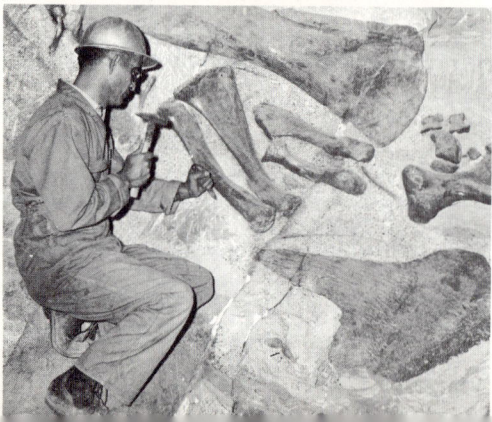

Figure 19–23 *Dinosaurs of the Mesozoic Era have been discovered in various places. The man in the photo is carefully digging out the bones of a dinosaur in Dinosaur National Monument, Utah.*

Figure 19-24 (Right) The first bird, Archaeopteryx, as conceived by an artist. (Far right) Early mammals of the Mesozoic drawn from fossil evidence.

of energy available today. Coal and shale beds formed during the Pennsylvania Period are shown on page 440.

19-13 Reptiles rule the earth.

As the Paleozoic Era drew to a close, the reptiles, which had evolved from the amphibians, became the leading animals. Fossil-bearing Mesozoic rocks found in many places on the earth have provided a fairly detailed picture of life in this era. Beginning with the Triassic Period some 225 million years ago, the Mesozoic Era opened with a large reptile population. Climate aided the development of reptiles, for it was much warmer during Mesozoic time than it is today.

Ranging from less than a meter to over 30 meters in length, the reptiles had undisputed rule of the land. The presence of flying as well as sea and land forms of reptiles showed that they had adapted to life in different environments. Considering their numbers, it is not surprising that the Mesozoic Era is called the Age of Reptiles. (See Figure 19–23.)

Among the many reptiles that evolved, the dinosaurs were particularly numerous and varied. Dinosaur National Monument in Utah is one of the few places in the world where dinosaur skeletons are almost completely exposed. They are embedded in the rock at the same place and in much the same position as

when the sediment was washed over them tens of millions of years ago. (See Figure 19–23.)

The skeleton of the first bird was found in a Jurassic limestone in southern Germany. This primitive bird would have been classified as a reptile but for impressions in the rock that showed it was heavily covered with feathers. This was a most remarkable find, not only because it is the earliest known bird, but also because it shows clearly that birds evolved from reptiles.

During the Jurassic Period the mammals also appeared. Like the early birds, the first mammals were primitive and reptile-like. (See Figure 19–24.) What did this change from reptile to mammal involve? Reptiles and mammals are living today. How do they differ?

Although the fossil remains of the first mammals are fragmental, evidence indicates that these creatures were about the size of a mouse. Although they evolved rapidly during Jurassic and Cretaceous time, they were overshadowed by the reptiles. It was not until the Cenozoic Era that the mammals began to spread and increased in number.

The advancement of Mesozoic life was not confined to the vertebrates. The invertebrates of this era were generally more complex than those of the Paleozoic. Land plants increased in number and variety, and during the Cretaceous Period flowering plants appeared. Before this time there were no grasses, fruit trees, or flowering shrubs.

The relatively sudden disappearance of the dinosaurs, flying reptiles, most of the marine reptiles, and several invertebrate groups took place at the end of the Cretaceous Period. Although these creatures had ruled the earth for more than 140 million years, their rapid decline brought the Age of Reptiles to an end. Why should these animals, which had so successfully adapted to such a wide variety of habitats, come to such an abrupt end at the peak of their development? Can you propose any explanation for their sudden extinction?

19–14 The Cenozoic Era is called the Age of Mammals.

The Cenozoic Era is the Age of Mammals just as the Mesozoic Era was the Age of Reptiles, and as the Paleozoic before that had been the Age of the Invertebrates. It has been characterized by a great increase in the number and variety of mammals. As you learned in Section 19–13, mammals had lived for millions of years before Cenozoic time, but only during this era did they become dominant. They had developed into forms capable of adapting to a wide variety of environments. Could the extinction of the dinosaurs and many other reptiles have had something to do with the relatively rapid rise of the mammals?

Some mammals, like the giant ground sloths, woolly mammoths, and saber-toothed cats, flourished for several million years and then became extinct. (See Figure 19–25.) Others, like the camels and horses (Figure 19–20), evolved into the modern forms living today. Their geographic distribution, however, has not always been as it is today.

Figure 19–25 *Statues of giant ground sloths in a Los Angeles park. Such extinct animals, together with woolly mammoths and saber-toothed tigers, once roamed the area. Their fossilized remains were found in tar pits there.*

The fossil record indicates that camels and horses may have originated in North America. It also shows that both of these groups became extinct in North America only a few thousand years ago. The horse was reintroduced as a domestic animal by the early Spanish explorers. Later an unsuccessful attempt was made to bring back the camel as a beast of burden in the desert areas of southwestern North America.

As time passed in the Cenozoic Era, flowering plants and grasses increased. Many of today's trees—poplar, maple, elm, and oak—began to spread rapidly over the land. These developments in

Woolly mammoths roamed the North American continent during the last Ice Age.

the plant kingdom possibly played a part in the rapid rise of the mammals.

Late in the Cenozoic Era man appears to have evolved from a group of man-like mammals. During Pleistocene time, man continued to develop into his present form. Today, man is the most complex form of life on earth. Will some other animal be more successful than man in some future era?

Unsolved Problems When, where, and how did the different animal groups develop hard parts? By the end of the Cambrian Period these had been developed in most of the major groups of invertebrates, yet in Precambrian time most organisms had poorly developed hard parts or lacked them entirely.

Did the vertebrates evolve from ancient relatives of the starfish or did they evolve from segmented worms like earthworms? Various scientific authorities have suggested different answers to this question. Paleontologists are constantly searching for such missing bits of evidence in the fossil record.

At various times in geologic history organisms, such as the dinosaurs, have

Thought and Discussion . . .

1. How can ancient environmental conditions be interpreted by the kinds of fossils found?
2. Which animal can adapt to the widest range of environments? Make a list of the evidence to support your answer.
3. Discuss some of the relationships between plant and animal development during the Mesozoic era.

become extinct. Although several explanations for this have been proposed, none can be proved. Causes of worldwide extinction of a single group of animals cannot be explained from the available evidence. Mountain building, climatic changes, and migrations of predators cannot affect all the individuals in a group. What single or combined agents, then, caused extinctions? Perhaps the answer will be found in a study of population, environment, and genetics, the study of heredity.

Scientists do not yet know exactly how plant and animal substances are changed into fossil fuels. If this problem could be solved, organic wastes might be used to manufacture similar fuels.

CHAPTER REVIEW

Summary

Although life surrounds us, it is not always easy to distinguish living from non-living objects. In general, however, living objects are characterized by growth, response to outside stimulation, and the ability to reproduce. Living matter is composed of organic compounds.

During the more than three billion years that life has been present on earth, it has spread to all parts of the earth. Organisms have interacted with the atmosphere, lithosphere, and hydrosphere to become involved in a number of earth processes.

Although the record of past life is not complete, fossils have provided valuable clues to earth history. In studying fossils the paleontologist uses many techniques of the biologist, and he assumes that plants and animals of the past lived in much the same manner as their living relatives.

The way an organism becomes fossilized depends somewhat on the original composition of its body and the physical and chemical conditions that surrounded the animal before and after burial. Most organisms have not been preserved. Of those that have been fossilized, many have been destroyed through chemical and physical

What types of fossils will someday provide evidence of present conditions and forms of life?

processes, or will never be found by the paleontologist. In general, the older the rocks, the less evidence of life they contain.

Since plants and animals were restricted in time, space, and environment, their fossil remains are valuable aids in interpreting earth history. Some of these fossils are used in the search for coal, petroleum, and mineral deposits.

Organisms vary in an orderly fashion. The consistent variation in horses is an example of the adaptation of organisms to a changing environment and supports Darwin's theory of organic evolution.

Rock records indicate that the first organisms to appear on earth were probably much less complex than those that developed during later geologic periods. Although the record of Precambrian life is scarce, the fossil record is relatively clear from the beginning of the Cambrian Period. Although marine plants and animals were the dominant forms of Paleozoic life, vertebrate animals appeared early in the era and expanded rapidly. Fish, amphibians, and reptiles evolved in the order listed. Starting in the Silurian Period plants evolved rapidly and covered much of the land.

Reptiles flourished in the warm Mesozoic climates, reaching the height of their development. The entire history of the dinosaurs is recorded in the rocks of this era. Mammals, although in existence during much of the Mesozoic, did not predominate until the Cenozoic. Then in a tremendous variety of forms they spread, along with grasses, modern types of trees, and flowering plants, throughout the world. The appearance of these new plants, the disappearance of the dinosaurs, and other changes apparently resulted in conditions ideal for the development of mammals. Man finally appeared late in the Cenozoic Era.

Questions and Problems

A

1. What is meant by the term biosphere?
2. What are fossils?
3. Why are fossils not likely to be found in metamorphic rocks?
4. Why are microfossils especially useful to the paleontologist?
5. From what group of animals did birds and mammals evolve?

B

1. What are three observable basic characteristics of life?
2. Distinguish between organic and inorganic compounds.
3. Explain the role of decomposers in the calcium cycle.
4. How do fossils support the theory of organic evolution?
5. What features developed by the amphibians permitted them to live on land?

C

1. Discuss the various ways in which the biosphere, lithosphere, hydrosphere, and atmosphere may interact with one another. Describe the interfaces.
2. Outline the process of photosynthesis and explain why it is important to both plants and animals.
3. Show how the carbon, calcium, and water cycles are necessary for the support and continuation of life.
4. Explain how the differences of the Galápagos finches supported Darwin's theory of natural selection.
5. Describe the adaptations made by the amphibians as they evolved into reptiles.

Suggested Readings

BOOKS

Barnett, Lincoln and the editors of *Life*. *The World We Live In*. Time, Inc., New York, 1955.

Beerbower, James R. *Search for the Past: An Introduction to Paleontology*. Prentice-Hall, Inc., Englewood Cliffs, N.J., 1960.

Biological Sciences Curriculum Study. *Biological Science: An Inquiry into Life*. BSCS Yellow Version. Harcourt, Brace & World, Inc., New York, 1963.

Biological Sciences Curriculum Study. *Biological Science: Molecules to Man*. BSCS Blue Version. Houghton Mifflin Company, Boston, 1963.

Biological Sciences Curriculum Study. *High School Biology*. BSCS Green Version. Rand McNally & Co., Skokie, Ill., 1963.

Colbert, Edwin H. *The Dinosaur Book*. McGraw-Hill Book Company, N.Y., 1951.

Farb, Peter. *The Story of Life*. Harvey House, Inc., Publishers, Irvington-on-Hudson, N.Y., 1962.

Fenton, Carroll L. and M. A. Fenton. *The Fossil Book, a Record of Prehistoric Life*. Doubleday & Company, Inc., Garden City, N.Y., 1959.

Fox, William and S. Welles. *From Bones to Bodies: A Story of Paleontology*. Henry Z. Walck, Inc., New York, 1959.

Heller, Robert L., ed. *Geology and Earth Sciences Sourcebook*. Holt, Rinehart & Winston, Inc., New York, 1962. Paperback.

Ludovici, Lionel J. *The Great Tree of Life, Paleontology: The Natural History of Living Creatures*. G. P. Putnam's Sons, New York, 1963.

Matthews, William H., III. *Exploring the World of Fossils*. Childrens Press, Inc., Chicago, 1964.

Matthews, William H., III. *Fossils: An Introduction to Prehistoric Life*. Barnes & Noble, Inc., New York, 1962. Paperback.

Moore, Ruth. *Man, Time, and Fossils, The Story of Evolution*, rev. ed. Alfred A. Knopf, Inc., New York, 1961.

Petersen, Kai. *Prehistoric Life on Earth*. E. P. Dutton & Co., Inc., New York, 1961.

Rhodes, Frank H. T., H. S. Zim, and P. R. Shaffer. *Fossils: A Guide to Prehistoric Life*. Golden Press, Inc., New York, 1962. Paperback.

Simpson, George G. *Horses*. Doubleday & Company, Inc., Garden City, N.Y., 1961. Paperback.

Simpson, George G. *Life of the Past*. Yale University Press, New Haven, Conn., 1953. Paperback.

PERIODICALS

Brues, Charles T. "Insects in Amber." *Scientific American*, November, 1951. (Also Scientific American Offprint #838, W. H. Freeman & Co., Publishers, San Francisco.)

Colbert, Edwin H. "The Ancestors of Mammals." *Scientific American*, March, 1949. (Also Scientific American Offprint #806.)

Eiseley, Loren C. "Charles Darwin." *Scientific American*, February, 1956. (Also Scientific American Offprint #108.)

Lack, David. "Darwin's Finches." *Scientific American*, April, 1953. (Also Scientific American Offprint #22.)

Kettlewell, H. B. D. "Darwin's Missing Evidence." *Scientific American*, March, 1959. (Also Scientific American Offprint #842.)

This giant Cretaceous fossil fish was found in Kansas. The smaller fish in its stomach is almost two meters in length.

Chapter 20 Development of a Continent

Changing shape of the North American continent. From left to right: Ordovician, Pennsylvanian, Tertiary, and Present. Where was material eroded from the continents being deposited in each case? Could land animals have crossed at any time from North America to Asia?

You have just seen the parade of life. Ordinary parades are parades through space, around the school grounds, along the street, or through the downtown area. The parade of life is a parade through time. It involves events and their relationship to one another in time. Some of the most difficult questions for earth scientists to answer involve the relationship of events in space. These questions ask *how* and *where* the events occurred.

Camels are found in the desert regions of Africa and Asia. Evidence indicates that they originated in North America. How did they migrate to the other continents? Did they swim? Even if the Bering Strait were much warmer in the past than it is now, the shortest swimming distance is about 85 kilometers. Did camels travel on rafts of matted vegetation carried out to sea by rivers

and across oceans by currents and winds? Were there times when more of the continents were connected by "bridges" like the Isthmus of Panama between North and South America? Were the existing continents once a part of one or two much larger continents? If so, is it possible that the migration of animals took place before the continents separated? All ideas suggested by these questions must be considered. The questions cannot be answered finally until some problems about the continents have been solved.

For instance, how old are the continents? Have they always been where they are? Is there evidence that can lead to conclusions about their ages and the ways in which they developed? Answers to these questions would help not only to unravel the history of the continents but also to provide information about animal and plant migration over the surface of the earth.

Figure 20–1 *Canyon of the San Juan River in Utah. If you found evidence for unconformities, how could you reconstruct the parts of the record that are missing?*

Early History of North America

20–1 North America: a sample continent.

In reconstructing the development of continents, earth scientists work with records like those pictured in Figure 20–1. In the photograph the pages of the record look quite complete. It appears too, that the pages, or rock layers, can easily be correlated across the canyon. It should be easy to reconstruct the history of this area. But suppose that you were to examine the canyon more closely. Could there be layers missing?

The canyon pictured in Figure 20–1 is in North America. It is possible to find similar canyons in many parts of the world. Although these canyons differ in detail, there are many features that they have in common. Similarly, all continents differ in certain details but resemble one another in general. Hence North America can serve as a sample to examine problems typical of the geology of all continents.

You can begin by looking at the entire continent and then at some of its parts. Suppose you were in a spaceship over North America, moving from time to

Figure 20–2(A) *A relief map of North America, and (B) a map showing the distribution of the major rock types of North America. What similarities can you find between the two maps?*

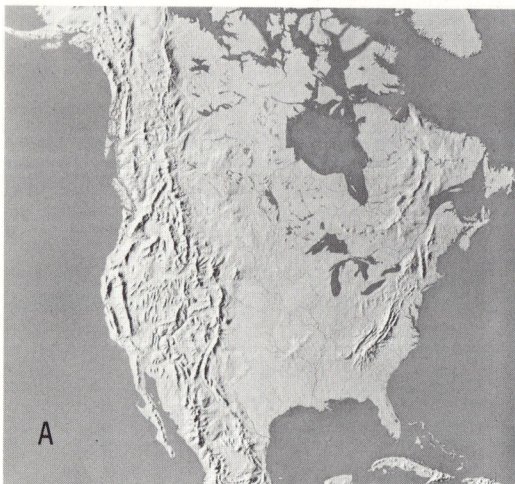

A

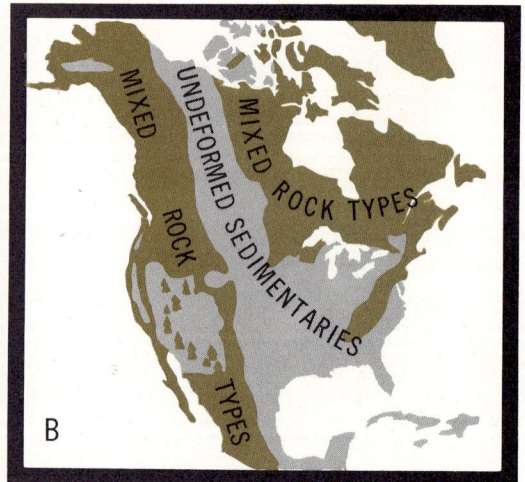

B

time for a view of different parts of the land. What would be the most noticeable features of the continent? (See Figure 20–2A.) Mountain ranges, plains, and lakes stand out as the most obvious aspects of the terrain. Large rivers drain the interior of the continent, carrying sediments to the seas that border it.

The distribution of the different kinds of rock in North America is shown in Figure 20–2B. Areas in which igneous, sedimentary, and metamorphic rocks are found together correspond roughly to the mountain regions. Areas in which nearly horizontal layers of sedimentary rocks are found lie within the plateau and plains areas or in the coastal regions. Rocks that make up the plains and plateaus in northeastern North America are almost all igneous and metamorphic like those found in mountainous areas. What might this mean?

20–2 Investigating Precambrian rocks.

Figure 20–3 shows a series of cross sections that represent Precambrian rocks found along the north shore of Lake Huron near Blind River, Ontario. Information gathered from the study of many outcrops has been pieced together to make each of these cross sections that earth scientists now believe best represent the geology of this area.

Procedure

(1)List the rocks shown in each of these cross sections in the order in which they formed. Do the relationships shown in the cross sections permit you to put all of the rock units in a relative time sequence? If you are not sure of the order in which some of the rocks formed, indicate these rocks and tell why you are not sure.

(2)Your teacher will provide you with a list of the radioactively determined ages of some rocks shown in the Precambrian cross sections. Does the sequence indicated by these ages agree with the order you worked out from the cross sections? Why or why not?

Figure 20–3

20–3 The Precambrian record.

The sequence of rocks found near Blind River, Ontario, is typical of Precambrian rocks found at many places in northeastern North America. It is common to find within the Precambrian some older, folded, metamorphic rocks under younger Precambrian rocks that are not as highly metamorphosed. In most places, the two rock types are separated by an unconformity.

Figure 20–4 *Unconformity between Precambrian and Cambrian rocks that are exposed along the edge of the Canadian Shield.*

Figure 20–5 (*Top*) Eroded, folded Precambrian rocks in the Canadian Shield.
Figure 20–6 (*Above*) Precambrian rocks exposed at the surface in North America.
Figure 20–7 (*Below*) Distribution of radioactive dates from Precambrian rocks.

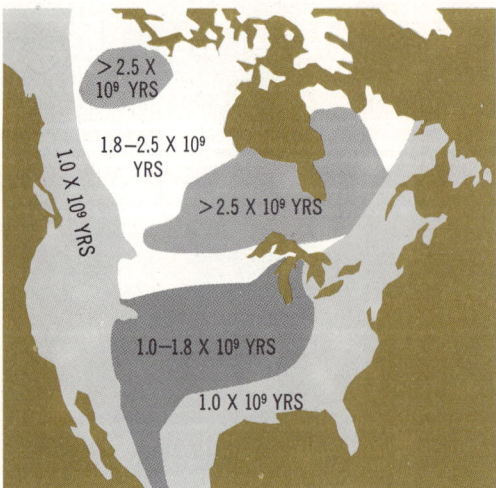

> 2.5 X 10⁹ YRS

1.8–2.5 X 10⁹ YRS

1.0 X 10⁹ YRS

> 2.5 X 10⁹ YRS

1.0–1.8 X 10⁹ YRS

1.0 X 10⁹ YRS

Around the borders and at some places within the region, Cambrian and younger rocks lie on the Precambrian as you can see in Figure 20–4. What evidence in the figure suggests that a long time passed between the formation of Precambrian and Cambrian rocks?

Unconformities and other evidence indicate that almost no sediments have been deposited over most of northeastern North America since the early Paleozoic. This suggests that the region has been quite stable for a long time, at least since the close of the Proterozoic Era about 600 million years ago. Large areas that have been stable since the beginning of the Paleozoic and in which Precambrian rocks are now exposed over thousands of square kilometers are called **shields.** Every continent includes a shield within its boundaries. Because the shield in North America is found almost entirely within Canada, it is known as the Canadian Shield. (See figures 20–5 and 20–18.)

In some places within the Canadian Shield, interlayered lava flows and sedimentary rocks are over 5000 meters thick. After they accumulated, these rocks were folded, intruded by igneous rocks, and metamorphosed. Exposed now in low-lying areas like that shown in Figure 20–5, they appear to be the roots of old mountains formed so long ago that the parts formerly raised to high elevations have been eroded away. The long narrow belts in which the roots are found are probably sites of former geosynclines. If these conclusions are correct, the Canadian Shield was far from stable during Precambrian time. Mountain building occurred several times and at many places in the Shield.

The map in Figure 20–6 shows the areas in North America in which Precambrian rocks are found at the surface.

No fossils have been found in these rocks with which to correlate the ages of the rocks. Few radioactive dates have been established, but there are enough to attempt correlating some of the Precambrian rocks. Dates shown within the area of the Canadian Shield in Figure 20–7 were obtained from exposed Precambrian rocks. Some dates outside the Shield were obtained from samples taken from wells drilled through younger rocks down to the Precambrian layers. Radioactive dates indicate that the time interval between the formation of the youngest Precambrian rocks and the oldest Cambrian rocks is about 500 million years in some places.

Although fossils are rare in Precambrian rocks, more and more fossils are being found. The oldest fossils known are remains of algae and bacteria. They have been found in rocks in Africa that are more than 3 billion years old! (See Figure 20–8.) Although algae and bacteria are primitive organisms, they must have evolved from even more primitive types, possibly viruses. Fossils have been identified in Precambrian rocks on other continents also. For example, fossils of more complex but still primitive organisms such as sponges have been found in rocks that are believed to have been deposited in very late Proterozoic time. In Precambrian rocks of Australia and in the Grand Canyon, fossils of some strange invertebrate animals have been found. (See Figure 20–8, right.)

As you can see, there has been life on earth for a very long time!

20–4 Four billion years of history.

From your work with the Precambrian rocks of the Blind River area you have seen that the record for the early history of the North American continent is incomplete. Scientists have evidence that the earth is at least 4.5 billion years old. If there were a North American continent before about 3 billion years ago, rocks in which the record is preserved have not yet been found. However, the Precambrian record shows that erosion, sedimentation, volcanic activity, intrusion, and metamorphism have combined to build and shape the continent. The oldest rocks known are metamorphosed sedimentary rocks. The land area from which the sediments forming these rocks were derived has not been found.

Figure 20–8 *Precambrian fossils.* (*Left*) *Fossil algae over 3 billion years old.* (*Right*) *A fossil worm found on the Australian Continent.*

Figure 20–9 *Three stages in the growth of the North American continent. (A) about 2.5 billion years ago, (B) 1.8 billion years ago, and (C) about 1.4 billion years ago during the Proterozoic.*

Most of the radioactive dates shown in Figure 20–7 are from igneous rocks believed to have been intruded during mountain building. The way the dates are grouped suggests that parts of North America may have been added to the continent at different times in the past. In Figure 20–9 possible stages of growth are outlined on maps of North America. The hypothesis on which these maps are based is that the North American continent developed from several small nuclei. According to this hypothesis, the first stage of development included rocks that are 2.5 billion years old or older. (See Figure 20–9A.) From this beginning the continent grew, so that by the early Paleozoic it may have looked as in Figure 20–9C.

If growth occurred in this fashion, the presence of geosynclinal rocks in the Shield suggests that growth may have taken place at the edges of the continent. Early in each stage geosynclines may have developed at the margins and received thick accumulations of sediments and volcanic rocks. Later, during mountain building, the geosynclinal rocks were lifted and folded to become part of the continent. Along the newly established margins new geosynclines developed and the mountain-building processes were repeated.

As continents grew, the evolution of organisms proceeded also. As the organisms became more complex and numerous, they spread to new environments. In adapting to these new environments, the organisms evolved more diverse forms. Thus, the rate of evolution may have increased with time. Although it appears that algae, bacteria, and other primitive plants were perhaps the sole inhabitants of the earth for most of Precambrian time, more diversified forms of life gradually evolved from them. Although invertebrate animals lived in Proterozoic waters, the fossil record is so scant that little is known of their abundance or form. What evidence can you think of to support the conclusion that many different kinds of animals existed during the late Proterozoic? Why are fossils so rare?

Thought and Discussion . . .

1. What evidence leads to the conclusion that the Canadian Shield has been stable since the early Paleozoic?

2. What evidence suggests that the Canadian Shield has not always been stable?

3. What evidence suggests that North America may have developed from a smaller continent?

Later History of North America

20–5 Investigating Paleozoic rocks in Michigan.

When you worked out the sequence of events of Precambrian rocks in Investigation 20–2, you used several cross sections of an area. Cross sections are constructed by first mapping the surface rock units and drawing a map like the one in Figure 20–10. After many observations are made on the earth's surface, cross sections interpreting conditions below the surface can be constructed. This is roughly the procedure that you will follow in this investigation. You used a similar type of evidence to trace the course of an ancient stream channel in Investigation 18–4.

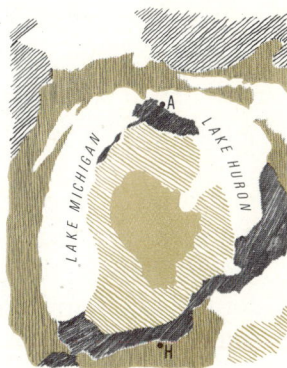

Figure 20–10

Procedure

Examine Figure 20–10, a generalized map of the rock units in the state of Michigan.

(1)If you had to make a model of the area represented in this map, in how many different ways could you account for the surface rock pattern? (Remember the techniques used in Investigation 18–8.)

(2)Table 20–1 gives the thicknesses of four subsurface rock layers along a cross section from A to H. Using modeling material make a cross-section model of each rock unit.

(3)Once you have made the cross section of each of these units, try to see how they could all fit together. Use some kind of modeling material and make cross section strips. (See Figure 20–11.) Put them together so that they show what a complete cross section of these units would have looked like after they had been deposited. Make a drawing of your structure.

Figure 20–11

(4)Since all the rock units were deposited in water, what must the upper surface of the deposits have been like at any stage of deposition?

(5)Summarize the apparent behavior of the crust in this area during deposition of each of the four units.

TABLE 20-1 THICKNESS OF ROCK UNITS IN MICHIGAN BASIN

ROCK UNITS	THICKNESSES IN METERS AT STATIONS							
	A	B	C	D	E	F	G	H
IV (YOUNGEST)	0	450	900	1200	750	450	150	0
III	300	200	150	80	30	30	75	75
II	150	250	300	400	400	350	350	350
I (OLDEST)	30	300	450	500	600	600	600	600

20–6 The Paleozoic record.

The map in Figure 20–12 shows areas of Paleozoic rocks in North America as well as areas containing Precambrian rocks. Over most of the continental interior, the Paleozoic sequence is similar to that in Michigan, although at many places it is thinner. The earliest sediments, deposited in a Cambrian sea, formed sandstones and shales. They contain fossils of trilobites and brachiopods.

Figure 20–12 *Precambrian and Paleozoic rocks exposed at the surface in North America.*
Figure 20–13 *Paleozoic rocks. (A) Paleozoic reef. (B) A salt mine under Lake Erie. (C) Pennsylvanian shale and coal beds in Michigan.*

A very thick sequence of limestone overlies the Cambrian layers. Reefs like that shown in Figure 20–13A are common in these limestones, extending from the Arctic Circle to Kentucky. Salt deposits, although less abundant than other rock types, extend over thousands of square kilometers in the rock layers of some regions. (See Figure 20–13B.) The youngest Paleozoic rocks are mostly sandstones and shales containing thin coal beds like those shown in Figure 20–13C. (See Section 19–12.) This sequence of rock types is characteristic of Paleozoic rocks in the interiors of all continents between their shields and geosynclinal mountains.

The most unusual feature of this Paleozoic sequence is the widespread presence of limestone. Never before or since have limestones been deposited so extensively on the continents. There must have been something very different about the atmosphere and seas during this interval of time. The reason for the great abundance of calcium carbonate is one of the great unsolved problems of the earth's history. It seems unlikely that calcium was being carried to the sea in greater amounts than at other times. The older rocks from which the calcium would have come do not contain an unusually large amount of calcium. The fossil record shows that animals and plants that formed calcium carbonate were abundant in the early Paleozoic seas. (See Section 19–12.) However, they have become increasingly abundant as geologic time has progressed. If their abundance was the reason for the great amount of calcium carbonate deposited during this age, limestone should be much more abundant in recently formed rocks. Yet this is not the case.

Paleozoic rocks of the continental margins are up to eight times thicker

Figure 20–14 *The location of Paleozoic geosynclines of North America. Where would you expect mountain systems to form?*

than those in the interior. (See sections 14–1 and 14–2.) These geosynclinal rocks provide evidence for several episodes of mountain building, extensive volcanic eruptions, and other events. Such events indicate the unstable, mobile character of these belts during Paleozoic times. Look at the map of North America in Figure 20–14. It shows the locations of geosynclines along the eastern and western borders of the continent during the Paleozoic Era. What kinds of evidence do you suppose were used to draw the map?

In reconstructing the history of the continent it is important to know not only where geosynclines were and what

they were like but also *when* they existed. (See Table 19–1.) Near the boundary between the United States and Canada in the Rocky Mountain region more than 13,000 meters of Proterozoic rocks are exposed. They lie beneath thick Paleozoic rocks that formed in the western geosyncline. Evidence in the Appalachian area suggests that a similar thickness of Precambrian rocks is found beneath the Cambrian there. It seems likely that geosynclines were in existence along both continental margins during the late Proterozoic.

The thick sedimentary rocks in the Appalachian geosyncline were folded, faulted, intruded by igneous rocks, and uplifted into mountains during the Paleozoic Era and probably the early Mesozoic Era. In contrast, thick sediments continued to accumulate in the western geosyncline, which was not added to the continent by mountain-building processes until late Mesozoic and early Cenozoic time.

The presence of fossils makes it possible to correlate geosynclinal rocks with those of the continental interior. Figure 20–15 is a cross section of rocks in Nevada and Arizona drawn across the margin of the ancient geosyncline. *Olenellus*, a kind of trilobite, and other fossils associated with it are found only in the very oldest marine Cambrian rocks. If the *Olenellus* were not present, it is doubtful that there would be any way to correlate the thick sediments in the

Figure 20–15 *Cross section of Precambrian and Cambrian rocks in Nevada and Arizona.*

geosynclines with thinner sediments in the continental interior.

In a similar way fossils are used to show that within the continental interior there are some regions where Paleozoic rocks are much thicker than at others. For instance some of the thick beds of the Michigan area correlate with much thinner beds in the Cincinnati arch and Ozark dome regions. (See Figure 20–18.) Reefs in one place correlate with sandstones and shales in other places. They also correlate with unconformities in other regions. Hence we can see that all of these features—reefs, sand deposits, and shale deposits—were forming at the same time in different locations just as they are today.

20–7 The Mesozoic-Cenozoic record.

Areas where Precambrian, Paleozoic, and Mesozoic rocks are found at the surface in North America are shown in Figure 20–16. For much of the Mesozoic, the record consists of rocks that were deposited on land. Stream, lake, and wind deposits are spread across several of the states and provinces. Some areas, such as most of the eastern half of North America, were above sea level and being eroded during much of the Mesozoic Era. Marine sediments were deposited along the east and Gulf Coasts and in an arm of the sea reaching across what is now the Rocky Mountains.

The geologic map of North America shown in Figure 20–17 (page 452) indicates areas where rocks of each of the major subdivisions of geologic time are found at the surface. Deposits distributed by ice during the last Ice Age have been omitted. Cenozoic rocks, deposited over the Great Plains and in areas between the western mountain ranges, contain fossils of horses, camels, cats, dogs, and ancestors of other familiar land animals and plants. The rocks containing these fossils are conglomerates, sandstones, and shales deposited in lakes and streams that flowed from the growing mountain ranges.

Cenozoic rocks in North America containing marine fossils are restricted almost entirely to the coastal plains. During this time invertebrate animals found in the oceans and seas today were evolving, and the records are more complete than those for any other part of geologic time. Why? Many of the Cenozoic marine fossils are related to animals that live in the sea today. Humans are relatively new to the coastal scene.

Sir Charles Lyell used fossils to subdivide Cenozoic rocks into three sequences that he named Eocene, Miocene, and Pliocene. The subdivisions were based on the percentages of certain marine invertebrate fossils that can be related to living forms. Eocene rocks contained the smallest percentage and Pliocene rocks the largest. Other subdivisions of the Cenozoic have been added since Lyell proposed the original three. (See Tables 17–2 and 19–1.)

MESOZOIC
PALEOZOIC
PRECAMBRIAN

Figure 20–16 *Precambrian, Paleozoic, and Mesozoic rocks exposed at the surface of North America. Compare this map with those in figures 20–6 and 20–12. Note successive patterns.*

Changes in the distribution of Cenozoic fossils, especially those of plants, have been studied to learn about climatic changes that took place. Evidence indicates that early in the Tertiary Period, northern climates became warmer. Southern North America, from Texas to North Carolina, was tropical and most of the northern United States was subtropical. Canada and Alaska were in the temperate zone! However, later in the Tertiary the trend was reversed. Climates grew cooler. The warmer belts were crowded toward the equator and the polar regions became colder. (See Figure 18–18.)

20–8 North America
in space and time.

The four maps on the title page of this chapter show the changing shape of the North American continent at various stages of its development. What type of evidence could establish whether an area was above or below sea level during a given period of time? Compare these maps with those in Figure 20–9.

In the process of reading the record in the rocks much information has been assembled about the geologic history of North America. The Canadian Shield, where the oldest rocks are found, is bordered by Paleozoic rocks of the continental interior. The continental interior apparently acted as a slowly and unevenly subsiding "platform" after the Proterozoic ended. Seas encroached on parts of it and a relatively thin sequence of sediments was formed. Sometime earlier, during the Proterozoic, geosynclines developed along the borders of the continent. Thick accumulations of sediments collected in them until each was finally uplifted into mountains. During the Mesozoic, the Gulf of Mexico developed along the southern border of

Sir Charles Lyell

Charles Lyell was born in Forfarshire, Scotland, in 1797. While at Oxford studying law, he became interested in geology, and in 1819, he became a fellow of the Geological Society.

After passing the bar exam, Lyell became a circuit lawyer and traveled through France and Italy. As he continued to observe earth processes during his travels, he gradually became convinced that James Hutton's theories were correct. By 1827 Lyell had already begun to plan his chief work, The Principles of Geology, published in 1830.

Lyell felt that the landscape had been created not by a series of catastrophes, as people believed, but rather by slow, continuous earth processes that had been going on since the beginning of geologic time. The same idea had been proposed more than a generation before by James Hutton. Lyell's data supported Hutton's theory, and his three-volume book brought it to the attention of the world.

Through Lyell's careful work, the principle of uniformity of process became widely accepted. In 1838 Lyell published the Elements of Geology, now regarded as a classic geologic work. Lyell traveled to the United States and Canada in 1841, and wrote a number of papers about the geologic features of North America.

Figure 20–18 *Major structural features of the North American continent. 1. Michigan Basin. 2. Cincinnati Arch. 3. Illinois Basin. 4. Ozark Dome. 5. Llano Uplift. 6. West Texas Basins. 7. Central Kansas Uplift. 8. Williston Basin. 9. Colorado Plateau. 10. Columbia Plateau. White bars are ancient and modern mountains.*

the continent. Some characteristics of the Gulf region lead some geologists to call it a modern geosyncline. (See Figure 14–5.) In what ways does the Gulf region resemble a geosyncline?

Late in the Mesozoic Era, the Rocky Mountains began to rise out of the sea (Table 19–1) and erosion was initiated. By early Cenozoic time they had reached lofty heights. Sediments from the Rockies were carried into the basins between mountain ranges and spread eastward over the Great Plains. Some were carried by streams into the Gulf of Mexico and Arctic Ocean.

The major features of this continent have developed over a long period of time and are still developing. What evidence suggests that mountains are still growing? Which structural features shown in Figure 20–18 are the youngest? Mountains that have been uplifted since the close of the Proterozoic Era formed toward the outer margins of North America. The continental interior lies

between them and the Canadian Shield. Scattered domes and basins in the interior mark areas of greater or lesser crustal rising and sinking.

Coral reefs and plant fossils are found in Paleozoic rocks in belts extending from the Arctic Circle to the present temperate and subtropical climatic zones in North America. Under what conditions do corals grow in seas today? What does this suggest about water temperatures, depths, and salinities in Arctic regions during the Paleozoic?

In order to account for the apparent changes in positions of climatic belts, some scientists have suggested that continents were once oriented differently. As you learned in Chapter 16, one theory proposes that all present continents were once part of one or two much larger continents. Existing continents were formed and drifted to their present positions on the earth's surface when the original masses broke up. Study Figure 16–16. Can you find evidence there to support this hypothesis?

There are other types of evidence, some of which support the hypothesis of continental drift and some of which do not. Some of the evidence for continental growth was presented in Section 20–4. Is it possible that both growth and drift could help to account for the present continents? The origin of continents will not be understood until we learn much more about the earth.

Thought and Discussion . . .

1. What can the relative thicknesses of sedimentary rocks tell us about the time of development of basins, domes, and geosynclines?
2. What evidence shows that thicker rocks in the geosyncline were formed during the same time interval as thin rocks in the continental interior?

3. What happened to destroy the geosynclines that existed along the east and west coasts of North America during the Paleozoic and Mesozoic eras?

4. What might happen in the future to the Gulf coastal region where the present land surface is nearly flat and is very close to sea level?

5. When did North America reach its present size and shape?

The Great Ice Age

20–9 Glaciers and glaciation: theory and evidence.

In 1836, Louis Agassiz, a young Swiss scientist, began a study of glaciers in the Alps. His discoveries were to result in the acceptance of a theory that had been hinted at for many years but one that people had been reluctant to accept. The possibility that glaciers had once been very extensive in the Northern and Southern hemispheres had been ridiculed by scientists for a long time.

Agassiz compared the deposits of glaciers in the Alps with those that cover the bedrock in northern Europe. In both places he found the deposits to consist of loose material composed of a mixture of fragments ranging in size from clay particles to boulders.

Many boulders on the plains of northern Europe are composed of igneous or metamorphic rock, but they are found hundreds of kilometers from the nearest outcrops of such rocks. By comparing rock types Agassiz was able to show that these boulders could have originated only in Scandinavia. Somehow they had been carried from the region of Norway, Sweden, and Finland rather than from the Alps. From this, Agassiz reasoned that glaciers had once covered much of northern Europe and that they had spread from a source on the northern part of the continent. Although the glaciers in Alpine valleys had been much greater in size and length during the Pleistocene, they were not the agents responsible for spreading most of the loose material.

This glacial material long had been called **drift** because people thought it was deposited by melting icebergs drifting through water. Through Agassiz's work, drift was finally accepted as evidence of Pleistocene glaciation. Although its glacial origin is now recognized, the name drift is still used.

The Pleistocene Epoch, the time during which today's glacial landscapes were produced, is believed to have begun about one million years ago, perhaps about the time that man appeared on the earth. At least four times, great sheets of ice spread over more than half of North America. (See Figure 20–19.) At the same time similar ice sheets covered northern Europe.

How did the ice sheets change the land surface and where did the material that they deposited come from? In

Figure 20–19 *Glacial map of North America showing the maximum advance of the four great Pleistocene ice sheets over the continent.*

some places ice sheets moving over the surface picked up soil and weathered rock material. This material was carried over the bedrock beneath the glacier, polishing, scratching, and grooving its surface. (See Figure 20–20.) It also scoured valleys and other low areas over which the ice flowed, deepening some by hundreds of meters. In this way the basins of the Finger Lakes in New York and the Great Lakes were enlarged from stream valleys. (See Figure 20–21.)

Around each of the basins of the Great Lakes there is a series of ridges that parallel the shores of the basin. The ridges are made of unsorted mixtures of clay, sand, and boulders called **till.** (See Figure 20–22.) Many of the larger fragments are angular and covered with scratches and grooves. Does water deposit unsorted, unrounded material like this? How do you think the till might have been deposited? How did the ice in a glacier pile up material in ridges in this manner?

Because ice picks up more rock fragments from some places than from others, some parts of glaciers carry a larger load than others. When the ice deposits this unevenly distributed material, the resulting blanket of rock debris is thicker in some places than in others.

This is one reason why surfaces of glacial deposits are irregular and bumpy.

Water-deposited gravel and sand associated with till are called **outwash.** How would these differ from till? (See Figure 20–23.) Where did the water come from that transported and deposited the gravel and sand? Why is there very little clay in these deposits?

The direction of the grooves and scratches, the general orientation of ridges and other glacial deposits, and the rock types found all indicate that the glaciers of North America originated in Canada. They flowed outward from centers near Hudson Bay and in the Canadian Rocky Mountains. (See Figure 20–19.) During the Pleistocene the glaciers expanded and melted at least four times. Each of the four ice sheets that covered the land remained for thousands of years. (See Figure 20–24.) Between glacial advances there were even longer periods when the land surface was free of ice, and climates were warmer than they are now. Radiocarbon dates of plant remains buried in and under glacial deposits show that the last ice sheet melted from the northern states only about 10,000 years ago.

Comparison of glacial deposits in New England mountains with modern ice sheets in Antarctica and Greenland indi-

Figure 20–20 (*Below*) *Grooves made by a glacier in bedrock, Kelley's Island, Lake Erie.*
Figure 20–21 (*Right*) *Lake Cayuga, one of the Finger Lakes in New York State. These lakes formed when glaciers deepened stream valleys.*

cates that at times the ice over Hudson Bay was more than 3300 meters thick. The weight of this mass of ice was so great that it depressed the crust. Where the ice was thickest the surface was depressed more than 500 meters. Hudson Bay occupies a depression created at least partly by the ice. As the last glacier melted and the ice load decreased, the surface began to return to its original position. The land surface still has not reached its original level and is rising very slowly. The land near Niagara Falls is rising about 25 centimeters per century. At this rate it will probably be a long time before this movement stops. Can you think of any areas on other continents of the world where ice might have depressed the land surface?

When the immense ice sheets were accumulating on the continents, much water was temporarily stored in the form of ice. Sea level gradually was lowered on at least four different occasions. Beach deposits, wavecut cliffs, and similar features along the coasts of all of the continents, some submerged and some above sea level, provide evidence for this. Why are some of the old beaches and other types of coastal features still above sea level? (Refer to Figure 13–17.)

In addition to the continental ice sheets that cover Greenland and Antarctica today and smaller ice caps such as that on Iceland, there are thousands of valley glaciers in mountain ranges in many parts of the world. These valley glaciers are grinding away their floors and shaping their valleys and the enclosing mountain ranges into distinctive landforms. Earlier in the Pleistocene when the continental glaciers were widespread, there were many more valley glaciers than there are now. Where the valley glaciers have melted, the landforms that they created can be seen, as in the Rocky Mountains and in other high mountains on all continents.

During the Pleistocene Epoch, about 25 to 30 percent of the earth's land surface was covered by ice. Today 10 percent is ice-covered. Are we still in an Ice Age? Are we entering another stage between ice advances? Will large sheets of ice again spread over the continents in the near future, again changing the landscape and exerting their unusual effects on the water cycle?

Figure 20–22 *Glacial till. Note how the material varies in size, from boulders to fine clay.*
Figure 20–23 *Glacial outwash. The material has been deposited by melt water from a glacier.*
Figure 20–24 *The west coast of Greenland shows the remains of the last great ice sheet.*

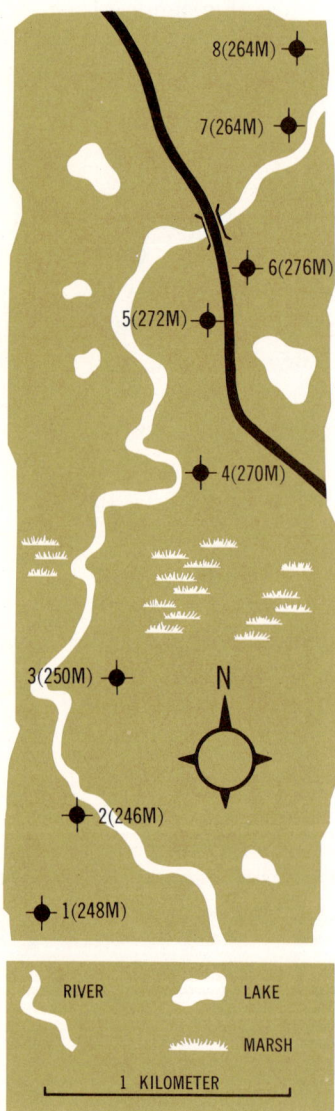

Figure 20-25

Additional Investigation

20-10 Investigating the Ice Age puzzle.

Imagine a giant scraper made of ice several thousand feet thick moving slowly over the earth. Vast areas of land have been completely changed by the scouring and grinding of huge continental ice sheets and smaller valley glaciers. Today about a third of the world's landscape exhibits modification by the last great glacial advance.

In this investigation you will examine an area that was formerly covered by part of a continental ice sheet.

Procedure

A map of a glaciated area appears in Figure 20-25. Across the map are numbers indicating certain stations on the landscape. Information is given for each station in Appendix D. The stations represent road cuts, stream banks, or drill holes where information has been obtained about the materials beneath the surface.

Using a scale of 1 centimeter = 10 meters, plot the elevation of each station on some graph paper. Connect the elevation points to form a topographic profile. A **topographic profile** is a drawing made to show the shape of the land surface along a given line.

Plot on the profile the information from the data table for each station. Make a cross section using different colors or symbols for the rock and glacial deposits. Be sure to include a key to show which material is represented by each color or symbol in your cross section.

Note that two kinds of till are distinguished by their color.

(1)Which till layer is apparently older?

(2)What is the evidence that a considerable length of time elapsed between deposition of the two layers?

(3)Recalling what you have learned about glaciers, can you think of the sequence of events that would explain this lapse of time between periods of deposition?

At stations 5, 6, 7, and 8 the bedrock has deep grooves.

(4)Refer to your cross section. With which till are the south-trending grooves associated? the southwest-trending grooves?

(5)How do you explain the absence of south-trending grooves at localities 7 and 8?

(6)Develop your interpretations of this model into a history of glacial activity in this area.

Thought and Discussion . . .

1. What evidence is there that the drift that covers the northern states and southern Canada was deposited by glaciers? What principle supports this interpretation?
2. Why is outwash believed to have been deposited by water rather than by ice?
3. What evidence indicates that there were several glacial advances during the Pleistocene Epoch rather than just one glacial advance?
4. How can earth scientists locate the centers from which ice sheets have advanced so many years ago?
5. Are you living during an Ice Age, at the beginning of a period between two glacial advances, or at the end of an Ice Age? What is your evidence?

Unsolved Problems Although broadly defined time relationships can be established for Precambrian rocks, it still is not possible to correlate such rock units precisely. Therefore, historical events that occurred at different places on the continent during Precambrian time cannot yet be correlated. Until more can be learned of the detailed history of the Precambrian continent, many of the problems of continental origin and early development must remain unsolved.

In the shields of all continents, the rocks record long periods when these regions were sites of geosynclinal development and mountain building. Having been unstable for so long, why did these regions become the most stable parts of the continents? Why, throughout the histories of the continents, have the successive growth stages consisted of the development of unstable regions, or geosynclines, that were subjected to mountain building and became part of the stable continental area?

During much of geologic time, mountain building has occurred frequently and perhaps almost continuously. However, the latest Precambrian mountain building took place in North America about one billion years ago and the earliest Paleozoic mountain building about 500 million years ago. The interval of time during which no mountains were built on the continent is about 500 million years, almost equal in length to all of the Paleozoic, Mesozoic, and Cenozoic eras. Why was there so long a period of time when the continent was so stable? Were the ocean basins equally stable during that time?

Basins like that in Michigan develop in the interiors of continents. Sediments accumulate in them at different rates during different intervals of time. There seem to be no common factors in their development that explain their existence or histories. They may be stable for a time and receive little sediment, and then subside very rapidly and receive immense volumes of sediment. We still do not know why this occurs.

What factors produce the changes in climate that cause continental glaciers to originate, develop, and expand over large areas? What conditions cause the process to reverse—glaciers to shrink in size and finally disappear? In order for glaciers to form there must be enough precipitation to supply snow. Average annual temperatures must be low enough so that more snow accumulates during winter than melts during summer. Glaciers shrink when precipitation decreases, temperatures increase, or both. The factors that alter climatic conditions and cause these changes must affect the entire earth at the same time because glaciation has occurred simultaneously in both polar regions.

CHAPTER REVIEW

Summary

The North American continent has been in existence a long time, but there is no evidence to indicate whether or not it was a feature of the earth's crust at the time the planet was formed. The ages of the rocks that make up the continents suggest that the continents may have grown in stages. If so, they may have grown as new crustal material was added by mountain building at the margins. It is also possible that the continents broke away from a much larger continent and drifted to their present positions on the earth.

All rocks found on the continents, including the oldest, were formed by the same processes that are believed to be forming rocks at the present time: sedimentation, volcanism, intrusion, and metamorphism. Characteristics of rocks and fossils give information about the processes and environments of rock formation.

Perhaps during the Precambrian eras, and certainly in later eras, seas alternately advanced and retreated over the interior of the continents. In these seas and on the land that lay outside their shores, animals lived and died and sediments were deposited in relatively quiet environments.

On the other hand, materials erupted from volcanoes and thick sequences of rocks indicate that geosynclines were mobile belts that remained unstable for long periods of time. In North America the eastern geosyncline ceased to exist during mountain-building processes of the Paleozoic and early Mesozoic Eras. Similar events destroyed the western geosyncline during the Mesozoic and early Cenozoic Eras.

North America did not assume its present outlines and extent until late in the Cenozoic. Earthquakes, volcanic activity, and movement along active faults, especially along the Pacific Coast, provide evidence that its formation has not ended. Not enough is known about earth processes to allow prediction of future developments.

The most recent major events in the development of North America were the advances of immense glaciers over its surface. These advances have profoundly affected man's activities. Most of North America is now free of ice. However, the presence of extensive continental ice sheets on Greenland and Antarctica leaves open the question of whether North America will be covered again in the near geologic future or whether the ice has retreated and will not return until another "Great Ice Age."

Questions and Problems

A

1. What types of rocks are generally associated with plains and plateaus? with mountain ranges?

2. Why is the trilobite *Olenellus* so useful for rock correlation?

3. What principles are used to interpret the order and environments in which rocks have formed?

4. In what ways are glacial deposits different from ordinary water-deposited sediments?

5. What evidence indicates that the Pleistocene ice sheets made several advances rather than only one?

6. What features of glaciation can be used to interpret the direction in which the ice moved?

7. The Great Lakes and Hudson Bay occupy large depressions. How were these depressions formed?

B

1. Describe the arrangement of mountains and lowlands in North America. Why are they arranged in this way?

2. What evidence indicates that the Canadian Shield has been relatively stable since early Paleozoic times?

3. Igneous and metamorphic rocks commonly are exposed in mountain ranges. How do you explain the presence of

these rocks at the surface over most of the Canadian Shield?

4. Why is the rock record of the geologic history of a continent less complete for earlier than for later eras?

5. What might the earliest living things have been like? Why have no fossil traces of them been found?

6. Why are some fossils useful for correlating sedimentary rocks but not for explaining the environments in which the rocks formed? Why are other kinds of fossils useful for explaining the environments in which rocks formed, but not for correlation?

7. There have been several explanations suggested to account for the migration of animals and plants from continent to continent. List some of them and explain what kinds of evidence are needed to support each.

8. Describe some of the evidence that indicates the presence of extensive glaciation in the Northern Hemisphere during the Pleistocene Epoch.

9. Parts of the North American continent are still reacting to the presence of the tremendous weight of the Pleistocene ice. What are these reactions and where are they evident?

C

1. If the oldest known rock originally was sedimentary, does this mean that the first rock-forming process that affected the earth was sedimentation? Why?

2. What does the presence of fossil coral reefs in arctic regions *probably* indicate about the ancient climate of those regions? What other possible explanation could there be?

3. How will studies of the ocean floor help to explain the origin of continents?

4. There are indications that climates in the Northern Hemisphere are gradually becoming warmer. What effects could this have on the remaining glaciers and sea level? How might this be related to the Pleistocene ice age?

Suggested Readings

BOOKS

Clark, Thomas H. and Colin W. Stearn. *The Geological Evolution of North America.* The Ronald Press Company, New York, 1960.

Dyson, James L. *The World of Ice.* Alfred A. Knopf, Inc., New York, 1962.

Fenton, Carroll L. *Our Amazing Earth.* Doubleday & Company, Inc., Garden City, N.Y., 1938.

Gamow, George. *A Planet Called Earth.* The Viking Press, Inc., New York, 1963. Chapter 5.

Milne, Lorus J., Margery Milne, and the Editors of *Life. The Mountains.* Time, Inc. (Life Nature Library), New York, 1962.

Moore, Ruth and the Editors of *Life. Evolution.* Time, Inc. (Life Nature Library), New York, 1962.

Powell, J. W. *Down the Colorado!* Princeton University Press (Science Reading Series), Princeton, N.J., 1964.

Sanderson, Ivan T. *The Continent We Live On.* Random House, Inc., New York, 1961.

Shelton, John S. *Geology Illustrated.* W. H. Freeman & Co., Publishers, San Francisco, 1966.

PERIODICALS

Glaessner, Martin F. "Precambrian Animals." *Scientific American,* March, 1961. (Also Scientific American Offprint #837, W. H. Freeman & Co., Publishers, San Francisco.)

Harland, W. B. and M. J. S. Rudwick. "Great Infra-Cambrian Ice Age." *Scientific American,* August, 1964.

Schaeffer, B. and M. Mangus. "Fossil Lakes from the Eocene: Green River Formation." *Natural History,* April, 1965.

PAMPHLET

Page, Lou W. *The Earth and Its Story.* American Education Publications, Education Center, Columbus, Ohio, 1961.

Figure 20–17

GEOLOGIC MAP OF NORTH AMERICA

Legend:

- CENOZOIC
- CENOZOIC LAVA
- MESOZOIC-CENOZOIC INTRUSIVES
- MESOZOIC
- UPPER PALEOZOIC IN INTERIOR
- PALEOZOIC
- PALEOZOIC INTRUSIVES
- PRECAMBRIAN

APPROX. SCALE

0 — 500 MILES

0 — 500 KILOMETERS

Azimuthal Equal Area Projection

© Lilli Tanzer, 1967

452

NORTH AMERICA
WITH RELIEF IN OBLIQUE PERSPECTIVE

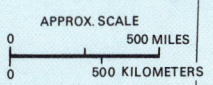

ARCTIC OCEAN

U.S.S.R.

GREENLAND

ICELAND

CHUKCHI SEA

Bering Strait

ST. LAWRENCE I.

Barrow

BEAUFORT SEA

QUEEN ELIZABETH ISLANDS

ELLESMERE I.

BANKS I.

PARRY ISLANDS

VICTORIA ISLAND

BAFFIN BAY

BAFFIN ISLAND

Davis Strait

ARCTIC CIRCLE

SURTSEY

ALASKA (U.S.)

Yukon R.

Anchorage

KENAI PENIN.

Gulf of Alaska

KODIAK I.

ALEXANDER ARCHIPELAGO

QUEEN CHARLOTTE IS.

Tanana R.

YUKON TERR.

BRITISH COLUMBIA

ROCKY MTS.

Great Bear L.

Mackenzie R.

NORTHWEST TERRITORIES

Back R.

Great Slave L.

HUDSON STRAIT

Leaf R.

NEWFOUNDLAND

Peace R.

MANITOBA

HUDSON BAY

LABRADOR

Churchill R.

Nelson R.

Thompson R.

CANADA

ALBERTA

SASKATCHEWAN

Saskatchewan R.

L. Winnipeg

ONTARIO

Albany R.

QUEBEC

Gulf of St. Lawrence

NEWFOUNDLAND

VANCOUVER I.

Fraser R.

Columbia R.

WASHINGTON

MT. HOOD

COLUMBIA PLATEAU

OREGON

CRATER LAKE

MT. SHASTA

MONTANA

Yellowstone R.

Madison R.

Hebgen L.

YELLOWSTONE NAT'L PARK

IDAHO

Snake R.

Great Salt Lake

NORTH DAKOTA

SOUTH DAKOTA

BLACK HILLS

WYOMING

Missouri R.

MINNESOTA

WISCONSIN

L. Superior

Blind River

MICHIGAN

L. Michigan

L. Huron

Ottawa

Ottawa R.

L. Ontario

ST. LAWRENCE

ADIRONDACKS

VT.

N.H.

ME.

NEW BRUNSWICK

NOVA SCOTIA

CAPE COD

MASS.

R.I.

CONNECTICUT

San Francisco

Reno

NEVADA

SIERRA NEVADA

CALIFORNIA

Humboldt R.

Mead L.

Los Angeles

DEATH VALLEY

MOJAVE DESERT

Yuma

BAJA CALIFORNIA

UTAH

GRAND CANYON

DINOSAUR NAT'L MON.

COLORADO

Denver

Colorado R.

ARIZONA

Meteor Crater

PETRIFIED FOREST NAT'L PARK

NEW MEXICO

NEBRASKA

Platte R.

KANSAS

Arkansas R.

OKLAHOMA

St. Louis

MISSOURI

Mississippi R.

IOWA

ILLINOIS

Chicago

IND.

OHIO

Ohio R.

Cleveland

Erie

PENN.

W. VIRGINIA

VIRGINIA

Wash. D.C.

MARYLAND

DELAWARE

NEW JERSEY

Philadelphia

NEW YORK

New York

Niagara Falls

APPALACHIAN MTS.

UNITED STATES

TEXAS

Red R.

Pecos R.

Rio Grande

ARKANSAS

TENNESSEE

KENTUCKY

N. CAROLINA

S. CAROLINA

MISS.

ALABAMA

GEORGIA

Atlanta

Savannah

LOUISIANA

New Orleans

Houston

FLORIDA

CAPE KENNEDY

L. Okeechobee

MEXICO

Mexico City

PARICUTIN

TROPIC OF CANCER

GULF OF MEXICO

Florida Straits

BAHAMA IS.

GR. EXUMA

CUBA

JAMAICA

HAITI

DOMINICAN REPUBLIC

PUERTO RICO

CARIBBEAN SEA

BERMUDA

GUATEMALA

EL SALVADOR

BR. HOND.

HONDURAS

NICARAGUA

COSTA RICA

PANAMA

PANAMA CANAL

CENTRAL AMERICA

PACIFIC OCEAN

ATLANTIC OCEAN

SOUTH AMERICA

APPROX. SCALE

0   500 MILES

500 KILOMETERS

Azimuthal Equal Area Projection

© Lilli Tanzer, 1967

453

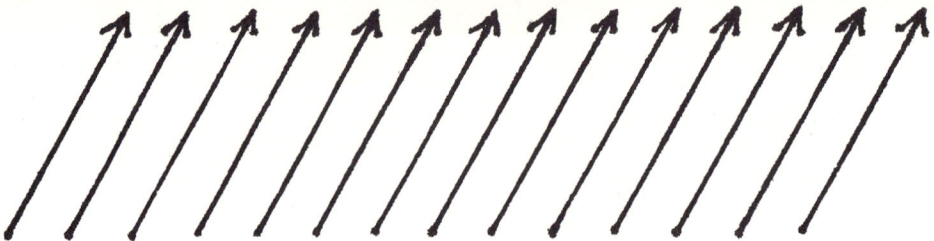

Chapter 21 Evolution of Landscapes

What makes landscapes? Which processes that you have studied have helped to shape the face of the land shown in this photograph? Can you identify the effects of weathering? of erosion by water, ice, or wind?

Landscapes are formed at the interface where the lithosphere meets the atmosphere. This interface is also where you live. What you see as you look out across the landscape is like a very short part of a very long motion picture. The movie began long before you arrived, and it will continue long after you leave. Yet from this brief glimpse of the story you can easily describe the plot of this landscape motion picture. It is the constant interplay between the rock cycle below and the water cycle above.

Through many investigations you have observed a variety of processes that result in earth changes. You have recorded evidence for changes in the atmosphere in the Weather Watch, and for changes below the earth's surface in the Earthquake Watch. You have duplicated the action of processes at the earth's surface in causing rocks to wear. In this chapter you will concentrate on the landscape and study the many interrelated processes of change that make the landscape look as it does.

If you make a list of all the things you can think of that might influence the shape of the land, you will find that it includes nearly everything you have learned about the properties of rocks and about the processes that affect them in and on the earth. If the shape of the land surface is determined both by what has happened beneath it and what has happened upon it, then by studying that shape you should be able to interpret past events and changes as well as to understand what is happening now. By making certain assumptions, you should even be able to make reasonable predictions about what will happen to the landscape in the future.

Major J. W. Powell, a one-armed civil war veteran, led the first expedition down the unexplored Colorado River in 1869. His study of these canyon lands led to new theories of landscape evolution.

Processes that Shape the Land

21–1 A first look at landscapes.

Look at the landscape in Figure 21–1. What is going on? Two kinds of landscapes appear in this scene. One, mostly in the background of the scene, is relatively rough and cut by several gullies and one major valley or canyon. In terms of earth processes this landscape is undergoing erosion. The second kind of landscape, mostly in the foreground of the photograph, is relatively smooth. Obviously it is the surface of sedimentary deposits that occupy the low places. It includes the deposits on the floor of the canyon and their extension in the shape of a fan beyond the canyon's mouth. The fan, in turn, seems to be spread over a broader area of sediment that appears to have come from outside the area. Apparently this second area is not undergoing erosion but is receiving sediment instead.

Place a piece of thin paper over Figure 21–1 and lightly draw a line around the borders of the picture. Now carefully trace a line across it that will separate the two kinds of landscape. On one side of the line the land is undergoing erosion. On the other side it is receiving sediment. Will this landscape change? Judging from the pole, how wide is the canyon?

In Figure 21–2 you see the effects of erosion and deposition that have been going on for thousands of years. A road runs along the edge of the fan. Notice the patch of light colored gravel that has been deposited on the steep fan at the mouth of the canyon. This is perhaps the only important addition of material to the fan in the last 100 years. It probably represents about 1/500 of the volume

Describe the processes that produced this landscape in these mountains, located east of Kirkuk, Iraq.

Figure 21–1 (Right) Can you distinguish two kinds of landscape in this photograph? Figure 21–2 (Far right) Are the same kinds of landscape visible in this view of the steep east wall of Death Valley, California? How long would you guess it took for each of these landscapes to form?

of the whole deposit. If it has taken a century to add this amount of material, how long has it taken to build the fan to its present size? How many factors can you think of that would affect the accuracy of your answer?

Again it is possible to draw a line separating areas of erosion from areas of deposition. Although the noticeable effects of processes are intermittent and very slow by human standards, it is clear that this landscape is also changing, like the one in Figure 21–1. How are the two landscapes different? Would it surprise you to learn that Figure 21–1 shows an area only about one meter square? The "pole" in the photograph is a pencil. This miniature landscape with its canyon and fan was sculptured in loose soil by a single rainstorm. Thus, the two scenes differ in that the second is 1000 times larger than the first and took much longer to form. Yet note that these two scenes have the same basic characteristics.

At any scale of observation you can divide a landscape into areas losing material and areas gaining material—or areas of erosion and areas of deposition. A good first step in analyzing any landscape is to distinguish between the areas of erosion and deposition.

ACTIVITY *In your environment identify locations that are giving up material and areas that are receiving it. Look at landscapes of all scales, ranging from only a few square centimeters to very large areas.*

21–2 Investigating areas of erosion and deposition.

In Section 12–7 you used a stream table to investigate the processes of stream action. In this investigation you will use similar materials in the stream table to investigate the miniature landscapes that are formed. Concentrate on the boundary line between erosion and deposition. What causes this line to change its position? Try to predict the kinds of changes that will occur in your miniature landscape as the stream flows through the materials in your stream table.

21–3 Investigating the leveling processes.

Areas of erosion can be recognized by their exposures of bedrock and such features as steep slopes, cliffs, and ridges. The areas of deposition are recognized by the presence of loose sediment that from time to time is either added to or shifted. Usually areas of deposition are found on low ground with gentle slopes, such as valley floors, floodplains, lake floors, and beaches.

Since the higher areas undergo erosion and the lower areas receive sediment, the overall result is a tendency for the landscape to become more nearly level. For this reason weathering, erosion, and deposition are sometimes grouped together as *leveling processes*. Although running water is the most widespread and the most important *leveling agent*, you often notice the effects of other agents such as ice, wave action, ground water, wind, or gravity alone.

Procedure

(1)Examine Figure 21–3A through F. Study each one and decide which process, erosion or deposition, has been more important in shaping each landscape.

(2)Determine which leveling agent was most responsible for the features you see.

(3)List all the evidence you can see in each of the photographs that supports your conclusions. Can you find any evidence that seems to suggest other conclusions?

Figure 21–3 *Can you determine the principal agent responsible for sculpturing each of these landscapes?*

Figure 21–4 *(Right)* *Three stages in the development of a cloud.*

Figure 21–5 *(Below)* *The development of a landscape. What is the proper order of this sequence?*

21–4 Interpreting landscape development.

When you try to read the life story of a landscape from the features around you, one factor soon becomes obvious. This factor is *time*. Landscapes do not change rapidly enough for anyone to have seen the entire history of change from beginning to end. Compare the rates of change shown in figures 21–4 and 21–5. Change in a cloud is much more apparent to you than change in a mountainside. Changes can take place in the atmosphere in minutes or hours. It may take years or centuries to detect even minor landscape changes.

Since landscapes are the places where the hydrosphere, atmosphere, and lithosphere come together, the landscapes that you see are expressions of the way the three spheres interact. Because landscapes do not change rapidly enough for you to watch them, other methods must be found to interpret them. One method is to examine miniature landscapes in the field or in a stream table. You can assume that many of the same processes operate in a miniature landscape as in a major one. The rates of change, however, are increased in a miniature landscape.

Another method is to look at landscapes in different areas that have formed under similar conditions and predict how a particular structure will wear away and change. Look at the landscapes shown in Figure 21–5. If you assume that the rocks and the climates are similar in each case, which area has been subjected to weathering and erosion for the longest period of time?

Look at Figure 21–6 and try to determine the history of Santa Elena Canyon. The most prominent feature in this landscape is the canyon cut by the stream across the limestone block that slopes gently away from you. In how many ways can you account for the stream cutting across this limestone barrier? If crustal movement does not lift the land higher, what can you predict about the future of the landscape?

It is likely that the steep sides of the canyon will gradually weather and collapse, as will the cliff on the front of the block. Already small streams have begun to cut gullies into the sloping top of the block. (See Figure 21–6.)

Figure 21–6 (Above, left) Santa Elena Canyon.
Figure 21–7 (Above) Niagara Gorge below the Falls. In each of these two scenes, a canyon is cut in gently tilted limestone strata.

Compare the view of Santa Elena Canyon with the scene shown in Figure 21–7. This is a view of the gorge of the Niagara River near Niagara Falls, New York. In what way is this scene similar to the one shown in Figure 21–6? In what way is it different? What factors influence one landscape but do not seem to affect the other?

The Niagara River flows from Lake Erie into Lake Ontario. Almost every year a meter or so of rock breaks away at the falls, causing the falls to migrate upstream a little. (See Figure 21–7). When the falls reach Lake Erie, the lake's outlet will be lowered and as the lake is drained, more and more land around its shores will be exposed to erosion. If conditions remain unchanged, the floor of the lake will someday become a wide valley crossed by a stream carrying sediment to the sea.

In some places the relationship between uplift and downcutting can be worked out in even greater detail. An example is provided by Figure 21–8. You are looking northward across a low ridge. The ridge is part of an east-west trending anticline that descends gently to the east (right). The drainage in the foreground slopes away from you, and most of the channels join to flow through the lower notch in the ridge. The larger notch to the west is now merely a pass. Both of these notches have been cut by

streams flowing away from you. Why has the stream ceased to flow through the larger notch?

The two notches divide the ridge into three parts. Notice that the western part at the left is deeply cut by canyons, whereas the central part has only a few gullies on its slopes. The upper surface is smooth and almost as high as its neighbor to the west. The low eastern part at the far right has no gullies at all. The

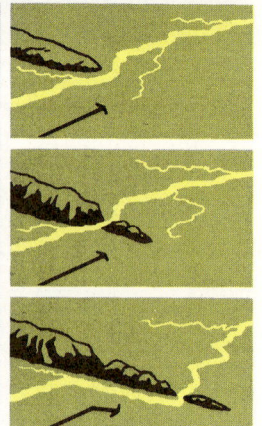

Figure 21–8 (Above) Wheeler Ridge at the south end of San Joaquin Valley, California. (Right) Trace the stages of development of this growing ridge.

Figure 21–9 *The Canadian Rockies, a region of high elevation, very steep slopes, and great differences in potential energy of the land surface.*

Figure 21–10 *Salt marshes along the New Hampshire coast. The land is low with only small differences in the potential energy of the landscape.*

most likely explanation for these contrasting conditions is that the western part of the ridge was uplifted first and has been undergoing erosion the longest, while the parts toward the east are progressively younger. This suggests that the ridge has been extended eastward as it was being uplifted. These events have occurred during the past one or two million years. Someday, if the ridge continues to rise, all the drainage may be diverted eastward once again. A new channel still farther to the right may then become the only place where streams can cross the ridge.

Part of the early history of an area is recorded *within* the rocks. From the rock types, fossils, and amount of deformation you can learn much about what happened to the rocks within the crust before they reached the surface. Once the rocks become part of the landscape, most or all of the remaining history of the area is recorded in the changing shape of the land. Landscapes bear the mark of recent earth movements, changing climates, and the tendency of the leveling processes to subdue a restless crust. The interplay among these factors, which is recorded in the landscape, brings the story up to the present time.

21–5 How low can a landscape get?

You can think of a landscape as being a potential energy surface. Places where the landscape is high are areas of high potential energy. Low landscapes have low potential energy.

Forces within the earth produce different elevations of the land and thus create a potential energy surface on which the leveling agents work. Each high elevation or steep slope is a place where potential energy is stored. (See Figure 21–9.) Water, snow, and ice resting on the mountains also have high potential energy. Whereas the mountain gained its position of high potential energy from forces inside the earth, the leveling agents on the mountain gain potential energy from the sun, through the action of the water cycle. As the leveling agents carry material downward and deposit it in low places, they reduce the potential energy of the landscape. (See Figure 21–10.) Mountain-building processes thus tend to increase the potential energy of an area, whereas the leveling processes tend to reduce it.

You can see that the leveling processes would eventually reduce all irregularities in the land surface and produce a smooth landscape at the lowest possible elevation—one on which no particle

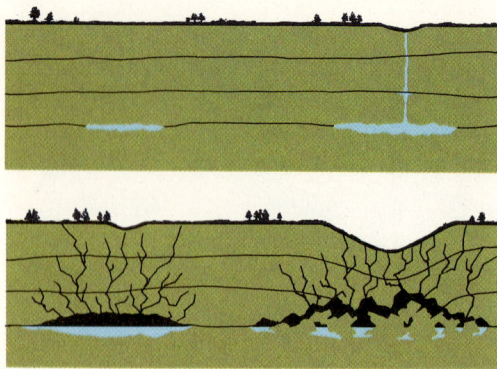

Sinkholes make an unusual landscape on some areas underlain by limestone. What processes cause sinkholes to form?

could fall or roll anywhere. On such a surface there would be no differences in potential energy. Is there such an area on the earth? Under what conditions could such a surface exist?

If the leveling processes were the only ones in operation, they would eventually remove all the high land on earth. As long as a landscape remains above sea level, streams and rivers flowing to the sea can move parts of the landscape to lower elevations and eventually into the ocean basins. Unless sea level itself changes greatly, the sediment can only become a part of the continents again through uplift of the ocean floor as part of the rock cycle.

The lowest level to which a landscape can be cut is usually considered to be sea level. Leveling processes, however, do not stop at sea level. You saw in Chapter 13 that the ocean floor has a strange and varied landscape. The sea bottom scenery is in many ways more dramatic than that on land. Just as landscapes on land occur at an interface, so do those of the ocean bottom. In this case, however, the overlying fluid is the hydrosphere. What difference does this make in the work of leveling agents? Materials still move from high to low potential energy regions. On the land the dominant level-

ing agent is running water. Wind and ice are also important in many places. Which of these agents do you think are at work in sculpturing the bottom of the ocean?

Near the shore on the continental shelf wave action predominates. Glaciers entering the sea can also gouge valleys below sea level. But since ice floats, can this gouging continue very far from the land? What about wind? Along most of the ocean bottom the only important leveling agent affecting the undersea landscapes is gravity acting on materials of different densities. However, you can separate areas of erosion and deposition beneath the sea just as you can on land. From what you know about the undersea landscapes, can you answer the question, "Where is the potential energy on the earth's surface the lowest?"

As for the low areas above the sea, if the center of a continent were reduced to only a few hundred feet above sea level, rivers flowing through the area would have such low gradients and be so sluggish that most of the weathered material could be removed only in solution. The process would be very slow. At low elevations the leveling processes produce extensive areas of nearly level land, because downcutting is limited and sidecutting predominates. The result is wide, shallow valleys. At higher elevations the leveling agents produce deep, narrow valleys.

Have the leveling processes ever washed a whole continent into the ocean? No continent today is so eroded that its entire surface is nearly at sea level. However, there are many places where large areas have been almost leveled by surface processes. From Washington, D.C., to Atlanta, Georgia, the broad lowland east of the Appalachian Mountains is composed of igneous

Figure 21–11 *Rocks formed beneath the surface were lifted into lofty mountains and later eroded to this low plain in South Carolina.*

and metamorphic rocks. (See Figure 21–11.) The existence of such rocks at the earth's surface is proof that this area has been uplifted many thousands of meters. The fact that the thick cover under which these rocks formed has been removed is proof that erosion can effectively level the land.

Much of the surface of the Canadian Shield is also low and flat and composed of igneous and metamorphic rocks. (See Figure 20–5.) However, patches of nearly horizontal early Paleozoic rocks lie on it here and there. This proves

that these parts have been low and level for about 500 million years.

Do you suppose that similar plains have been formed in the past and have since been covered up? One answer can be found in the Grand Canyon. On its walls you can follow the edge of an extensive unconformity for more than 300 kilometers. (See Figure 21–12.) For most of this distance the trace of the unconformity is almost horizontal. In places this surface cuts across metamorphic and igneous rocks. This means there must have been a great thickness of rocks removed before the sediments of the overlying rocks were deposited. Since rocks above the unconformity are of Cambrian age, the erosion must have occurred at least 600 million years ago, before the Cambrian period.

These examples show that more than once, over a long span of time, the leveling processes have reduced large areas of the land to low-lying plains.

Figure 21–12 *An unconformity in the north wall of the Grand Canyon. Drawings (A), (B), and (C), suggest stages of development. Relate the landscape in the photograph to the drawings.*

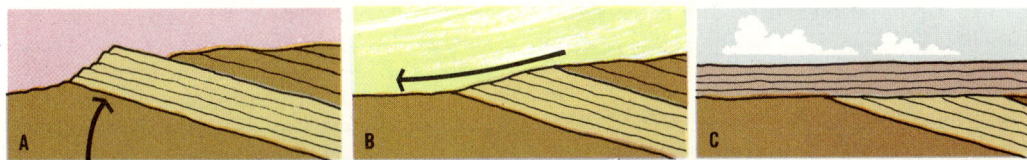

Thought and Discussion . . .

1. What differences between Niagara Gorge and Santa Elena Canyon are solely the result of climate? Do you think the climates were different while the canyons were being cut or became so only recently? Why?

2. The limestone into which the Niagara Gorge is cut is Silurian, and is over 400 million years old. The limestone into which Santa Elena Canyon is cut is Cretaceous, or about 100 million years old. Do these facts reveal anything about the ages of the two canyons?

3. Look again at the three segments of the ridge in Figure 21–8. Consider an alternative to the explanation given in the Text. Suppose that uplift of all parts of the ridge began at the same time but that the uplift was more rapid toward the west (left) end. Would this account equally well for the present landscape? If not, how might the two different histories be revealed in the resulting landscapes?

Landscapes in Perspective

21–6 Internal and external processes are in conflict.

The landscape is obviously a place of conflict between the rock cycle and the water cycle at the interface of the lithosphere, hydrosphere, and atmosphere. Basically, three factors determine the shape of the land. The first factor is the kind of rock at the earth's surface and its degree of resistance to weathering and erosion. It makes a difference, for example, whether the rock of the landscape is uniform like granite or layered with different sedimentary rocks such as in the walls of the Grand Canyon.

The second factor is a group of dynamic processes operating *within* the crust. These include movements that produce uplift, subsidence, tilting, bending, and breaking, as well as volcanic eruptions. As we have seen, they tend to *unlevel* the land.

The third factor is a group of external dynamic processes operating *upon* the crust. These tend to level the land through all the natural changes brought about by weathering, downslope movements such as creep and sliding, and the effects of running water, ice, waves, and wind. These processes are powered by gravity and energy from the sun.

Figure 21–13 (*Left*) *The east wall of Death Valley, California, shows very recent uplift.*

Figure 21–14 (*Right*) *New England mountains elevated by the Paleozoic upheavals that produced the Appalachians. Contrast this scene with the fresh appearance of Figure 21–13. (See Table 19–1.)*

Every landscape may be thought of as a kind of battleground between the internal and external processes. Whenever the internal forces of the rock cycle elevate the land, the influence of the water cycle increases. If uplift is more rapid than erosion, the elevation of the land surface will increase. If the rate of erosion exceeds uplift or if uplift is not occurring, the elevation of the land surface will decrease. Because these processes vary from time to time and place to place, there is a great variety of landscapes in the world. In spite of this variety, however, landscapes can be divided into three main groups: mountains, plains, and plateaus.

Under what conditions of the battle can *mountains* exist? The lofty peaks of the Sierra Nevada or the Andes are evidence that at this moment in history the internal processes in these areas are far ahead of the external ones. These areas have been lifted faster than erosion could cut them down. Faulting, earthquake activity, and volcanism suggest that forces beneath the earth's surface are still active in these places. Particularly spectacular examples of this occur in places where uplift is so recent that erosion has cut only small valleys in the uplifted rocks as in Figure 21–13. The Appalachian Mountains, by contrast, appear to be the remains of a once large mountain range uplifted long before the Rockies and Sierra Nevada. Your Earthquake Watch showed that there is relatively little crustal disturbance there now. (See Figure 21–14.)

Recall from your study of the stable regions in Section 14–9 that extensive *plains* coincide roughly with zones of little crustal movement. What can you conclude then about the conditions that allow plains to exist? You can probably think of two possibilities. One is that a plains region has never been elevated far enough above sea level for streams to have cut deeply into its surface. You are familiar with another possibility from your study of the Canadian Shield. The internal forces have been quiet for so long that a once-mountainous region has been reduced to a low plain by the external processes.

A *plateau* is an elevated plain. It is similar to a mountain in that the rock cycle is ahead of the water cycle. A plateau is different from mountains since it is the result of broad, gentle uplift over a wide area with little folding and faulting. Often it is cut by deep canyons.

How fast do crustal movements take place? Fixed points on the land have been accurately measured many times over the years. Near Cajon Pass in California such measurements, begun in 1906, show that the land is being uplifted by nearly one centimeter per year. The so-called Temple of Jupiter Serapis, Naples, Italy, shows evidence of both subsidence and uplift since Roman times. The average movement here has also been about one centimeter per year. (See Figure 21–15.) The anticline in Figure 21–16 has been rising at a slower rate. Can you compute the rate from

Figure 21–15 *What evidence can you see in the remains of the Temple of Jupiter Serapis that the relative level of the land and sea has changed?*

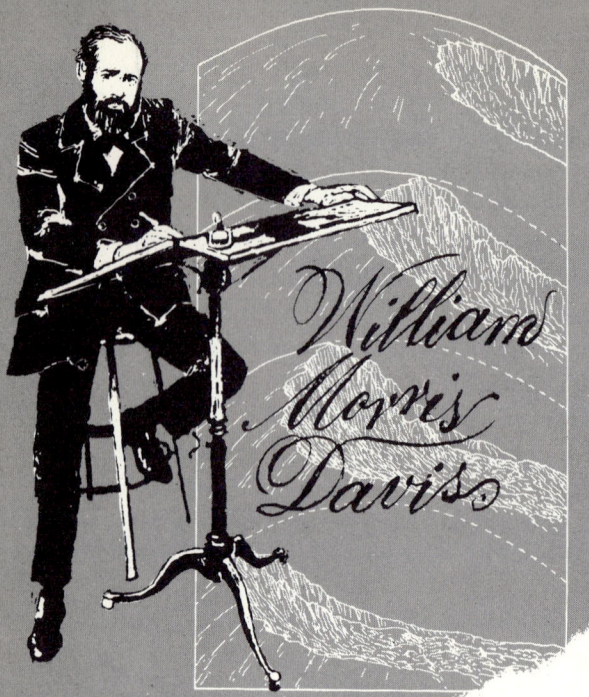

William Morris Davis

The famous American geographer and geologist, William Morris Davis, was a pioneer in the study of land-form development, the science of geomorphology. Born in Philadelphia in 1850, Davis became professor of physical geography and geology at Harvard. In 1912, he retired to travel, lecture, and do research.

The idea of the evolution of land forms was developed from studies of the arid American Southwest by a Civil War veteran, Major J. W. Powell. Inspired by the work of Powell and the geologist G. K. Gilbert (see Chapter 22), Davis extended the idea to land forms in humid regions.

Perhaps Davis' greatest contribution was the notion that the complex land-shaping processes can be broken down into three main factors: (1) the kind of rocks at the surface, (2) the kinds of processes acting on them, and (3) the length of time the processes have been acting on the rocks. Davis elaborated on the stages of development by proposing that after uplift the landscape went through distinct stages of youth, maturity, and old age finally becoming a low, eroded plain.

Although his ideas on stages of development have been challenged, most of his work is still very useful. Davis was a master at presenting his interpretation of landscapes in clear description and fine sketches. His Geographical Essays were published in 1909.

the information given in the caption? By comparison with volcanic activity these rates are all slow. A single volcanic outpouring may add a thickness of several meters. These examples demonstrate how fast the crust *can* move or be built up. At the other extreme is the Canadian Shield, most of which has probably moved very little in the last 500 million years.

How do rates of erosion compare with rates of uplift? In Chapter 12 you learned that rivers carry great quantities of sediment to the sea. The loss of the volume of sediment would lower the United States on the average about six centimeters in a thousand years. The average elevation of the United States is about 700 meters. You might conclude that if the average lowering is 0.00006 meter per year, the United States would be eroded to a very low plain near sea level in about 12 million years. Why will this probably not happen?

You have been considering the gross features of the landscape resulting from uplift and leveling. Other factors affect the detail of the land and help determine its appearance. Climate, for example, affects the rate of weathering; it also influences the kind and amount of vegetation. If you look at a landscape closely, you will realize the importance of vegetation in affecting the rate of erosion. Where vegetation is thick, erosion is slowed. Where vegetation is sparse, erosion is more rapid. Infrequent rains in arid regions support little vegetation so that a heavy rain can wash away large quantities of sediment. Thus arid landscapes are angular, as shown in figures 21–5 and 21–6. Under a protective cover of vegetation, landscapes tend to be somewhat rounded because runoff is less violent and soils are thicker. (See figures 21–11 and 21–14.)

Figure 21–16 (*Top*) *The youngest rocks at Kettleman Hills, California, involved in the upfolding shown (bottom) are 1 to 3 million years old. If the rocks have been arched about 3000 meters, what has been the average rate of uplift?*

21–7 Investigating regional landscapes.

If the landscape is the result of internal and external processes working on rock materials at the surface, then you should be able to examine a landscape and say something about (1) the nature of the surface rocks, (2) the effect of the internal forces, and (3) the kinds of external processes or agents at work there. You may also be able to say which processes, internal or external, dominate the landscape at present.

In this investigation you will study several different areas in the United States. The areas represent typical mountains, plains, and plateaus. You will examine each landscape by means of aerial photographs and topographic maps (Figure 21–17). Describe the landscape in each area and interpret the processes that created the features you observe.

Procedure

(1)Using the map provided showing the principal land forms of the United States, divide the country into areas of similar landscapes. Compare your landscape classification with those of other students and discuss the basis for your divisions.

With the help of the photographs and maps, answer the following questions about each area:

(2)Is the area a plain, a plateau, or a mountain?

(3)What evidence can you find for rock cycle activity?

(4)What leveling agent is dominant?

(5)Which processes, uplift or leveling, have been most active in forming the landscape you see?

(6)How has the landscape influenced man's activities?

(7)Mark on the landform map where you think this area might be. After you have finished all the areas, see if you still find acceptable the landscape boundaries you drew earlier.

Figure 21–17

Figure 21–18 *(Far left) Lake-filled depression caused by melting of an ice block on an outwash plain. (Left, top) Crater of Zuni Salt Lake south of Gallup, New Mexico. (Left, below) A solution pit or sinkhole near Roswell, New Mexico.*

21–8 Craters—an unusual landform.

Are all landscapes on earth formed by mountain-building and leveling processes? What formed the landscapes shown in Figure 21–18? A number of depressions have been found that probably were not formed by earth processes. Many scientists believe they were developed by extraterrestrial forces.

Over 20 impact craters have been found on the land surface of the earth. They present a slight variation on the theme of this chapter. Although subject to modification by all the normal leveling processes, these landforms do not owe any part of their shape or origin directly to internal movements of the crust. Those that occur in moist climates usually contain lakes. Are the features in Figure 21–19 of impact origin? Some craters look recent, like the one pictured in Figure 21–20. Others have been so modified by weathering and erosion that proof of their origin rests entirely on clues within the shattered rock.

Interest in the geology of the moon has led to intensive study of impact craters on the earth. In the depression of Meteor Crater in Arizona, exploratory drilling has failed to reveal any huge chunk of a meteorite beneath its floor. It is estimated from sampling the surrounding area that thousands of tons of very small meteoritic particles are mixed with the soil. Furthermore, all of the sandstone exposed in the rim of the crater is greatly shattered and some of it has even been fused to glass.

Some of the quartz in the sandstone has also been converted to rare high-density forms of silica. From the results of laboratory experiments, we know that these forms of silica can be produced only by conditions that occur naturally at well over 100 kilometers below the earth's surface. Since these forms of silica occur in this sandstone only at the crater, a logical conclusion is that the necessary heat and pressure were supplied by the impact of a meteorite.

Figure 21–19 *Scientists are still debating the origin of these oval depressions in North Carolina. How might they have been formed?*

Figure 21–20 *(Above) The cup of Meteor Crater west of Winslow, Arizona. How was this landscape feature formed?*

Figure 21–21 *(Right) Dome, Sundance, Wyoming.*

Calculations of the energy required to produce Meteor Crater, nearly 180 meters deep and almost 1.6 kilometers in diameter, indicate that it could have been caused by a meteorite about 25 meters in diameter traveling 50,000 kilometers per hour. If it had traveled faster, as many meteors do, it might have been smaller. In any case it was evidently largely destroyed by the impact, which tossed out the lumpy deposit of light-colored rock debris visible in this view of the crater. Can you think of ways to distinguish impact craters from depressions formed in other ways?

As you turn away from the earth and look toward our neighbors in space, you must bear in mind that although most landscapes represent the surface expression of the conflict between mountain-building and leveling processes operating within and upon the crust, there are a few land shapes that owe their origin partly to extraterrestrial agents.

Thought and Discussion . . .

1. Explain the origin of the feature in Figure 21–21 in terms of the rock and water cycles.
2. On a sheet of paper draw a vertical cross section representing a slice through the middle of the dome (Figure 21–21) from left to right.
3. Explain the landscapes shown below in terms of the rock and water cycles. Bring in as many processes as you can from this and previous chapters that will help to explain the landscapes.

Unsolved Problems Since landscapes are the product of many interacting processes, they present many unsolved problems. The things we do not know about the causes of deformation in the crust, especially the patterns that deformation produces and the timing of the movements, complicate the study of landscapes, for these processes influence the shapes we see. Similarly, the causes and timing of ice ages and other climatic changes and the origin and history of the ocean basins are also problems in the study of landscapes.

One of the major difficulties in trying to understand landscapes is the way the many factors influencing their development interact. Various specialists have examined certain aspects of the landscape with great care. The geologist has acquired considerable knowledge of how rocks weather, erode, and move to lower elevations. The soil scientist has studied soil formation, and the biologist has learned much about soil and plant relationships. They have really only begun to study the complex ways in which all these and other elements interact.

All of the processes interacting at the land-air-water interface need to be studied together, both where man has been acting as an agent and where he has not. Only through the examination of the combined influence of rock type and structure, soil formation, moisture, insolation, plant growth, and even animal activity can many of the details of landscape development be understood.

CHAPTER REVIEW

Summary

Two fundamental groups of external processes continually shape the land surfaces of the earth. One is the weathering and erosion of solid rock, the other is transportation and deposition of sediment. Both are closely related to the water cycle and both are strongly influenced by gravity. Together these processes tend to move rock material from high to low places and make the land more nearly level. For this reason they are called the leveling processes.

The exact shape of the land at any particular place and time is not determined by the leveling or external processes alone. The shape of the land also depends on the kinds of rocks exposed at its surface, how the resistant rocks are arranged, and how recently and in what way they have been elevated by internal processes. Thus the shape of the land is also dependent upon that part of the rock cycle that takes place deep within the earth's crust.

To best interpret the shape of the land you must recognize what is going on now, and then work back through time looking for evidence of different conditions in the past. Was this land surface once under ice, under the sea, or under sand dunes? If so, did this occur before, during, or after the latest uplift, tilting, or faulting? In this way you can often reconstruct a step-by-step sequence of events growing out of the interplay between internal and external processes.

Impact craters are a special kind of landscape. While not created by normal rock cycle processes, they are destroyed by weathering, erosion, and deposition.

Questions and Problems

A

1. How can areas of erosion be recognized? Describe such an area.
2. How can areas of deposition be recognized? Describe such an area.

3. What are the leveling processes? Why are they called this?
4. What limits the lowest elevation to which the leveling processes could possibly erode the land?
5. How may energy from within the earth increase the potential energy of rocks on the surface?
6. What evidence indicates that much of the Canadian Shield has been low and level for hundreds of millions of years?
7. What do unconformities indicate?

B

1. Describe the leveling processes from the point of view of energy relationships.
2. Is it likely that the leveling processes will ever lower all the land to sea level? Explain.
3. Once sediments are dumped into the ocean, can they ever again be exposed to the leveling processes? If so, how? If not, why?
4. What does a region look like in which internal forces dominate external forces? Give an example of such a region.
5. What does a region look like in which external forces dominate internal forces? Give an example of such a region.
6. If the processes of weathering and erosion have been acting on the earth's surface for billions of years, why isn't the surface flat and level today?
7. What evidence indicates that Meteor Crater in Arizona was actually created by a meteorite?

C

1. Describe the probable fate of Lake Erie. What could prevent this from taking place?
2. What leveling agent or agents work on the sea bottom? Explain the role of gravity and density there.
3. How does the kind of rock in a region help to determine the landscape to be found in that region?
4. How do processes within the crust help to determine the landscape of a region?

5. How do processes operating upon the crust help to determine the landscape of a region?
6. Can you think of conditions under which a region would be stable in terms of physical weathering?
7. Why might a region become stable in terms of physical weathering long before it becomes stable with respect to chemical weathering?
8. In a region of marine terraces, how is it possible to tell whether the terraces were formed by uplift of the land or by a lowering of sea level?

Suggested Readings

BOOKS
Dury, George H. *The Face of the Earth.* Penguin Books, Inc. (Pelican Book), Baltimore, Md., 1959. Paperback.

Dyson, James L. *The World of Ice.* Alfred A. Knopf, Inc., New York, 1962.

Folsom, Franklin. *Exploring American Caves.* Collier Books, New York, 1962. Paperback. Chapter 1.

Lobeck, Armin K. *Things Maps Don't Tell Us.* The Macmillan Company, New York, 1956.

Milne, Lorus J., Margery Milne, and the Editors of *Life. The Mountains.* Time, Inc. (Life Nature Library), New York, 1962.

Shelton, John S. *Geology Illustrated.* W. H. Freeman & Co., Publishers, San Francisco, 1966.

Shimer, John A. *This Sculptured Earth: The Landscape of America.* Columbia University Press, New York, 1959.

PERIODICAL
Dietz, Robert S. "Astroblemes." *Scientific American*, August, 1961. (Also Scientific American Offprint #801, W. H. Freeman & Co., Publishers, San Francisco.)

PAMPHLET
Page, Lou W. *The Earth and Its Story.* American Education Publications, Education Center, Columbus, Ohio, 1961.

UNIT IV *Earth's Environment in Space*

American Indians always respected the bear for his strength, courage, and intelligence. His strength and mental prowess made the bear a hunter equaled only by man himself. The bear feared no man or animal and was considered a powerful spirit by the Indians. Bears often raided Indian camps, taking food and sometimes killing people. Legends of these deeds naturally grew with each telling.

One legend pits a mysterious, game-stealing bear against three Iroquois brothers who had dreamed of finding and killing the giant beast. They followed the bear relentlessly through ice, snow, wind, and darkness, but each time they drew close enough to use their bows, the bear vanished without a trace. They did not stop, night or day. The braves chased the bear to the northern edge of the world where he led them into the sky. They climbed the icy paths upward into the cold sky of the north. They watched the bear moving ahead of them as he charged through the clouds and mist. Unknown to the braves the crafty bear was weaving an invisible net while he moved along. Becoming weary, the bear took refuge in a cave to rest. When the Indians saw this they thought that at last they had him. They planned to capture the bear while he slept. However, the bear heard them and burst out of the cave with the net in his paws. Hurling the net,

he gathered in the three hunters and their little dog, Jiyeh. With a mighty sweep the bear flung them high into the northern sky. Even today they are seen there following the great bear of the north who skillfully continues to elude them.

The Iroquois see the bear as the four stars we see in the bowl of the Big Dipper and the three stars in the handle represent the fearless Iroquois hunters. Only those who truly believe the legend can see the little dog as he follows the braves through the sky. Even the mouth of the cave where the bear rested is visible in the area of Corona Borealis. Perhaps if you study the northern sky you too can identify the bear and the Iroquois hunters pursuing him.

This myth of the bear and the hunters exists with some variations in the folklore of nearly all of the North American tribes including the Eskimos of Alaska, the Pueblos of Arizona, and the Yakimas of the Pacific Coast. The same myth of bear and hunters is found on the other side of the North American continent, in the legends of the Micmacs of Nova Scotia.

Modern stories to explain matter, space, and time seem to have all the excitement of a living legend. Space probes and ambitious research programs are adding new dimensions to man's understanding of the universe. Many scientists are at work all around the world. Our knowledge of the earth and its environment in space is increasing at a remarkable rate. Still, there is much that is unknown to us. Each of us in his own way bridges the unknown in his own mind. Our explanations may even be considered "myths" in a sense. Continued investigation brings new understanding, and new understanding takes us farther into the unknown.

Chapter 22

The Moon: A Natural Satellite

To an astronomer on Mars looking at the part of the solar system between himself and the sun, one of the most interesting features would be its only double planet—a very bright, bluish-white globe with a smaller white companion a short distance away. This double planet system is, of course, our earth and its moon. Let's look through the Martian astronomer's eyes and see how he would compare these two bodies.

Seen from space, the earth is a sparkling globe of blue, white, brown, and yellow, wreathed in spiral cloud patterns and largely covered with blue water. The continental areas, as you have seen, are in many places wrinkled by mountains, dissected by rivers, and studded with volcanoes. If our Martian astronomer watches the earth for a few days, he will be impressed by the ever-changing cloud patterns, the blinding reflection of the sun shimmering on the oceans, and perhaps even a volcanic eruption.

The moon presents a strikingly different appearance. The Martian astronomer sees a bewildering maze of craters, ranging in size from hundreds of kilometers in diameter to a few meters across. Parts of the moon are covered with smooth dark plains. There are no oceans, no great river valleys, and none of the wrinkled mountain belts so prominent on the earth. The Martian astronomer could watch the moon for days, months, and perhaps years before noticing any change in its landscape. The sun lights the same features over and over as the moon turns slowly on its axis.

Why are the earth and its companion so different? Is the moon merely a small, dead planet still scarred by the events of its birth? Or is the moon, like the earth, still evolving? In this chapter you will first look at the moon in much the same way that you looked at earth landscapes. Then you will study the moon's nature and evolution as astronomers have done and see how lunar research may help to answer many questions.

Figure 22–1 *A lunar landscape in the north central portion of the moon, the crater Archimedes on the edge of the Mare Imbrium.*

Lunar Landscapes

22–1 Investigating landscapes on the moon.

The landscape of the moon is remarkably different from any seen on earth. Only a very few places on earth have features that are at all like those on the moon. Does this mean that the methods used for determining the history of lunar landscapes are different from methods used for the earth? In this investigation you will try to answer this question.

Procedure

Examine the landscape shown in Figure 22–1.

(1)What seems to be the last feature that formed on the surface that you see? What seems to be the earliest feature?

(2)Starting with the most recent event list the sequence of events that took place to produce the landscape.

Compare the history you have developed with the history indicated on the geologic map provided by your teacher.

(3)In what ways did your interpretation differ from the map? In what ways was it similar?

(4)If you were to land in this area, what five spots would you visit to learn the most about lunar landscape features?

22–2 The face of the moon.

Look at the full moon with binoculars. You will see two major types of landscapes, one dark and the other much lighter. The light areas are generally called highlands or continents—although they are probably quite different from continents on earth. Close examination of the highlands in a photograph like that of Figure 22–2 shows that the light areas appear very rough because they are covered with craters of all sizes.

The word **crater** simply means a bowl-shaped depression.

The dark areas are much smoother and lower than the highlands. They also contain fewer large craters. Early astronomers called these dark areas **maria** (MAH-ree-ah), the Latin word for seas, mistaking them for bodies of water like oceans on earth. You can be quite sure, even without high-powered telescopes, that there are no oceans on the moon. The ancient name remains, however, and in fact a new *mare* (MAH-ray, singular of maria) was named only recently. This area, which was photographed by the Ranger 7 spacecraft, was called Mare Cognitum, the Known Sea. (See Figure 22–3.)

Study the photograph on page 474 taken with the 100-inch Mount Wilson telescope. At first the lunar topography appears to have no obvious pattern like the parallel ridges of the Appalachians or the ring of mountains around the Pacific. But on closer study you will see that a pattern does exist. Except for the material of the maria, most of the topographic features on the moon belong to, or are clearly associated with, circular depressions of some kind.

The crater Copernicus, named after the famous astronomer, is one of the most conspicuous lunar craters on the visible face of the moon, having a diameter of 92 kilometers. (See Figure 22–4.) It is a depression containing a central peak. The crater's inner wall is made up of a series of terraces formed when blocks of rock slumped toward the crater's center. The outside rim of Copernicus is a light-colored, rough blanket of material generally believed to consist of rock ejected, or thrown out, from the crater. This rock, called the **ejecta blanket,** gradually grades into the deposits of white material called rays. How were the rays formed?

Tycho is another crater like Copernicus. Because of its tremendous ray system, Tycho is easily visible with binoculars at or near full moon. Many craters look like Copernicus but have no visible rays. The crater Eratosthenes is one of these. Close study shows that Eratosthenes is somewhat rounded, as if by erosion. (See Figure 22–5.) What does this suggest about the rays? Eratosthenes and similar rayless craters are essentially the same as Copernicus, despite their apparent differences. Look again at another kind of crater, Archimedes, in Figure 22–1. Archimedes does not look very similar to craters like these others. However, closer study reveals that it too has a rim, a series of terraces one within the other, and at least part of an ejecta blanket. It looks different because it has been filled and partly surrounded by the dark mare material.

The crater Grimaldi is simply a much larger and probably older version of Archimedes. (See Figure 22–6.) Mare Crisium (Sea of Crises) seems to be a larger version of Grimaldi, and Mare

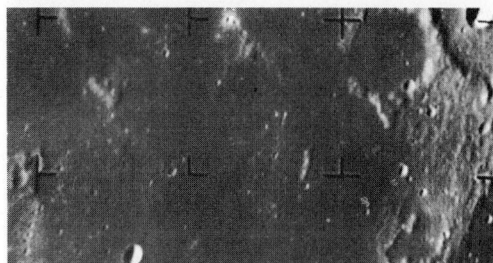

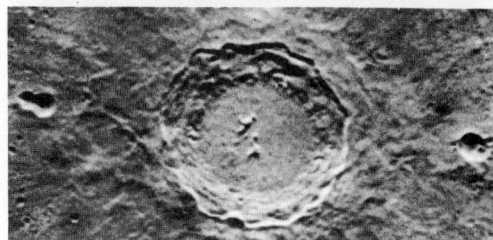

Figure 22–2 (*Right, top*) *The lunar highlands photographed with an earth-based telescope.*
Figure 22–3 *Mare Cognitum (center), the "Known Sea," showing the smooth nature of the mare. This photograph was made by the Ranger 7 spacecraft.*
Figure 22–4 *Crater Copernicus (below) photographed with the 200-inch telescope. Notice the slumped walls within the rim of the crater.*

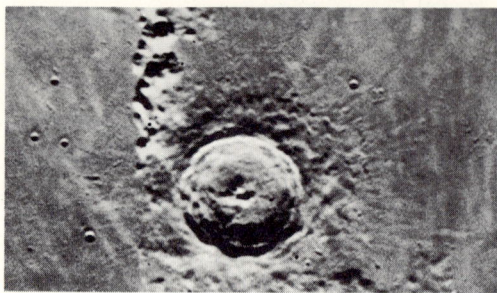

Figure 22–5 *Close-up view of the Crater Eratosthenes made with the 200-inch telescope on Palomar Mountain in California.*

Serenitatis (Sea of Serenity) and Mare Imbrium (Sea of Rains) larger versions of Mare Crisium. This family of circular depressions ranging from Copernicus to Mare Imbrium includes almost all the major topographic features of the moon.

Some topographic features are found only on maria. Prominent among these are the **mare ridges,** or wrinkle ridges. (See Figure 22–7.) These ridges are hard to see unless the sun's rays slant across the moon at a low angle. They are several kilometers wide and sometimes hundreds of kilometers long, but only a few hundred meters high. Of what features on earth do these remind you?

Chain craters are rows of relatively small craters only a few kilometers in diameter. (See Figure 22–8.) They may occur almost anywhere—in the highlands, on the maria, or in the floor of craters. Some chain craters are surrounded by deposits of dark material.

Another unusual feature of the lunar landscape are **rilles** or valley-like depressions on the moon's surface that in some places grade into chain craters. (See Figure 22–9.) Could they be related? The rilles are generally thought to be features bounded by faults and formed by subsidence of the surface. Lunar Orbiter 2 has revealed dome-like features that would seem to be related to eruptions of material from within the moon. (See domes in Figure 22–7.)

22–3 Evolution of the moon's topography.

You studied the evolution of landscapes on the earth in Chapter 21. See what you can infer about the moon's landscape. A detailed photograph of the lunar surface may appear to be a complicated maze of craters, rilles, and rays. The picture becomes clearer if you remember that the topographic features may be divided into two major classes— the maria and the circular depressions.

First, you must distinguish between the dark mare material and the circular depressions that it fills—the **mare basins.** The mare material itself has traditionally been thought to be lava because of its dark color, its flatness, and because it looks as if it has flowed over the moon's surface. However, it was recognized in the 1950's that radar reflections from the moon did not look like those from a rough, hard lava surface, but more like those from a smooth, powdery material. This led to the theory that much of the moon was covered with deep dust—a theory that became very

Figure 22–6 *(Left) Crater Grimaldi near the western edge of the side of the moon visible from earth.*
Figure 22–7 *(Below) Wrinkle ridges and domes.*

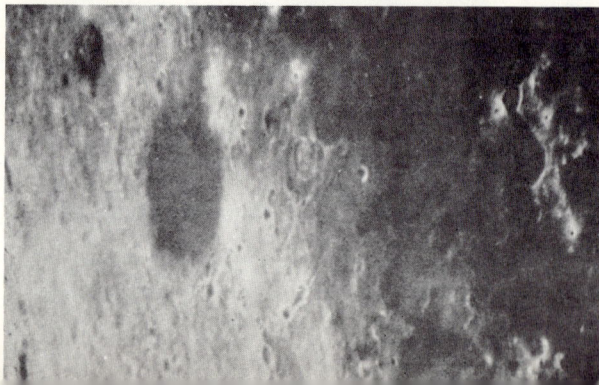

significant when it was decided to land spacecraft on the moon. The Ranger and Surveyor pictures somewhat reinforced the dust theory because they showed few features typical of lava.

Which theory is correct? Because of new information from lunar probes, probably both the lava and the dust theories need to be changed. The Surveyor 1 pictures in particular show that at least the spot where Surveyor landed is not a fresh lava flow. The material in this area seems typical of that of maria. (See Figure 22–10.) The evidence seems to suggest that surface material is much like soil—crumbly but firm. On the other hand, the general distribution and topography of maria still support the lava theory. A possible compromise between the lava and dust theories is that mare material is ancient lava that has been struck repeatedly by meteorites over many millions of years. This has reduced the lava to rubble. Another possibility is that the maria are vast deposits of volcanic ash and pumice deposited by glowing avalanches like the one that erupted from Mt. Pelée in 1902.

The question of the origin of maria will probably not be settled until astronauts can take a look at the material of the maria and bring some of it back to earth for analysis. Presently, however, most scientists agree that the maria are composed of some sort of volcanic material—either crushed lava or ash.

The origin of lunar craters is one of the major questions of lunar geology. There are two major theories. One is that the craters are large collapsed volcanoes, or calderas (call-DER-ahs), like the Darwin Caldera in the Galápagos Islands off the coast of Ecuador. (See Figure 22–11.) Another caldera is illustrated by Crater Lake in Oregon, seen in Figure 22–12. The other theory is that they are pits formed by the impact of large meteorites which produce effects much like explosions because of their high impact velocity.

What evidence is there that craters such as Copernicus are calderas? First, they look like calderas. Crater Lake, for example, has an almost central peak, which is actually a small cinder cone that developed after the formation of the main crater. It also has a surrounding blanket of pumice and lava ejected from the crater and geologists have discovered internal faults around the inner wall. Second, if the maria are volcanic rock, it would be unusual to find so much volcanic activity without craters of some sort. In particular, craters such as Archimedes (Figure 22–1) filled with mare material must have resembled active volcanoes at one time if the material is actually lava or volcanic ash. A final bit of evidence comes from the glowing pink spots that have reportedly been seen in various craters, including Aristarchus. Although these spots may not be volcanic eruptions, they may indicate that the moon is geologically active.

Figure 22–8 (Left) Rows of small chain craters.
Figure 22–9 (Center) Rilles on a crater floor.
Figure 22–10 (Right) Close-up of the lunar surface as photographed by Surveyor 1.

Several arguments can be made against a volcanic origin for lunar craters. Volcanoes on the earth tend to occur in well-defined areas, such as the "ring of fire" around the Pacific Ocean. (See Figure 14–10A.) Lunar craters, however, seem to be dotted randomly over the moon's face, except for the small chain craters that are generally thought to be volcanic. Many scientists believe that lunar craters such as Copernicus are too large to have been volcanoes. There are at least 72 craters on the visible face of the moon with diameters over 80 kilometers, but no recent volcanoes of this size are found on earth. The Valles Caldera, one of the largest volcanic earth craters, is only about 29 kilometers in diameter. However, much larger volcanoes, perhaps as big as 80 kilometers in diameter, may have existed in the past. Some scientists think that ring-like structures of volcanic rock discovered in Africa and Australia are the exposed roots of such large volcanoes. Thus the great size of lunar craters does not necessarily mean that they may not have been volcanoes.

What evidence is there to support lunar crater formation by the impact of meteorites or comets? Perhaps the strongest piece of evidence is the existence of many impact craters on earth, such as Meteor Crater in Arizona. (See Figure 22–13.) Of course, Meteor Crater is very small compared to many lunar craters. In fact, if it were on the moon, it would barely be visible through a large telescope. However, ancient ring-like structures in Canada, for example, are as large as 65 kilometers in diameter. Many scientists are sure that these are the roots of old impact craters. If such craters have been formed on the earth, it would seem that they would have been formed on the moon as well.

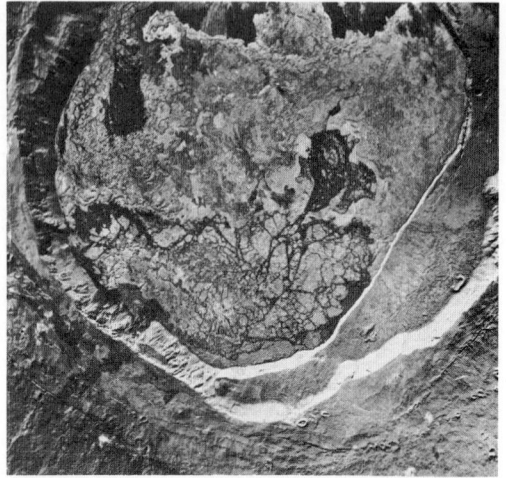

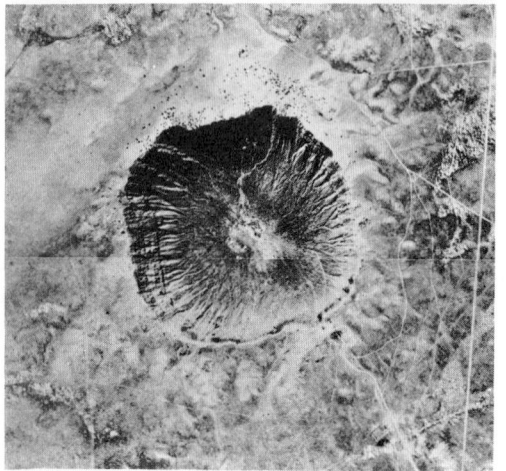

Figure 22–11 (Top) Air view of active Darwin Caldera in the Galápagos Islands near Ecuador.
Figure 22–12 (Center) Crater Lake in Oregon.
Figure 22–13 (Bottom) Meteor Crater in Coconino County, Arizona. Metallic fragments indicate it was formed by a meteoritic impact.

Another point in favor of the impact theory is that the large lunar craters seem to be randomly located with no obvious relation to other features. In addition, they appear to have been formed by one event, although most volcanoes on earth have long histories of alternating periods of eruption and quiet. Finally, lunar craters look like terrestrial impact craters. To test this reasoning, compare Meteor Crater with Copernicus. (See figures 22–4 and 22–13.) What similarities do you see? What differences? How might you account for these differences?

One reason that scientists disagree on the origin of lunar craters is that they still do not know enough about the moon. For example, they do not know just what the types of lunar rock are, or how old they are. What rock types might you expect if the craters are calderas similar to those on earth?

Another reason for scientific disagreement about the origin of craters on the moon is that scientists with different backgrounds study the problem. Scientists who study volcanoes on the earth tend to relate craters on the moon to volcanoes. Geologists who have studied impact craters on the earth tend to relate craters on the moon to impact.

What conclusions have scientists reached about the origin of lunar craters? First, most agree that there are some volcanic craters on the moon. The chain craters fit most of the requirements for volcanic origin on the basis of their size, appearance, and association with geologic structures. Second, most scientists agree that much of the rock on the lunar surface, in particular that of the maria, is volcanic. Most scientists believe that the impacts of meteorites or comets are the primary cause of typical craters like Copernicus. Many scientists

favor an impact origin for the circular maria as well, because as we have seen, it is difficult to draw a sharp distinction between them and the ray craters. However, if the maria are volcanic rock, there must have been extensive volcanic activity after the dark-floored craters and the mare basins were formed. This would be true even if the craters had been produced by impact. The general opinion is that most lunar rocks are volcanic, but that most lunar land forms are the result of impact. In some cases, impact may have resulted in disturbances that caused some volcanic activity.

Research presently being done suggests that rocks are altered by the shock of impact and these can be readily recognized. This will be useful in determining how lunar features were formed.

Thought and Discussion . . .

1. If you were the first person to land on the moon, what kind of samples would you bring back for analysis?
2. How can your knowledge of landscape processes on earth help you understand the development of lunar landscapes?
3. Explain the effect of the water cycle on sculpturing lunar landscapes. How do you think erosion occurs on the moon?
4. The diameter of Copernicus Crater is 92 km and the diameter of Meteor Crater, Arizona, is 1.6 km. Can you find a crater in Figure 22–4 that is the same size as Meteor Crater, Arizona?

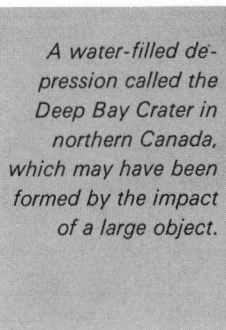

A water-filled depression called the Deep Bay Crater in northern Canada, which may have been formed by the impact of a large object.

The Moon as a Satellite

22–4 Investigating the motions of the moon.

The moon is the brightest object in the sky whose shape appears to change at regular intervals. How and why does the moon's shape seem to change night after night? Does its apparent size change as well? To answer these questions you can use astronomical data on the moon's position, shape, and distance, based on angular diameter.

To determine the angular diameter of an object you measure its apparent width from your observation point, as shown in Figure 22–14. The angular diameter of any object can be determined without reference to distance. However, if the angular diameter of the object you are measuring varies, then you can assume that either the distance between you and the object is changing or that the object is changing diameter. If the observer in Figure 22–14 remained stationary, how would the angular diameter of the sphere change if it were half as far away from him? twice as far away? How do you think that the distance to the moon is related to its angular diameter as measured from the earth?

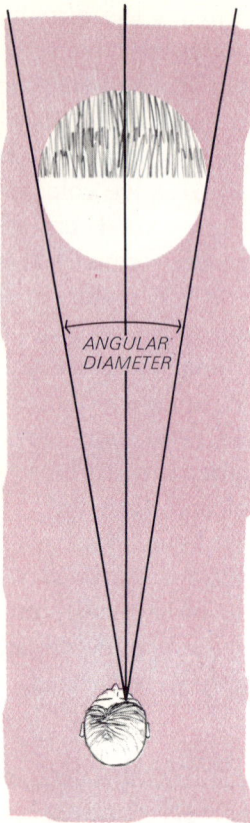

Procedure

In this investigation, you will plot the data from the table in Appendix E on circular graph paper. Imagine that the earth is located at the center of the graph. Plot the positions of the moon for each of the days given in the table.

(1)Indicate where the moon will be at (A) full phase, (B) quarter phase, and (C) new phase.

(2)At what positions might eclipses occur?

(3)The apparent position of the sun will shift about 30 degrees in a month. Locate where the next full moon will be.

(4)With a drawing compass, try to draw the best orbit that you can through all the moon's positions. Explain your results.

ANGULAR DIAMETER

Figure 22–14
*Angular diameter
of an object.*

*The various phases of
the moon as seen from
planet earth.*

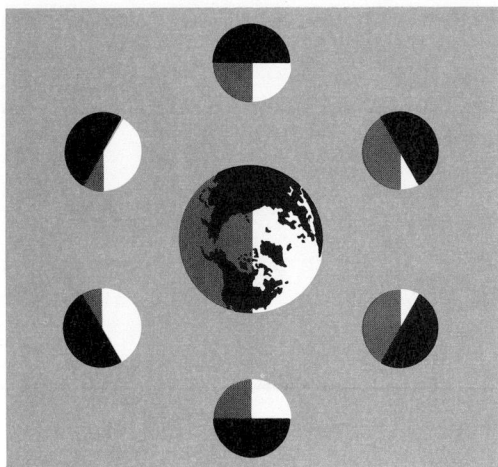

Figure 22–15 *The hidden side of the moon (shown in black) can never be seen from earth. How does the hidden side differ from the dark side?*

22–5 What is the moon's path?

The moon rotates on its axis in the same time that it revolves in its orbit around the earth (27.3 days). Because of this, the moon keeps the same face turned toward the earth at all times. Many people think that the hidden side of the moon is always dark. They talk about the "dark side of the moon" when they mean the side hidden from the earth. However, the two are not the same. The relation between the hidden and dark sides is shown in Figure 22–15. Relate this to the results of Investigation 22–4.

The term "month" comes from the same root as "moon." It refers to the time taken for a complete revolution of the moon. However, you know that to describe a motion such as revolution, you must specify the motion relative to a frame of reference. If you measure the moon's revolution with respect to the stars—that is, the time necessary for it to return to the same position among the stars—you will find it to be 27.3 days. This is the **sidereal month.** However, as you may have noticed in Investigation 22–4, the time from one new moon to the next is about 29.5 days. This period, called the **synodic month,** is measured relative to the apparent position of the sun. Can you see from Figure 22–16 why the sidereal and synodic months have different lengths?

Does the earth cast a shadow? You know that it does. You spend every night in the earth's shadow. How far into space does this shadow extend? Eclipses of the moon prove that the earth's shadow extends at least as far as the moon because they occur when the moon enters this shadow. During a lunar eclipse, the moon disappears, partly or wholly, depending on whether it is in the central part or on the edge of the earth's shadow. Lunar eclipses are valuable for astronomers studying the moon because the eclipses cut off the sun's light to points on the moon in a few minutes—much more rapidly than normally happens during lunar sunsets.

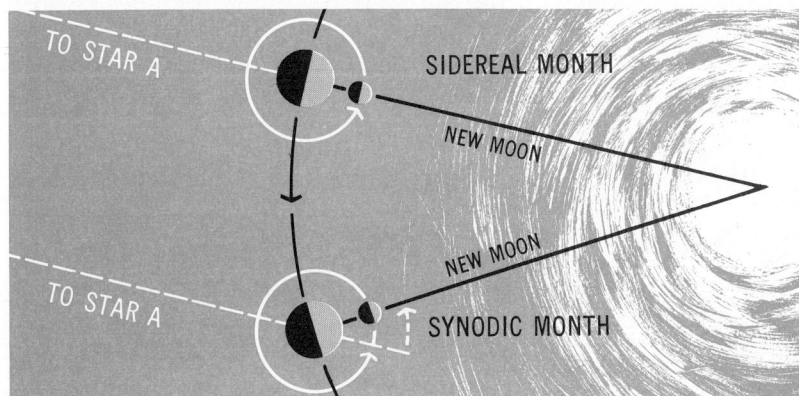

Figure 22–16 *It takes the moon about two days longer to return to its same position relative to earth and sun than it does for it to revolve once in its orbit in space.*

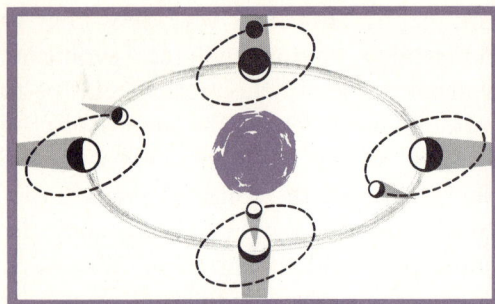

Figure 22–17 (*Left*) *Relationship between the shadows of the earth and the moon. At what positions can eclipses occur?*
Figure 22–18 (*Right*) *The sun's corona seen during a total solar eclipse.*

An eclipse of the sun occurs when the moon's shadow falls on the earth. The relationship between the shadows of the earth and the moon is shown in Figure 22–17. Total eclipses of the sun take place somewhere on the earth at intervals of between one to five years, but at any one spot a total eclipse is a very rare event. For instance, Chicago will have a total eclipse of the sun on the average of only once in 350 years, and only two total eclipses will be visible in the United States between 1967 and 2000. Partial eclipses, in which the sun is only partly covered by the moon, are much more common.

Total eclipses of the sun are magnificent spectacles to those lucky enough to see them. The moon's shadow moves across the earth at several thousand miles per hour, cutting off the sun's light in just a few minutes. In the small area of the total eclipse, night falls suddenly in the middle of the day. A total eclipse allows the sun's corona, which is usually invisible, to be seen. (See Figure 22–18.) For this reason total eclipses of the sun are valuable to scientists, and astronomers frequently travel thousands of miles to observe them.

22–6 The earth-moon system.

How far away from the earth is the moon? How much does its distance from the earth vary? Historically, the distance of the moon from the earth was determined very early by means of the parallax. Parallax is the apparent movement of a celestial object, or any other object, caused by a change in the position of the observer.

ACTIVITY *You can demonstrate parallax for yourself. Hold a pencil up close to your face and look at it, first with one eye and then with the other. You will notice that it appears to move from side to side in relation to background objects. Now hold the pencil about 30 centimeters away, and then hold it at arm's length, repeating the experiment each time. Can you tell how the apparent movement, or parallax, varies with the distance of the pencil? Why does the parallax vary in this way?*

As used by two observers, the parallax method involves measuring two angles and the distance between them, as shown in Figure 22–19. The third angle can then be calculated and the length of the sides of the right triangles, whose common side is approximately the moon's distance, can be found.

A more direct method of measuring the moon's distance is by means of radar. A short radio signal, or radar pulse, is sent to the moon. Its travel time to the moon and back is measured. Radio signals are known to travel at the speed of light (300,000 km/sec). If the round-trip time of the radar pulse is 2.5 seconds, what is the moon's distance?

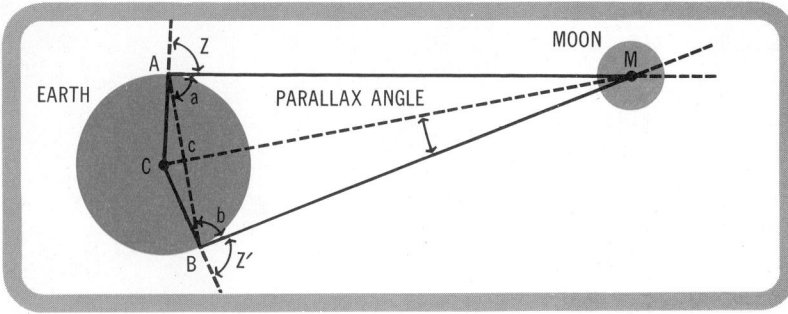

Figure 22–19
Observers A and B find angles a and b from the angles Z and Z' between their zeniths and the moon. Knowing the distance AB and the angles a and b gives the distance cM.

Like all objects in the universe, the moon is not stationary. Repeated measurements of the distance and position of the moon are needed to determine its orbit. The common phrase, "orbit around the earth," is not completely accurate because the earth and moon both revolve around a common center of mass, called the **barycenter.** (See Figure 4–20.) It is really the barycenter that makes an elliptical orbit around the sun. (See Figure 22–20.)

The average density of the moon has been calculated to be 3.3 grams per cubic centimeter. Is this greater or less than the average density of the earth? The moon's density should indicate something about its internal composition. Unfortunately, many materials come close to this density, including stony meteorites and the upper mantle of the earth. It seems clear, however, that the moon's density is too low for it to have a large iron core such as the core the earth is believed to have. Instead, the moon's overall composition may be something like that of stony meteorites. Their composition resembles that of silicate rocks rich in iron and magnesium.

The force of gravity at the moon's surface is about one-sixth that of the earth's gravity. Can you verify this value? The low force of gravity on the moon has many effects. Because of the low gravitational attraction, the moon cannot retain an atmosphere. The velocity of gas molecules depends on temperature. The high temperatures during the lunar day cause the velocity of the gas molecules to exceed escape velocity from the moon. Therefore, they fly off into space.

The weak lunar gravity field may also have affected the way the moon has evolved. For example, rock pressure in the interior of the moon would be considerably lower than pressure at a corresponding depth within the earth.

22–7 The moon has been studied in other ways.

So far you have studied the moon by looking at it. What other methods can be used to learn something about its composition and evolution?

Measurements of temperatures on the moon's surface provide useful information. Temperatures can now be measured directly with soft-landing space

Figure 22–20 *The barycenter of the earth-moon system orbits the sun in an elliptical path.*

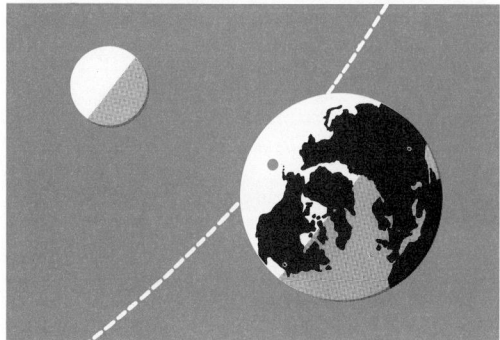

craft such as Surveyor, although for many years astronomers have done this by using telescopes with sensitive instruments that convert heat into electricity. Lunar surface temperatures during the day are surprisingly high, over 100°C. When and where on the moon's surface would you expect these maximum temperatures? At night or during an eclipse, however, the surface temperature drops rapidly to −150°C. These extreme temperatures allow astronomers to infer at least two things about the moon. First, the moon has little or no air, since the presence of air would moderate the temperature. (See Section 22–6.) Second, most of the lunar surface cannot be mainly solid rock, because solid rock would take a long time to warm up or to cool off. The next time you have a campfire or a fire in a stone fireplace, notice how long it takes the hot stone to cool after the fire is out. Many areas of the moon, however, like the floor of the crater Tycho, do not change temperature rapidly. These may be areas in which there is considerable solid rock at or near the surface.

In 1946 a U.S. Army Signal Corps antenna in New Jersey bounced the first radar pulses off the moon and received them back on earth. This experiment has been repeated many times. Much has been learned about the nature of the lunar surface from the way it reflects radar energy. The material making up the moon has been found to depart from smoothness by only a few centi-

Figure 22–21 *The rough texture of the moon's surface, as photographed by Surveyor 1. The rock casting a shadow is several centimeters wide.*

meters. Only when the small features are photographed at close range, as was done by Surveyor I, are they seen to be rough. (See Figure 22–21.) This is not very surprising. A sandy beach may look smooth from a distance but the closer you get to it, the rougher it appears. Radar data have indicated that most of the surface material is a good electrical insulator and is not solid rock.

When you look at the moon with binoculars or a telescope, you will notice how sharp its edge is. This is further proof that it has no halo of surrounding air like the earth. Photographs taken from orbiting spacecraft, like that on pages 58 and 59, show how the earth's atmosphere looks from space. The density of the moon's atmosphere has been measured by studying the disappearance of stars behind the moon. Instead of fading gradually, stars disappear abruptly. This indicates that the density of the lunar atmosphere must be less than a millionth that of the earth's atmosphere at sea level. Recent evidence of how the moon affects radio waves changed this figure. It shows that the moon's atmosphere is less than a trillionth (10^{-12}) as dense as the earth's atmosphere.

Unmanned spacecraft have so far provided the most spectacular method of

A double lunar crater (center) and a large crater (top) appear in this Lunar Orbiter photograph.

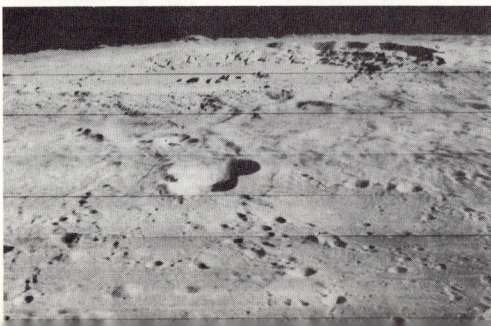

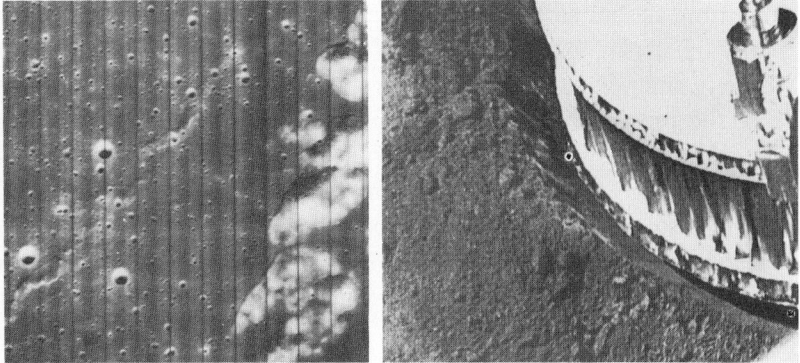

Figure 22–22 *Lunar Orbiter 1 reveals that the lunar surface is creased here and there with ridges and dotted with craters.*
Figure 22–23 *Surveyor 1's pad settled slightly into loose lunar material when it landed.*

investigating the moon. The information that Ranger, Surveyor, Lunar Orbiter, and the various Russian lunar probes have sent back to earth indicates that the nature of the lunar surface is very much as expected from the various earth-based techniques. A picture from the Lunar Orbiter 1 is shown in Figure 22–22. Ranger and Lunar Orbiter pictures have confirmed radar data by indicating that most of the moon's surface is fairly smooth, unconsolidated material containing occasional small craters. The Surveyor I picture in Figure 22–23 shows that a typical mare site consists of a relatively crumbly material, like sand or loose soil, rather than solid rock.

Surprising photographs made by Lunar Orbiter 1 showed that some of the highland areas are apparently smoother, with fewer craters, than the adjoining maria. Reasons for this are not yet clear. The highland material may weather faster than the mare material because of its greater slopes. This weathering may destroy the smaller craters. Or perhaps the highland material is younger than the mare material, and has been formed by volcanic activity.

You may be reading this chapter after men have landed on the moon. If so, have their discoveries greatly changed this picture of the lunar surface?

Thought and Discussion . . .

1. Can you develop a variation of the parallax method that could be used by only *one* observer to measure the distance of the moon? Illustrate it with a diagram corresponding to that in Figure 22–19.
2. If the earth's orbit around the sun and the moon's orbit around the earth were in the same plane, how often would eclipses occur?
3. If you were on the moon looking at the earth when observers on the earth were observing a solar eclipse, in what phase would you see the earth?

Lunar Research

22–8 What was the origin of the moon?

As you might expect, there are several theories about how the moon was formed. It is curious, however, that while scientists have in the past few decades reached considerable agreement about the formation of the planets,

they have disagreed more and more about the formation of the moon. Why should this be so? What are the main theories about the origin of the moon?

Perhaps the simplest theory is that the moon is part of a double planet that was formed by the accumulation of particles and that the moon grew at the same time as, but somewhat more slowly than, the earth. This theory has many strong points. However, as you have seen, the moon's density is considerably lower than that of the earth. So it is likely that the moon's overall composition is also different. It is difficult to understand why this would be so if the earth and moon were formed originally from the same cloud of material.

Another theory of the moon's origin was proposed in the nineteenth century by George Darwin, a son of Charles Darwin. Darwin suggested that if the earth had once rotated very rapidly— one rotation in about 4 hours—while still molten, it might have split into two bodies. He proposed that an increasing vibration that reinforced itself was the cause of the separation. Tides raised in the liquid earth by the sun might have been in time with the earth's rotation, and the two forces reinforcing each other would have caused a large blob of material to be torn from the earth. You may have demonstrated this accidentally yourself while walking with a plate of soup. If the soup happened to start

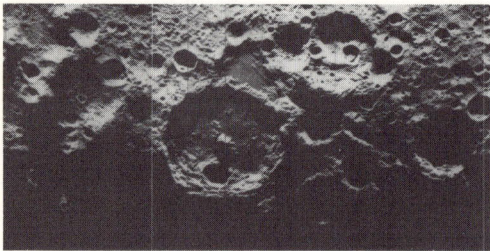

Closeup of an area near the center of the hidden side of the moon photographed by Lunar Orbiter 1.

sloshing back and forth in time with your steps, it may have sloshed right out of the bowl. Darwin's theory was first popular, then discarded, and finally revived again a few years ago. One of the main questions still not satisfactorily answered by this theory is why the earth should have been rotating so much

more rapidly than it does today. Another difficulty raised by Darwin's theory is that such an origin for the moon would have raised the earth's temperature considerably—so much, in fact, that we should still be able to detect the excess heat today, but we do not.

Still another theory proposed for the moon's origin is that the moon is an intruder from some other part of the solar system. As it came close to the earth, it was captured by the earth's gravitational field just as satellites like the Lunar Orbiters are captured by the moon. An advantage of this theory is that it overcomes the difficult problem of why the moon's composition seems so different from that of the earth. On the other hand, capture of the moon by the earth would require a very unusual balance of forces. Unlike the Lunar Orbiters, the moon has no retro-rockets to slow it down. Furthermore, if such capture did occur, much of the energy lost by the moon would have been converted into heat in the body of the earth by tidal friction. But, as in the case of Darwin's theory, this excess heat is not detected.

A compromise theory, proposed by the American geologist G. K. Gilbert as early as 1892, is that the moon was formed by the falling together of several smaller moons that once orbited the earth. While this theory seems to avoid some of the problems that have been discussed, it is still in a very general form and requires further research. So we still do not really know how the moon originated. You can see, therefore, that the familiar moon is one of the major mysteries of the solar system. After reading about all these theories and their weaknesses, you may find that it is very reassuring to go out of doors, look up at the sky, and make sure that the moon is really there!

22–9 What opportunities for research does the moon offer?

President Kennedy's decision to attempt a manned lunar landing by no later than 1970 was based on many reasons. Although scientific curiosity was probably not the most important of these reasons, most scientists feel that the manned lunar landing of the Apollo program will be scientifically valuable.

One reason why scientists have a great interest in the moon is that they can think of it as the earth's companion planet. Furthermore, it is a companion that has direct effects on the earth. Can you think of some of these effects the moon has on the earth? (See Section 4–12.) If scientists are to understand the history of the earth, they must study both members of this double planet system.

The moon's almost total lack of atmosphere offers many research opportunities. You know that most of the earth's land forms are the result of reactions between the earth's crust, air, and water. Furthermore, many rocks, such as sandstone, shale, and limestone, are formed by weathering, erosion, and sedimentation which could not take place in the absence of air and water. Even some igneous rocks, granite in particular, may be remelted sediments. Rocks and landforms on the moon, on the other hand, must be the result of different, nonatmospheric processes. By going to the moon, then, scientists will be able to observe the results of this different environment. They can then compare the earth's development to that of a planet lacking both air and water.

Another reason for studying the moon is to get a better idea of the composition of the solid matter making up the solar system. Because the moon has not been weathered and eroded in the same way as the earth, the analysis of carefully

The American geologist Grove Karl Gilbert became famous for his studies of the Henry Mountains in the Rockies, the ancient shorelines of the Great Salt Lake, the structure of the Great Basin, and erosion in the Sierra Nevada. Born in Rochester, New York, in 1843, Gilbert had little formal training in geology. His interest in the field, however, led him to work on various geological expeditions and then join the United States Geological Survey when it was set up in 1879.

Although most of Gilbert's work is considered classic for its combination of accurate observation with sound inductive reasoning, his theory for the origin of the moon has been largely ignored. Gilbert theorized that the moon resulted from the fusion of solid fragments of matter he called "moonlets," which had originally orbited the earth. He was convinced that the moon's surface materials must be fairly rigid to support the steep inner slopes of many of its craters. His theory was that such craters had been produced as the "moonlets" collided and fused. Gilbert thought that areas of the moon's surface had been fluid since its origin; this fluid had resulted from the impact of meteorites, not from high internal temperatures. Recent research indicates that Gilbert's proposal for a low-temperature origin of the moon may need to be taken more seriously.

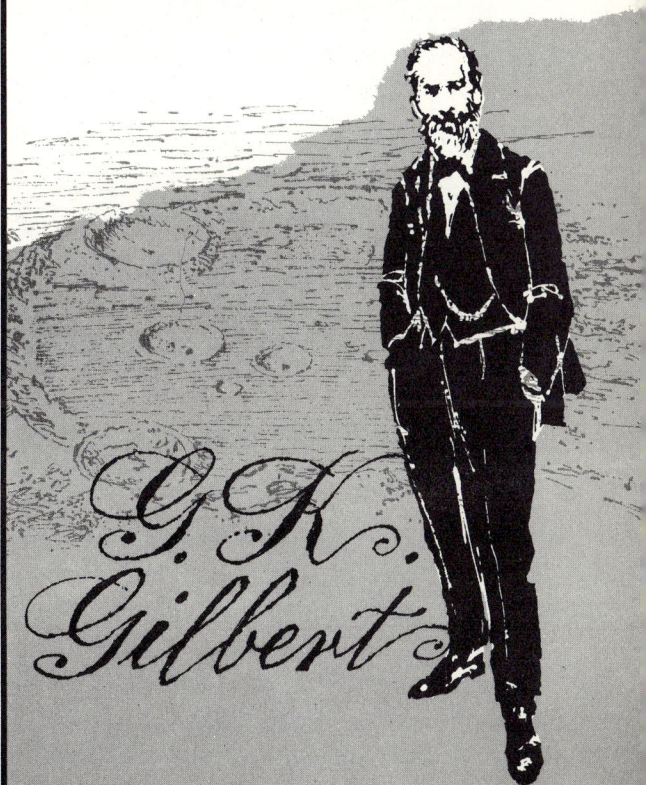

G. K. Gilbert

selected lunar rock samples might reveal its overall chemical composition. This of course depends on how much the composition of the material found on the moon's surface represents the total composition of the moon.

The moon should contain a more representative collection of meteoritic material than the earth. This will be valuable because meteorites provide important information about the origin and evolution of the solar system. Although most of the meteorites displayed in museums are iron, most of those that fall to earth are stone. Why is this so? On the earth it is difficult to form an accurate idea of the actual abundance of meteoritic types, especially of certain rare meteorites. The moon's more typical collection of meteorites, however, should provide a more accurate picture.

In addition to being an interesting object in itself, the moon offers a natural space platform for astronomical observation and other investigations of the universe. Again, the chief reason for the moon's value as an observatory is its lack of atmosphere. If you have looked at stars or planets through a telescope, you have noticed how the image shimmers. This is the result of atmospheric motion, a problem that will not exist on the moon. Even more significant, however, is the fact that the earth's atmosphere stops electromagnetic radiation of certain wavelengths, especially the very short and the very long waves. On the moon, astronomers should be able to observe the entire electromagnetic spectrum. The absence of an atmosphere and of a strong magnetic field, which act as shields, may also permit cosmic rays to reach the moon's surface directly.

Thought and Discussion . . .

1. Which theory of the moon's origin do you believe is the best? Why?
2. Why would the moon be of greater value for astronomical studies than a space platform orbiting the earth?

An oblique view of the Crater Copernicus as photographed by Lunar Orbiter 2. The mountains on the crater floor are about 300 meters high. The Orbiter was about 23,000 meters above the moon's surface when the photograph was taken.

Unsolved Problems This chapter has suggested that there are more questions about the moon than there are answers. This is part of the exciting challenge the moon offers. In an unending effort to gain more insight into the nature of this distant satellite, scientists have examined materials that have fallen upon the earth for clues to lunar composition. Tektites, small glassy blobs of strange material, have been the focus of a great deal of controversy. The tektites are found concentrated in a number of localities around the earth, such as Australia, the Philippines, and Texas. Some scientists believe they come from the moon, ejected by the smashing force of meteorite impacts. Others argue that the tektites are the product of large meteoritic impacts on earth.

Once man reaches the moon perhaps he will be able to answer many puzzling questions: What types of rock are there on the moon? Does the rock cycle as we know it on earth act on this satellite? Where did the moon come from and how was it formed? What new insight will the study of the moon provide about the earth's history?

Perhaps the most important question still to be answered about the moon is its chemical and mineralogical composition. As you will see in the next few chapters, quite a bit is known about the composition of stars because they glow by their own light, which can be analyzed with spectroscopes. But the moon shines by reflected sunlight, so spectrograms of moonlight tell us little. Other forms of radiation, such as microwaves and radar reflections, give us information chiefly about the physical condition of the surface, but not about its composition. To find out what kinds of rocks and minerals make up the moon, we shall have to wait until samples can be analyzed and studied.

Another unsolved problem is that of the moon's relation to the earth. One book has a chapter entitled "The moon: earth's fair child, or a foundling?" Was the moon formed from the earth, or did the earth capture it from somewhere else in the solar system? You know now, of course, that there are at least two other possibilities, and probably more. Probably a choice cannot be made among them until long after the first manned lunar landing.

Finally, one of the most important questions about the moon is that of how useful it will be as a scientific observatory site. Probably it will be a good place for telescopes and for various kinds of research, but to use it for these purposes more must be known about such things as meteorite infall rates, radiation, and the nature of the lunar soil.

CHAPTER REVIEW

Summary

The moon's surface, at least on the earthward side, seems to consist chiefly of two main types of landscapes. The maria are the relatively smooth, dark plains and the highlands are the heavily cratered lighter areas. At close range, this description does not necessarily hold true, because some parts of the highlands are smoother than nearby parts of the maria. Most of the highland features are part of, or related to, various types of circular depressions. The largest of these are the mare basins, which are filled with the dark mare material, but there seem to be all gradations between the mare basins and typical craters, such as Copernicus. Common smaller topographic features include the mare ridges, rilles, and chain craters.

There are various theories about the formation of the moon's surface features. Scientists generally agree that the maria themselves are volcanic rock of some kind, either lava or volcanic ash. However, the origin of the circular depressions is still unclear. One theory is that they are impact craters, similar to Meteor Crater, Arizona, which have been invaded in some places by the mare material. Another theory is that the craters are calderas, like Crater Lake, Oregon, Darwin Caldera, or some related type of volcanic feature.

Most of what is now known about the moon has been learned from the earth by various astronomical techniques. Measurements of the moon's distance and position show that the earth and moon both revolve around their common center of mass, the barycenter. Analysis of the moon's motions and application of the law of gravitation permit the calculation of the moon's mass, about ⅟₈₁ that of the earth, and the moon's density, which turns out to be substantially less than that of the earth. The force of gravity at the moon's surface is also much less than it is at the earth's surface. This is the primary reason why the moon cannot retain an atmosphere.

The moon's surface has been studied by several techniques. Radar tells us that it is smooth in most areas, at least on a scale of meters, with occasional rough spots. The rough spots prove to be the ray craters. Lunar temperatures suggest that ray craters are composed of rock more solid than that of the rest of the moon's surface.

The origin of the moon is not known but there are many theories. One theory is that it was formed near the earth in the same way and at about the same time through the accumulation of solid material. Another theory holds that the moon was captured by the earth's gravitation. Perhaps the most radical theory proposes that the moon was born early in the earth's history when the then-liquid earth vibrated and split into two fragments. None of these theories is completely satisfactory, leading to still another: that the moon was formed by the falling together and merging of several smaller moons. Solving the problem of the moon's origin will take a long time, even after landings have been made on the moon.

Perhaps the dominant aspect of landscapes on earth is that they are the result of the interaction of the water cycle and rock cycle. Without an atmosphere there would be no water cycle. In its absence, sedimentary rocks would be scarce or nonexistent. There would be no geosynclines, no Grand Canyon—and perhaps no continents. Igneous rocks might have different compositions. Probably there would be no life on earth.

These are speculations because the earth *does* have an atmosphere and all that an atmosphere entails. But the moon in effect furnishes a laboratory for studying the evolution of a planet that has no air and no water. For this reason, scientists feel that the exploration of the moon, in addition to satisfying man's curiosity about it, will also reveal much about the earth.

Questions and Problems

A

1. How do the moon's seas differ in appearance from the highland areas?
2. How much of the moon's surface is visible at the new moon phase? at full moon? Explain.
3. Why is it incorrect to refer to the "dark" side of the moon?
4. What is meant by the barycenter of the earth-moon system?
5. Why does not knowledge of the moon's density enable the moon's composition to be determined?
6. How is it known that the moon's surface is covered with a good insulator?
7. What processes that help shape the earth's surface are probably also active on the moon?
8. What processes that help shape the earth's surface are probably not active on the moon? Why?

B

1. Why don't total lunar eclipses occur once a month at the full moon phase?
2. How long does it take the moon to revolve? to rotate? What effect does this have on the part of the moon we see from earth?
3. Does the sun cast a shadow? Explain.
4. What is parallax? How is it used in making celestial measurements?
5. Compare the velocity necessary for a spaceship to escape from the earth with that needed to escape the moon. Why is there such a large difference?
6. How is it known that the moon has no halo of surrounding air?

7. Discuss the main theories of lunar origin and explain their weaknesses.
8. How is it known that there is no water on the moon's surface? Why can the moon's surface contain no water?
9. Why might the moon make an excellent platform for astronomical observations?

C

1. Outline the volcanic theory of lunar crater origin, discussing its weak and strong points.
2. Outline the impact theory of lunar crater origin, discussing its weak and strong points.
3. Total eclipses of the moon are visible from everywhere on the nightside of earth, whereas total eclipses of the sun are only visible from small areas of the earth. Explain.
4. Compare the densities of the moon and earth. What does this indicate about the cores of the two bodies and the gravitational force exerted by each?
5. What are some of the effects of the moon's low gravitational force?
6. Discuss in some detail several reasons why man wants to journey to the moon.

Suggested Readings

BOOKS

Alter, Dinsmore, Cleminshaw, and Phillips. *Pictorial Astronomy*, 2nd rev. ed. Thomas Y. Crowell Company, New York, 1963.

Alter, Dinsmore. *Pictorial Guide to the Moon*. Thomas Y. Crowell Company, New York, 1963.

Binder, Otto. *The Moon: Our Neighboring World.* Golden Press, Inc., New York, 1959.

Boeke, Kees. *Cosmic View: The Universe in 40 Jumps.* John Day Co., N.Y., 1957.

Branley, Franklyn M. *The Moon: Earth's Natural Satellite*. Thomas Y. Crowell Company, New York, 1960.

Gamow, George. *The Moon.* Abelard-Schuman Limited, New York, 1959.

Hynek, J. Allen. *Exploring the Universe.* American Education Publications, Columbus, Ohio, 1961.

Moore, Patrick. *A Guide to the Moon.* W. W. Norton & Company, Inc., New York, 1960.

Moore, Patrick. *A Survey of the Moon.* W. W. Norton & Company, Inc., New York, 1963.

Trinklein, Frederick E. and Charles M. Huffer. *Modern Space Science.* Holt, Rinehart & Winston, Inc., New York, 1961.

Whipple, Fred L. *Earth, Moon, and Planets,* rev. ed. Harvard University Press, Cambridge, Mass., 1963.

Wilkins, Hugh P. and Patrick Moore. *The Moon.* The Macmillan Company, New York, 1955.

PERIODICALS

Dryden, Hugh L. "Footprints on the Moon." *National Geographic,* March, 1964.

Klemperer, W. B. "The Solar Eclipse from a Jet." *National Geographic,* November, 1963.

Kopal, Zdenek. "Luminescence of the Moon." *Scientific American,* May, 1965.

Lowman, Paul D., Jr. "The Origin of Tektites." *School Science and Mathematics,* January, 1964.

Ronan, Colin A. "Phoenix of Astronomers." *Natural History,* January, 1965.

Shoemaker, E. M. "The Moon Close Up." *National Geographic,* November, 1964.

Shoemaker, E. M. "The Geology of the Moon." *Scientific American,* December, 1964.

Stubbs, Peter. "Enigma of the Moon, How Did it Get There?" *New York Times Magazine,* March 28, 1965.

The old moon in the new moon's arms. Why is the dark side of the moon partially illuminated?

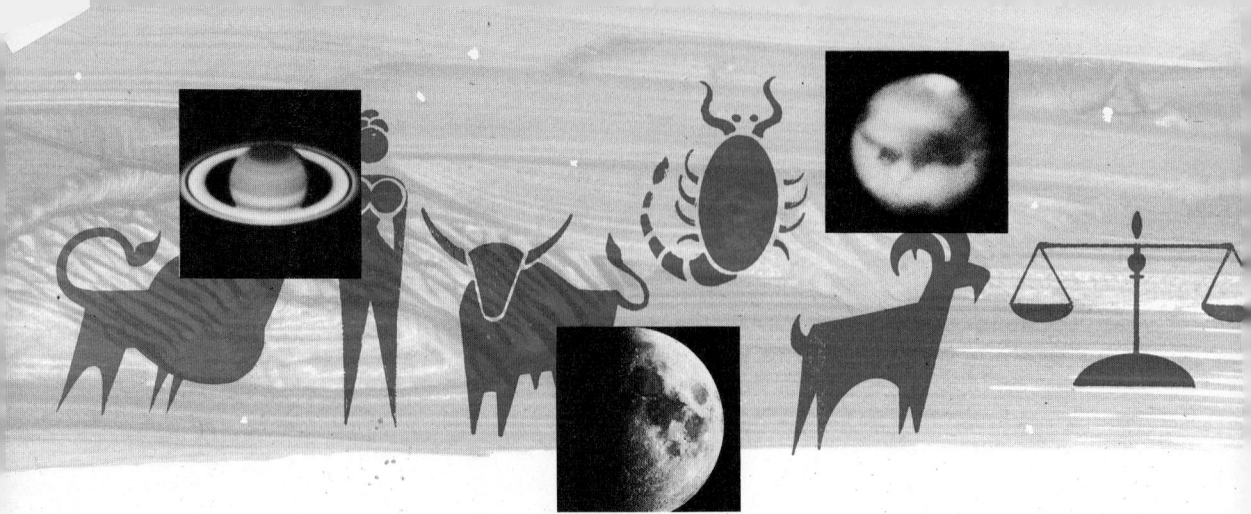

Chapter 23 The Solar System

The solar system is the family of all the objects including the twin planets, earth and moon, that orbit the sun. The solar system has often been compared to a gigantic clockwork. This comparison is a good one in many ways. The earth's motion around the sun is the fundamental basis of our timekeeping. All clocks are keyed to the motions of the master clock, the solar system. This master clock needs no winding and has no gears or wheels. It contains more parts than any clockwork, however, all of them moving over vast distances with astounding precision year after year.

The timekeeping of the solar system is more accurate than that of the most expensive watch. And to top it off, its main working parts operate in a thin disk, far thinner, in proportion to its diameter, than the thinnest watch.

How does this clockwork move? The story of how man came to understand its motions is one of keen intellectual adventure. It begins with primitive man, who probably knew the stars and constellations far better than most of us do today. It is likely that he was aware of a few bright "stars" that did not keep their places in the sky but slowly changed their positions in relation to other stars night after night. Their motions were always confined to a narrow belt in the sky, now called the zodiac, which was regarded with awe and reverence. Considerable attention was given to the constellations

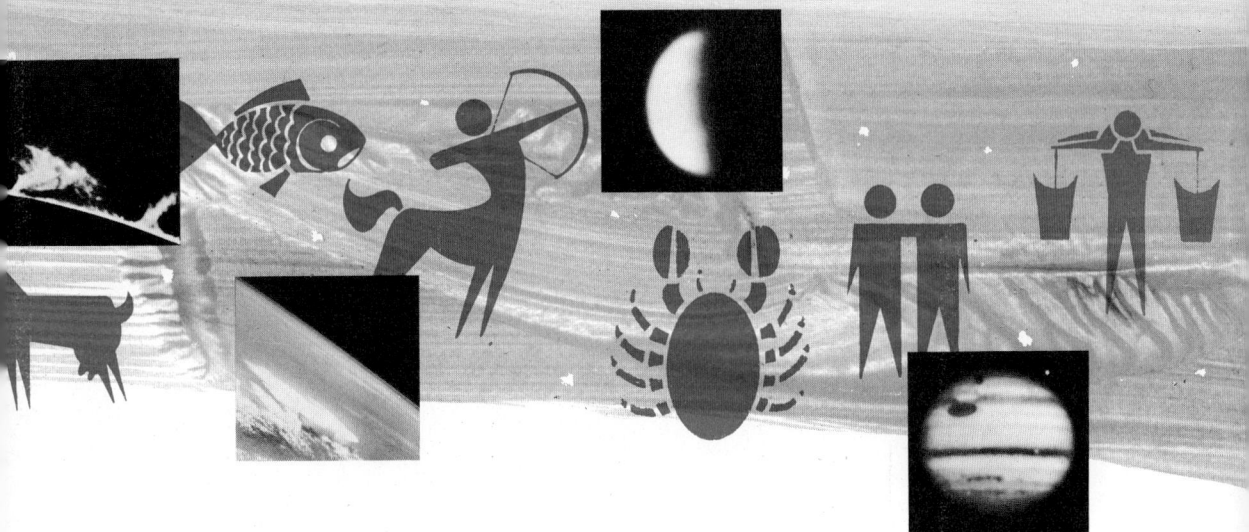

along this belt. They are the twelve constellations of the zodiac or "celestial zoo." The planets, or "wanderers," are found among these constellations.

It was natural for early man to associate these lights that wandered through the zodiac with his gods. The Greeks named the planets after their gods: Mercury, the fleet-footed, the fastest moving planet; Venus, the goddess of love, often seen shining brightly in the sky just before sunrise or after sunset; Mars, the god of war, glowing red and bright high in the sky every other year; Jupiter, king of the gods, moving more slowly than Mars; and Saturn, the grandfather of the gods, moving even more slowly.

There were seven objects in the sky moving among the stars: sun, moon, and the five planets known at that time. This may account for the special regard often shown for the number seven. It almost certainly accounts for our having seven days in the week. Sunday is clearly the sun's day; Monday, the moon's day; Saturday, Saturn's day; and the other days are named for Norse gods. Tuesday, for Tiw, is Mars' day; Wednesday, for Woden, is Mercury's day; and Thursday is Thor's day. Thor is the Norse equivalent of the god Jupiter. That leaves Friday for Freya or Venus' day. The fact that the seven brightest objects in the sky were worshipped as gods has given us the names for the days of the week and the order of the days.

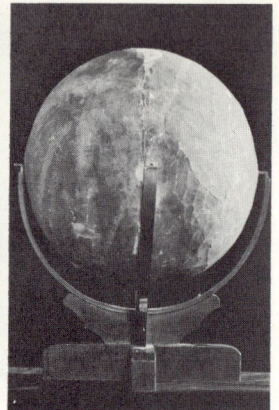

Motions of the Planets

23–1 The puzzling motion of the planets.

As the planets change their positions among the stars, they appear to move in a strange and puzzling way. A planet may move eastward *among the stars* for many months. Then it may slowly come to a stop, seemingly pause, and start westward. After a time it may again slow down, stop, and finally resume its eastward motion.

ACTIVITY *The actual places in the sky occupied by Mars from December through August of a year are shown in the sky maps (A to D) in Figure 23–1. Mark the positions of the stars and of Mars on a piece of tracing paper placed over Figure 23–1A. Then place the tracing paper exactly over B, C, and D by matching the stars.*
Mark the successive positions of Mars. How did Mars move? Draw the apparent path of Mars. Why does Mars appear to move in this back-and-forth manner?

The Greeks tried hard to make sense out of these motions. This was a real puzzle to the ancients. What happens to make a planet back up? The Greek astronomer, Ptolemy, determined a way that this motion might take place. He described the system in his book, *The Almagest,* written about A.D. 150 and accepted as correct until about A.D. 1700. Ptolemy's system is illustrated in Figure 23–2. He theorized that a planet travels on a small circle called an **epicycle,** the center of which orbits the earth on a much larger circle, a **deferent.**

Figure 23–1 *Sky maps showing the positions of Mars from December to August. The stars serve as a frame of reference.*

We know that Venus travels in an orbit between the earth and the sun and, therefore, can never be seen on the side of the earth opposite the sun. Ptolemy accounted for this by having the center of Venus' epicycle always lie on a line connecting the earth and sun. (See Figure 23–2.) That appeared to keep Venus on a kind of leash.

For planets farther from the sun than the earth, no such restriction was necessary. The "backing up" of planets like Mars was explained by their motion in their epicycles. See how in Figure 23–2 Mars appears from the earth to be traveling backward. This is an illusion that is caused by the fact that Mars is moving backward faster on its epicycle than its epicycle is moving forward.

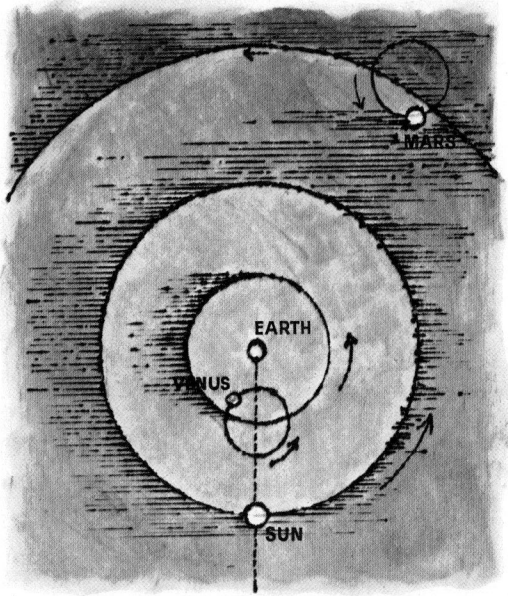

Figure 23–2 *According to Ptolemy's ancient theory each planet moved in a small circle, or epicycle, which in turn moved in an orbit around the earth.*

23–2 Motions and phases of Planet X.

In 1610, Galileo, using his newly constructed telescope, reported that a certain planet changed appearance in a full cycle of phases just like our moon. He reported further that at full phase the diameter of this planet was only one-sixth as great as it appeared to be in its new phase. Like other scientists of the time, Galileo used an anagram, or coded sentence, to make his findings known. The anagram read, "The mother of love imitates the forms of Cynthia." Perhaps you will be able to decipher this anagram after you have completed this investigation.

Procedure

In working through this investigation, try to put yourself in Galileo's place. The only information you have is that the object you are viewing in Figure 23–3 is a wandering planet moving across the sky in a path different from those of the stars. The photographs represent what Galileo observed through his telescope.

In attempting to explain the information you have, it should help if you construct a model. You can make a simple model to represent Planet X as shown in Figure 23–4. Since you are an observer on the earth, your position can be considered that of the earth. Try to make the sphere look like Planet X in the photos. While you are doing this, keep in mind that you are attempting to answer the same question

Figure 23–3 *Phases of Planet X.*

Galileo asked himself: "Where is this planet in relation to the other objects around or near it?"

After you have examined the relationships between Planet X and the "sun," study your observations and attempt to draw some conclusions:

(1)Sketch your part of the solar system (the sun, the earth, and Planet X) as you believe it to be.

(2)Is the orbit of Planet X in the same plane as the earth's orbit? How do you know?

(3)What planet in our solar system could Planet X be? Explain your answer.

(4)What is the reason for the difference in phases between Planet X and the moon?

(5)How would a planet orbiting between the earth and sun differ in appearance from a planet at a greater distance from the sun than the earth?

(6)How does Galileo's anagram, "The mother of love imitates the forms of Cynthia," relate to this investigation?

Figure 23–4

23–3 An intellectual relay race.

Even before Galileo had recorded his observations, the astronomer Copernicus in Poland had already proposed the earth as one of the planets in his book *On Revolutions*. In this book, written in 1543, he developed a sun-centered theory of planetary motion. Galileo showed the correctness of Copernicus' idea that the earth and the other planets moved around the sun. This explained the backward or **retrograde motion** of the planets very simply. (See Figure 23–5.)

It took nearly 200 years for the ideas of Copernicus to be fully accepted, even with the help of Galileo's observations.

The replacement of the old ideas by new ones was much like a relay race in which one runner handed the baton of knowledge to the next.

Copernicus was the first runner. The next was the Danish astronomer Tycho Brahe. He would not accept the ideas of a moving earth, but he was a superb observer of the skies and made detailed observations of the night-by-night positions of Mars. The telescope had not yet been invented, but he lined up long and very accurate sighting rods with Mars' position among the stars each clear night. His observations were made over a period of many years.

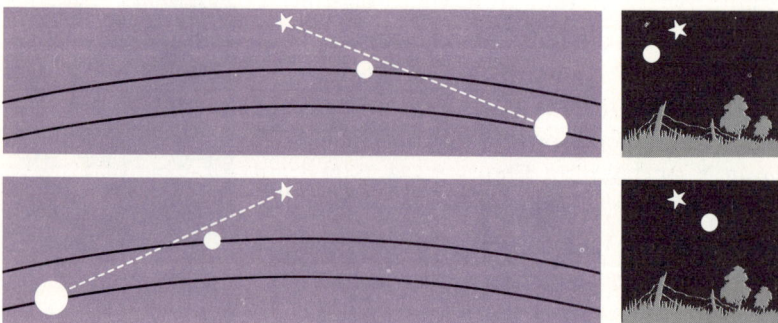

Figure 23–5 *The earth moves faster in its orbit than Mars, so Mars appears to go backward as the earth passes. This backward motion of Mars is shown using a star as a reference point (right).*

The reasons for Brahe's rejection of Copernicus' ideas were scientifically sound at the time. Brahe's main argument was that if the earth went around the sun, the nearer stars should shift positions with respect to the more distant stars. It should be possible to measure the parallax of a star. (See Section 22–6.) Brahe was correct but did not realize that the expected parallax shift would be more than 100 times smaller than any he could measure because the stars are so far away. The measurement of this shift requires the use of large telescopes and was not accomplished until more than 200 years after Brahe's death.

Tycho Brahe's observations actually held the answer, but he did not have the mathematical knowledge needed to find it. The next "relay runner" was Johannes Kepler who, on Brahe's death in 1601, took the fine catalogue of Mars observations that Brahe had compiled. Kepler alone knew their tremendous value. He worked for years using painstaking methods of plotting Mars' positions to see what theory would fit the facts. Finally, in 1609, Kepler was able to announce the first two laws of planetary motion that now bear his name. In 1619 Kepler published his third and most famous law —the law of planetary motion.

Copernicus had argued that planets would naturally move in circular paths around the sun. Following beliefs of the early Greeks, Copernicus thought that circles were perfect curves and that planets would have to move on circles. Holding on to this idea cost Kepler several years' work. There is a famous story that the measured positions of Mars almost fitted the theory but missed by a very small amount. Kepler insisted that "The master (Brahe) could not have made so great an error as eight minutes of arc." Eight minutes

Born in 1564, the gifted Italian scientist Galileo Galilei entered the University of Pisa in 1581 to study medicine.

In that year, he discovered that the time of swing of a pendulum depends on its length, not on the extent of its swing. Knowledge of this principle led later to the pendulum clock.

As he developed the principle of the pendulum, Galileo realized his need to learn mathematics. In fact, mathematics was basic to much of his later work on motion, floating bodies, the path of projectiles, and the speed of falling objects.

As an astronomer, Galileo made his own observations instead of relying on accepted opinions based on the Ptolemaic theory of the solar system. The newly-invented telescope in 1610 provided Galileo with strong support for the Copernican theory. Finding four moons revolving around Jupiter indicated that the earth was not the only center of motion. Venus' moonlike phases also fitted the Copernican but not the Ptolemaic system.

Galileo's belief in the reality of the Copernican system, however, brought him into direct conflict with official Church policy, which supported Ptolemy. Galileo was called before the Inquisition in 1633 and forced to retract his views. Until his death in 1642, however, he privately worked and wrote according to his beliefs.

of arc is not much more than the limit of the accuracy of the human eye. Finally Kepler gave up trying to make his observations fit into circles and announced his first law. This law states that the planets, including the earth, move around the sun in elliptical paths. Note that the sun is at one focus of the ellipse and not at the center. (See Figure 23–6.)

Kepler's second law describes *how* planets move in their orbits. Still using Brahe's observations, Kepler proved that each planet moves in such a way that a line joining the planet to the sun passes over equal areas of space in equal times. This relationship is shown in Figure 23–7.

Keplers' third law—How is the orbit of one planet related to that of another? Is the time it takes a planet to go around the sun once in its orbit, called its **period,** completely independent of the period of another planet in its orbit? Kepler was sure there was some relationship between the orbits of planets, and after several years he found it. This relationship became his third law, which states that the square of the periods of the planets are to each other as the cube of their distances from the sun. This can be said more easily in a formula: $P^2 = D^3$. P is the period of a planet measured in years and D is the distance of a planet from the sun measured in Astronomical Units. The average distance of the earth to the sun equals one **Astronomical Unit** (A.U.), about 150 million km.

Does it work? Try it and see. The period of Mars is 1.88 earth years. Square it: $1.88 \times 1.88 = 3.54$. The distance of Mars from the sun is 1.52 times the earth's distance. Cube it: $1.52 \times 1.52 \times 1.52 = 3.54$.

Test it for yourself on some other planet. Jupiter's period is 11.86 years and its distance is 5.20 Astronomical Units (A.U.).

The final runner in this relay race was Isaac Newton. You have already learned in Chapter 5 about his development of the laws of motion and the law of gravitation. Newton applied these laws to the solar system by using a new form of mathematics he invented, called the calculus. In so doing, he showed that Kepler's laws are a natural consequence of the law of gravitation and the laws of motion. Basing his conclusions on observations and mathematical calculations, Kepler showed that planets move on ellipses. However, he never knew *why* this was so. Newton's law of gravitation explained the reason for this behavior and showed that the planets could only move in ellipses.

Newton's development of the mathematics of planetary motion is called **celestial mechanics.** These mathematical expressions explain the mechanics of the "celestial clockwork" we know as the solar system. They also apply as the mechanics of the Space Age. When an astronaut goes into orbit, his capsule obeys Kepler's and Newton's laws just as the moon and planets do. Our relay race runners actually set the stage for the Space Age. They provided the science and the mathematics necessary for the launching of artificial satellites. Now, more than 200 years later, engineering and technology have finally developed to the point where man can apply the laws of Kepler and Newton to the artificial satellites he himself has placed in orbits in the sky.

Thought and Discussion . . .

---

1. How do the laws of Newton and Kepler apply to artificial satellites?

2. Describe the astronomical contributions made by the men of the "intellectual relay race."

3. What do Kepler's laws tell us about planetary motion?

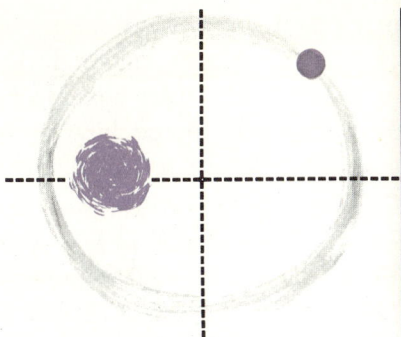

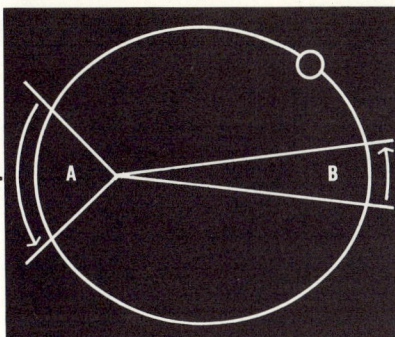

Figure 23–6 (*Far left*) *The elliptical path of the earth's orbit illustrates Kepler's first law.*
Figure 23–7 (*Left*) *Kepler's second law. The area A is equal to the area B.*

The Sun's Family

23–4 Creating a model of the solar system.

Look out the window at a distant place. How long would it take you to get to that place? Now try to visualize the distance from your home to the next town. For some, this may not be too difficult. For others, it may be quite a problem. Why? Obviously, the more familiar you are with the trip from town to town, the easier it is to imagine. Can you now visualize the distance from the earth to another planet?

In order to get a better idea of interplanetary distances, make as accurate a model of the solar system as possible on a scale you can understand. Then you may see some of the problems that face the astronomer and the astronaut in their exploration of our solar system and beyond.

Procedure

Table 23–1 gives the average distances of the planets from our sun in Astronomical Units. The earth, by definition, is one Astronomical Unit (A.U.) from the sun. Since the earth's average distance from the sun is 150×10^6 kilometers, Mars, which is 1.5 Astronomical Units from the sun, must be 1.5 times the earth-sun distance, or about 225×10^6 kilometers from the sun. The table also shows planetary diameters in terms of the earth's diameter.

Make up your own table like Table 23–1, adding columns for scale distance from the sun and scale diameter of the planets. Use scales of 1 meter = 1 earth-sun distance, and 0.1 millimeters = 1 earth diameter. Then calculate the scale distances and diameters and enter them in your table.

Plot the values from the scale-distance column of your table on a long piece of ticker tape or adding-machine tape. Label the position of the sun at one end of the tape and locate and label the positions of all the planets according to the scale distances. Draw in the planets to scale.

TABLE 23-1 PLANETARY DISTANCES FROM SUN AND PLANET DIAMETERS (APPROXIMATE)

OBJECT	DISTANCE FROM SUN (EARTH = 1)	DIAMETER (EARTH = 1)
SUN	—	110.
MERCURY	0.4	0.4
VENUS	0.7	1.0
EARTH	1.0	1.0
MARS	1.5	0.5
JUPITER	5.2	11.2
SATURN	9.5	9.5
URANUS	19.2	3.7
NEPTUNE	30.1	3.5
PLUTO	39.5	1?

23-5 The planets form two distinct groups.

Newton's law of gravitation shows how gravitational force depends on mass ($F = \dfrac{G\,M_1\,M_2}{d^2}$). If the earth were twice as massive as it is, its gravitational pull on the moon would be twice as great and the orbit of the moon around the earth would be altered.

By reversing this reasoning, scientists can figure out what the mass of the earth must be to allow the moon to have the kind of an orbit it has. Whenever a planet has a moon, the mass of that planet can be accurately obtained by means of celestial mechanics. When a planet has no moon, then its mass can be determined in a similar way by the pulls of other planets upon it. Knowing the gravitational forces allows the mass of a planet to be calculated from the amount it veers in its course under the pull of other celestial bodies.

Venus has no satellites, but the close passage of the Mariner space probe in 1964 made it possible to get a much more accurate value for the mass of Ve-

nus than ever before. By noting the amount by which Venus changed the orbit of the Mariner, it was possible to "calculate backward" to see how massive Venus must be in order to have produced the observed change.

The masses of the planets have been calculated and are given in Appendix E in terms of the earth's mass. You notice immediately that planets form two distinct groups. The massive planets are Jupiter, Saturn, Uranus, and Neptune, which are often called the **major planets.** The much less massive planets, which are called the **terrestrial** or **earth-like** planets, are Mercury, Venus, Earth, Mars, and Pluto. The major planets have low densities much like the average density of the sun, while the smaller planets have much higher densities. Venus is a near twin of the earth in mass, whereas Mars and Mercury are much less massive and much smaller than the earth. (See Appendix E.)

Many of the physical properties of a planet are closely related to its mass. If the mass is small enough, the surface gravity of the planet will be too low to retain an atmosphere. Mercury is not able to hold an atmosphere and Mars has only a very thin one. The giant planets have very extensive atmospheres. The amount and kind of atmosphere a planet has almost completely determines the sort of surface it has. The density of its atmosphere also determines whether we can see its surface from the earth.

Venus and Mars come relatively close to the earth, but you cannot see much detail on Venus because it is entirely covered by clouds. (See Investigation 23-2.) We can deduce something of what it might be like on the surface of this planet, for it is very much like the earth in size and mass. Mariner II, as well as radio telescopes on earth, indicate that the temperature on the surface must be very high, about 600°C, or hot enough to melt lead. It seems that there would be little chance of life on Venus.

A large telescope reveals a good deal of surface detail on Mars, as shown in Figure 23–8. The most obvious features are the polar caps that are believed to be very thin layers of frost rather than thick ice caps like those of the earth's polar regions. Observations of the dark markings near the center of Mars, sometimes called seas and bays, show that Mars spins like the earth, turning on its axis once in 24.62 earth hours. Mars' equator is tilted 25 degrees from the plane of its orbit around the sun. How many degrees does the earth's equator tilt from the plane of its orbit? The planet has seasons in its northern and southern hemispheres much like the seasons on the earth, although the Martian year is 687 earth days. When it is summer in the southern hemisphere of Mars, as shown in Figure 23–8, the southern polar cap is smaller than it is during the winter. This has led observers to conclude that Mars has an atmosphere containing some water vapor.

The Martian seasons are accompanied by a darkening of certain surface markings. This has led to speculation that there are plants that grow green leaves in the summer just like plants on earth. However, careful study of the spectrum of light reflected from Mars, and especially from these dark areas, has yielded little evidence of water vapor and no evidence of chlorophyll. (See Section 19–2.) Water vapor and chlorophyll always absorb certain wavelengths of light and produce a definite spectrum. Spectra are described in Section 6–12. Other parts of Mars' spectrum show that there is carbon dioxide in the Martian atmosphere. The planet's atmosphere probably contains other gases such as nitrogen (N_2), argon (A), and possibly a small amount of oxygen (O_2), as is found in the earth's atmosphere. In addition, astronomers have seen clouds and dust storms moving across Mars.

Speculation about life on Mars has also been based on the "canals," fine dark lines on the surface that have never been clearly photographed. A few astronomers claim to have had brief glimpses of these fine lines in a telescope when the visibility conditions on earth were nearly perfect. Other astronomers say that no such fine lines exist. The Mariner IV space probe passed within 15,000 kilometers of Mars on July 14, 1965, and transmitted 21 closeup photographs back to earth. These pictures were taken along a path running roughly from the South to the North Pole of Mars. One of these photographs appears in Figure 23–9. The photographs show craters very much like those on the moon but no canals or signs of life.

Figure 23–8 *Dark markings and polar caps can be seen on this photo of Mars made with a telescope.*
Figure 23–9 A Mariner IV photo of a portion of the *surface of Mars, showing craters.*

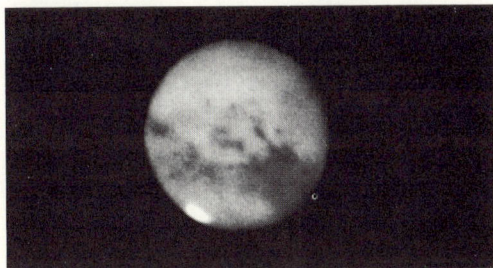

Other instruments carried by Mariner IV showed that Mars' atmosphere is very thin and exerts a pressure of about 20 millibars, which is only two percent of the atmospheric pressure at earth's surface. Mars' magnetic field was found to be either nonexistent or very weak.

The temperatures on the surface of Mars are lower than those on earth because Mars is farther from the sun and has a thin atmosphere. For only a few hours each day—near noon at the Martian equator—is the summer temperature above freezing. Experiments on earth have shown that several kinds of algae can survive under these conditions, but the extreme cold on Mars makes it seem unlikely that living organisms would have evolved to the same extent there as they have on earth.

23–6 The major planets differ from the others.

About 550 million kilometers past Mars, or 3½ times the distance of the earth from the sun, we find Jupiter. Saturn lies 650 million kilometers beyond Jupiter. These are large planets, easy to see in the sky with the naked eye and interesting to view with a telescope. The next two planets, Uranus and Neptune, are farther away and appear very faint and small even in large telescopes although they are also giant planets with diameters nearly four times as great as the earth's. After Uranus was discovered with a telescope in 1781, it was found that its orbit showed a swing away from a perfect ellipse that could not be attributed entirely to the effect of Saturn's gravitational pull. (See Figure 23–10.) Two young astronomers, an Englishman and a Frenchman, calculated where another planet would have to be in order to produce this wiggle of Uranus. Finally, in 1846, a German astronomer located

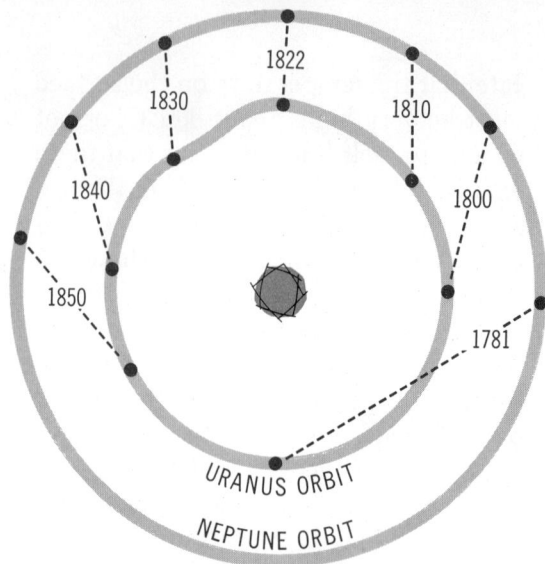

Figure 23–10 *Compare the positions of Uranus and Neptune for the years shown. Can you see the evidence that led to the discovery of Neptune?*

Neptune where it was predicted to be. Later Neptune's orbit was found to have a small wiggle, similar to that of Uranus. After a 25-year survey, Pluto was discovered in 1930 on photographic plates made with a telescope.

The four major planets are remarkably similar. (See Appendix E.) Their densities are low like the sun's and they show bands of clouds in stripes that run parallel to their equators. They are all spinning rapidly, rotating once in from 10 to 16 hours. The comparative sizes of these and the other planets may be obtained in Appendix E. Note that the orbits of the major planets are farther apart than those of the smaller planets. This may have something to do with their origin.

Recently, Jupiter has been found to emit strong bursts of long-wavelength radio waves that radio telescopes directed toward it receive as static-like noise. No one has a complete explanation for this radio noise. One guess is that it comes from lightning in Jupiter's atmosphere. Some of it seems to be triggered when Io, one of the four largest of Jupiter's 12 moons, is in certain positions relative to Jupiter and the earth. Radio telescopes also show that Jupiter has a strong magnetic field and a Van Allen belt like the earth's, which may be the source of the radio bursts. (See Section 5–10.)

The atmospheres of the major planets are very different from those of the earth and Mars. We cannot see through them to any solid surface and their gases contain much more hydrogen than any other element. Methane (CH_4), ammonia (NH_3), and hydrogen (H_2) have been detected in these atmospheres by careful analyses of their spectra. The total hydrogen content in this mixture is about 80 percent, the same proportion of hydrogen contained in the sun. If the earth ever had such a large proportion of hydrogen in its atmosphere, it is likely that it escaped after a few million years. The earth's surface gravity is low when compared with that of the major planets and the molecules of light gases move rapidly at the high temperatures in the earth's upper atmosphere. The major planets can hold on to these light gases, because their temperatures are lower (since they are farther from the sun) and their surface gravities are higher than the earth's. (See Appendix E.)

23–7 Asteroids and meteoroids.

There is a large gap between the orbits of Mars and Jupiter. In 1801, a small body was discovered going around the sun in this gap. Since then, astronomers have tracked over 1500 other minor planets, or **asteroids**, most of which travel around the sun between the orbits of Mars and Jupiter. They are found as little streaks on long-exposure telescopic photographs. There are so many that it is difficult to keep track of them, because this involves calculating each one's orbit and allowing for deflections in orbit when they pass close to Jupiter or Mars. It is estimated that there are 50,000 asteroids, ranging in size from a few hundred kilometers in diameter for Ceres, the largest, down to small chunks. Almost all the asteroids move in nearly circular orbits around the sun in the same direction as the earth and very nearly in the same plane as the earth's orbit. A few of the asteroids have unusual orbits, some occasionally passing fairly close to the earth.

Where could these chunks have come from? It was first thought that a large planet broke up or that two planets collided. If all the asteroids were packed together, they might make one small planet the size of Mars. Since there is a great deal of space between the orbits of Mars and Jupiter, two planets there would not be likely to collide. A near collision would only swing the planets around each other into two new orbits. The forces involved would not cause them to break into fragments.

Another explanation is that the asteroids have been there since the beginning of the solar system. They might collide with each other from time to

The heating of this large iron meteorite as it plunged through the earth's atmosphere melted its surface and produced the deep pits and holes.

time, breaking into smaller bits and chunks. These chunks would go off in different directions. Some of them might hit the earth, our moon, and other planets. The impact of large chunks could explain the craters on Mars (Figure 23–9), on the moon (Chapter 22), and a few similar craters found on the earth, such as the Meteor Crater in Arizona. Such great collisions must be rare, because no new craters have been observed on the moon in the past 100 years. Now that we can observe the moon's surface from much closer, we may find that smaller craters are being formed at the present time.

However, smaller bits of material called **meteoroids** while outside the earth's atmosphere collide with the earth in large numbers. Most of them burn as **meteors** high up in the earth's atmosphere, giving off flashes of light. You often see meteors, traveling several kilometers per second, streak across the sky. Meteors are sometimes called shooting stars. Some of the large, slower-moving ones can reach the surface of the earth. When they do, they are called **meteorites.** They are made up of familiar chemical elements—the metals iron and nickel and silicate minerals like those found in basalt. Meteorites do have a peculiar structure and surface that show the effect of the heat produced by friction as they travel through the earth's atmosphere. Some are almost pure iron and have the appearance of a metal that has cooled slowly from a molten stage while under high pressure. This was once the best evidence that a larger body, such as a planet or large asteroid, was broken up into fragments in the past. This planet may have had a core like the earth's. (See chapters 3 and 16.) However, very recent studies have shown that what were

thought to be high-pressure patterns can be produced at lower temperature and pressure. Studies of the radioactive materials in meteorites show that some of them are four or five billion years old. This is the best evidence we have of the age of our solar system.

Most meteors never reach the earth's surface to become meteorites. On the average, about 20 million meteors burn up in the atmosphere every 24 hours. Sometimes they occur in showers of many thousands per hour. These **meteor showers** occur each year at the same time. You can usually see more meteors after midnight because, as the earth rotates, you are then on the side of the earth facing in the direction it is moving in its orbit around the sun. This indicates that not all meteoroids are moving in nearly circular orbits of the sun like the earth's. The earth runs into them just as a moving car runs into insects. If the insects were flying at the same speed as the car, and in the same direction, they would not be hit. Similarly, the earth would not collide with meteoroids traveling at similar speeds and in the same direction.

Meteoroids are a hazard to artificial satellites. Space probe vehicles must be designed to protect astronauts and delicate instruments from being damaged by meteoroids. Meteors also bring a great deal of material into the earth's atmosphere—about 10^6 kilograms per day—mostly as a fine dust. Deposits of this dust have been detected in the upper atmosphere and in the polar ice caps of the earth. Of course, such material is a small addition to the earth's total mass of 6×10^{24} kilograms. Even in five billion years meteoric dust would have added only 2×10^{18} kilograms, a layer about 30 centimeters deep over the entire surface of the earth.

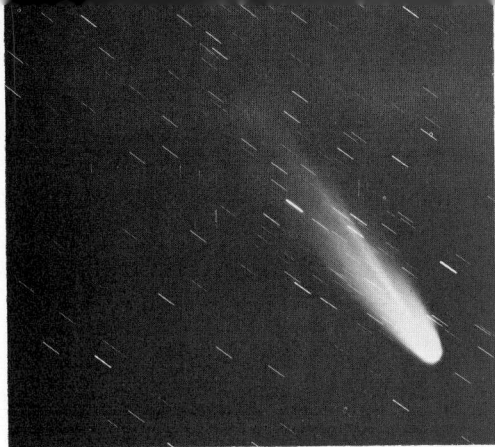

Figure 23–11 *A photograph of the Arend-Roland Comet that was visible to the naked eye over most of the United States in April of 1957.*

23–8 Are comets members of the solar system?

Comets travel toward the sun from great distances and from all directions. A recently observed large comet is shown in Figure 23–11. Most comets have orbital paths that cause them to miss the sun and swing around it in a long, narrow ellipse. At the outer end of their orbits comets are too faint to be seen, but as they approach the sun, the cloudlike haze of their heads grows larger and brighter. Then a tail grows out of this haze in the direction away from the sun. (See Figure 23–12.) This is caused by the pressure of solar radiation and the solar wind described in Section 6–9. Near the sun some comets grow very bright and long, although others remain small and dim. Analysis of their light shows that the tail and the haze around the head are formed of fine dust and gases. This gas boils out of a solid nucleus that is believed to be a few kilometers in diameter.

Three or four small comets are discovered by professional and amateur astronomers each year. Usually a large bright comet appears every 5 to 10 years. A particularly bright comet that has returned every 75 years is Halley's Comet, which is mentioned in records as far back as 240 B.C. It is due to return again in 1985.

Some comets move in orbits that cross the earth's orbit. Comets leave a trail of meteoroids made up of fine dust that continues to go around the sun near the comet's orbit. (See Figure 23–12.) When the earth passes through this trail of debris, fragments of the material enter the atmosphere as meteors. Because the average number of meteors increases remarkably, these events are called **meteor showers.** The motions of shower meteors can be measured from photographs and by radar, and the direction of these motions often associates the meteors with the orbits of comets.

From all of these observations of shower meteors and comets it is inferred that a comet is a chunk of material composed of dust, frozen water, frozen gases, and other compounds of hydrogen, carbon, oxygen, and nitrogen. The hydrogen content of comets is proportionately much higher than the earth's. The sun's radiation heats up the surface of this clump of "dirty snow" as it approaches and boils off gases that carry along free dust particles. The sunlight causes the comet's gases to shine and is also reflected from the snowy material that makes up the center of the comet's head.

Comets differ from planets and asteroids both in composition and in motion.

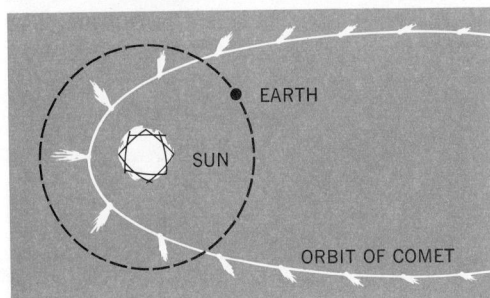

Figure 23–12 *Why does the tail of a comet point away from the sun regardless of its position?*

Their motions are not confined to the disklike region around the sun in which the planets move and their orbits are extremely long, narrow ellipses.

Thought and Discussion . . .

1. Besides the distance of Mars from the sun, what else can influence Martian surface temperatures? How can such temperatures be measured without sending instruments to Mars?
2. In what ways do the four inner planets differ from the five outer planets? What significance does this pattern have in relation to the various theories of the origin of the solar system?
3. What is the significance of the fact that the orbits of the nine planets are nearly circular and that all lie in nearly the same plane?
4. Describe how an understanding of the universal law of gravitation helped to discover Neptune.
5. How do comets differ from the other members of the solar system?

Origin of the Solar System

23–9 Theories of origin.

The goal of any theory is to fit together all observed facts. The following are major facts about the solar system that any theory of its origin must explain.

1. The solar system is isolated from other celestial objects and is composed mainly of empty space.
2. Planets revolve and rotate in the same direction and their orbits lie nearly in the same plane.
3. Planets are divided into two groups based on mass and composition.
4. Most of the comets we see have elongated orbits and short lives.
5. The solar system is about 5 billion years old.

For hundreds of years, theorists have struggled to create theories that matched the observed facts. As new evidence was gathered, new facts were added to the list that had to be considered in forming the theories.

A German philosopher, Immanuel Kant, in 1755, and a French mathematician, Pierre Laplace, in 1796, advanced similar theories that the solar system might have condensed from a spinning disk of gas thrown out by the sun. (See Figure 23–13.) There were many objections to this **nebular theory.** One of the most important was that if the planets formed from rings of gas that were spun off from a rapidly rotating sun, then today the sun should still be spinning rapidly instead of very slowly. Also, such rings of hot gas would just spread out in space, like the air that is let out of a tire, rather than condense into solid planets.

About 1900, T. C. Chamberlin, a geologist, and F. R. Moulton, an astronomer, proposed a different explanation for the origin of the solar system. Chamberlin thought that the structure and composition of the earth could be better explained by the falling together of

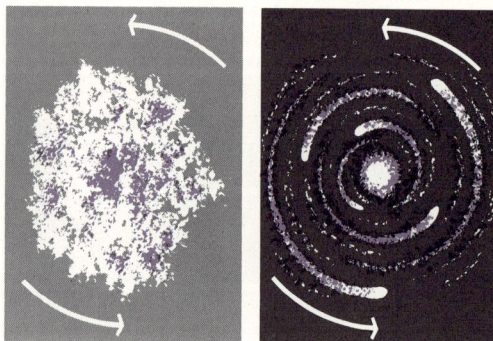

Figure 23–13 *Kant theorized that the solar system formed from huge clouds of dust and gas that condensed into planets. According to this hypothesis, the main part of a nebular cloud contracted in the central region to form the sun.*

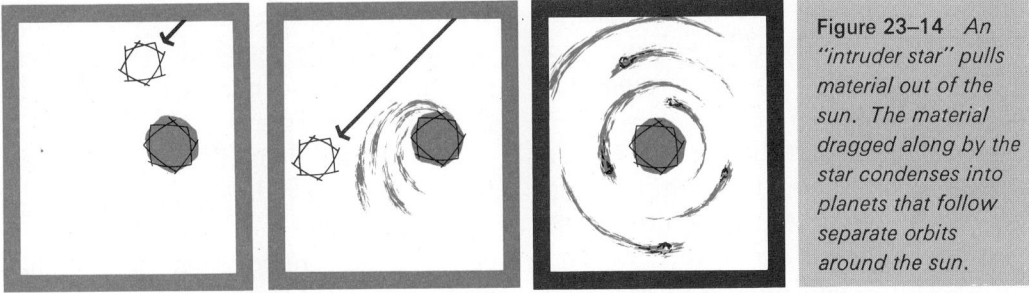

Figure 23–14 An "intruder star" pulls material out of the sun. The material dragged along by the star condenses into planets that follow separate orbits around the sun.

many small chunks of cold material that had been orbiting around the sun as the asteroids do today. This process would leave less original heat in the newborn earth than if the earth had condensed from hot gas. (See Section 6–8.) Where could such cold chunks come from? If they came from outside the solar system, they would not all be orbiting around the sun in the same direction. Also, these chunks of cold material would move in long ellipses like the orbits of comets rather than in the nearly circular orbits of planets.

Chamberlin and Moulton assumed that before the sun had any planets, another star, an "intruder," passed nearby and its gravitational force pulled material out from the sun. (See Figure 23–14.) This material later condensed into small chunks orbiting the sun in the same direction that the intruder had moved. The intruder was going so fast that it was deflected only slightly and during the next few million years it raced off to the distance of other stars. The small chunks then began to collect in groups. When two or three large ones were close enough together, their combined gravitational attraction pulled in a third or fourth from nearby, and so on until the planets were formed. According to Chamberlin and Moulton, the major planets are large because they swept up material from larger regions. Because there was far too little material beyond 35 to 40 Astronomical Units

from the sun, it was unlikely that more planets could be formed.

The **intruder hypothesis** explains the development of planets and asteroids and avoids the difficulty of accounting for a slowly rotating sun. However, it has been discredited because it assumes a highly unlikely event, the passage of another star close to the sun. In addition, careful calculations have shown that the intruder star could not give enough sideways thrust to the material it pulled out of the sun. Without this thrust, the material would just fall back into the sun instead of going into orbits to form planets as we know them.

23–10 A new look at the nebular theory.

In recent years astronomers have returned to the idea that the sun and planets came from a large, cold mass of gas and dust, or **nebula.** In addition to having much observational evidence, astronomers are now armed with a clearer understanding of the chemical nature of the solar system. Whereas earlier theories were focused on the physical behavior of the system, this newer view includes its chemical composition.

Observations with large telescopes have revealed many large gas clouds (true nebulas) between the stars, some of which are actually condensing into stars. If such a nebula does not rotate at all, it will condense to form a single star with no planets. If it is *rapidly* rotating, large eddies or whirlpools will form and the nebula will break into two or more parts and a double or triple star might be formed.

According to this theory, if a nebula had a moderate amount of rotation, a regular pattern of eddies would form in the rotating disk of gas and dust. (See Figure 23–15.) The larger eddies spaced farther apart would form large planets. These large eddies would develop smaller whirlpools inside. The whirlpools would then become the satellites of the large planet. This might explain why the giants Jupiter and Saturn have 12 and 10 moons respectively, whereas the inner planets have no "moon families." The earth is a special case, more like a double planet than a planet and relatively tiny moon. Mars' two very tiny moons may be captured asteroids rather than regular moons.

The motions in this rotating disk are complicated and have not been worked out in detail. However, the eddies seem to keep most of the rotational motion out in the spinning disk and allow the central material to shrink and form the slowly spinning sun. A large fraction of the more rapidly spinning disk would spin off and escape from the gravitational pull of the system. The rest would begin to pile up in several places because of the eddies. Then the gravitational attraction would cause this material to collect by pulling it toward centers of accumulation. Different energy conditions of the young solar system would allow different kinds of molecules to exist. Some scientists believe that methane (CH_4), ammonia (NH_3), and water (H_2O) were common when our planetary system was forming. These three compounds may have played an important part in causing other materials to collect together in the eddies.

Heat energy released in this compaction would heat the material of each new planet and cause chemical changes in the planets and their atmospheres.

At this stage it is likely that the sun would begin to radiate at the center of the system. The sun's outpouring of energy would create solar winds that would drive off most of the hydrogen and other light gases from the region of the inner planets. This would probably prevent the formation of a larger planet in an eddy between Mars and Jupiter, leaving the asteroids. However, the eddies forming the major planets would be too far away to be affected. Hence Jupiter, Saturn, Uranus, and Neptune would retain their hydrogen. This would account for their low density.

After many millions of years the planets would become more compact. The inner four would have higher densities than the four major planets because of the loss of the low-density material. The eddy pattern should have left all the planets spinning in the same direction with their satellites going the same way. Orbits of rotation around the sun would

Figure 23–15 *The nebular theory. Eddies formed in a rotating disk of dust and gas concentrated material in different parts of the disk. This material formed the planets and their satellites.*

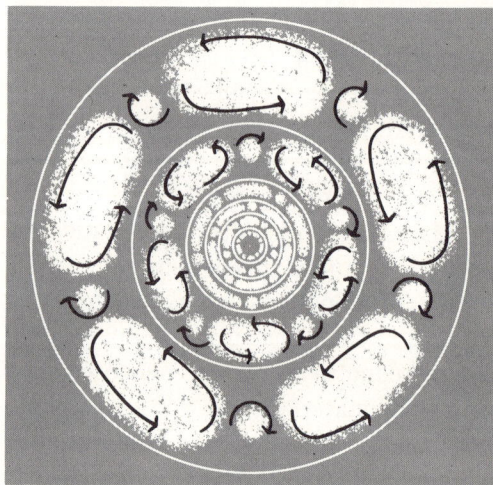

be in the same direction as that of the original nebula. The few exceptions, Venus, Uranus, and the outer satellites of Jupiter and Saturn, need special explanation. For instance, gravitational forces of Jupiter and Saturn may have captured asteroids that came too close and some of these may now be their outer moons. The explanations for these gravitational captures and other occurrences are not yet worked out in detail under the nebular theory.

Where did the comets come from? One guess is that some of the light gases and dust did not escape the system completely but formed a shell several hundred Astronomical Units from the sun where the temperature is very low. The gases condensed into blobs of snow, frozen gases, and other loose solids together with the dust particles that account for meteor showers. Each time these comets fall in toward and swing around the sun, they lose gases and dust and are slowly used up. Aside from these gradual changes in comets, the solar system seems to have remained essentially the same for several billions of years.

23–11 The early atmosphere and hydrosphere of the earth.

The present theory of the origin of earth and planets is imperfect, but it has already led to interesting studies of the origin of the earth's atmosphere and hydrosphere, closely connected with the origin of life. The study of the evolution of living things as indicated by fossils, traces them all back to a few types of living organisms in pre-Paleozoic time. (See chapters 19 and 20.) It seems likely that the first of these simple one-celled organisms were formed in early seas. What were the atmosphere and hydrosphere like when the earth was newly formed?

This space laboratory was designed to land on the planet Mars and test for the existence of life.

Today, the earth's atmosphere is 78 percent nitrogen (N_2) and 21 percent oxygen (O_2). But the solar nebula from which the sun and planets were formed was mostly hydrogen (H_2) and helium (He). Where did the nitrogen and oxygen come from and what happened to the hydrogen and helium?

As the earth formed, many chemical reactions took place between the dust particles, hydrogen, and the other gases that were heated as they were compressed by the earth's gravitational field. The newly formed sun brightened and heated the gases. Lighter molecules like hydrogen and helium escaped, leaving heavier molecules like nitrogen behind. This did not happen suddenly, so during this time the earth had a thin atmosphere of methane (CH_4), ammonia (NH_3), water (H_2O), a little hydrogen, nitrogen, and carbon dioxide (CO_2). It was in this mixture that the first living organism may have been formed.

Lightning in this early atmosphere may have provided the energy to reorganize the material into larger organic molecules. Other experiments suggest that ultraviolet radiation might have contributed the energy needed to form these molecules. Such molecules could not have formed in the presence of free oxygen, for they would have "decayed" as quickly as they formed. However,

A common species of lichen that has been growing for a year in an atmosphere of carbon dioxide.

most of the available oxygen was combined in water, carbon dioxide, and other molecules. These organic compounds would then have served as food for the first living things.

Once living organisms started to reproduce, new species evolved that could break up carbon dioxide (CO_2) into carbon (C) and oxygen (O_2). Another source of oxygen was water vapor (H_2O) broken up by ultraviolet solar radiation. These two processes might account for the oxygen in the atmosphere today.

23–12 Other worlds, other civilizations.

What are the chances that there are other worlds like our earth and other civilizations like or more advanced than ours elsewhere in the universe?

Chance or probability must be considered because even if every star in the universe had its own system of planets, it would be impossible for us to discover it at this time. Other planetary systems could not be seen even through our most powerful telescopes. They would be much too small for observers to detect their reflected light.

If the present theory of the origin of the solar system is correct, then planets might be expected to exist around many stars. In many cases planets would be a natural by-product of the formation of stars. Even if only 1 out of 10 stars had planets, there would still be more than ten billion planetary systems in our galaxy alone.

It is quite another question whether life would develop on any of the planets in each of these planetary systems. If temperature and atmospheric conditions were similar to those on the earth, would life naturally develop? Or is life a special and unique thing? Many biologists think that, given the right conditions, living things are almost certain to develop. At the present time, there is no conclusive evidence that such favorable conditions exist on any other planet in our solar system. But even if life develops on only 1 out of 10 of the 10 billion solar systems, there would still be at least a billion life-bearing planets in our galaxy. Since our galaxy is basically no different from the millions upon millions of other galaxies, they too may be the home of countless life-bearing planets. We do not know. The earth may turn out to be unique. It does seem extremely unlikely, however, that in this vast universe life would exist only on our tiny earth. The chances against this being the only planet with life on it are tremendously great.

Life on a planet does not necessarily mean an advanced civilization. Life may have developed on many planets but may have taken quite a different course in the long process of evolution. Or is it possible that evolution and natural selection would tend to result in intelligent beings that looked at least something like man? If beings like us exist elsewhere in the universe, communication with them might be impossible or highly unlikely. The distances between the stars presently seem to eliminate any thought of actual interstellar travel. This is not merely because of the long time needed for such a journey, but also because of the great energy that would be required for the trip. Such an engineering accomplishment would be far beyond our present capabilities. But the universe may hold many surprises for us. The human race is in its infancy and before it stretches a long future of possible accomplishment.

Unsolved Problems What are the exact stages in the formation of the observed features of the solar system? This question has been discussed for several centuries but no one theory is satisfactory. Even the current nebular theory of the origin of the solar system does not explain all the features of the system that we observe today.

Does life exist elsewhere in the solar system? The present answer is that most scientists do not think so. But no one really knows. What about one of the satellites of Jupiter or Saturn? Could the color changes and the unusual mark-

Thought and Discussion . . .

1. Explain the older theories of the origin of the solar system. What are their strong and weak points?
2. What is the modern theory of the origin of the solar system?
3. Contrast the early atmosphere of the earth with the present atmosphere.
4. What is the possibility of life on other planets in our solar system? in other planetary systems?

ings on the surface of Mars be caused by life forms found on the planet? These questions can be answered only by close-up photography or by landing on the planets or their satellites.

Do any other stars have systems of planets like our sun? A few stars have been discovered with deflections that indicate they may have planetary systems. If so, do these planets have life? So far, this last question is completely unanswerable. Perhaps through radio astronomy, radio signals or other communications from outside the solar system will be detected.

CHAPTER REVIEW

Summary

Along with other planets and satellites, the earth and the moon are members of the sun's family, the solar system. Because their strange motions in relation to the stars were observed by ancient peoples, the planets were known as wanderers in the sky.

Ptolemy used an earth-centered system with epicycles to explain the motions of the planets. His explanation was accepted for many centuries. Then Copernicus proposed a sun-centered system. Galileo's observations with the aid of a telescope supported this system, as does your investigation of the phases and motions of Planet X. Brahe's accurate observations provided the

basis for Kepler's three laws of planetary motion. These laws were then explained by Newton with his laws of motion and gravitation, which founded celestial mechanics.

A model of the solar system demonstrates how vast the distances are within it and how relatively empty it is, despite the planets, satellites, comets, asteroids, and meteoric chunks and dust that move in orbit around the sun. The terrestrial planets are composed of heavier materials and have greater densities than the major outer planets. The densities of these giants are so low that they must be composed largely of gases like hydrogen and helium. Although very little can be observed of Mercury and Venus, more is being learned about Mars, its surface features, and its atmosphere. The meteoroids in space sometimes pass into the earth's atmosphere and burn up as meteors. Larger meteors may even reach the earth's surface as meteorites. A number of comets move in toward the sun each year, pass around it, and then retreat in their elongated orbits toward the outer reaches of the solar system.

A theory of the formation of the solar system from a cold, thin, whirling nebula of gas and dust has replaced an older nebular theory and an intruder-star theory. Planets formed gradually, it is believed, by the collection of this material. The early atmosphere of the earth has changed with the loss of lighter gases and the addition of oxygen from plants as life evolved. Life may exist, too, on planets in other planetary systems.

In the chapters that follow, you turn from our sun, the center of its planetary system, to other suns, the stars that twinkle in the night sky. Is our sun a typical star? What are the billions of other stars like? What methods can be used to find out?

Questions and Problems

A

1. What evidence led Galileo to discover a flaw in Ptolemy's geocentric theory?
2. Explain retrograde motion.
3. Describe how the period of revolution of a planet can be measured.
4. Saturn has a period of revolution of 29.5 years and is about 9.5 times farther from the sun than the earth. Does Kepler's third law of planetary motion hold true for Saturn?
5. Describe the two distinct groups into which the planets can be divided. In which group would you place Pluto? Why?
6. Describe two ways of detecting the atmosphere of a planet.
7. What are some possible explanations for the existence of the asteroids?

8. Distinguish the terms meteoroid, meteor, and meteorite.
9. Describe the original nebular theory of Kant and Laplace. What were the shortcomings of this theory?

B

1. How do the phases of Venus prove that the earth is not the center of the solar system?
2. How do earth-centered (geocentric) and sun-centered (heliocentric) theories of planetary motion differ?
3. What kept Tycho Brahe from accepting a heliocentric theory? Why was he unable to resolve this problem?
4. Explain why Kepler's second law of planetary motion can be called the law of equal areas.
5. If the distance of Venus from the sun is 0.7 times the earth's distance, then what is its period (year)?
6. From information we have about Venus' surface, discuss the possibility of the presence of familiar life forms on that planet.
7. How were scientists able to determine Venus' mass from the Mariner space probe to that planet?
8. In what ways do comets differ from other members of the solar system?
9. Describe the intruder hypothesis. Why has it been abandoned?

C

1. After you watch the sky day and night for several years, what do you see that shows the solar system to be a small group of things separate from the rest of the universe?
2. Why has Venus been able to retain most of its atmosphere whereas Mars has not retained much?
3. Jupiter is about 318 times more massive than the earth and its diameter is about 10 times that of the earth. How many times more would a 50-kilogram mass weigh on Jupiter than on Earth? (Refer to Section 5–6.)

4. Write down the characteristics of the solar system under two headings: (A) those features that fit under Newton's laws and would be true no matter how the system was started, and (B) those features that are clues to the origin of the system.

Suggested Readings

BOOKS

Allen, Thomas. *The Quest.* Chilton Books—Educational Division, Philadelphia, 1965.

Broms, Allan. *Our Emerging Universe.* Dell Publishing Co., Inc., New York, 1964.

Inglis, S. J. *Planets, Stars, and Galaxies.* John Wiley & Sons, Inc., New York, 1961.

Nininger, Harvey H. *Ask a Question about Meteorites.* American Meteorite Lab, Denver, 1961. Paperback.

Nininger, Harvey H. *Out of the Sky: An Introduction to Meteoritics.* Dover Publications, Inc., New York, 1952. Paperback.

Ohring, George. *Weather On the Planets.* Doubleday & Company, Inc., Garden City, N.Y., 1966.

Page, Thornton and Lou W. Page. *Wanderers in the Sky.* The Macmillan Company, New York, 1964.

Page, Thornton and Lou W. Page. *Neighbors of the Earth.* The Macmillan Company, New York, 1965.

Page, Thornton and Lou W. Page. *Origin of the Solar System.* The Macmillan Company, New York, 1966.

Ronan, C. A. *Man Probes the Universe.* Doubleday & Company, Inc. (Nature and Science Library), Garden City, N.Y., 1964.

Sullivan, Walter. *We Are Not Alone.* McGraw-Hill Book Company, New York, 1966. Paperback.

Trinklein, Frederick E. and Charles M. Huffer. *Modern Space Science.* Holt, Rinehart & Winston, Inc., New York, 1961.

Watson, Fletcher G. *Between the Planets,* rev. ed. Doubleday and Company, Inc. (Natural History Library), Garden City, N.Y. Paperback.

Whipple, Fred L. *Earth, Moon, and Planets.* Harvard University Press, Cambridge, Mass., 1963.

PERIODICALS

Barnes, Virgil E. "Tektites." *Scientific American,* November, 1961. (Also Scientific American Offprint #802, W. H. Freeman & Co., Publishers, San Francisco.)

Brown, Harrison. "The Age of the Solar System." *Scientific American,* April, 1957. (Also Scientific American Offprint #102.)

Gingerich, Owen. "The Solar System Beyond Neptune." *Scientific American,* April, 1959. (Also Scientific American Offprint #295.)

Nicholson, T. D. "Early 20th-Century Discoveries are Keys to Star Evolution." *Natural History,* August, 1965.

Reynolds, John H. "The Age of the Elements in the Solar System." *Scientific American,* November, 1960. (Also Scientific American Offprint #253.)

Sky and Telescope. Sky Publishing Corp., Cambridge, Mass.

Urey, Harold C., "The Origin of the Earth." *Scientific American,* October, 1952. (Also Scientific American Offprint #833.)

to Strive to Seek to Find...

TENNYSON . . . ULYSSES

Chapter 24 Stars as Other Suns

What do you see when you look at the next nearest star? only a point of light. Even through the world's largest telescope, the 200-inch reflector on Palomar Mountain, the stars are so far away they are all only tiny points of light.

How can scientists hope to learn what stars are like and how they compare with the sun when they cannot even see their surfaces? "There are some things," said the nineteenth century French philosopher Auguste Comte, "of which the human race must forever remain in ignorance, for example, the chemical constitution of the heavenly bodies." Comte was wrong. We know what the stars are made of. We also know something about their sizes and temperatures, their masses and brightness, and how they move in space.

How was this information obtained? It certainly did not come from space travel to the stars. Even in this age of space exploration, moving from star to star will prove to be much harder than going from planet to planet within our solar system. This is because of the fantastically great distances between the stars. When the planet Mars is closest to the earth, sunlight reflected from its surface takes only three minutes to reach our planet. Light from distant Pluto takes about five and a half hours. But the radiation from the star nearest the sun, traveling at the speed of light, takes more than four years to reach the earth. Astronauts trying to reach this star would have to travel at speeds near the speed of light or face the possibility of dying of old age before getting back to earth. Propelling a spaceship at such high speeds from star to star will require a tremendous fuel supply. Even if rocket motors powered by nuclear energy are available such trips will have to wait until the distant future.

It looks as if many years will go by before astronauts will reach the stars. Scientists, therefore, must continue to use planet earth and possibly the moon as observing platforms with help from satellites or space stations to collect the only information available from stars—their radiation. Fortunately, this radiation can supply a great deal of information. Radiation has three characteristics that can be studied: how much there is (its quantity), where it comes from (its direction), and what kind it is (its quality). Investigating each of these characteristics with the help of large telescopes has provided astronomers with many different kinds of information about the stars. Taken together, this information provides a picture of the universe in which we live.

An astronomer inside the prime-focus cage of the giant 200-inch telescope. The reflecting surface of the mirror is seen in the background.

Measuring the Amount of Radiation

24–1 How luminous are the stars?

Have you ever looked carefully at the starry sky on a clear, dark night? To the unaided eye some stars appear as brilliant, dazzling objects while others can be only dimly seen. How much brighter is one star than another?

Scientists want to know not only how bright stars look, but how bright they actually are. The energy output of the sun was calculated in Section 6–10. How does the energy output of the stars compare with that of the sun? Sirius, the brightest star in the sky, for example, appears about four times as bright as the bright star Rigel (RY-gel). Does this mean that Sirius actually gives off more light or that it is closer to us than Rigel? To compare the light radiated by any two stars, the luminosity of each must be known. **Luminosity** is the total amount of energy radiated into space every second by a celestial object.

To calculate the luminosity of a star, an astronomer must measure the amount of light received and the distance of the star from the earth. Suppose you are standing 3 meters from a 100-watt light bulb with a light meter such as photographers use. The light meter tells you how much light the bulb gives off at that distance. If you now walk away from the bulb, your meter will indicate that less light is reaching you. If you used a 50-watt bulb you would get a lower light-meter reading at the same distance. Knowing the distance to the light bulb and the reading on your light meter, you could actually calculate the luminosity of the light bulb.

An astronomer does essentially the same thing for the sun and stars. As you must have guessed, the sun appears to be billions of times brighter than any other star only because it is so close to the earth. Comparing Sirius with Rigel, you will find that Rigel is actually about 2000 times more luminous than Sirius, even though it appears to be only one fourth as bright. This is explained by the fact that Rigel is over 90 times farther away than Sirius.

When the luminosities of stars are compared, enormous differences become evident. Some stars, like Rigel, are real beacons in the sky, pouring 40,000 times more energy into space each second than does the sun. Others are feebly-shining objects with less than $\frac{1}{10,000}$ of the luminosity of the sun. How did such facts come to be discovered? What sort of "light meters" does an astronomer use and how does he calculate the distance to a star?

In estimating how bright a star looks to you, it is convenient to use the *magnitude system*. This system actually goes back over 2000 years to the Greek astronomer Hipparchus who divided the stars he saw in the sky into six magnitude classes. The brightest he called first magnitude, those somewhat fainter second magnitude, and so on, all the way to the stars just barely visible to the naked eye, which he called sixth magnitude. Modern astronomers still use this system but have expanded it to include the very brightest objects in the sky (given minus magnitudes) as well as stars too faint for Hipparchus to have seen. Magnitudes for certain celestial objects are listed in Table 24–1, and compared in brightness with Polaris, the North Star, which is a second-magnitude star and with the limits of various instruments.

TABLE 24–1 MAGNITUDES OF SOME CELESTIAL OBJECTS

OBJECT	MAGNITUDE	TIMES BRIGHTER OR FAINTER THAN POLARIS
SUN	—26.5	250,000,000,000
FULL MOON	—12.5	1,000,000
VENUS (AT BRIGHTEST)	—4	250
JUPITER	—2	40
MARS (AT BRIGHTEST)	—2	40
SIRIUS	—1.5	25
ALDEBARAN	1	3
ALTAIR	1	3
POLARIS	2	↑ BRIGHTER / ↓ FAINTER
NAKED-EYE LIMIT	6	40
BINOCULAR LIMIT	10	1,800
10 INCH TELESCOPE LIMIT	14	60,000
200-INCH TELESCOPE LIMIT (PHOTOGRAPHIC)	23.5	400,000,000

ACTIVITY   *In order to measure stellar luminosities, astronomers must measure how bright the stars appear. You can also estimate stellar brightnesses just by looking at the stars. You know that the stars in the sky do not all look equally bright. How much brighter is one than another? What about color? Are all stars white or are some yellowish or even reddish in color?*

You can find Polaris by following the line of the two pointer stars in the bowl of the Big Dipper. (See Appendix E and Figure 4–2.) (1)*How many stars do you see in the Big Dipper?* (2)*Are all these stars of equal magnitude?* (3)*Are they all the same color?* (4)*What are the magnitudes of the six stars in addition to Polaris in Ursa Minor (the Little Dipper)?* (5)*How many times brighter is Polaris than the faintest star of the six?* (6)*Find as many of the following bright stars as you can and estimate their magnitudes: Rigel, Castor, Pollux, Procyon (PRO-see-yun), Sirius, Aldebaran (All-DEB-ah-run), Betelgeuse (BET-el-gerse), Regulus, Spica, and Arcturus (ARK-tour-us.) Did you notice any differences in the colors of these stars?* (7)*Can you guess why stars have different colors?*

24–2 Stars vary in brightness.

Most stars keep the same brightness from night to night. The stars in the Big Dipper look the same night after night and year after year, for example. However, certain stars do go through a cycle of brightening and dimming. The bright star Algol (ALL-gaul) in the constellation Perseus is a good example. Find Algol on the star charts in Appendix E.

In 1782, the English astronomer John Goodricke (1764–1786) discovered that Algol appeared fainter than usual for several hours at a time. This dimming occurred at regular intervals of 2 days, 21 hours. His explanation, which turned out to be correct, was that Algol was really two stars. They revolved around one another and eclipsed each other regularly. Each time a star is eclipsed, the light that would normally come to us is blocked and we notice that it dims. We know some 3000 of these pairs of stars, called **eclipsing binary** systems. The way in which the light of such a pair of stars changes with time is shown in Figure 24–1.

Eclipsing binary stars help the astronomer learn about the sizes of the stars. Although the eclipsing binary star appears only as a point of light, the accurate measurement of the changes in its light with time can be used to calculate the diameters of stars. Can you see how this could be calculated? Examine Figure 24–1 again.

Using this and other methods, astronomers have found a wide range in star sizes. Some, like Antares (AN-TARE-eez), are so huge that the sun plus the earth's orbit could easily fit inside one of them. Other stars are much smaller than the sun and in some cases they are not much bigger than the earth. Figure 24–2 compares the sizes of some stars, illustrating how greatly they vary.

Eclipsing binary stars change their brightness only because one star actually blocks the light of the other. Other stars behave differently from eclipsing binaries. Imagine a huge, glowing balloon that swells up and then shrinks again every few days, becoming bright each time it expands and faint when it con-

tracts. Certain stars that behave like this are called **pulsating variable stars.** They pulsate in and out because they expand and contract, and they are called variable stars because it has been found that their brightness changes as they go through their change in size.

Several kinds of pulsating variable stars are known. Some are giant red stars that change their brightness only every year or two. Others are smaller, white stars that brighten and dim regularly every few hours. An important class of pulsating stars is the **Cepheid** (SEE-fee-id) **variable star** named after the bright star Delta Cephei. You can find this star on the star charts in Appendix E. If you watch Delta Cephei for a few weeks, comparing its brightness with the stars around it, you will notice that it changes from fourth to fifth magnitude and back again to fourth every 5.4 days. Most Cepheid variable stars are giant yellow stars that change brightness regularly every week or two.

Cepheid variable stars are important because astronomers can estimate their distances from the way they change in brightness. The most luminous Cepheid variable stars pulsate slowly whereas less luminous ones pulsate rapidly. Accurate measurements of the changing light from these stars can therefore tell astronomers how luminous they are. A comparison of their luminosity (how bright they actually are) with their average brightness (how bright they look)

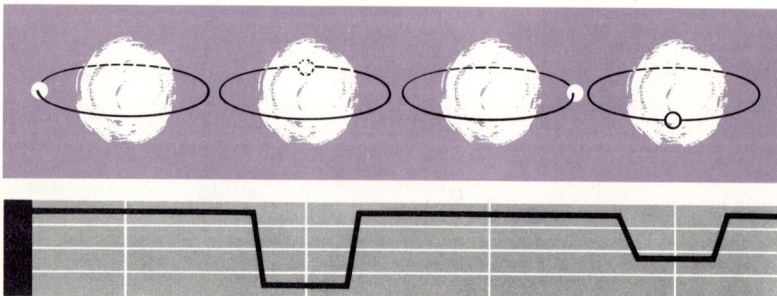

Figure 24–1 *Each time one star eclipses the other, the total light of the system is cut down. The way the light changes with time indicates the diameters of the stars.*

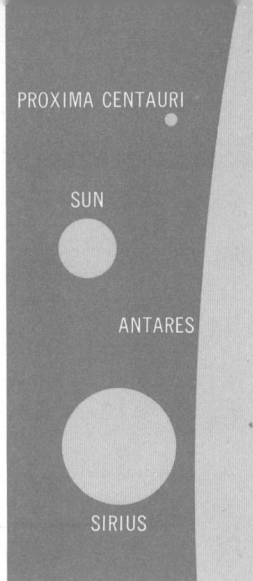

PROXIMA CENTAURI

SUN

ANTARES

SIRIUS

Figure 24–2 *Stars vary widely in size. Compare the size of our sun with that of the giant star Antares. Other stars are so small that they would not show at this scale.*

then allows their distance from earth to be calculated. Cepheid variable stars frequently appear in other star systems very far from our own. If the distance to the Cepheid variable star can be estimated, the distance to that entire star system of which it is a part is known. Since such distances are very difficult to measure in any other way, Cepheid variable stars are among those most useful to astronomers.

Other stars called novas go through tremendous changes in brightness. **Nova** means "new star," because observers first thought they were watching the birth of a new star when a nova suddenly flared up. Actually, novas are small hot stars that occasionally blow off their outer layers. When this happens the nova may increase in brightness by 50,000 times, stay that way for a few days, then dim slowly back to its original brightness. A typical nova is shown in Figure 24–3. Astronomers are not

Figure 24–3 *The star Nova Herculis as it appeared before and after its outburst in 1934. How would you determine the change in magnitude?*

certain why novas explode as they do but think that these great explosions may be a way for stars to shed mass before dying of old age.

An even more spectacular kind of exploding star is the **supernova.** As you might expect from the name, this is a super kind of nova—a star that actually blows itself to pieces. Supernovas flare up to hundreds of millions of times the luminosity of the sun. Supernovas can be seen over enormous distances, like a slow-motion flashbulb, flaring up brightly and then fading out.

Supernovas are rare. Only three have been observed in our Milky Way galaxy in the past 1000 years. The most spectacular supernova was recorded in Chinese and Japanese literature of A.D. 1054. Although very far away, it reached a brightness in the sky greater than the brilliance of Venus and could still be seen two years later. The remains of this enormous explosion are now visible as a large cloud of gas, called the Crab Nebula. The Crab Nebula emits strong radio waves. Instruments in rockets have also detected powerful X-ray radiation from the nebula. Perhaps when more observations are made, the puzzle of why some stars become supernovas may be solved.

Thought and Discussion . . .

1. What can be learned about stars from accurate measurements of the amount of light received from them on earth?
2. How is the luminosity of stars measured and calculated?
3. Compare the luminosity and size of the sun with other stars.
4. Why do astronomers use minus magnitudes?
5. Of what special use are Cepheid variable stars to astronomers?

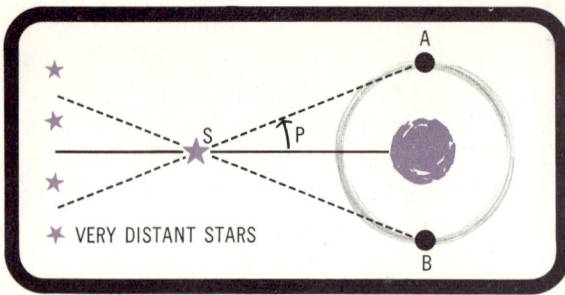

Figure 24–4 *The stellar parallax angle (P) is measured by locating the star in relation to other stars, first from point A, then from Point B.*

Measuring the Direction of Radiation

24–3 How far away are the stars?

How would you measure the distances to the stars? You know that astronomers can estimate the distances to Cepheid variable stars. But how about ordinary stars on your star chart like Sirius and Altair (ALL-tare)? Could you bounce a radar beam from a star and calculate its distance as is done for the moon? The answer of course is no, because the stars are so much farther from earth than the moon. No radar beam is powerful enough to reach even the nearest star and return an echo strong enough to be measured. This would be like whispering across the Grand Canyon and trying to hear the echo.

Astronomers measure the distance to nearby stars by the parallax method, which was described in Section 22–6. Instead of measuring the parallax angle from widely separated points on the earth's surface, they make measurements from opposite sides of the earth's orbit around the sun as shown in Figure 24–4. Astronomers measure the tiny shifts in the direction to the star on photographs taken six months apart. This means that they can separate their observing stations by 300 million kilometers, the diameter of the earth's orbit, rather than merely 12,000 kilometers, the diameter of the earth.

Even with this great distance between observing stations, the stars are so very far away that the parallax angles can barely be measured. In Section 23–3 you read that Tycho Brahe tried to measure stellar parallax angles and failed. This is no wonder, because the nearest star is still so far away that its parallax angle is only 0.76 second of arc (0.00021 degree). This is like measuring the diameter of a dime 2.5 kilometers away. Tycho never had a chance!

How far away is Proxima Centauri, (Sen-TAW-ree), the nearest star? Its distance can be calculated by measuring the parallax angle and knowing the distance of the earth from the sun. It turns out to be 4×10^{13} kilometers. This is such a large number that it is more convenient to use a larger unit of distance. A **light-year** is the distance that light travels in one year. Since the speed of light is 3×10^5 kilometers per second, Proxima Centauri is 4.3 light-years away. This means that even the nearest star is so distant that its light takes over four years to reach us! The nearest star visible to the naked eye from most parts of the United States is the bright star Sirius, about eight light-years away.

As you might expect, the parallax angles are so small for distant stars that they become impossible to measure ac-

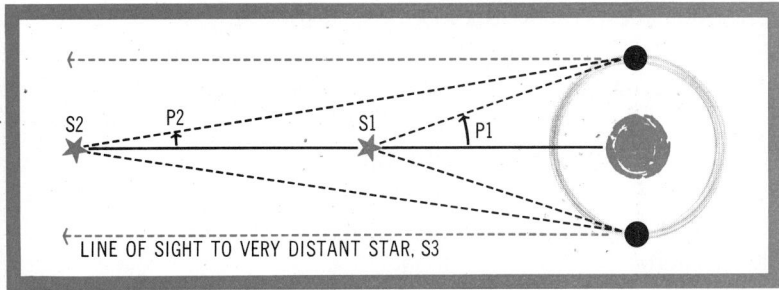

curately even with the largest telescopes. (See Figure 24–5.) Although the distances of about 6000 stars have been measured by the parallax method, distances to stars farther than about 300 light-years away cannot be measured accurately with it. For more remote stars there are other, although less accurate, methods of measuring distance.

24-4 The stars move in space.

Have there been any changes in the shape of the Big Dipper since you first saw it? Actually, the answer is yes, but the distance to these stars is so great that you will not have noticed any of these changes. Figure 24–6 shows the Big Dipper today and 100,000 years from now. The stars actually do move with respect to one another, but their motions appear very slight because of their immense distances from us.

Figure 24–6 *The stars in the Big Dipper (A) are slowly changing their positions. In 100,000 years they will appear as shown in B.*

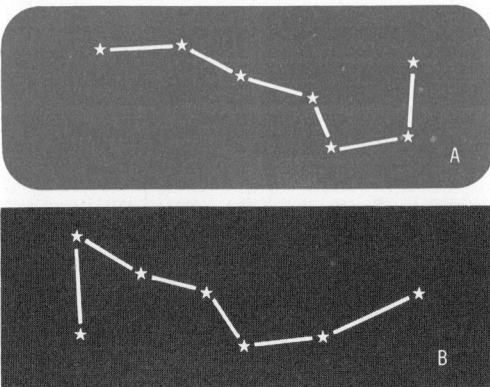

The great English astronomer Edmund Halley (1656–1742), whom you read about in Chapter 7, was the first to show that stars really do move in the sky. He compared ancient star positions, listed by Ptolemy in A.D. 150 for the bright stars Arcturus and Sirius, with positions measured in the early eighteenth century. Halley was able to show that Arcturus had moved about one degree (twice the apparent size of the moon in the sky) and Sirius half a degree during that interval. Astronomers have calculated similar motions for many stars by measuring the tiny shifts in the position of star images on photographic plates made with large telescopes. The star with the greatest known motion in the sky is a faint red object known as Barnard's star, shown in Figure 4–3. In 180 years, Barnard's star moves through an angle of about 0.5 degree, which is the angular size of the full moon in the sky.

The discovery by Halley that individual stars move in space destroyed forever the ancient idea of a sphere of "fixed stars" in the sky.

What do motions in the sky tell us about the actual motions of the stars in space? They tell part of the story, but not all of it. Suppose you see an airplane flying over your house and note that it takes one minute to move from a point directly overhead and disappear behind a tree in your backyard. How fast is the plane flying? You cannot answer this question unless you also know how high the plane is flying. If its altitude is 10 kilometers, it must be a very fast jet flying near the speed of sound. But if it is a small plane at an altitude of one kilometer, it only needs to move at a little over 100 kilometers per hour to sweep across the same portion of sky just as fast as the jet. Draw a diagram of this situation so that you will understand better how the plane's altitude and speed are related.

Similarly, the distances to the stars must be known in order to calculate how fast they really move from how fast they appear to move in the sky. Stars that seem to move rapidly across the sky may actually be moving very fast in space, like Arcturus, or may only appear to be going fast because they are so close to earth, like Sirius, or may be both close and moving fast, like Barnard's star.

In addition to moving across the sky, stars also move toward or away from the earth. How can such motions be detected? You can tell if an airplane is moving toward or away from you because it will appear to grow either larger or smaller. Stars, however, are so distant that they will not become measurably brighter or dimmer as they move toward or away from you unless you wait hundreds or thousands of years.

Nevertheless, there is a method of discovering this. Remember that the Doppler effect was described in Section 4–5 (Figure 4–11) to help prove that the earth revolves around the sun. Like the pitch of an auto horn as it moves toward or away from you, light waves are also affected by rapid motion. Stars approaching you will look just a little bluer than normal, while those moving away from you will look somewhat more red. You cannot see these tiny changes in the color of starlight, but astrono-mers can analyze the light spectra and discover not only whether the star is moving toward or away from us but also how fast the star is moving.

Knowing the speed of a star toward or away from us as well as its speed across the sky, you can calculate the actual space motion or velocity in space with respect to the sun. Those stars near the sun seem to move in all directions. Some apparently move toward us, some away from us, and others across our line of sight. While the average speed of these stars is about 20 kilometers per second, a few, like Barnard's star, move with speeds of over 100 kilometers per second. (See Figure 4–3.)

Would you expect the sun to be fixed in space or do you suppose it too is in motion? An analysis of the motions of the stars around us shows that the sun is also moving. Carrying its family of planets with it, the sun is speeding at 19 kilometers per second with respect to its neighboring stars in the general direction of the constellation Hercules.

If the earth revolves around the sun while the entire solar system moves through space, how do you think the earth would appear to move to an observer outside the solar system? You can see from Figure 4–18 that this would be a kind of spiral path.

24–5 How massive are stars?

Suppose you had a large telescope and were measuring the small changes in direction of the light from the bright star Sirius caused by its motion in the sky. If you continued your observations for perhaps 40 years, you would notice that Sirius moves in a wiggly rather than in a straight line across the sky. How would you explain this?

You read in Section 5–4 that any object will travel with constant speed in a straight line unless an outside force acts on it. Some outside force must be acting on Sirius. Do you know what caused it? You have probably guessed that the force was produced by the gravitational attraction of another star. Sirius has a companion star so faint that it is visible only at certain times. Sirius and its companion revolve around one another as both move through space together, like the earth-moon system.

Just as the masses of the sun and moon are calculated by the way in which they swing the earth around, the masses of stars can be calculated from measurements of their gravitational effects on each other. You read in Section 24–2 that many stars are actually double rather than single and sometimes block each other's light. In addition to these eclipsing binary systems, more than 20,000 double stars have been discovered. In each case, two stars move around each other, sometimes taking hundreds or thousands of years to make a complete orbit. One example is Krüger 60, shown in Figure 24–7. Measurements from such photographs give the astronomer the data needed to calculate the masses of the stars. In this way astronomers have learned that the masses of the stars range from less than a tenth of the sun's mass for the smallest stars to over 50 times the solar mass for the largest.

Figure 24–7 *The double star indicated in these photographs is Krüger 60. The system is made up of two stars that slowly revolve around each other.*

ACTIVITY *Assuming that the two stars in Figure 24–7 revolve around each other in circular orbits, see if you can estimate from the photographs how long it takes them to make one complete orbit. What would a light intensity curve look like for these stars?*

If the size and mass of a star have been measured, its average density can also be calculated. As you might expect, some stars are more dense and others are less dense than the sun. Antares, for example, has an average density of less than a millionth that of the sun. This density is about a thousandth that of air at sea level. The companion of Sirius, on the other hand, has an average density nearly 50,000 times as great as that of the sun. If you were this dense you would weigh several thousand tons! In each star the density is greater at the center of the star than in its outer layers.

Thought and Discussion . . .

1. What is a light-year? Why do astronomers use this unit to measure stellar distances?
2. What are the limitations of the parallax method for measuring stellar distances? Why do these limitations exist?
3. If some stars are moving as rapidly as 20 kilometers across our line of sight, why do their positions seem to remain constant from night to night?
4. Describe the path of the earth as seen by an observer in another galaxy.

1908   1915   1920

Measuring the Quality of Radiation

24–6 Colors are a clue to stellar temperatures.

If you have good weather with clear nights, you may notice that different stars have different colors. For example, Betelgeuse is a red star, Capella is yellow, and Spica is bluish-white.

What causes these different colors? The answer is related to temperature. Have you ever seen a piece of metal being heated? It glows first with a dull red color, which turns to orange, then yellow, and finally to bluish-white as the temperature increases. In the same manner, cooler stars look red while the hottest stars look blue.

Do stars shine only with red or blue light? No, but they may emit more red or blue light than any other color. The radiation from any star, like that from the sun shown in Figure 6–18, consists of an entire spectrum. This spectrum ranges from shortwave gamma rays, X-rays, ultraviolet, and blue radiation on the high-energy side, to longwave red, infrared, and radio radiation on the low energy side. High temperature stars emit mostly high-energy radiation, whereas radiation from low temperature stars is mostly of low energy.

This is easy to see from energy curves like the ones shown in Figure 24–8. Notice that the hotter stars not only emit more blue than red radiation and hence look bluer, but that they also emit more radiation of every kind because they pour out more energy from each square centimeter of their surfaces.

Just as they do for the sun (Section 6–12), astronomers use these facts to measure the temperatures of the stars. The astronomers analyze the quality or kind of radiation received from the stars. From this they can then calculate their surface temperatures.

Such methods have shown that the temperatures of the stars range from 50,000°C or more for the hottest blue stars to 1500°C or less for the coolest red stars. Do you remember reading in Section 6–12 that the sun, a yellow star, has a surface temperature of about 6000°C? Our nearest star is neither among the hottest nor among the coolest of the stars.

Figure 24–8 *Energy is emitted in different wavelengths by hot sources at different temperatures. These wavelengths correspond to different colors.*

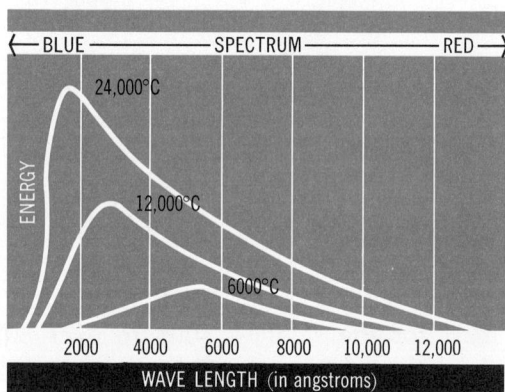

Figure 24–9 *A light bulb shows a continuous spectrum in a spectroscope. If light passes through a cooler gas cloud, a dark-line spectrum is produced. Energy emitted by the cloud itself yields a bright-line spectrum. These different spectra provide different kinds of information.*

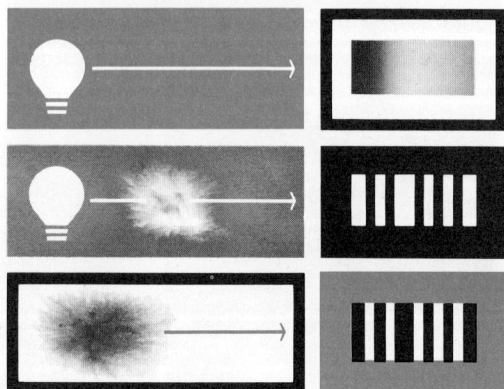

24–7 Investigating spectra.

About 300 years ago Newton passed sunlight through a glass prism. Although sunlight looks yellowish-white, Newton showed that it actually contains all the colors of the rainbow. A century and a half passed before scientists thought of placing a narrow slit in front of the prism to make the first spectroscope. With this instrument the sun's spectrum was discovered to be not a continuous rainbow of colors but to be crossed by many dark lines. In this investigation you will examine the dark-line spectra of several stars to see if you can see any relationships among them.

Procedure

Using the spectra strips provided for you, try to place the spectra in order with reference to the lines on them. Answer the following question:

(1) What is the basis for the order you chose?

Read the following definition of dark-line spectra: **Dark-line** or absorption spectra are produced when radiation from the underlying layers of a star passes through the cooler outer layers on its way to earth. The continuous spectrum from the lower layers is then broken up by a series of dark lines. These result from the cooler outer layers absorbing certain radiations that would normally have reached us.

(2) What do the dark lines on your spectra strips represent?

(3) Which of the stars are probably the hottest?

A **continuous spectrum** is a rainbow of radiation in which each color merges smoothly into the next without interruption. Continuous spectra are emitted by glowing solids or liquids, such as the filament of a light bulb, or by the hot underlying layers in a star. **Bright-line** or emission spectra consist of individual colored lines with dark places between them. The bright lines are produced by hot gases at low pressure, such as the gas in a neon light tube, or a celestial gas mass such as the great nebula in Orion. The three kinds of spectra are shown in Figure 24–9 and on page 533.

Look at an ordinary light bulb with a small hand spectroscope. Now look at a fluorescent light tube. (4) How do the spectra differ? Look also at sodium, mercury, and neon lights with the spectroscope, if these are available. (5) Describe the variations among them. The spectrum of sky-light is similar to that of direct sunlight. Look at the spectrum of the sky as close to the sun as possible without looking directly at the sun. (DO NOT LOOK DIRECTLY AT THE SUN BECAUSE YOU MAY DAMAGE YOUR EYES.) (6) Describe the sun's spectrum. (7) How can spectra assist you in studying stars?

24–8 What are stars made of ?

It was discovered about a century ago that the spectral lines produced in the laboratory by heating certain chemical elements were the same as those observed in stellar spectra. Each chemical element has its own set of spectral lines that are different from those of any other chemical element. The yellow lines of sodium vapor, for example, are radiated only by sodium vapor. If you observe these yellow lines anywhere in the universe with your spectroscope, you can be certain that sodium vapor is present.

The spectral lines for each chemical element are like a set of fingerprints. No two elements have the same fingerprints, and once he knows what those for a particular element look like, the astronomical detective can recognize that element by the character of its radiation. Figure 24–11 (page 533) shows a number of different kinds of spectra.

There is great variety in stellar spectra. Blue stars show spectral lines consisting almost entirely of those of hydrogen and helium, whereas the spectra of yellow stars like the sun are filled with the lines of iron, nickel, and other metals. Red stars often show the fingerprints of titanium oxide and carbon molecules in their spectra as well as the lines of metallic elements. Does this mean that blue stars are made mostly of hydrogen and helium, yellow stars of metals, and red stars of titanium oxide?

No, because temperature also influences radiation from the stars.

Imagine a box that contains a sample of solar material—mostly hydrogen, some helium, and traces of all the other chemical elements. Suppose you heat the box and examine the contents, which cannot escape from the box, with a spectroscope. What would you see?

Even though you would always be looking at the same material in the box, its spectrum would look very different at different temperatures. For a temperature of 1500° to 2000°C the spectrum would consist mainly of red light, crossed with spectral lines caused by titanium oxide and other molecules. At 6000°C the radiation from the box would turn yellowish and the spectral lines of the molecules would be replaced by lines of iron, nickel, and other metals, as in the spectrum of the sun. At 30,000°C the spectrum of radiation would be mostly bluish and the spectral lines of iron and the other metals would be replaced by the lines of hydrogen and helium atoms.

These differences in the spectra are obviously due not to a difference in chemical composition but to differences in temperature only. Molecules exist and glow only at relatively low temperatures but atoms of hydrogen and helium require very high temperatures before they will glow at all. Reexamine the spectra strips of Section 24–7.

The differences among stellar spectra are caused almost entirely by differences in temperature. Actually, most of the stars are made of about the same materials as the sun—mostly hydrogen (50 to 75 percent), with helium the next most abundant element (20 to 45 percent), and with all the other elements together making up less than five percent of the total mass of any star.

24–9 Comparing the sun with other stars.

You have studied how the luminosities, diameters, masses, and temperatures of the stars are measured. Would you expect any of these quantities to be related? It was learned many years ago that the masses and luminosities of most stars are related. The more massive the star is, the greater is its luminosity. In this investigation you will study another relationship, that between the luminosity and temperature of a star. This was first investigated by the Danish astronomer Ejnar Hertzsprung and the American astronomer H. N. Russell over a half century ago and resulted in the *Hertzsprung-Russell,* or H-R, diagram. By plotting the sun in an H-R diagram, you will see quickly how it compares with other stars. In addition, you will investigate the location of stars of various temperatures on the diagram in the next chapter when you study how stars evolve.

Procedure

Using a blue pencil mark for each star, plot the data on each of the 20 brightest stars, given in Appendix E, on a piece of graph paper with luminosity on the vertical scale and temperature on the horizontal scale. Plot the sun in the diagram. (1)Is the sun more or less luminous than the brightest stars in the sky? (2)Is it hotter or cooler than most?

Now on the same graph plot the data on each of the 20 nearest stars in Appendix E, using a red pencil mark for each star. (3)Is the sun more or less luminous than the nearest stars in the sky? (4)Is it hotter or cooler than most? (5)In what ways do the H-R diagrams for the brightest and for the nearest stars differ? (6)Which are more common in space, stars like those in the brightest star list or stars like those in the nearest star list? (7)How does the sun compare with the average star in space?

(8)How do the locations on the H-R diagram of these stars compare with the ones you plotted on the large H-R diagram? The location of stars on the H-R diagram provides clues to the evolution of stars, as you will see in Chapter 25.

The Pleiades are a group of high temperature young stars.

An astronomer looking through the eyepiece of a spectrograph on a large telescope.

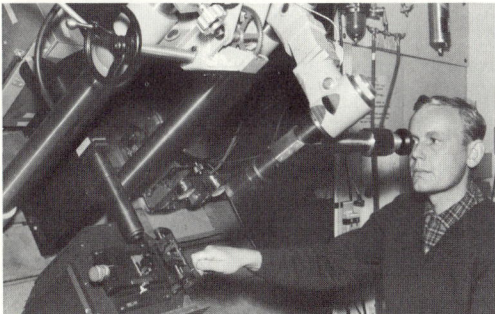

Thought and Discussion . . .

1. What is the relationship of star color to temperature?
2. Compare the temperature of our sun with that of other stars.
3. How are the spectral lines for chemical elements similar to sets of fingerprints?
4. What is the main cause for observed differences in stellar spectra?

Figure 24–10 *Setup for measuring the diameter of the sun.*

Additional Investigation

24–10 Measuring the diameter of the sun.

How can anyone on earth possibly measure the diameter of the sun? The sun is millions of kilometers away! But it can be done. By using certain characteristics of that part of the sun's energy that reaches the earth, a great deal of information about the sun can be obtained. In this case it is the sun's visible energy, light, that we will use. Light can be assumed to travel through space in a straight line and therefore you can represent it by a line drawn with a straightedge. (See Investigation 3–5.) Using this principle and simple proportions you can measure the diameter of a distant object that gives off light—in this instance the sun.

Procedure

The meter stick and cards are to be assembled as shown in Figure 24–10.

Place the cards on the meter stick with the pinhole card at the zero end. Aim the zero end of the meter stick at the sun. (*DO NOT LOOK DIRECTLY AT THE SUN BECAUSE YOU MAY DAMAGE YOUR EYES.*) Move the stick around until the shadow of the big pinhole card covers the card with the circle on it. Move the circle card toward the pinhole card until you can see the bright dot of light formed by the pinhole.

Now carefully move the circle card away from the pinhole card until the bright image just fills the circle.

When the bright image just fills the circle, measure the distance between the pinhole card and the circle card.

(1)What is the value of the distance from the earth to the sun in centimeters?

(2)What is the distance between the circle card and the pinhole card in centimeters?

(3)What is the size of the sun's image?

(4)Calculate the sun's diameter by using the above measurements in a proportion.

(5)What is the percentage difference between your calculated value for the diameter of the sun and the value of its diameter given elsewhere in this book?

(6)Could you measure the diameter of a star by this method? Explain.

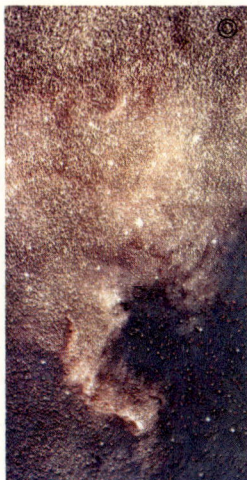

The dark gaseous nebula in the constellation Cygnus blocks out the light of stars behind it. Because of its shape, it is called the North American Nebula.

Unsolved Problems Because the stars are so far away, only a small portion of their total radiation reaches our planet. The radiation that does reach the earth is then often either blocked or distorted by the earth's atmosphere. Astronomers are constantly struggling to use all the radiation from the stars that they can gather. Larger and more efficient telescopes with new electronic and optical devices are being used often in satellites and space probes above the earth's atmosphere. New techniques are continually being sought to help measure the direction, quantity, and quality of radiation with the highest sensitivity and precision.

Much work also remains to be done on understanding variable stars. Why do some stars pulsate whereas others do not? Why do some stars explode? Are novas unusual or do all stars of a certain mass eventually become novas? What kinds of stars become supernovas?

Although most stars have about the same chemical composition, some have more carbon in their atmospheres, while others have more silicon or chromium. Might such differences in chemical composition provide clues to the way in which stars age?

The Danish physicist, Niels Bohr (1885–1962), revolutionized atomic theory. While working in England under Ernest Rutherford in 1913, Bohr developed a scheme of the atom in terms of energy. Bohr accepted Rutherford's atomic model of electrons orbiting a nucleus like planets around a sun. However, he saw these electrons as capable of absorbing energy and jumping to a higher energy level in an orbit more distant from the nucleus. The electrons would eventually fall back to their lower energy levels, emitting the energy they had absorbed as radiation of a certain wavelength. This wavelength was always the same for the same decrease in electron energy. Since each kind of atom had only certain orbits that its electrons could occupy, changes in energy level for a given element would produce unique emissions that could be used to identify the element. For this process, known as atomic "fingerprinting," Bohr won the Nobel Prize in physics in 1922.

Bohr was in the United States in 1939 when nuclear fission was discovered. Soon after he returned to Denmark, it was occupied by the Nazis. He fled the country in 1943 and worked on the American atomic bomb project. His work in Denmark after the war brought him the first Atoms for Peace award in 1957.

Niels Bohr

CHAPTER REVIEW

Summary

In this chapter you left planet earth and the solar system behind and moved out to the stars. Because of their great distances from the earth, the stars appear only as points of light even through our largest telescopes. Yet we can learn a great deal about stars by analyzing the direction, quantity, and quality of stellar radiation received on earth. By measuring these characteristics carefully, the astronomer obtains information about the luminosities, diameters, distances, motions, masses, temperatures, and chemical composition of the stars. He learns that the average distance between stars in space is incredibly large; that all stars are in motion with respect to one another; that all stars are hot globes of gas like our sun but differ in mass, luminosity, diameter, and temperature; that most stars are stable but some pulsate and others explode; that many stars are actually double; and that most stars have about the same chemical composition as the sun.

The H-R diagram, in which the luminosities of the stars are related to their temperatures, shows how the sun compares with its neighboring stars in space. This same diagram will be used in the next chapter to show how stars change as they grow older.

Questions and Problems

A

1. What is the luminosity of a star?
2. Why must the distance to a star be known to determine its luminosity?
3. Where are the "pointer" stars? To what do they point?
4. Describe an eclipsing binary system. What information can an astronomer get by studying such a system?
5. What is a nova? How did the name originate and why is it misleading?
6. Why cannot radar be used to measure stellar distances?
7. Why is not parallax used to measure stellar distances over 300 light-years?
8. How did Halley show that stars really do move in the sky?
9. How is the mass of a star determined?

B

1. How do novas and supernovas differ? What is the Crab Nebula?
2. Would measuring the distance to a nearby star result in greater or less accuracy if the measurements were made from Jupiter instead of from the earth? Explain your reasoning with a drawing.
3. Why must the distance to a star be considered when determining how fast the star is moving through space?
4. Describe the path traced by the earth through space. Is the moon's path similar? Explain.
5. How is star color related to star temperature?
6. If all stars are composed of the same elements, how do you account for the differences in their spectra?
7. What are stars made of? How do we know?

C

1. What are pulsating variable stars? Of what importance are Cepheid variable stars to astronomers?
2. Is a light-year a measure of time or distance? Explain. How many kilometers are there in a light-year?
3. If a star 20 light-years from earth suddenly stopped emitting radiation, how long would it be before we saw the star stop shining here on earth? Why?
4. Assuming that the bright star Vega, which is 26.5 light-years from us, is not moving with respect to the stars around it, how long will it take the sun to reach the vicinity of Vega?

5. If the bright star Sirius has a mass of 2.45 times the sun's mass and a diameter of 1.8 times the sun's diameter, what is its average density in comparison to the sun? in comparison to water?
6. Describe the three kinds of spectra. What causes bright-line and dark-line spectra?

Suggested Readings

BOOKS

Abell, G. O. *Exploration of the Universe.* Holt, Rinehart & Winston, Inc., New York, 1964.

Bergamini, David and the Editors of *Life. The Universe.* Time, Inc. (Life Nature Library), New York, 1962.

Elementary School Science Project. *Astronomy.* University of Illinois Press, Urbana, Ill., 1962–65. (6 volumes)

Hoyle, Fred. *Astronomy.* Doubleday & Company, Inc., Garden City, N.Y., 1962.

Hynek, Joseph Allen and Norman D. Anderson. *Challenge of the Universe.* McGraw-Hill Book Company, New York, 1962.

Kruse, Willie and Wilhelm Dieckvoss. *The Stars.* The University of Michigan Press, Ann Arbor, Mich., 1957.

Menzel, Donald H. *A Field Guide to the Stars and Planets.* Houghton Mifflin Company, Boston, 1963.

Miczaika, Gerhard R. and William M. Sinton. *Tools of the Astronomer.* Harvard University Press, Cambridge, Mass., 1961.

Page, Thornton. *Stars and Galaxies.* Prentice-Hall, Inc., Englewood Cliffs, N.J., 1962.

Trinklein, Frederick E. and Charles M. Huffer. *Modern Space Science.* Holt, Rinehart & Winston, Inc., New York, 1961.

Zim, Herbert S. and Robert H. Baker. *Stars.* Golden Press, Inc., New York, 1962.

PERIODICALS

Limber, D. Nelson. "The Pleiades." *Scientific American,* November, 1962. (Also Scientific American Offprint #285, W. H. Freeman & Co., Publishers, San Francisco.)

Sky and Telescope. Sky Publishing Corp., Cambridge, Mass.

Wilson, O. C. "A New Scale of Stellar Distances." *Scientific American,* January, 1961. (Also Offprint #254.)

PAMPHLET

Science and Superstition. Adler Planetarium and Astronomical Museum, Chicago Park District, 1962.

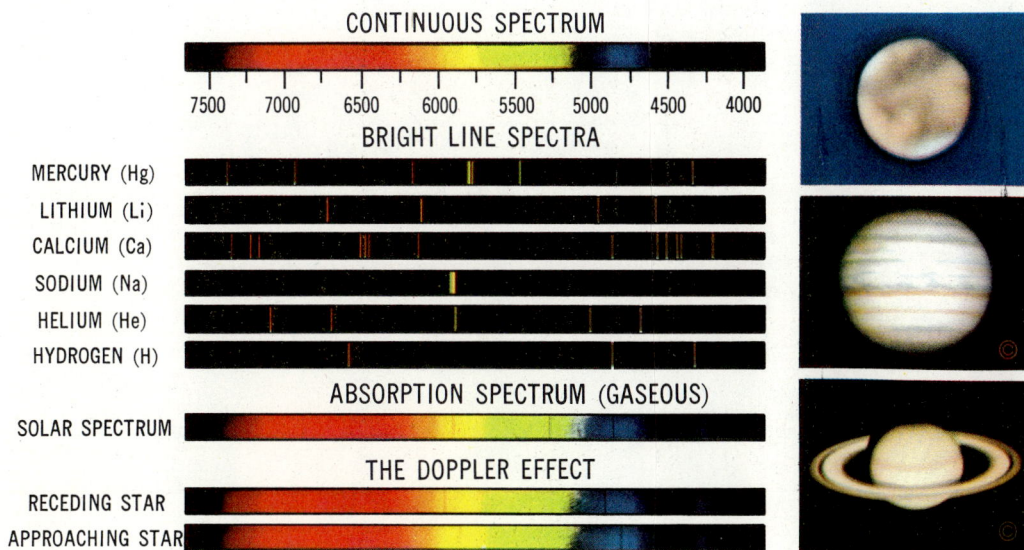

Figure 24–11 (*Left, below*) *Different kinds of spectra, and* (*right, below*) *the planets Mars, Jupiter, and Saturn.*

Chapter 25 Stellar Evolution and Galaxies

In 1944 astronomer Walter Baade was working with the 100-inch telescope, then the largest in the world, at the summit of Mount Wilson, California. Because of World War II, the lights of Pasadena and Los Angeles below were blacked out. Baade was trying to push the 100-inch telescope to its limits, so the blackout was helpful. It permitted him to expose his photographic plates longer without their being fogged by the sky glow produced by city lights. With this longer exposure time he found that he could record the light coming from much fainter stars on his photographic plates.

Baade was looking about two million light-years out into space at the great galaxy in the constellation Andromeda. This huge system of billions of stars clustered together in space appears in this photograph. About twenty years earlier, Edwin Hubble, using the same telescope, had photographed the same galaxy and found that the spiral arms forming the outer parts consisted of countless numbers of individual stars. Furthermore, the brightest of them were hot blue stars of great luminosity—true celestial beacons.

Baade was interested in the hazy-looking central regions of the Andromeda galaxy. These regions had never shown individual stars on any photographs. There were evidently no blue, luminous stars there of the kind that Hubble had discovered in the outer parts of the galaxy. Were there, then, any stars at all in the central regions? If so, what kind of stars would they be?

Baade thought he knew the answers to these questions. He suspected that the brightest stars in the center of the Andromeda galaxy must be red giant stars, neither as blue nor as luminous as the brightest stars in the outer parts of the galaxy. Because of the great distance to the galaxy, these stars toward its center would be very faint—so faint that they could be photographed only under the very best of conditions.

Using photographic plates that were especially sensitive to red light and waiting for the finest clear dark nights, Baade photographed the center of the Andromeda galaxy. His care and patience were rewarded, for barely visible on his photographs were large numbers of faint red stars.

Why are Baade's observations important? They led him to believe that the stars in the Andromeda galaxy, as well as the stars in our Milky Way and other galaxies, consist of two basic types. The main difference between the two types was age, Baade thought. From these ideas came our modern theories of the evolution of stars—where they come from, how they change, and what happens to them as they grow old.

Stellar Evolution

25–1 Clues to stellar evolution.

Every second the sun converts over four million tons of its mass into radiant energy. (Section 6–11.) The hot blue stars of high luminosity convert more than 10,000 times that much mass into radiation each second. Stars obviously cannot keep this up forever. What happens to them when their nuclear fuel runs out?

The answer to this question can best be found with the help of H-R diagrams like the one you plotted in Section 24–9. Notice that most of the stars lie along one stretch in the H-R diagrams, which astronomers call the **main sequence.** (See Figure 25–1.) What does the main sequence tell about the way stars age?

Suppose you did not know how people age, but wanted to find out, just as the astronomer wants to find out how stars age. It takes stars millions or billions of years to age, whereas the lifespan of astronomers is much shorter than that. Observations with telescopes are like a single snapshot taken at a particular stage in the lives of the stars. From this one snapshot the astronomer must reconstruct the lives of the stars. Suppose you had only a snapshot taken yesterday of all the people in your city or town—could you work out a theory of how people age? (See photo above.) How is this similar to the way you read the life story of landscapes in Chapter 21?

In the photograph some people are much smaller than others. Most of these would be children. Since there are fewer of them, you might decide that childhood is a short stage of life. What fraction of the people show wrinkled skin? Perhaps such people, since the number is not large, also represent another short stage of life. Most of the people in your snapshot would be adults, all about the same size and with similar physical characteristics. Since there are so many of the adults, relatively, this must be the stage of life in which people spend most of their time.

How does this analogy fit the life history of stars? Look again at the H-R diagram in Figure 25–1 and notice the larger number of stars on the main sequence. If stars change as they use up their fuel, the long main sequence must be the region of the H-R diagram in which stars spend the greatest proportion of their lifetimes.

Many of the stars you know are on the main sequence of the H-R diagram. These stars, like the sun, Sirius, and Spica, are all "adult stars" in the prime of life. But Spica is almost 2000 times more luminous than the sun, and it burns its nuclear fuel at a much faster rate. Although more massive than the sun, all stars like Spica at the hot, blue end of the main sequence are celestial spend-thrifts, using up their fuel very rapidly. The cooler red stars of small mass at the other end of the main sequence burn their nuclear fuel and evolve much more slowly than the sun.

What happens to a star when it uses up its nuclear fuel? Will it become cooler, or dimmer, or both? Its temperature and luminosity must change, which means it will leave its position on the main sequence of the H-R diagram. But which way will it go?

A clue to the answer to these questions came from a study of the H-R diagrams of globular clusters some years ago. A **globular cluster,** like the one shown in Figure 25–2, is a collection of thousands of stars all held together by their mutual

Figure 25–2 *The star cluster M13 is an example of a globular cluster. It is composed of many thousands of stars held together by their mutual gravitational attraction in space.*

Figure 25–1 *The Hertzsprung-Russell (H-R) diagram shows the relationship between the luminosities of stars (in units of the sun's luminosity) and their temperature. Compare this diagram with yours from Investigation 24–9.*

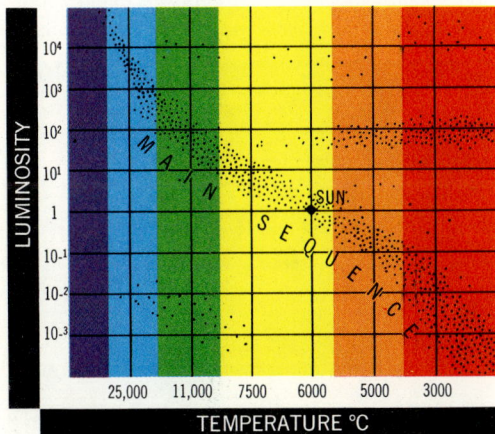

gravitational attraction, like a swarm of bees flying through space. Star clusters make a perfect testing ground for theories of stellar evolution because astronomers believe that all the stars in any one of them must have been born at about the same time. Any differences that are observed in the stars in the cluster must have come about because some stars grow old faster than others.

The H-R diagram of a typical globular cluster is shown in Figure 25–3A. How does this diagram differ from that for the ordinary stars in space, like the one shown in Figure 25–1? What has happened to the hot, blue stars of high luminosity in Figure 25–3A?

This is the kind of question Baade asked when he started his observations of the Andromeda galaxy. The H-R diagram that he plotted for the stars in the central parts of the Andromeda galaxy looks much like Figure 25–3A. Could it be, asked Baade, that the stars in globular clusters and in the center of the Andromeda galaxy are old? We know that the hot, blue luminous stars use up so much nuclear fuel each second

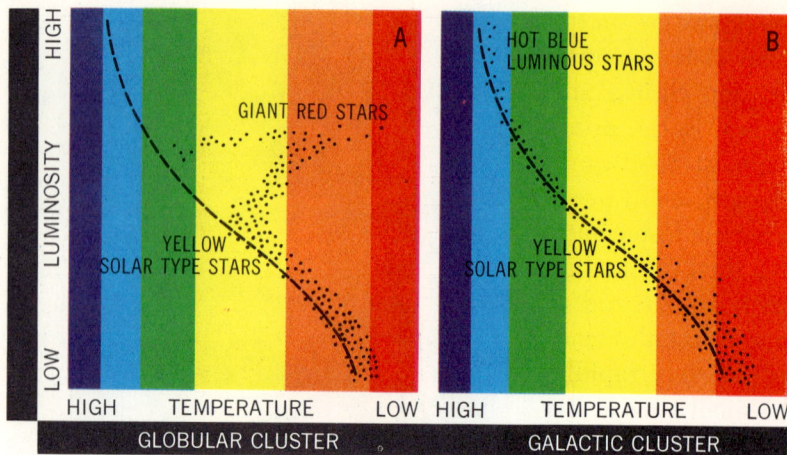

Figure 25–3 (A), far left, H-R diagram for a typical globular cluster and (B), left, H-R diagram for a galactic cluster. What does a comparison of the two diagrams tell you?

that they cannot radiate at that rate for very long. Perhaps they are young stars and arrived on the main sequence only recently. Since they do not appear in the globular cluster H-R diagrams, they have probably evolved into something else by this time.

H-R diagrams of galactic clusters give additional clues. A **galactic cluster** like the famous Pleiades (PLEE-yuh-deez) pictured on page 540, is also a group of stars traveling together in space, like a globular cluster. However, galactic clusters do not contain as many stars. These galactic clusters frequently contain hot, blue stars of high luminosity, such as those blue stars in the Pleiades and in the H-R diagram in Figure 25–3B.

Compare the H-R diagrams in Figure 25–3. Is there any relationship between the two H-R diagrams? Could hot, blue luminous stars evolve into red giant stars when their nuclear fuel supply runs low?

25–2 Where do stars come from?

Have you ever seen the constellation Orion, the hunter? This beautiful star group, which you will find on the star charts (Appendix E), dominates the winter sky and can still be seen during spring evenings. If you have binoculars or a small telescope, look at the central

star in the sword of the hunter. Does it look starlike? Probably you will notice that it looks rather hazy. This is the famous Orion Nebula, which appears in Figure 25–4 as it looks when photographed with the Mount Palomar 200-inch telescope. This large cloud of dust and gas is 1600 light-years away from us and is about 30 light-years in diameter. It contains many hot stars that make the cloud glow.

Many such bright clouds occur along the band of the Milky Way. Another, shown on page 543, is the Trifid Nebula in the constellation Sagittarius. Evidently there are large quantities of dust and gas as well as stars in space.

Figure 25–4 The Great Nebula (M42) in the constellation of Orion. This nebula is about 1600 light-years distant. How many kilometers is this?

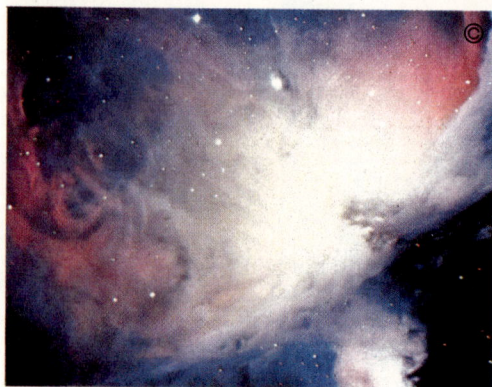

In addition to bright clouds, dark clouds of dust and gas also exist in space. These clouds in interstellar (between the stars) space look dark when there is no star nearby to illuminate them. The Horsehead Nebula, shown on page 543, is a beautiful example. You can see dark interstellar clouds without a telescope. Look at the Milky Way in the region of the constellation Cygnus (SIGnuss) on a dark summer night and you will notice that it seems to split into two parts. This apparent splitting is caused by a string of dark interstellar clouds that block the light of the stars behind them, as shown in Figure 25–5.

Astronomers can also detect interstellar dust and gas from their effect on the radiation of distant stars that must pass through the gas and dust on its way to the earth. Starlight passing through the great interstellar distances is scattered by dust and gas along the way and the scattering produces a reddening. This reddening can be measured. It is generally greater for the light from the more distant stars and for that from stars surrounded by interstellar clouds. Why should the reddening be greater for the more distant stars? Do you recall the effects that dust from Krakatoa had on the appearance of sunsets? (See page 13.)

Even the chemical composition of the matter between the stars can be determined. Do you remember from Section 24–8 how the gases in the outer layers of stars were identified from their spectra? In a similar way, when the radiation from distant stars passes through the interstellar gas on its way to the earth, some of it is absorbed by the gas. The interstellar gas then leaves its "fingerprints" behind in the form of dark spectral lines that identify the chemical elements making up the gas. Hydrogen gas can be identified from its

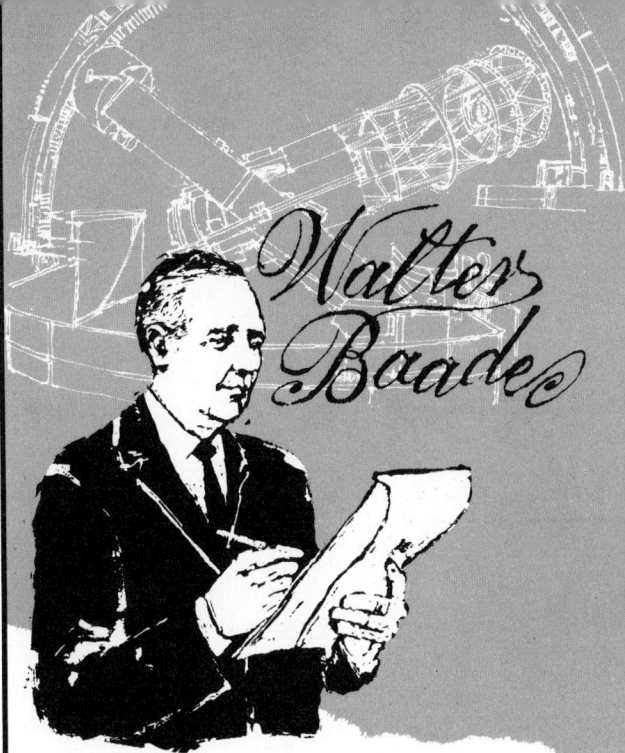

Walter Baade

Walter Baade exerted a great influence on recent astronomical research. Born in Germany in 1893, Baade received his doctorate at the University of Göttingen and spent the next dozen years at the Observatory in Hamburg. In 1931, Baade came to the United States to the Mount Wilson Observatory. With the 100-inch telescope, then the world's largest, he observed galaxies and nebulas.

Baade was particularly interested in the spiral Andromeda galaxy, which is much like our own Milky Way. His examination of this galaxy in 1944 led him to form a theory of stellar evolution. The two types of stars he noticed — massive, bright blue stars in the spiral arms, and reddish, generally smaller stars in the halo and hub of the galaxy — Baade saw as distinctly different groups or populations. The blue stars he considered young or in the process of being born from the dust and gas of space. The red stars he considered old and dying. Although this strict division of the stars of a galaxy into only two populations was an oversimplification, it has proved useful for analyzing other galaxies, including our own. The types of stars remaining in a given group can thus be used to determine the stage of evolution of that group.

Baade also made important contributions to our knowledge of the distances to galaxies and the nature of supernovas and radio-emitting sources.

Figure 25–5 *A portion of the Milky Way in the region of the constellation Cygnus is dimmed by dark clouds of dust and gas that cut off light from the stars behind them.*

emission of radio waves. These are detected with special radio telescopes, as shown in figures 25–6 and 25–7.

Now we can answer the questions: What makes up interstellar matter, and how much of it is there? The gas between the stars has about the same chemical composition as the sun and stars themselves. About three-quarters of it is hydrogen and the rest is mostly helium, with a small percentage of the heavier elements. There is only about one atom of gas per cubic centimeter of interstellar space, and one dust particle in a volume of interstellar space equal to that of a cubic city block. If you compare this with the 10^{19} gas molecules in each cubic centimeter of the earth's atmosphere at sea level, you can appreciate how low the density of matter is in interstellar space. However, be-

cause the distances between stars are so great, there is an enormous number of cubic centimeters in interstellar space and therefore a great quantity of matter. Within a few light-years of the sun, the total amount of mass of gas and dust between the stars may be as much as half the total mass of matter that is contained within the stars themselves.

Where do stars come from? You now have two clues: There is a great deal of matter between the stars, and it is made of about the same material as the stars. A further clue, noticed by Baade, is that the hot, blue luminous stars like the Pleiades are usually found in or near interstellar clouds. Would you conclude just as Baade did that the stars are born from the interstellar dust and gas? This is what modern theories of stellar evolution suggest to astronomers.

25–3 What is the life history of a star?

Astronomers today think that the life history of a star probably begins in a dark nebula. Such nebulas are turbulent, like a boiling liquid. Pockets or globules of concentrated dust and gas form within the nebulas. Some globules are visible in the photographs of nebulas on page 543. Once formed, such a globule pulls itself together as gravitational forces act on the matter. As the material becomes compressed into a smaller and smaller volume, the internal temperature and pressure rise. As you learned in Section 6–11, the temperature and pressure eventually become so great that hydrogen is converted to helium. This conversion results in the production of radiant energy. A star has been born.

The cluster of the Pleiades in the constellation Taurus. The Pleiades are hot, blue stars surrounded by nebulous clouds. These clouds have been found to be about 400 light-years away.

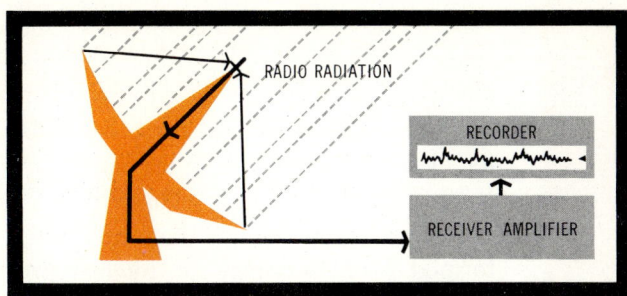

Figure 25–6 (*Above*) *A radio telescope gathers information by radio waves instead of light waves. Radio waves can pass through interstellar dust.*
Figure 25–7 (*Right*) *The 300-foot-diameter radio telescope of the National Radio Astronomy Observatory in Green Bank, West Virginia.*

The contraction of a globule in a nebula is believed to be only a short stage in the life history of a star. The pressure of the hot gas and radiation pushes outward and resists the matter being pulled inward by gravitation. This is similar to the situation when you squeeze a tennis ball. You can only squeeze so much before the internal pressure matches the pressure you exert. When the inward and outward pressures balance, the star has reached the main sequence on the H-R diagram. It is a stable star, like the sun. By this time, the nuclear furnaces of the star are going full blast and the star is pouring radiation out into space. The hydrogen gas at the core of the star provides the nuclear "fuel," which turns into helium gas as the "ashes." (See Section 6–11.) The star now spends most of its life on the main sequence as it uses up the nuclear fuel in its core.

How long does a star remain on the main sequence? Because of their high core temperatures, massive stars use up their fuel very fast, perhaps in only one or two million years. Less massive stars, like the sun, radiate at least 10 billion years before their cores run out of hydrogen. Scientists estimate that the sun has consumed at least half of its hydrogen fuel. Still less massive stars, with lower core temperatures, may take many billions of years to use up the hydrogen fuel in their cores. What happens then? When the hydrogen in the core has turned into helium, the core begins to contract. The temperature of the core rises with this contraction, and the hydrogen in a shell around the core feeds the nuclear furnaces once again. The star becomes more luminous. This means that the outward pressure within the star is greater than the inward pressure. This would be like a tennis ball swelling up in your hand regardless of how hard you squeezed it. This expansion causes the star's surface to cool and it moves off the main sequence to become a red giant star.

Astronomers are not sure what happens next. Perhaps the star goes through a pulsation stage and becomes a Cepheid variable star. (See Section 24–2.) Perhaps the star becomes a nova near the end of its life, blowing off its outer layers into interstellar space. Whatever the process, it will probably end its life as a tiny **white dwarf** star. These compact little stars, some no larger than the earth, have no available nuclear energy sources left. Their crushed atoms are packed so tightly that a piece of white dwarf star material the size of a golf ball would weigh more than a car. These small stars radiate energy away and cool slowly until they become cold and dark.

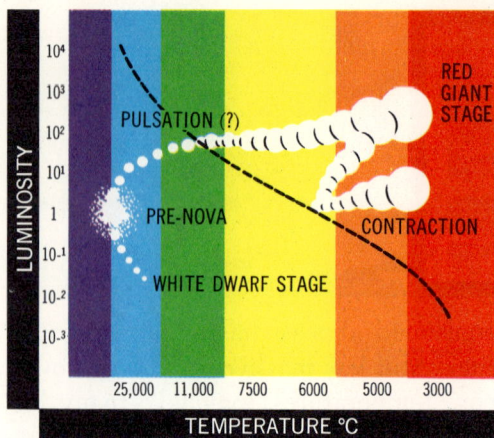

Figure 25–8 *Stellar evolution is shown above as it appears in the H-R diagram for a star somewhat more massive than the sun.*

Such a life history, of a star somewhat more massive than the sun, is shown on an H-R diagram in Figure 25–8. The story will be similar for a star of greater or smaller mass. If the original globule contains more mass than the sun, the evolution proceeds faster; if it has less mass, then it takes place more slowly.

Can any amount of interstellar gas and dust condense to form a star? As you might expect, the answer to this question is no. Only a limited range of stellar masses are actually observed. (See Section 24–5.) Masses less than about 1/100 of the sun's mass never get hot enough at their cores to start the nuclear furnaces going. Such small masses would always remain cold, as even large planets like Jupiter do. Masses greater than about 100 times the sun's mass would be so hot at their centers that the outward pressure of gas and radiation would prevent a stable star from forming.

25–4 Are heavy elements formed in the cores of stars?

Hydrogen and helium make up all but a small percentage of the matter in the sun, in other stars, and in interstellar space. Where did the other chemical elements come from? Did oxygen, carbon, silicon, iron, and all the other heavier elements always exist, or were they created as the universe evolved?

Because you know that helium is formed from hydrogen by nuclear processes in the centers of stars, you might ask whether the heavier elements could be built up in the same way. Calculations of conditions inside stars suggest that this probably does occur. As an evolving star reaches the red giant stage, the temperature at its core climbs to 100 million °C or more. The helium nuclei in the core of the star are then moving at such high speeds that they are capable of fusing to form still heavier elements. In this way, carbon and heavier elements can be built up at the centers of red giant stars.

Considerable evidence confirms that the stars do produce heavy elements. One of these lines of evidence has to do with the chemical element, technetium (tek-KNEE-shee-um). A heavy element of atomic number 43, technetium is not found on earth. It is an unstable element whose longest-lived isotope has a half-life of only 216,000 years. Technetium has been produced artificially by scientists studying the makeup of atoms.

Imagine the surprise of astronomers who identified the unmistakable spectroscopic lines of technetium in the light from stars that are many times older than 216,000 years. These stars are so much older, in fact, that any technetium that might have been present when the stars formed would have long ago been lost by radioactive decay. They concluded that technetium is being produced by nuclear reactions in the stars.

If these ideas are correct, how do the heavy elements get out of the cores of stars? Perhaps supernovas and novas throw off these heavier elements. We know that these exploding stars eject considerable amounts of matter out into interstellar space. Other types of stars shed mass into space more gradually. Even the sun, with its solar wind, is sending matter out into space. In these ways the abundance of heavy elements in interstellar space is gradually increasing, it is believed.

As one generation of stars goes through its evolution, the next forms from its discarded matter. Each generation of stars contains a greater proportion of heavy elements than the last and adds still more of these elements to interstellar space for the next generation. The sun with its planets may be a second, third, or even later generation star, and the carbon in your body may have formed inside some now-dead star.

ACTIVITY *Many objects are visible in the nighttime sky. Probably you have seen many members of our own solar system and you may have noticed differences in individual stars. But beyond our own neighborhood of stars are other stars and groups of stars at enormous distances from us. Although they are not always easy to see, with the help of the star charts in Appendix E you can look at light that left its source thousands and even millions of years ago. If you are interested in learning more about the stars, choose a clear, dark moonless night, away from lights of any kind. If possible, use binoculars or a telescope.*

Look for the broad band of faint light stretching across the sky that is the Milky Way. (1) Are some parts of it brighter than others? (2) In what constellations are the brightest parts? (3) Is the Milky Way a continuous band across the sky or is it patchy? (4) Can you see the dark interstellar clouds in the constellation Cygnus? (5) Now look at the Milky Way through binoculars or a telescope. What do you see when you can observe more detail?

The globular cluster M13 in the constellation Hercules is just visible to the naked eye. Look at it also with binoculars or a telescope and describe its appearance. You are looking about 25,000 light-years into space.

The Andromeda galaxy (M31) is visible only in the fall sky. (6) If you have the opportunity, examine and describe this galaxy whose light began its journey about two million years ago.

Great nebulas in interstellar space. The Horsehead Nebula in Orion, the Trifid Nebula in Sagittarius, the Dumbbell Nebula in Vulpecula, and a gaseous nebula in Serpens.

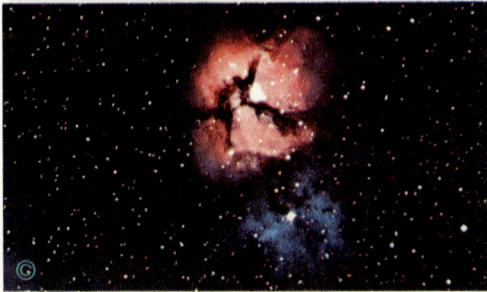

Thought and Discussion . . .

1. In what stage of development are most of the stars on the main sequence of the H-R diagram? What has led scientists to this conclusion?

2. What are the differences between a globular cluster and a galactic cluster?

3. How do astronomers know that dust and gas exist in space between the stars?

4. How can the composition of interstellar matter be determined? How does the composition of interstellar matter compare with stellar composition?

5. At what stage of stellar evolution are white dwarf stars believed to be?

We Live In a Galaxy

25–5 What do observations of the Milky Way tell us?

You have heard of scientific breakthroughs in which discoveries are made that lead to whole series of new ideas and forward steps. Galileo's discovery in 1610 that the Milky Way really consists of millions of very faint and distant stars must be ranked among the greatest breakthroughs of all time. His discovery started astronomers along the path to understanding the kind of star system in which we live.

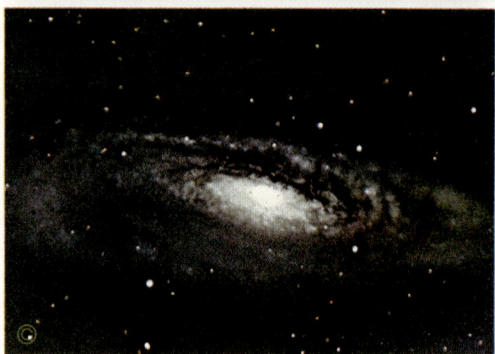

Suppose you have only the information that Galileo provided—that you are surrounded by a band of distant stars stretching all the way across the heavens. Could you decide for yourself what kind of star system you live in? Would you expect to see such a band of stars if you lived in the center of a globular cluster? Why would you conclude that we live in a huge flattened sheet of stars?

Are we at the center of this sheet? To answer this question, you need to know whether the Milky Way is uniformly bright or brighter in some parts than in others. In fact, the Milky Way appears brightest in and near the constellation Sagittarius (Sah-jit-TARE-ee-us) and faintest in the opposite part of the sky near the constellations Auriga (Oh-RY-guh) and Cassiopeia (Kas-i-oh-PEE-uh). Since the brighter part of the Milky Way results from larger numbers of faint stars, you might conclude that the center lies toward Sagittarius.

How far is our solar system from the center of the Milky Way galaxy? This question was not answered until about 50 years ago. You saw how astronomers could estimate the distances of Cepheid variable stars from the way in which they change brightness. (Section 24–2.)

A spiral galaxy in the constellation Sculptor, photographed with a 48-inch telescope, and another in Pegasus, photographed with the 200-inch telescope on Palomar Mountain.

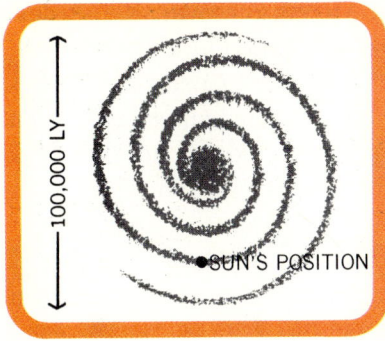

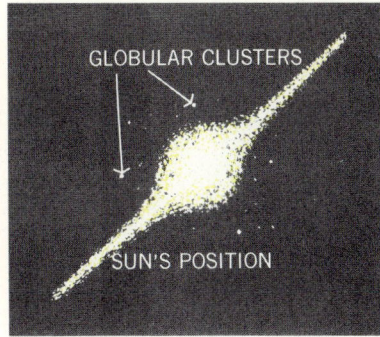

Figure 25–9 *The sun's position in one of the spiral arms appears in these simplified diagrams of the Milky Way galaxy. LY stands for light-years.*

The discovery of Cepheid variable stars in globular clusters led to the first knowledge of the distances to them and their distribution. When the American astronomer Harlow Shapley in 1917 mapped out the distribution in space of the 93 globular clusters then known, he found that they did not cluster around the sun but around a point about 30,000 light-years from us in the direction of the constellation Sagittarius.

What does this mean? Remember that each globular cluster is a massive system of thousands of stars. Just as the planets circle the sun, which is the mass center of the solar system, the globular clusters must circle the center of mass of the Milky Way galaxy. Apparently the center of our galaxy is nowhere near the sun but 30,000 light-years from us in the direction of Sagittarius. Observations involving the use of both radio waves and ordinary light have since proved this picture to be correct.

Now you know that our Milky Way galaxy is a flattened system of stars surrounded by a halo of globular clusters with our solar system near one edge. Would you expect any additional structure in the galaxy? The photograph of the Andromeda galaxy at the beginning of this chapter shows what our galaxy might look like if we could see it from a great distance. Notice that the stars are arranged in long, curved bands called **spiral arms.** Does our Milky Way galaxy have spiral arms too? According to evidence of both visible light and radio waves, the Milky Way does. Baade pointed out that the spiral arms in the Andromeda galaxy are outlined by hot, blue stars of high luminosity, surrounded by clouds of interstellar dust and gas. Studies of similar stars in the Milky Way galaxy show that they too are lined up along spiral arms.

Even more convincing is the evidence from radio waves. You learned in Section 25–2 that hydrogen gas in space can be identified from the "fingerprints" that the radio telescope detects. Observations of this kind have located hydrogen gas in the Milky Way galaxy. Like the hot blue stars, the hydrogen gas occurs in lanes that curve around the center of our galaxy, similar to the spiral arms in the Andromeda galaxy. These radio observations are especially significant because radio waves travel across long interstellar distances with less interference from dust and gas than do ordinary light waves. Therefore, astronomers have been able to map spiral arms not only in the neighborhood of the sun, but all the way across the Milky Way galaxy.

Our present picture of the Milky Way galaxy is shown in Figure 25–9. The entire system is believed to be about 100,000 light-years in diameter and several thousand light-years thick. The sun

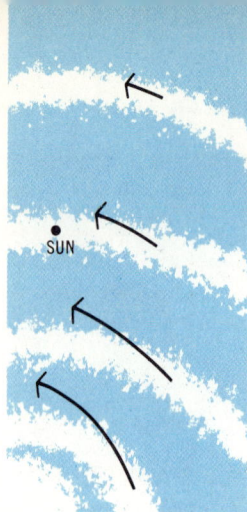

Figure 25–10 *Measuring the rotation of the Milky Way galaxy. The longer the arrow, the faster the stars are moving. Is the sun passing or being passed by the stars outside it? inside it? on a line with it?*

is in the flat sheet or disk of the galaxy, about 30,000 light-years from the center, in one of the spiral arms. In addition to the stars in the disk, a kind of spherical haze of stars exists around the center. This **halo,** as it is called, consists of globular clusters and individual stars.

25–6 Is our galaxy rotating?

What does the flattened system of our Milky Way galaxy suggest to you about its rotation? You know from Section 3–4 that the earth is somewhat flattened at its poles because of its rotation. Jupiter, with its rapid rotation, can easily be seen to be flattened in Figure 3–14. Would you expect the Milky Way galaxy to be rotating also?

Other flattened galaxies, such as the Andromeda galaxy, have been shown to be rotating from the Doppler shifts of their spectral lines. Observations with spectographs attached to telescopes show that the spectral lines from one edge of the galaxy are shifted to the blue end of the spectrum, while those from the other edge are shifted to the red. This means that one edge of the galaxy is approaching us while the other edge is moving away from us—in other words, the entire galaxy is rotating around its center. However, we are inside our Milky Way galaxy and that makes the problem of measuring our rotation with the galaxy much more difficult.

Just as Mercury moves the fastest around the sun and Pluto the slowest, imagine that the inner parts of the galaxy rotate around the center faster than the outer parts. Could you not then look at the stars around you to measure your rotation? Those closer to the center should be passing you while you should be passing the stars farther out, as shown in Figure 25–10. This is exactly what astronomers observe. The sun and its neighboring stars are all circling the center of our galaxy at a speed of about 240 kilometers per second. Because the sun's orbit is so large, it takes about 200 million years to make one revolution. This means that when the sun and planets started around the center of the galaxy on the revolution that we are now finishing, dinosaurs were just beginning to roam the earth. (See Table 19–1.)

Knowing that our galaxy rotates, can you think of ways in which its mass might be measured? Remember that the mass of the sun is calculated by the way in which it swings the earth around. Since the sun is located near the edge of the Milky Way galaxy, the mass of the galaxy inside the sun's orbit can be calculated by the way it swings the sun around. This mass of the Milky Way

A galaxy in the Constellation Virgo. Note the band of dust and gas in the disk.

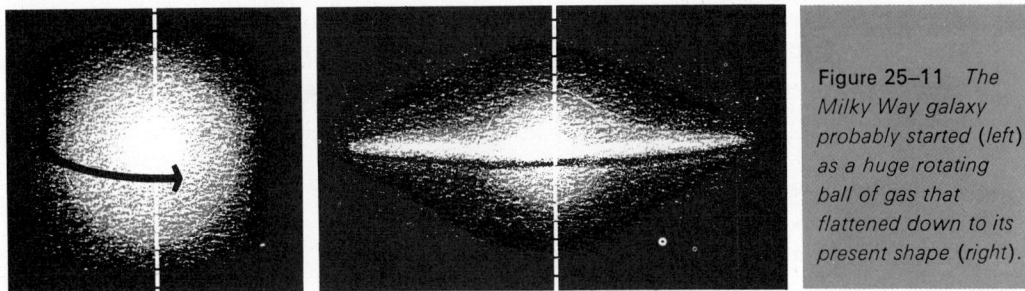

Figure 25–11 *The Milky Way galaxy probably started (left) as a huge rotating ball of gas that flattened down to its present shape (right).*

galaxy is calculated to be about 200 billion times the mass of the sun. Our Milky Way galaxy is truly an immense collection of matter.

Now that you know something about the size and structure of our galaxy, its mass, and its rotation, can anything be said about how it developed? Our galaxy probably started as a huge spherical cloud of rotating gas, as shown in Figure 25–11. The globular clusters must have formed early in the history of the galaxy, for they are now the oldest. Stars in the globular clusters probably formed rapidly in a brilliant burst of star formation. Because the galactic cloud was originally a huge ball of gas, these oldest stars formed in a sphere around the center of the galaxy. Today these stars still follow their original orbits in the galactic halo. Meanwhile, the ball of gas flattened down to a disk because of its rotation, and all star formation since then has taken place in that disk. It is within this disk that the younger stars are found, as well as the dust and gas that eventually will form new stars.

Are there any similarities between the formation of galaxies and planetary systems (Chapter 23)?

Thought and Discussion . . .

1. Explain how you might decide the shape of our galaxy just by looking at the Milky Way.
2. What indications do astronomers have that the sun is not at the center of the Milky Way galaxy?
3. Give some evidence that the Milky Way galaxy is rotating.
4. Relate the probable evolution of our Milky Way to that of the solar system.

Our Galaxy Among Its Neighbors

25–7 Investigating galaxies.

With one exception, the stars you can see in the sky from the earth's Northern Hemisphere without a telescope belong to our own Milky Way galaxy. The exception is the Andromeda galaxy that is barely visible and appears to the unaided eye as a fuzzy patch of faint light. Yet there are many such galaxies within the range of binoculars or a small telescope.

In 1781, the French astronomer Charles Messier prepared a catalogue of 107 fuzzy-looking celestial objects. Messier was a comet hunter and he made his catalogue so that he would not mix up these diffuse objects with comets, which also look fuzzy. Many conspicuous star clusters, gaseous nebulas, and galaxies are listed in his catalogue, including the famous Andromeda galaxy or M31 (for Messier 31). Other lists followed and today there are catalogues that list and describe many thousands of galaxies.

Procedure

The galaxies shown on the galaxy cards provided you represent the common types of star systems that can be seen through a telescope. One of the tasks of a scientist is to develop classification systems based on observable characteristics of different objects, materials, and processes. For this investigation try to place all of these galaxies in a sequence that relates characteristics you observe. After you have done this, answer the following questions.

(1) What is the basis of your classification?

(2) If you assumed that the sequence you set up was related to the relative age of galaxies, which galaxies would you judge to be the oldest and which the youngest?

25–8 The Local Group of galaxies.

You saw in Chapter 24 how astronomers learn what stars are like, and in Section 24–9 you compared the sun with neighboring stars. Let's ask a related question about our own galaxy: How does the Milky Way system compare with the neighboring galaxies in space?

How far away are the other galaxies? Fifty years ago, astronomers were arguing about this question. Some thought galaxies were located on the fringes of the Milky Way galaxy, while others claimed that they were much farther away. The question was settled in the 1920's when Hubble, using the 100-inch Mount Wilson telescope, discovered that there were Cepheid variable stars in M31 and in several other bright galaxies.

Again the Cepheid variable stars came to the rescue! Knowing how often they pulsate, astronomers can estimate their luminosities and from this their distances. This distance is then the distance to the galaxy in which they are located. The question of how far away was settled: very far away! The distance to M31 and other nearby galaxies was found to be millions of light-years. At these enormous distances, galaxies can only be giant systems of billions of stars, like our own Milky Way galaxy.

Since Cepheid variable stars can be observed in the nearby galaxies, their distances can be calculated.

All the known galaxies within about two million light-years of the Milky Way galaxy appear in Figure 25–12. This

Figure 25–12 *The collection of 17 galaxies within about two million light-years of the Milky Way galaxy is known as the Local Group.*

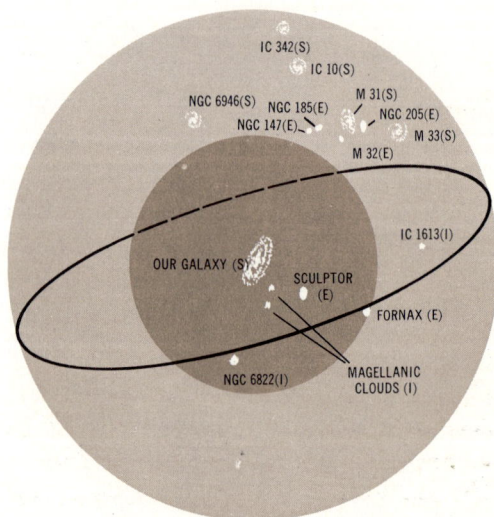

collection of 17 galaxies is known as the **Local Group.** In this group there are three spirals, four irregulars, four ordinary ellipticals, and six "dwarf" ellipticals. These latter galaxies are much smaller and contain fewer stars than ordinary elliptical galaxies. They may exist in large numbers in space but are difficult to detect at great distances because of their small luminosities.

How does our Milky Way galaxy rank with its neighbors? It is a spiral galaxy, like many others in space, including M31. It is a large galaxy—most of its neighbors are smaller. But M31 is of about the same size or slightly larger, and galaxies elsewhere in the universe are known that are much larger and more massive. Just as you have found the sun to be a rather average star, the Milky Way galaxy, though somewhat larger than most of the galaxies, can be classified as a rather typical galaxy.

Thought and Discussion . . .

1. Why is it that a galaxy like Andromeda, which consists of billions of stars, appears to the naked eye as a single hazy star in our nighttime sky?
2. How do astronomers determine distances to other galaxies?
3. How many galaxies are included in the Local Group? How many of each type of galaxy are there?
4. How does the Milky Way compare with the neighboring galaxies in space?

Unsolved Problems Although astronomers have a general understanding of how stars evolve, the details are far from clear. How do large interstellar clouds break up to form individual stars? What happens to a star after it reaches the red giant stage? By what process does it eventually become a white dwarf?

Many questions about the Milky Way galaxy and other galaxies have not yet been answered. Do galaxies begin as pure hydrogen gas? How do spiral arms form and what prevents them from winding up as the galaxy rotates? Why do some galaxies take the spiral form while others are elliptical or irregular? Are some galaxies in a later stage of evolution than others? More observations with both optical telescopes (using ordinary light waves) and radio telescopes, together with a lot of thought, will be required to solve these problems.

CHAPTER REVIEW

Summary

Learning about what individual stars are like brings up such questions as: Where do stars come from? What happens to stars when they grow old? Evidence from H-R diagrams of star clusters suggests the following picture: Stars form from globules of concentrated dust and gas within interstellar clouds. Once formed, the globules develop high enough temperatures inside to start nuclear reactions and give off radiation. The star spends most of its lifetime on the main sequence but eventually runs out of hydrogen fuel at its core. It then briefly becomes a red giant star and finally ends its life as a white dwarf star. Probably the heavier chemical elements are created in the hot cores of stars in late stages of evolution and afterwards are spread out into space by supernova and nova explosions.

The sun is one of over 100 billion stars in a flattened, rotating system called the Milky Way galaxy. Our galaxy is about 100,000 light-years across, a few thousand light-years thick, and is of the spiral type. The sun is located about 30,000 light-years from the center in one of the spiral arms and revolves about the center once every 200 million years.

The Milky Way galaxy is a fairly typical spiral galaxy although somewhat larger than most of its near neighbors in space. The Milky Way is a member of a Local Group of 17 galaxies, clustered within about two million light-years of it. One of these is Andromeda, a spiral galaxy of about the same size. The changing luminosities of Cepheid variable stars have enabled the distances of these galaxies to be estimated.

In the next chapter you will explore the farthest depths of the universe, passing millions of galaxies as you go. You will study the way galaxies are distributed in space, how they move, and finally the most basic questions of all: What is the universe in which we live really like—where and when and how did it originate and what will finally happen to it?

Questions and Problems

A

1. Describe the differences between the H-R diagrams of globular star clusters and galactic star clusters.
2. Explain how the differences in Question 1 can be understood.
3. Compare the density of interstellar gas and that of the air in your classroom.
4. What do you think will happen to the earth when the sun finally becomes a red giant star?
5. In what stage of its evolution is the sun now? Describe your evidence.
6. If the sun is in a flattened star system, how do you explain the presence of all the stars in the sky that do not lie along the Milky Way?
7. What are the advantages of using radio telescopes to study the structure of the Milky Way galaxy?
8. What is the difference between a nebula and a galaxy?
9. What kind of life existed on earth when the light that you see now from M31 left that galaxy? Look back at the Geologic Time Scale in Table 19–1.
10. The photographs of galaxies in this chapter show many bright stars in addition to the stars in the galaxy. Where do these stars come from?

B

1. Why do astronomers study H-R diagrams of star clusters instead of H-R diagrams of ordinary stars in the neighborhood of the sun to learn about stellar evolution?
2. Describe the processes by which the carbon, iron, and other elements in your body might once have formed inside a star.
3. How would the Milky Way appear in the sky if the sun were on the very edge of the disk of our galaxy instead of inside the disk? if the sun were at the center of the galaxy?
4. Fewer galaxies are observed along the belt of the Milky Way than anywhere else in the sky. Why?
5. Do you think that star formation in our galaxy will eventually stop? Why?
6. Do you think that elliptical galaxies might be in a more advanced stage of evolution than spiral galaxies? Why?

C

1. If there is one hydrogen atom per cubic centimeter in interstellar space, how many hydrogen atoms are there per cubic light-year? If each hydrogen atom has a mass of 1.67×10^{-24} grams and the mass of the sun is 1.99×10^{33} grams, what fraction of the sun's mass does this represent?
2. The Crab Nebula (Section 24–2) is observed to be expanding with a speed of 1300 kilometers per second. How many light-years has this nebula expanded since the original supernova explosion was first observed 900 years ago?
3. If galaxies like our own and M31 were the size of pie plates, how far apart would they be in space?

Suggested Readings

BOOKS

Abell, G. O. *Exploration of the Universe.* Holt, Rinehart & Winston, Inc., N.Y., 1964.

Bergamini, David and the Editors of *Life. The Universe.* Time, Inc. (Life Nature Library), New York, 1962.

Boeke, Kees. *Cosmic View: The Universe in 40 Jumps.* The John Day Company, Inc., New York, 1957.

Bok, Bart J. and Priscilla F. Bok. *The Milky Way,* 3rd ed. Harvard University Press, Cambridge, Mass., 1957.

Elementary School Science Project. *Astronomy.* University of Illinois, 1962–65.

Hoyle, Fred. *Astronomy.* Doubleday & Company, Inc., Garden City, N.Y., 1962.

Hynek, J. Allen and Norman D. Anderson. *Challenge of the Universe.* McGraw-Hill Book Company, New York, 1962.

Menzel, Donald H. *A Field Guide to the Stars and Planets.* Houghton Mifflin Company, Boston, 1963.

Page, Thornton. *Stars and Galaxies.* Prentice-Hall, Inc., Englewood Cliffs, N.J., 1962.

Physical Science Study Committee. *Physics,* 2nd ed. D. C. Heath & Company, Boston, 1965.

Shapley, Harlow. *Galaxies,* rev. ed. Harvard Univ. Press, Cambridge, Mass., 1961.

Trinklein, Frederick E. and Charles M. Huffer. *Modern Space Science.* Holt, Rinehart & Winston, Inc., New York, 1961.

PERIODICALS

Burbidge, Geoffrey and Margaret Burbidge. "Stellar Populations." *Scientific American,* November, 1958. (Also Scientific American Offprint #203, W. H. Freeman & Co., Publishers, San Francisco.)

Fowler, William A. "The Origin of the Elements." *Scientific American,* September, 1956. (Also Scientific American Offprint #210.)

Greenstein, Jesse L. "Dying Stars." *Scientific American,* January, 1959. (Also Scientific American Offprint #216.)

Sky and Telescope. Sky Publishing Corp., Cambridge, Mass.

Westerhout, Gart. "The Radio Galaxy." *Scientific American,* August, 1959. (Also Scientific American Offprint #250.)

Chapter 26 The Universe and Its Origin

The universe is everything that is: space, galaxies, stars, our solar system, the earth, and all the things on it and in it—including you and me. We are all part of one vast organization and collection of things called the universe.

Have you ever wondered how it all came to be? And why is it *this* particular universe and not some other totally different arrangement of things? Could the universe have been made of an entirely different set of elements? Instead of the iron and carbon we know, could there have been "oolion" and "zeran" instead? Have you ever asked yourself, "What would be here if all this weren't?", or, "If I had been born on a different day or into a different family, would I still be me?" These are philosophical questions. In some ways they are the most interesting questions of all. They often lead to very practical inquiries that can be tested in laboratories.

The analysis of meteorites and the study of the spectra of stars and galaxies reveal an astounding fact: Chemical elements are the same throughout the universe. As far as we can tell, even the most distant galaxies are composed of the same elements—like calcium, hydrogen, and nitrogen—that are found right here on earth. So we see that the universe, including you and me, is made up of the same "world-stuff." It is pretty wonderful stuff at that. In different combinations it makes forests, waterfalls, and stars.

This same "world-stuff" also makes man, and the things and patterns that man creates, works of art like the Mona Lisa, the music of Beethoven, the plays of Shakespeare, and masterpieces of inquiry like Newton's law of gravitation and Einstein's theory of relativity. In the form of man, after ages of evolution, this strange world-stuff has developed the ability to wonder about itself, to investigate the earth, and even to guide its own evolution.

General Picture of the Universe

26–1 Galaxies galore.

Before you ask how the universe was formed, suppose you take a look at the universe as a whole and think of everything that can be seen through the world's largest telescopes. Wherever you look, in those parts of the sky where your vision is not blocked by Milky Way dust (see photo above) you see galaxies, more galaxies, and still more galaxies. Often you see more galaxies than stars. The stars, of course, belong to our own galaxy, the Milky Way galaxy. It is only one of billions of other galaxies, and the sun is but one star out of billions and billions of stars in that one galaxy.

Suppose you were a cosmic navigator in search of the planet earth. From at least a billion galaxies (Figure 26–1), you would have to choose the right one, the galaxy we live inside of, called the Milky Way. That would be your first big problem—to find the right galaxy! You would have to have enormous and accurate three-dimensional charts of all the galaxies in the universe.

Your next problem would be to find one particular star out of more than a hundred billion—our sun. This would be no easy task. Even a billion is an extremely large number. How large? Think how fast seconds tick off. Yet you will not have lived one billion seconds until you are 31 years old. If you set out

to count the stars in our galaxy, one every second, it would take more than 3000 years of steady counting!

Once you located the sun, your task would be just a matter of finding the third planet out from it. That would be our own planet, the earth. How many planets like the earth do you think there are near other stars in our galaxy? How many planets orbit around stars in the billions of other galaxies?

As far as our telescopes can reach, we see fainter and fainter, more and more distant galaxies. Are they like our own galaxy? Many of them are, but galaxies come in many shapes and sizes. They are all huge collections of stars and often also contain great quantities of dust and gas, as discussed in Section 25–2.

The space between galaxies, called intergalactic space, seems relatively clear. There is some gas, and occasional stars may wander in the awesome spaces between galaxies, like lonely travelers in open country between large cities.

Our Milky Way galaxy is a member of a clump of galaxies called the Local Group. (See Section 25–8.) One of the galaxies in our Local Group is shown in Figure 26–2. Usually galaxies belong to large groups or clusters of hundreds or thousands of galaxies. There is even some indication that there may be clusters of clusters of galaxies!

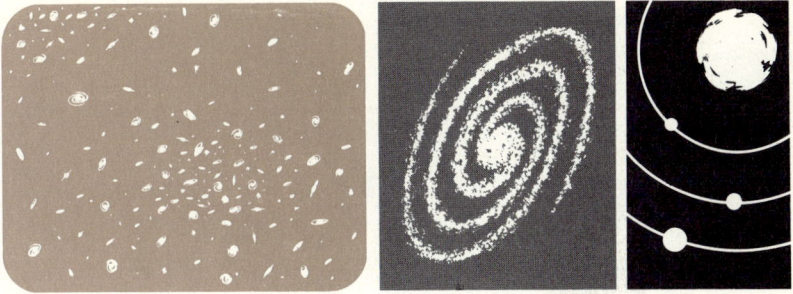

Figure 26–1 *The earth's position in space. Do you think you could find the planet earth orbiting a single star among the countless galaxies in space?*

As far as we can see, there appears to be no end to the realm of the galaxies. Is this really true? With even larger telescopes would we probe eventually to a place where there are no more galaxies—just "space"? We don't know, but you will soon see that you have to change your everyday way of thinking about space and time.

How far away are the farthest visible galaxies? Are they stationary or moving through space? The two questions are very closely related. You will find for yourself that the farther away a galaxy is, the faster it is moving away from us.

Some methods used for finding distance depend on observing individual stars in galaxies, such as Cepheid variables, and novas. These do not work for distant galaxies in which individual stars cannot be seen through a telescope. The astronomer must use less exact methods that depend on the average apparent size and brightness of galaxies in clusters. He can then obtain the average distance to a cluster of galaxies.

26–2 The red shift is discovered.

A very interesting part of the investigation of galaxies is the story of the red shift, one of the most exciting astronomical discoveries of all time. All distant galaxies and the recently discovered quasars (quasi-stellar radio sources) show the red shift. The quasars, first discovered by radio telescopes, were identified as objects radiating light as well as intense radio waves. The red shift appears to be a key to determining the structure of the universe. To appreciate the significance of the red shift, you must understand exactly what the term means. The red shift is designated by the symbol $\Delta\lambda$. The Greek letter delta, Δ, is the general symbol for difference or change in value. The Greek letter lambda, λ, is the symbol for wavelength. Delta $\lambda(\Delta\lambda)$ means the difference, Δ, or shift, between the *observed* wavelength of light, λ, in the spectrum of a galaxy and the wavelength it *ought* to have. The wavelength it ought to have is its *laboratory* value, λ_0.

What would cause such a shift in wavelength? Consider a light source A (Figure 26–3), one light-second away from you. (How far away from you would this light source be in kilometers?) This means it takes light exactly one second to travel from the source to you.

Figure 26–2 *This galaxy in the constellation Cassiopeia, like the Milky Way, is a member of our Local Group of galaxies.*

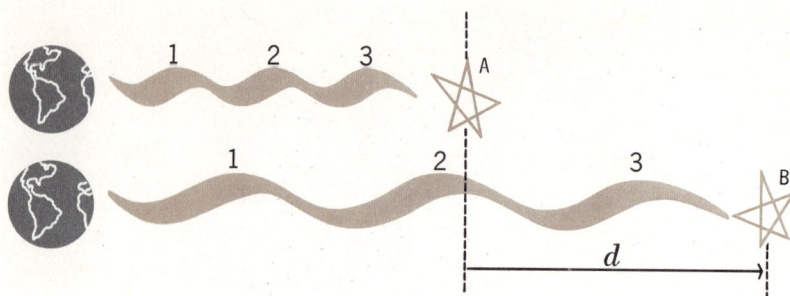

Figure 26–3 *Source (A) is stationary and Source (B) moves away from the observer. Each source sends out exactly the same number of light waves per second.*

In Figure 26–3, light source A is not moving in relation to the observer. Light source B is traveling *away* from you and in one second travels the distance d. In both cases, A and B, the source *remains lighted for exactly one second*, and both sources have sent out *exactly* the same number of waves. But in case B this same number of waves is spread out over a greater distance d the light source has traveled in one second. Since the same number of waves are spread out over a longer distance, each wave must be some $\Delta\lambda$ longer. This shift toward a longer wavelength is called the **red shift**. In Figure 26–3 the light source is going away, so the light waves are lengthened. The light would appear redder, showing the red shift, due to the fact that red light has a longer wavelength than yellow light.

In 1913, a program began to observe wavelength shifts in galaxies. It was noticed that the fainter the galaxy, the greater the shift in wavelength. The Doppler shift was *always* toward longer wavelengths, that is, it was always a red shift. This would indicate that the galaxies are going *away* from us.

This startling result was confirmed in the 1920's by an astronomer, Dr. Edwin P. Hubble, using the Mount Wilson 100-inch reflector, then the world's largest telescope. When Hubble plotted the red shift against the distances to the galaxies, he found a most interesting relationship.

26–3 Investigating the motion of galaxies.

Using the red shift shown in the spectrograms of distant galaxies, Hubble determined how fast they were going away from us. By plotting the velocity of the galaxy against its distance from the earth, he demonstrated the relationship between the amount of red shift and the distance from us.

Figure 26–4 shows the spectrograms of three distant galaxies. Using the same procedure as Hubble did, determine the relationship between distance and velocity.

Procedure

The long horizontal streaks in Figure 26–4 are the spectrograms of three galaxies. Two black spots appear in each spectrogram because the light at these two wavelengths is absorbed by material within the galaxy. These spots have been identified as the calcium H and calcium K spectral lines.

The three identical series of vertical lines are reference spectra photographed in a laboratory. The first two lines on the left end of each series are the calcium H and calcium K spectral lines. Use these as reference lines.

(1) Measure the red shift of each galaxy in angstroms (A) and compute its velocity (V), using the formula shown below. The speed of light is indicated by the letter c.

$$\frac{\Delta\lambda}{\lambda_0} = \frac{V}{c}$$

(2) Plot velocity against distance and see what relationship (if any) exists between them.

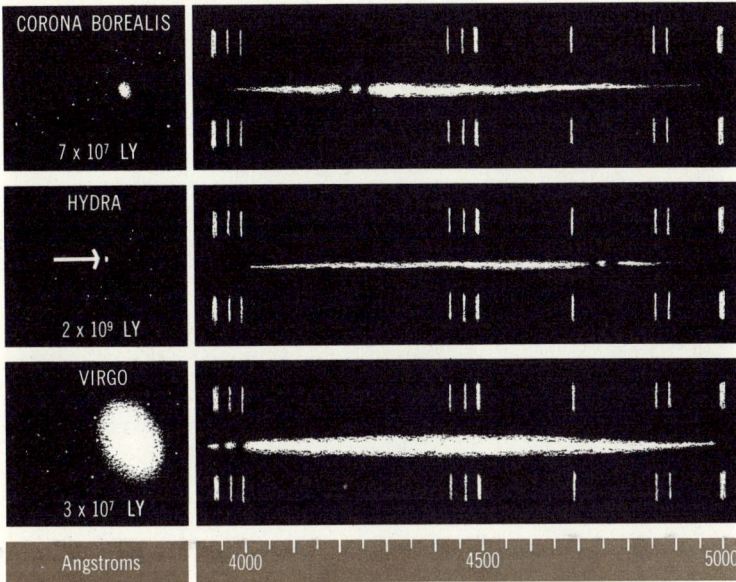

Figure 26–4
Spectrograms of three distant galaxies.

26–4 Is the universe expanding?

The great 200-inch telescope has made it possible to measure the red shifts of many galaxies more distant than Hubble was able to observe, and as far out as we can look his law holds. **Hubble's law** states that for every million light-years farther out we look into space, the speed with which galaxies move away from us increases by about 30 kilometers per second.

Remember that what is observed is the red shift, and not the speed of the galaxy. Astronomers generally agree, however, that the red shift is caused by the actual motions of galaxies and not by some unknown principle of nature.

But why should the universe be expanding all around us? Wherever we look, no matter what direction, galaxies are rushing away from *us*, and the farther away they are, the faster they go! Are we truly in the center of the universe? Not at all. This is merely an illusion, as you can easily see for yourself in the following example.

Imagine a very large theater with an infinite number of seats. Suppose that the interior of this theater were to begin expanding. At the end of each minute, every seat would be twice as far from its neighbor as it was the minute before. Then, no matter where you sat, every other seat would appear to be going away from you. The farther away a seat was, the faster it would seem to be rushing away from you. A diagram may make this clearer. The circles in Figure

26–5 (left) are the theater seats. Suppose you were in seat A. Now, suppose a minute later the theater had expanded to the size shown in Figure 26–5 (right). Then, persons in seats B and C would be twice as far away from you as they were one minute earlier. Also notice that C moved twice as far as B moved during that time. Why is this so? How would A and B appear to move from a person seated at C? Notice that you can start with a seat anywhere in the theater. No matter where you sit in the theater, the other seats will appear to be going away from you.

ACTIVITY *Using rubber cement, bits of cotton, and a balloon, construct a model of the principle illustrated in Figure 26–5.*

The theory of the expansion of the universe based on the red shift implies that the universe has *no* center.

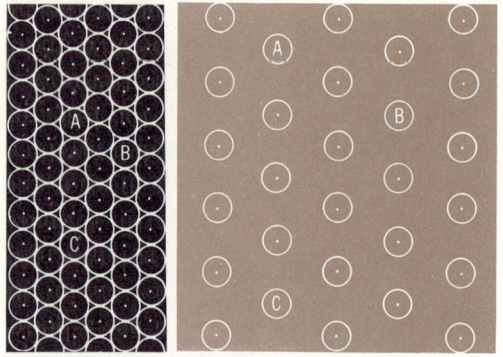

Figure 26–5 (*Left*) A, B, and C are seats in a theater. (*Right*) The theater has expanded. How have distances between seats A, B, and C changed?

Thought and Discussion . . .

1. Why do ordinary methods of measurement of stellar distances fail for distant galaxies?
2. What is meant by red shift?
3. Describe the motions of the galaxies of the universe relative to the earth.
4. Why does it appear that we are at the center of the universe?

Relativity

26–5 Faster than light?

Almost everyone has heard that nothing can travel faster than the speed of light. Some of you, however, may want to challenge this conclusion. Suppose, you may say, you have the same situation as that shown in Figure 26–6. Surely, an observer in galaxy A will see galaxy B going away from him at 1½ times the speed of light! Just figure it out for yourself: Where the letter c equals the speed of light, $\frac{3}{4}c + \frac{3}{4}c = 1\frac{1}{2}c$.

Actually the observer in galaxy A will see galaxy B speeding away at only $\frac{24}{25}$ the speed of light. This is explained by the theory of relativity developed by Albert Einstein. Although called a theory, most of the predictions of relativity have been so thoroughly tested in the

laboratory that the theory of relativity is accepted as solidly as the other laws of physics. The concepts of relativity seem strange to us only because the human race has evolved without experiencing the high speeds at which the effects of relativity become noticeable. But today, in the construction of an atom-smashing cyclotron, for instance, in which electrons travel at very high speeds, the prediction of relativity that the electrons will become much heavier at high speeds must be taken into account. Otherwise the cyclotron will not work. The electrons *do* behave as though they were much more massive as their speed increases. If they moved with the speed of light, they would behave as if they were infinitely massive.

The theory of special relativity deals with uniform motion, whereas the theory of general relativity deals with accelerated motion. The theory of special relativity was proposed by Einstein to explain, among other things, a very surprising conclusion from careful measurement of the velocity of light. This measurement was made in 1887 in Cleveland, Ohio, by two Americans, Michelson and Morley. They expected to find that light would go more slowly past the earth when it comes from behind the earth than when it meets the earth from the front. Remember that the earth moves at 30 kilometers per second in its orbit around the sun.

The investigators, Michelson and Morley, expected that light would behave like a bullet shot at a moving object such as an airplane. Such a bullet would pass the plane faster if it were shot in the direction of the oncoming plane than if it were shot toward the plane from behind.

Michelson and Morley found that light does not act in this way. The speed of light has been measured under many different conditions of speed for the observer and for the light source. The answer obtained is always the same. The speed of light always remains the same. It is a universal constant. It is equal, in round numbers, to 3×10^5 kilometers per second. From this one fact alone, a whole series of "Alice in Wonderland" results arise. They can be summed up in a nutshell: For instance, the faster you travel, the more massive you get—infinitely massive if you travel with the speed of light. This theory of relativity suggests that speeds greater than that of light are impossible, for if mass increases to infinity, no force could move it!

And another odd result: The faster you travel, the thinner you get in the direction of your motion, until you become as thin as paper as you approach the speed of light. And if that isn't enough—the faster you travel, the slower your clock or watch goes. At the speed of light time ceases to pass! These happenings in the wonderland of relativity have been tested many times. You cannot escape the results: The length and mass of an object are not definite, fixed quantities. The measurement of these properties and the measurement of time intervals depends on the *speed of the person making the measurements relative to the thing being measured!* As relative speeds increase, the length of the speeding objects shortens, in the direction of motion only, and becomes almost infinitely short as the speed of light is approached. The mass of the speeding object increases, as measured by the "stationary" observer, and becomes almost infinitely massive as the speed of light is approached. Remember the actual experimental increased mass of the electrons observed in the cyclotron, as measured by the "stationary" physicist. Finally, time intervals lengthen, or the passage of time slows down, in a speeding body when compared to the passage of time for the "stationary" observer. Why do all these strange results take place?

Figure 26–6 *Why doesn't the observer at A see galaxy B going away from him at $1\frac{1}{2}$ times the speed of light?*

You are in a train at a railway station. Suddenly the train appears to move. Yet, you experience no sensation of motion. Then you realize the train on the next track is sliding past you the other way, while you are standing still. Already in 1905, Albert Einstein (1879–1955) dealt with the problem of what is moving and what is standing still in his special theory of relativity. Einstein's ideas on relativity brought the first new look at the mechanics of the universe since Newton. Newton and Einstein each revolutionized the thinking of his age about time, space, mass, and motion. Einstein did most of the work that made him famous while employed in the Swiss Patent Office in Zürich, Switzerland. Later he worked at the Institute for Advanced Studies in Princeton. In conjunction with his work on the special theory of relativity, Einstein developed the formula, $E = Mc^2$ (energy equals mass times the square of the speed of light). United States government leaders did not know that this formula could be applied to nuclear energy until Einstein was persuaded to suggest the possibility early in World War II. Deeply concerned with peace and the problems of mankind, Einstein feared misuse of this knowledge, which marked the beginning of the atomic age.

Many people think that relativity is impossible to understand. It is true that some of the ideas of relativity are surprising. But no one should be afraid of an idea because it is surprising. If the idea is good, the scientific approach will explain and demonstrate it. Just think, less than a hundred years ago, how strange the ideas of television, nuclear energy, and radioactive dating of rocks would have seemed to the people of that day. What things do you suppose people a hundred years from now will regard as commonplace that today are completely unknown to us?

For the speeding galaxies A and B (Figure 26–6) it is just *because* time and length are relative and not fixed quantities that the observer on galaxy A will not see galaxy B going away faster than the speed of light. His measurements of speed, which is distance divided by time, are changed under the principles of relativity.

26–6 The traveling twin and the relativity of time.

One of the strangest predictions of relativity concerns the different rates of aging of the twins, Peter and Paul. Paul stays at home on earth, but Peter travels away from and back to the earth at very high speeds. When he returns to earth, Peter finds he is still quite young, but his twin, Paul, is old and gray.

Relativity shows that, relative to the earth twin, Paul, the space twin's clocks went more slowly, as well as the rate at which his body aged. Since it was the space twin, Peter, who speeded up with respect to the earth, and not the earth twin, it was only the traveling twin's clock that slowed down.

Is this too strange to believe? Well, it has been proved, not by a twin in a rocket, but by measuring the lifetimes of atomic particles called mesons, which are produced by cosmic rays very high in the earth's atmosphere. Calculations and experiments on earth indicate that the mesons created high above the earth should not live long enough to reach the earth's surface. Yet they do. This must mean that since the mesons travel with nearly the speed of light, their "clocks" run very slow, and they *do* have time enough to reach the earth on their time scale. Like the traveling twin, they live much longer than the mesons that "stayed at home."

There might be a practical side to the relativity of time. If a rocket ship can be made to move at almost the speed of light, an astronaut could reach the Andromeda galaxy in just 30 years, shipboard time. But when he returned to earth, what a difference he would find. It would be more than four million years later! His historic launching would probably have long been forgotten or have become a part of legendary history.

26–7 Time: the fourth dimension.

By now you realize that time is quite an interesting thing. It is, in fact, another dimension—the fourth dimension. If the speed of light is constant, lengths can be expressed as time—the time it takes light to travel a given length. One "light-second" is 3×10^5 kilometers. The moon is about 1.3 light-seconds away. You can express all lengths as times if you wish, so it is quite natural to think of time as a dimension. But now suppose you think of it as a fourth dimension, in addition to the ordinary three dimensions of space, length, height, and width.

Why should you want to do this? The reason is that in relativity, time is completely interwoven with space. We speak of space-time in relativity, in-

Figure 26–7 *The light from these galaxies has taken millions of years to reach the earth.*

stead of space and time. We need to do this because we cannot consider space alone when we think about the universe as a whole. Finding suitable models of the universe requires that we think in terms of the theory of relativity. We must think of space and time as interlocked and not as completely separate and different things.

This is really quite simple to do. As a start, we already know that space and time are closely connected when we look at distant galaxies. We do not see them as they are tonight, but *as they were* when light we are receiving on earth left there. When we look at the Andromeda galaxy, we see it not as it is now, but as it was over 2 million years ago. Saber-toothed tigers roamed the earth then, and man as we know him had not yet made his appearance. For every one of those two million years, the light from Andromeda we see tonight has been racing along at 3×10^5 kilometers per second!

Yet, Andromeda is one of the closest neighboring galaxies. In Figure 26–7 you see a cluster of galaxies in the constellation of Hercules. The light you see now from some of these galaxies probably left there when dinosaurs walked the earth. You can even go back to the time when life first appeared on earth. For every fossil that the geologist can uncover from the past, the astronomer can point his telescope to some galaxy, the light from which left there when that fossil was a living thing. As you go farther out into space, you go farther back in time. Right away you see how it is impossible to separate space and time. But space and time in relativity are even more closely connected.

How would you answer this question, "How far is it from the launching of astronauts at Cape Kennedy on Tuesday morning to a firecracker exploding on London Bridge on Sunday afternoon?" This may seem like a meaningless question, but it really isn't. It seems odd only because the earth is such a tiny speck in the universe and the distances and times involved are small. In relativity we speak of the distance, or *interval*, be-

tween "events." An "event" in relativity means the crossing of "world lines."

Let's look at your world line. Suppose you are sitting still in your chair. Then your world line with respect to the earth is represented by the dotted line shown in Figure 26–8. Although you are sitting still, you are growing older. You are moving upward in the time dimension. Now suppose someone runs toward you and crashes into you. He is moving in space as well as in time. His world line is shown as the solid line. When his world line crosses yours, that is an "event."

In the question about London Bridge and the astronauts, the "distance" between the launching at Cape Kennedy on Tuesday and the exploding firecracker in London on Sunday is shown in Figure 26–9. The "space distance" between Cape Kennedy and London is the arrow S. The "space-time" distance, or interval, is the longer arrow ST.

We have used a very simple example to illustrate that time and distance (space) can be considered together. In the universe, every star, planet, and galaxy has its own world line as it travels through space and time. A world line, remember, is simply the *path* of an object in four dimensions rather than our very familiar paths in the ordinary world of three dimensions.

The trouble is that you cannot draw world lines on two-dimensional paper. You must use your imagination. Do you think you can imagine four dimensions and your own path in space-time—your world line? Sometimes it helps your imagination to do something like this:

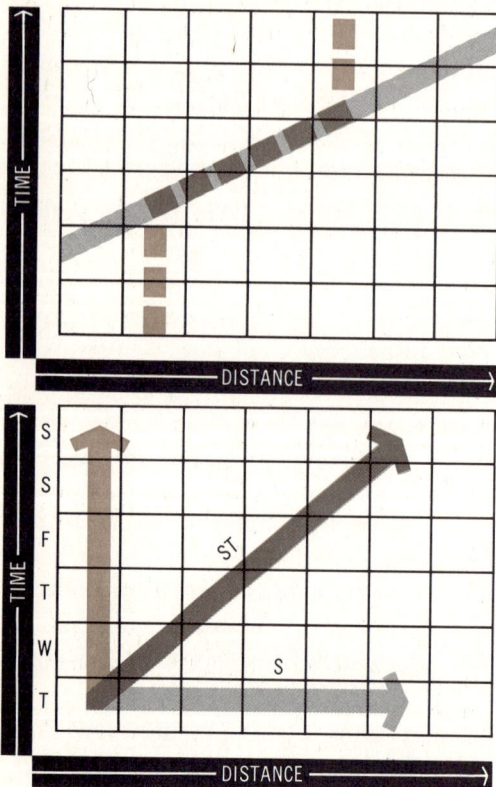

Figure 26–8 (*Above*) *The intersection of two separate world lines describes an event that involves both.*

Figure 26–9 (*Below*) *A graphical representation of two different events in a framework of space and time.*

Pretend that you have painted a landscape on the surface of a balloon—rivers and mountains and a road going off in the distance. You have *represented* the three-dimensional world on a two-dimensional surface—the surface of the balloon. Now blow up the balloon. You are moving the landscape through another dimension, time, since it takes time to blow up the balloon.

To make it easier for your imagination, just draw a graph like Figure 26–9. Let the vertical line represent time and the horizontal line just one dimension of space, left to right. Draw a straight diagonal line on the paper, as shown. That can be the world line of the earth or of a galaxy. Now wrap the paper around a doorknob. What happens to the world line? It curves and bends. The earth or galaxy traveling on that line would also curve in its path through space-time.

26–8 Curved space-time.

That space-time is curved is precisely what the theory of relativity says. The presence of matter in space warps, or curves, space-time just as the doorknob warped the flat sheet of paper. The sun is a massive body that warps space-time around it just enough to make the earth, which "thinks" it is moving on a straight world line, curve ever so slightly as it accompanies the sun on its journey through space. In the course of a year that slight curvature makes it appear that the earth has gone completely around the sun. Hence, in the theory of relativity there is no need for a special force of gravity. The same results are obtained by the curvature of space-time.

The sun, too, "thinks" it is going along a straight world line. But the Milky Way galaxy is very massive, so the sun's path in the space-time is also slightly curved. This causes the sun to make one complete trip around the galaxy in a little more than 200 million years.

Here is an interesting idea. Would it be possible to have a body so massive and so dense that it would curve space-time enough to completely close around the object, as an eggshell encloses an egg? This is certainly theoretically possible. There may be such massive "super-stars" that have completely closed space around themselves! Their light could never reach us, because it could never escape from the closed neighborhood of the super-star. There is a real "Alice in Wonderland" result of relativity for you to think about!

What about the galaxies? Here is where relativity and space-time become important. The combined mass of all the galaxies warps or curves the entire universe of space-time. We do not know whether the curvature is positive, negative, or zero. (See Figure 26–10.) If it were positive, space-time would close in

Figure 26–10 *Different models of space-time of the universe have different curvatures. An important question that may someday be answered is, "Is the curvature zero, positive, or negative?"*

around itself as the two-dimensional surface of a sphere curves around the third dimension. On a sphere like the earth you can travel forever without coming to a place where it stops. Centuries ago people would speak of the "four corners of the earth" and of what would happen if you traveled on and on. Many thought you would come to the end of the earth and fall off. Some people today ask, "Is there an end to space?" This is probably as meaningless as the question, "Where is the end of the earth?"

If space-time were curved negatively, like the surface of a saddle, instead of positively, like a globe, it would go on indefinitely and never close back on itself. Or it might have zero curvature and just go on and on like an infinite sheet of paper but in a four-dimensional sort of way. (See Figure 26–10.)

We still do not know what the geometry of space is. This problem has stretched the imagination and abilities of many scientists. To get some idea of the problem, let's make an imaginary model of everything that can be seen through the world's largest telescopes. Suppose we use the entire United States for building our model. You would be somewhere in Kansas. Looking out in one direction, the most distant galaxy you could see on your model would be in New York City. In the opposite direction your most distant visible galaxy would be in San Francisco.

On that model, the earth would be so small that no microscope could reveal it! You, looking out from that submicroscopic speck, ask: "What is the geometry of the world like?" Do you think you could answer the question? Our model is on a two-dimensional surface, the surface of the earth. From our submicroscopic speck in Kansas it looks flat, but we know that if we kept on

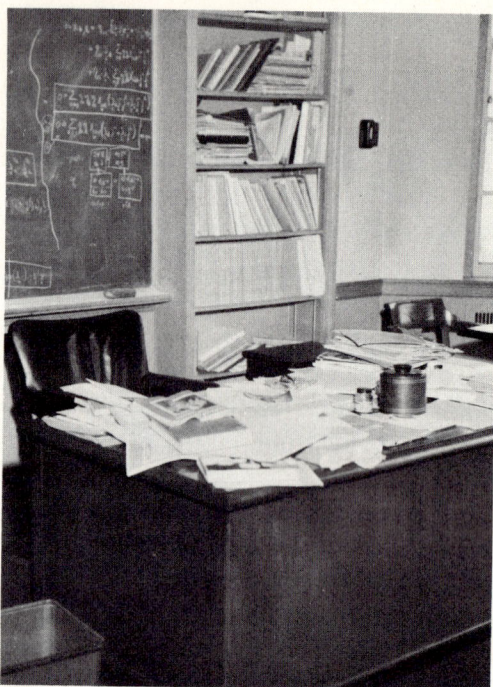

The desk of Albert Einstein as he left it shortly before he died. Here one of the greatest thinkers in the history of mankind did his work.

going past San Francisco, across the Pacific, we would eventually return to Kansas by way of New York, from the opposite direction in which we left. Our model is on a surface with positive curvature—it is a sphere. Does our actual universe have positive curvature too? That is the problem astronomers face. From this extremely tiny planet earth they must, like cosmic detectives, try to find out what the whole universe is like.

Thought and Discussion . . .

1. Why do the results of relativity seem so strange and difficult to understand?
2. How do the general relativity theory and special relativity theory differ?
3. On what factor does the length and mass of an object depend?
4. In what way are an object's mass and speed related?
5. What is the relationship between an object's length and its speed?

Origins

26–9 Did the universe have a beginning?

What chance is there of finding out how the universe started? Perhaps we can work backward from what we do know to what might have been. There are two possibilities: Either the universe was always here and had no beginning and will have no end, or the whole universe had a start sometime in the past and is evolving as are the stars and individual galaxies. Stars and galaxies cannot last forever. Stars are using up their hydrogen fuel and must someday end up in the cosmic ash heap as celestial clinkers. The same is true for the galaxies. Their ability to form new stars out of dust and gas must someday end. But can the universe become young and start over again?

There is another factor we must take into account: The universe is expanding and the space between galaxies is getting larger and larger. Someday, billions of years from now, our galaxy may appear to be alone in space. Does the expansion stop and the galaxies come closer together again for billions of years until they are crushed together, explode, and start the whole process over again? This sort of universe would be an **oscillating universe,** eternally expanding, contracting, and expanding, like a giant lung or balloon. (See Figure 26–11.)

Figure 26–11 (*Left*) *The oscillating,* (*center*) *big-bang or evolutionary, and* (*right*) *the steady-state theories of origin of the universe. How do the densities vary in each case?*

26–10 Big-bang or steady-state?

If the universe just keeps on expanding, then the galaxies will get farther and farther apart until each one is "alone" in space. Was there a time when they were all together? Suppose we "run the film backward," as is sometimes done in a movie of a man diving into a swimming pool. Played backward, the film shows the man come out of the pool and back onto the springboard. Our "cosmic film" would show the galaxies rushing together. How long would it be before they were all together? A rough calculation shows that this would have been about 10 to 12 billion years ago. Then the galaxies would have been right on top of each other. The **big-bang or evolutionary theory** states that when the universe began there were no galaxies or stars and not even much matter. Instead there was an intense globe of energy that exploded outward and "cooled down" into matter. (Recall that matter and energy are interchangeable.) At that time huge chunks of matter became galaxies. Finally individual stars were formed within the separate galaxies. Stars are still forming within our galaxy, but the day must come when all the material has formed into stars. What happens to an old galaxy according to this theory? Its stars go through their evolution, and eventually the galaxy becomes a vast collection of used-up stars.

That is one picture. Another, often called the **steady-state theory,** states that

as the galaxies move away from each other, new hydrogen is somehow mysteriously formed in space. Eventually new, young galaxies are formed to take the place of those that are disappearing in the distance and dying out. This might be called the perpetual universe.

If the big-bang theory is correct, then when we look out as far into space and as far back into time as we can, we should see younger galaxies than we see nearby. We would literally be looking into the past and seeing those galaxies as they were billions of years ago.

If the steady-state theory is correct, no matter where we look we should see on the average much the same proportion of old and new galaxies as we see around us. The steady-state theory appeals to many people, but truth in science does not depend on what is appealing. Observational tests are far from complete today, but evidence is mounting strongly in favor of the evolutionary, big-bang theory. It may turn out that the oscillating theory is the correct one and that we have an eternal universe, as in the steady-state theory, as well as an evolving universe, as in the big-bang theory. All of these theories are illustrated in Figure 26–11.

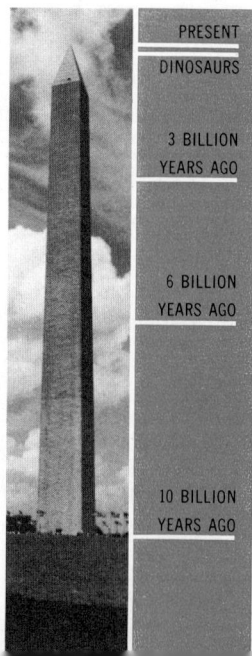

Figure 26–12 *If the Washington Monument represented the age of the universe, it would be divided as shown. Compare the time line shown here with the time lines you developed in Investigation 17–7.*

PRESENT
DINOSAURS
3 BILLION YEARS AGO
6 BILLION YEARS AGO
10 BILLION YEARS AGO

26–11 The long journey through time.

We know that the universe has been here a long time. Certainly the universe cannot be younger than its parts. It must be older than the individual galaxies, older than the earth, and older than the chemical elements. Many lines of evidence indicate that an important event occurred 10 to 12 billion years ago. Playing the expanding universe film backward also supports this idea.

We can look far backward down the corridor of time. But how far into the future can we look? The sun will probably shine much as it does today for many more billions of years.

Looking backward in time, let the height of the 169-meter Washington Monument represent these 10^{10} years since the big-bang. (See Figure 26–12.) The diameter of a silver dollar balanced on edge on the top of the monument represents the entire age of man, the time since manlike creatures appeared on the earth. The age of dinosaurs would come above the windows near the top of the monument and the appearance of the first living organisms, about three billion years ago, would be one-third of the way down. Imagine a thin sheet of tissue paper on top of the silver dollar. The thickness of the paper represents the 4000 years of recorded history.

Is there any limit to the future? The sun may last another 5 to 10 billion years, providing energy to the earth's surface as it does now. Therefore, you must imagine another monument above the sheet of paper—or better, a 169-meter stack of silver dollars—to represent the next 10 billion years. Beyond that, the sun may enter the red giant stage or change drastically in some other way.

As far as mankind is concerned, we are at the beginning and not the end of a long, long period of time. The adventure of mankind has just started even though it took billions of years of development to get this far. Only in the last few hundred years has man arrived at the point in his growth at which he is able to begin to control his environment. No longer will evolution be "blind" or accidental. With the great discoveries going on in biology, man may even begin to guide his own biologic development. It is a deeply thrilling thought.

The British astronomer, Sir James Jeans, in his book, *The Universe Around Us,* expressed this thought very well:

As inhabitants of a civilized earth, we are living at the very beginning of time. We have come into being in the fresh glory of the dawn, and a day of almost unthinkable length stretches before us with unimaginable opportunities for accomplishment. Our descendants of far-off ages, looking down this long vista of time from the other end, will see our present age as the misty morning of the world's history; they will see our contemporaries of to-day as dim heroic figures who fought their way through jungles of ignorance, error and superstition to discover truth, to learn how to harness the forces of nature, and to make a world worthy for mankind to live in. We are still too much engulfed in the greyness of the morning mists to be able to imagine, even vaguely, how this world of ours will appear to those who will come after us and see it in the full light of day. But by what light we have, we seem to discern that the main message of astronomy is one of hope to the race and of responsibility to the individual— of responsibility because we are drawing plans and laying foundations for a longer future than we can well imagine.

Astronomers examining the reflecting mirror of the 120-inch telescope at Lick Observatory, Mount Hamilton, California. This is one of the larger telescopes available for probing the universe.

Since that was written, the human race has unleashed, but only partly harnessed, the greatest force of nature— atomic energy. This makes our responsibility all the greater. Through the long ages down to the present time we have had nothing to say about how we evolved. Natural processes of selection have made us what we are. But from now on we can have something definite to say about how we will develop. Genetic guidance and control can shape our future physical features. But more important than that is how we guide our future by the way we think and what we think about. Unsolved problems are everywhere around us. The future of our race will depend on how we tackle those problems—and on how the human spirit is allowed freedom to search the unknown and to seek out the truth.

Thought and Discussion . . .

1. Do you think the universe has always been in existence or that it had a beginning? Explain your answer.
2. Discuss the three major theories of the origin of the universe and your reasons for or against any of them.
3. What do you think the future of mankind will be like?

CHAPTER REVIEW

Summary

We know that the observable universe consists of billions of galaxies, of which one is our own Milky Way, a member of a Local Group of galaxies in intergalactic space. The distances between galaxies are tremendous and largely empty, containing a little gas and occasional stars. The discovery of the red shift in the wavelength of light from galaxies has indicated that they are receding in accordance with Hubble's law ever more rapidly with greater distance from us. The conclusion can be drawn that the universe is expanding.

Einstein's theory of special relativity deals with uniform motion and his theory of general relativity with accelerated motion. The speed of light is treated as a constant under relativity. Light always moves at the same speed and it is assumed that nothing can move faster. The speed of a person making measurements of space or time is relative to the speed of the object being measured. Under relativity the three dimensions of space and the one dimension of time are affected by motion. Time is the fourth dimension and dimensions must be conceived in terms of space-time. The world lines of objects involve both space and time. Where world lines cross, space-time events take place, space is curved, and this curvature explains gravitation. It is still not known exactly how space-time is curved. What is the geometry that expresses this idea of the universe? This is one of the greatest unsolved problems of the universe.

Another unsolved problem is how the universe began. Is it in a steady state in which matter is constantly being created out of nothing to replace the matter in the galaxies speeding rapidly away from us in an expanding universe? The evidence at hand does not seem to support this theory. Did the universe then start with a big bang of highly condensed energy in which the matter composing galaxies was formed as it expanded? Or does the universe go back and forth between an expanding state and a contracting state in terms of the theory of an oscillating universe? No one knows whether one of these theories or some other theory will eventually be proved correct.

The quest for more and more evidence bearing on all features of the universe is one of the many exciting adventures in science in which we can all share.

Questions and Problems

A

1. How does the chemical composition of the earth compare with the composition of the entire universe?
2. What is the relationship between the distance of a galaxy from the earth and the speed with which it travels away from the earth?
3. What does the symbol λ represent? the symbol Δ?
4. How does the passage of time vary with increase in speed?
5. How much earth time would it take for a space ship traveling at the speed of light to make a round trip to the moon?

B

1. What causes the red shift of the light reaching us from other galaxies?
2. What is the limiting speed in the universe? Why?
3. How can lengths be expressed in terms of time? With what units are you already familiar that express distance in terms of time?
4. Give an example that illustrates the close connection between time and space in the universe.
5. What do you think is meant by the expression, "oscillating universe"?

C

1. Why is it that wherever you go in the universe it appears that you are in the center of the universe?
2. Describe the several possible shapes of the universe shown in Figure 26–10.
3. Describe the big-bang theory of the origin of the universe.
4. Describe the steady-state theory of the universe. What are some of its weaknesses?
5. If the big-bang theory is correct, why are you watching the youngest galaxies when you view light from the most distant galaxies? Which galaxy would appear oldest to us? Why?

Suggested Readings

BOOKS

Barnett, Lincoln. *Universe and Dr. Einstein*, rev. ed. The New American Library of World Literature, Inc. (A Mentor Book), New York, 1952. Paperback.

Bondi, Hermann. *The Universe at Large*. Doubleday & Company, Inc., Garden City, N.Y., 1960.

Bonnor, William. *The Mystery of the Expanding Universe*. The Macmillan Company, New York, 1964.

Coleman, James A. *Relativity for the Layman*. The New American Library of World Literature, Inc. (A Mentor Book), New York, 1959. Paperback.

Gamow, George. *The Creation of the Universe*, rev. ed. The Viking Press, Inc., New York, 1961.

Gardner, Martin. *Relativity for the Million*. The Macmillan Company, New York, 1962.

Hynek, J. Allen and Norman D. Anderson. *Challenge of the Universe*. McGraw-Hill Book Company, New York, 1962.

Jeans, Sir James. *The Universe Around Us*, 4th ed. Cambridge University Press, New York, 1960. Paperback.

Kahn, Fritz. *Design of the Universe: The Heavens and the Earth*. Crown Publishers, Inc., New York, 1954.

Messel, Harry and S. T. Butler. *The Universe and Its Origin*. St. Martin's Press, Inc., New York, 1964.

Page, Thornton and others. *Stars and Galaxies*. Prentice-Hall, Inc., Englewood Cliffs, N.J., 1962.

Russell, Bertrand. *The ABC of Relativity*. The New American Library of World Literature, Inc. (Signet Science Library Book), New York, 1959.

Thiel, Rudolf. *And There Was Light: The Discovery of the Universe*. Alfred A. Knopf, Inc., New York, 1957.

PERIODICALS

Gamow, George. "The Evolutionary Universe." *Scientific American*, September, 1956. (Also Scientific American Offprint #211, W. H. Freeman & Co., Publishers, San Francisco.)

Hoyle, Fred. "The Steady-State Universe." *Scientific American*, September, 1956. (Also Scientific American Offprint #218.)

Sandage, Allan R. "The Red-Shift." *Scientific American*, September, 1956. (Also Scientific American Offprint #240.)

Sky and Telescope. Sky Publishing Corp., Cambridge, Mass.

Aerial view of Lick Observatory at Mount Hamilton, California. Many kinds of astronomical research are conducted here.

APPENDIX A MATHEMATICAL INFORMATION

A-PART 1 METRIC AND OTHER UNITS OF MEASURE

The Metric System

Prefixes

Prefix	Meaning
kilo-	1,000 or 10^3
centi-	0.01 or 10^{-2}
milli-	0.001 or 10^{-3}

Units of Length

1 kilometer (km) = 1000 meters (m) = 10^3 m

1 centimeter (cm) = 0.01 m = 10^{-2} m

1 millimeter (mm) = 0.001 m = 10^{-3} m

1 angstrom (A) = 0.0000000001 m = 10^{-10} m

Units of Area

1 square meter (m^2) = 10,000 square centimeters (cm^2) = 100 cm × 100 cm

Units of Volume

1 cubic meter (m^3) = 1,000,000 cubic centimeters (cc) = 100 cm × 100 cm × 100 cm

1 liter (1) = 1000 milliliters

1 milliliter (ml) = approximately 1 cc

Units of Mass

1 metric ton = 1000 kilograms

1 kilogram (kg) = 1000 grams

1 gram (gm) = approximately the weight of 1 cc of water

1 milligram (mg) = 0.001 gm

Units of Time

1 hour (hr) = 60 minutes (min) = 3600 seconds (sec)

Metric-English Equivalents
(Values Are Approximate)

Length

1 kilometer = 0.621 mile (1 mile = 1.610 km)

1 meter = 1.094 yards = 3.281 feet (1 foot = 0.305 m)

1 centimeter = 0.3937 inch (1 inch = 2.54 cm)

1 millimeter = 0.0394 inch or approximately $\frac{1}{25}$ inch (1 inch = 25.4 mm)

Volume

1 cubic meter = 1.31 cubic yards (1 cubic yard = 0.76 m^3)

1 liter = 1.06 quarts (1 quart = 0.95 l)

Mass

1 kilogram = 1000 gm = 2.20 pounds (1 pound = 0.45 kg)

1 metric ton = 1.1 tons (U.S.) (1 U.S. ton = 0.909 metric ton)

Other Frequently Used Units of Measure

Distance

1 Astronomical Unit (A.U.) = 149.6 × 10^6 km (mean distance from earth to sun)

1 light-year = 9.46 × 10^{12} km or 5.88 × 10^{12} miles

Force

1 dyne (d) = the force that will produce an acceleration of 1 centimeter/second^2 when applied to a 1-gram mass.

1 newton (nt) = the force that will produce an acceleration of 1 meter/second^2 when applied to a 1-kilogram mass.

1 nt = 100,000 d

Energy

1 erg = the work done by a force of 1 dyne when its point of application moves through a distance of 1 centimeter in the direction of the force.

Angle Measurement

1 degree (1°) = $\frac{1}{360}$th of a circle = 60 minutes

1 minute (1′) = 60 seconds (60″)

Heat

1 calorie (cal) = the amount of heat that will raise the temperature of 1 gram of water 1 degree Celsius with the water at 4 degrees Celsius.

Pressure

1 millibar (mb) = 1000 d/cm^2

Average atmospheric pressure at sea level = 1013.6 mb

If you divide the difference between your answer to a problem and the correct answer by the correct answer, you obtain the *relative error*. If you multiply the relative error by 100, you obtain the *percentage error*. For example, in Investigation 3–5 you calculate the circumference of the earth. If you consider the actual value of the earth's circumference to be 40,000 km and your measurement was 38,000 km, the difference between them is 2,000 km. Dividing this difference (2000 km) by the actual value (40,000 km) gives a relative error of 0.05 ($\frac{2000}{40,000} = \frac{1}{20} = 0.05$). Multiplying this relative error by 100 gives a percentage error of 5% ($0.05 \times 100 = 5\%$). A student who obtained a measured value of 42,000 km

would have the same percentage error as your value of 38,000 km. Can you see why?

It is often desirable to calculate the percentage error to see if your answer is reasonable in relation to the possible sources of error of your instruments and measurements. If all your measuring instruments are reasonably accurate and your answer has a percentage error of 40%, you should review your work and look for errors. If, however, your measuring instruments are crude as in Investigation 24–10, and your percentage error is only 8% or so, then it is likely that your work is as accurate as your instruments will permit. As a general rule, the greater your percentage error, the more carefully you should recheck your work for mistakes.

A-PART 3 POWERS OF TEN

In earth science, it is often necessary to use very large and very small numbers. The area of the earth's surface is 361,000,000 square kilometers. A convenient shorthand for writing numbers like this one is to use powers of ten. For example,

Number	Equivalent Power of 10	Number	Equivalent Power of 10
$1000 = 1 \times 10^3$		$0.1 = \frac{1}{10^1} = 1 \times 10^{-1}$	
$100 = 1 \times 10^2$		$0.01 = \frac{1}{10^2} = 1 \times 10^{-2}$	
$10 = 1 \times 10^1$		$0.001 = \frac{1}{10^3} = 1 \times 10^{-3}$	
$1 = 1 \times 10^0$		$0.0001 = \frac{1}{10^4} = 1 \times 10^{-4}$	

Thus, 361,000,000 is the same as 3.61 times 100,000,000. Since this is 3.61 times $10 \times 10 \times 10 \times 10 \times 10 \times 10 \times 10 \times 10$ or 3.61 multiplied by 10 eight times, we call this 3.61×10^8.

$$\text{coefficient} \longrightarrow 3.61 \times 10^8 \overset{\nearrow \text{exponent}}{\underset{\searrow \text{base}}{}}$$

The *exponent* tells how many times to multiply by 10, which is called the *base*. To convert a number from the usual long form to the standard form, move the decimal point to the left until you have a number between one and ten. The number of places that you moved the decimal point is the exponent, or power of ten. The coefficient is the number between one and ten used with the power of ten. In the example, the decimal point was moved eight places to the left, so the exponent is 8. The base is 10 since we are using the decimal number system. The coefficient is 3.61.

If the original long number is less than one, it can be expressed as a number between one and ten *divided* by ten to some power.

$$0.008 = 8 \times \frac{1}{1000} = 8 \times \frac{1}{10^3} = 8 \times 10^{-3}$$

That is, if you have to move the decimal point to the *right* to get a number between 1 and 10, the exponent has a negative sign.

APPENDIX B WEATHER DATA

B-PART 1 RECORDING WEATHER WATCH DATA (INVESTIGATION 1–8)

Your teacher will provide you with the necessary wall chart on which to record your data for this investigation. Gather data carefully to avoid errors that might affect your analysis of the data later. Record data legibly on the chart.

The specific information to be gathered as part of the investigation includes:

1. *Date.* Record the day of the month at the top of each column.

2. *Time.* Record the exact time your observation is made. Use the 24-hour clock notation. In this notation, 10:15 A.M. is 1015 and 9:02 P.M. is 2102. The hours after noon (P.M.) are numbered from 1300 to 2400.

3. *Air Temperature.* A thermometer is commonly used to measure air temperature. Air temperature can also be measured by a thermograph, a thermometer that automatically records air temperature on a continuous graph attached to a rotating drum. Temperatures should be measured outdoors in a shaded shelter about 1.5 meters (5 feet) above the ground. The thermometer bulb should be kept dry and the air should be free to circulate through the shelter. All temperatures should be recorded in degrees Celsius. (See Appendix B, Part 2.) This information is then plotted on the chart in the appropriate place to provide a continuous record of temperature change.

4. *Atmospheric Pressure.* Air pressure can be measured with an aneroid or mercurial barometer or by a barograph. A barograph, like a thermograph, records air pressure on a sheet of paper attached to a revolving drum. Unlike the thermometer or thermograph, the barometer or barograph can be placed indoors. Air pressure should be measured and recorded in millibars.

5. *Wind.* Both wind direction and speed are needed in this observation. Record wind direction and speed along with sky condition for each day on your wall chart. *Wind direction* can be measured with a wind vane or some means you devise. It is recorded on the chart by a line representing the compass direction *from* which the wind is blowing,

with north at the top of the chart.

Wind speed can be measured with an anemometer or a wind speed meter. If neither is available, you can observe local conditions and estimate the velocity of the wind from the table shown on the back of a Sunday Daily Weather Map, published by the U. S. Weather Bureau. The "flags" indicating the wind speed as shown on the daily weather maps (see back of Sunday map for scale) should be drawn on the end of your wind direction line — the end from which the wind is blowing.

6. *Sky Condition.* This observation includes the amount of the sky covered by clouds and the type of cloud. For ease of recording, determine if the sky is clear, partly cloudy, or cloudy. Use the following symbols for your three categories, and record on your chart with these symbols:

SYMBOLS

(1) Cloudy	More than eight-tenths of sky covered	●
(2) Partly Cloudy	Two-tenths to eight-tenths of sky covered	◑
(3) Clear	Less than two-tenths of sky covered	○

The type of cloud should be noted as billowy or sheet-like. Sketch the type of cloud on the chart as simply as possible.

7. *Weather.* Observe and enter on the chart the state of the weather at the time of observation, such as rain, snow, thunderstorms, clear, cloudy, fog, haze, smog, and so forth.

8. *Precipitation.* Moisture that has fallen to the earth's surface in the form of rain, hail, drizzle, sleet, or snow is considered to be precipitation. Dew or fog is not. Precipitation is recorded as the quantity of water deposited in the gauge since the last reading. If the gauge has snow in it, melt the snow to secure a liquid reading.

Temperature is a measure of the amount of molecular activity in a substance. If molecules are moving slowly, the temperature of the substance containing them is said to be low. If molecular motion is rapid, the temperature is high. In general, when the temperature of a substance is high, the substance tends to expand; when cooled, the substance contracts.

Thermometers are marked (calibrated) with a scale. Scales that are commonly used are Fahrenheit and Celsius. The Fahrenheit scale is used in the United States and other English-speaking countries. The Celsius scale is sometimes called centigrade, because there are 100 divisions between the freezing and boiling points of water. The Celsius scale is widely used for temperature measurement throughout the world.

A third scale for temperature measurement, useful in some kinds of scientific work, is the Kelvin scale, called an absolute scale because the zero point is that at which there is no molecular motion. Kelvin scale divisions are the same size as Celsius divisions; the Kelvin zero is 273 degrees below the Celsius zero.

You can convert the temperature reading on one scale to the reading on another scale if you take into account the size of the degrees and the zero point. For example, as indicated below, Kelvin temperature is found by adding 273 to Celsius temperature. Remember that the degrees are the same size but counting starts at different places in the two scales. Converting Celsius temperature to Fahrenheit requires adjusting for different sizes of degrees and different starting points. You can convert from one to the other by using the formulas given.

There is also an easier method of finding the temperature on one scale that is nearly equivalent to the temperature on another scale. The drawing represents a thermometer marked with the three scales. To find the approximate equivalent temperature in other scales, move directly across the page from one scale to another.

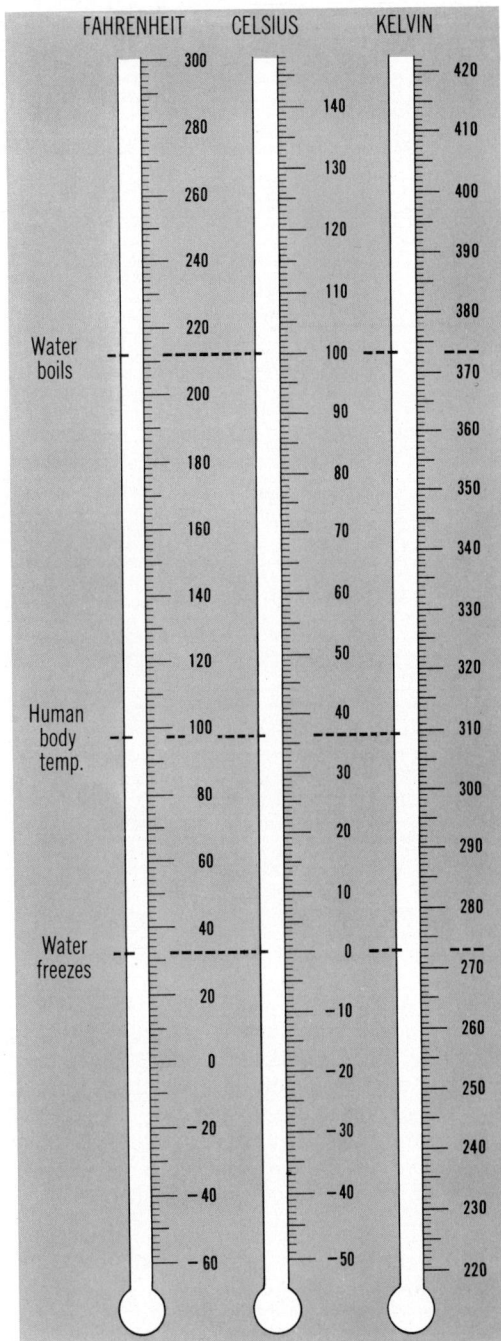

To change from Fahrenheit (F) to Celsius (C)

$$°C = \frac{(°F - 32°)}{1.8}$$

To change from Celsius (C) to Fahrenheit (F)

$$°F = (°C \times 1.8) + 32°$$

To change from Celsius (C) to Kelvin (K)

$$°K = °C + 273°$$

B-PART 3 DEW-POINT TEMPERATURE CHART

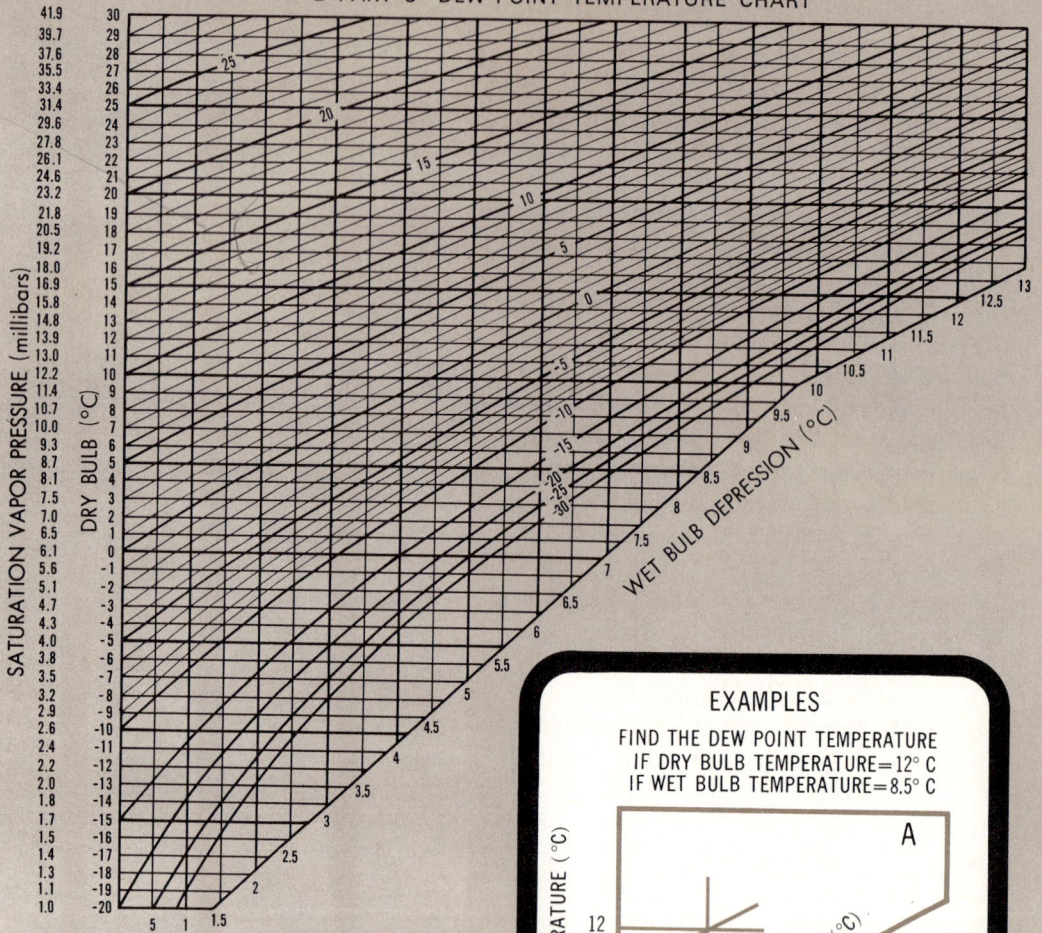

EXAMPLES

FIND THE DEW POINT TEMPERATURE
IF DRY BULB TEMPERATURE=12° C
IF WET BULB TEMPERATURE=8.5° C

A

ANSWER: DEW POINT
TEMPERATURE=5° C

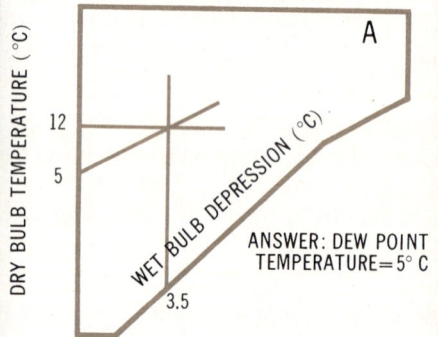

FIND THE RELATIVE HUMIDITY

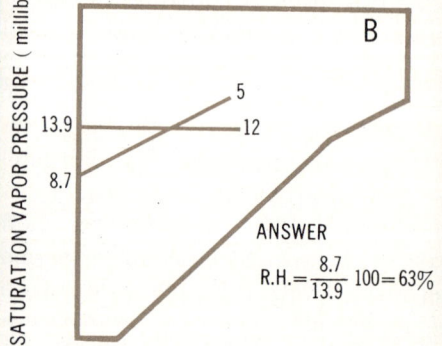

B

ANSWER

$$R.H. = \frac{8.7}{13.9} \times 100 = 63\%$$

1. To find dew-point temperature (See Example A): Find the dry-bulb temperature along the left side of the chart (12°C). Follow horizontal line to the vertical line for the wet-bulb depression (difference between dry-bulb and wet-bulb temperatures, or 3.5°C). Read the dew-point temperature from sloping line at this intersection (5°C).

2. To find the relative humidity (See Example B): Read the value of the saturation vapor pressure for the dry-bulb temperature at left side of chart. (13.9 mb is saturation vapor pressure for air at 12°C). Read the value of saturation vapor pressure for dew-point temperature also at left side of chart. (8.7 mb is saturation vapor pressure for air at 5°C.) Divide the second value (8.7) by the first (13.9) and multiply by 100. Answer: 63%.

APPENDIX C   MINERALS AND ELEMENTS

C-PART 1   PROPERTIES OF SOME MINERALS

Mineral Name	Color	Streak*	Luster	Hardness†	Composition	Remarks
Apatite	Green or Brown	White	Glassy	5	$Ca_5(F, Cl, OH)$ $(PO_4)_3$	Used in making fertilizer
Biotite	Black	Colorless	Glassy, Shining	$2\frac{1}{2}$-3	$K(Mg, Fe)_3AlSi_3$-$O_{10}(OH)_2$	Black mica-fractures in very thin plates
Calcite	Colorless, White	Colorless	Glassy, Pearly	3	$CaCo_3$	Effervesces in cold acid
Cinnabar	Red	Bright Red	Glassy, Earthy	2-$2\frac{1}{2}$	HgS	Mercury ore
Corundum	Brown, Pink, Blue	None	Sparkling, Dull	9	Al_2O_3	Gem stone-used as an abrasive
Diamond	Grayish-Black	None	Sparkling, Dull	10	C	Gem stone-industrial saws
Fluorite	Light Purple, Yellow, Green	Colorless	Glassy	4	CaF_2	Used in steel and glassmaking
Galena	Lead Gray	Gray-Black	Metallic	$2\frac{1}{2}$	PbS	Lead ore
Graphite	Steel Gray to Iron Black	Black to Gray-Black	Metallic, Earthy	1-2	C	Feels greasy-used as a lubricant
Gypsum	Colorless, White, Gray	Colorless	Silky	2	$CaSO_4 \cdot 2H_2O$	Used in making plaster of Paris
Halite	White, Red, Blue	Colorless	Glassy, Translucent	$2\frac{1}{2}$	$NaCl$	Common salt, tastes salty
Hornblende	Dark Green to Black	Colorless to Gray	Glassy	5-6	$Ca_2Na(Mg, Fe)_4$-$(Al, Fe, Ti)_3$ $Si_6O_{22}(0, OH)_2$	An amphibole-a common rock mineral
Magnetite	Iron Black	Black	Metallic	$5\frac{1}{2}$-6	Fe_3O_4	Magnetic
Muscovite	Tan, Green, Yellow, White	Colorless	Glassy, Silky	2-$2\frac{1}{2}$	$KAl_3Si_3O_{10}(OH)_2$	White mica-flakes in thin sheets
Olivine	Olive to Gray, Green, Brown	Colorless	Glassy	$6\frac{1}{2}$-7	$(Mg, Fe)_2SiO_4$	Green rock mineral
Orthoclase	White, Gray, Flesh-Red	White	Glassy	6	$KAlSi_3O_8$	A feldspar-common rock-forming mineral
Pyrite	Pale Brass, Yellow	Green or Brown-Black	Metallic	6-$6\frac{1}{2}$	FeS_2	"Fool's Gold"
Quartz	Colorless, White	None	Glassy	7	SiO_2	Gem stone-common rock-forming mineral
Talc	White, Green, Gray	Colorless	Glassy, Pearly	1	$Mg_3Si_4O_{10}(OH)_2$	Greasy feel-used in talcum powder
Topaz	Yellow, Pink, Blue, Green	None	Glassy	8	$Al_2SiO_4(F, OH)_2$	Gem stone
Wollastonite	Colorless, White, Gray	Colorless	Glassy, Pearly	5-$5\frac{1}{2}$	$CaSiO_3$	Associated with crystalline limestone

(See next page for notes ° and †.)

Notes for C-PART 1

† HARDNESS

The resistance that a mineral surface offers to scratching is its hardness.

To determine the hardness of any mineral, it is necessary to find which of the minerals in Mohs' scale of hardness it can scratch and which it cannot scratch.

* STREAK

The color of the fine powder left after a mineral has been rubbed on a piece of unglazed porcelain (streak plate) is known as its streak. This is useful in the identification of minerals, because the color of a mineral's streak is usually constant.

MOHS' HARDNESS SCALE

1 TALC	2 GYPSUM	3 CALCITE	4 FLUORITE	5 APATITE
6 ORTHOCLASE	7 QUARTZ	8 TOPAZ	9 CORUNDUM	10 DIAMOND

C–PART 2 THE ELEMENTS

(Listed alphabetically with the atomic number preceding them.)

89 Actinium (Ac)
13 Aluminum (Al)
95 Americium (Am)
51 Antimony (Sb)
18 Argon (Ar)
33 Arsenic (As)
85 Astatine (At)
56 Barium (Ba)
97 Berkelium (Bk)
4 Beryllium (Be)
83 Bismuth (Bi)
5 Boron (B)
35 Bromine (Br)
48 Cadmium (Cd)
20 Calcium (Ca)
98 Californium (Cf)
6 Carbon (C)
58 Cerium (Ce)
55 Cesium (Cs)
17 Chlorine (Cl)
24 Chromium (Cr)
27 Cobalt (Co)
29 Copper (Cu)
96 Curium (Cm)
66 Dysprosium (Dy)
99 Einsteinium (Es)
68 Erbium (Er)
63 Europium (Eu)
100 Fermium (Fm)
9 Fluorine (F)
87 Francium (Fr)
64 Gadolinium (Gd)
31 Gallium (Ga)
32 Germanium (Ge)
79 Gold (Au)

72 Hafnium (Hf)
2 Helium (He)
67 Holmium (Ho)
1 Hydrogen (H)
49 Indium (In)
53 Iodine (I)
77 Iridium (Ir)
26 Iron (Fe)
36 Krypton (Kr)
57 Lanthanum (La)
103 Lawrencium (Lw)
82 Lead (Pb)
3 Lithium (Li)
71 Lutetium (Lu)
12 Magnesium (Mg)
25 Manganese (Mn)
101 Mendelevium (Md)
80 Mercury (Hg)
42 Molybdenum (Mo)
60 Neodymium (Nd)
10 Neon (Ne)
93 Neptunium (Np)
28 Nickel (Ni)
41 Niobium (Nb)
7 Nitrogen (N)
102 Nobelium (No)
76 Osmium (Os)
8 Oxygen (O)
46 Palladium (Pd)
15 Phosphorus (P)
78 Platinum (Pt)
94 Plutonium (Pu)
84 Polonium (Po)
19 Potassium (K)
59 Praseodymium (Pr)

61 Promethium (Pm)
91 Protactinium (Pa)
88 Radium (Ra)
86 Radon (Rn)
75 Rhenium (Re)
45 Rhodium (Rh)
37 Rubidium (Rb)
44 Ruthenium (Ru)
62 Samarium (Sm)
21 Scandium (Sc)
34 Selenium (Se)
14 Silicon (Si)
47 Silver (Ag)
11 Sodium (Na)
38 Strontium (Sr)
16 Sulfur (S)
73 Tantalum (Ta)
43 Technetium (Tc)
52 Tellurium (Te)
65 Terbium (Tb)
81 Thallium (Tl)
90 Thorium (Th)
69 Thulium (Tm)
50 Tin (Sn)
22 Titanium (Ti)
74 Tungsten (W)
92 Uranium (U)
23 Vanadium (V)
54 Xenon (Xe)
70 Ytterbium (Yb)
39 Yttrium (Y)
30 Zinc (Zn)
40 Zirconium (Zr)

APPENDIX D-DATA FOR INVESTIGATION 20-10

ROCK DESCRIPTION FROM SURFACE DOWNWARD

STATIONS	1	2	3	4	5	6	7	8
SURFACE ELEVATIONS IN METERS	248 METERS	246 METERS	250 METERS	270 METERS	272 METERS	276 METERS	264 METERS	264 METERS
LAYER I DESCRIPTION	WEATHERED GRAY OUTWASH	WEATHERED GRAY OUTWASH	WEATHERED GRAY OUTWASH	WEATHERED GRAY TILL	WEATHERED GRAY TILL	WEATHERED GRAY TILL	WEATHERED GRAY TILL	WEATHERED GRAY TILL
THICKNESS	2 METERS	2 METERS	2 METERS	3 METERS	2 METERS	3 METERS	2 METERS	1 METER
LAYER II DESCRIPTION	UNWEATHERED GRAY OUTWASH	UNWEATHERED GRAY OUTWASH	UNWEATHERED GRAY OUTWASH	UNWEATHERED GRAY TILL	UNWEATHERED GRAY TILL	UNWEATHERED GRAY TILL	UNWEATHERED GRAY TILL	UNWEATHERED GRAY TILL
THICKNESS	2 METERS	2 METERS	3 METERS	15 METERS	15 METERS	20 METERS	5 METERS	3 METERS
LAYER III DESCRIPTION	WEATHERED RED OUTWASH	WEATHERED RED OUTWASH	WEATHERED RED TILL	WEATHERED RED TILL	WEATHERED RED TILL	WEATHERED RED TILL	BEDROCK SW GROOVES	BEDROCK SW GROOVES
THICKNESS	7 METERS	7 METERS	4 METERS	7 METERS	7 METERS	7 METERS		
LAYER IV DESCRIPTION	BEDROCK	BEDROCK	BEDROCK	BEDROCK	SOIL	BEDROCK S GROOVES		
THICKNESS					1 METER			
LAYER V DESCRIPTION					BEDROCK S GROOVES			

APPENDIX E-PART 1 STAR AND CONSTELLATION CHARTS Hold overhead so arrows point to directions on horizon.

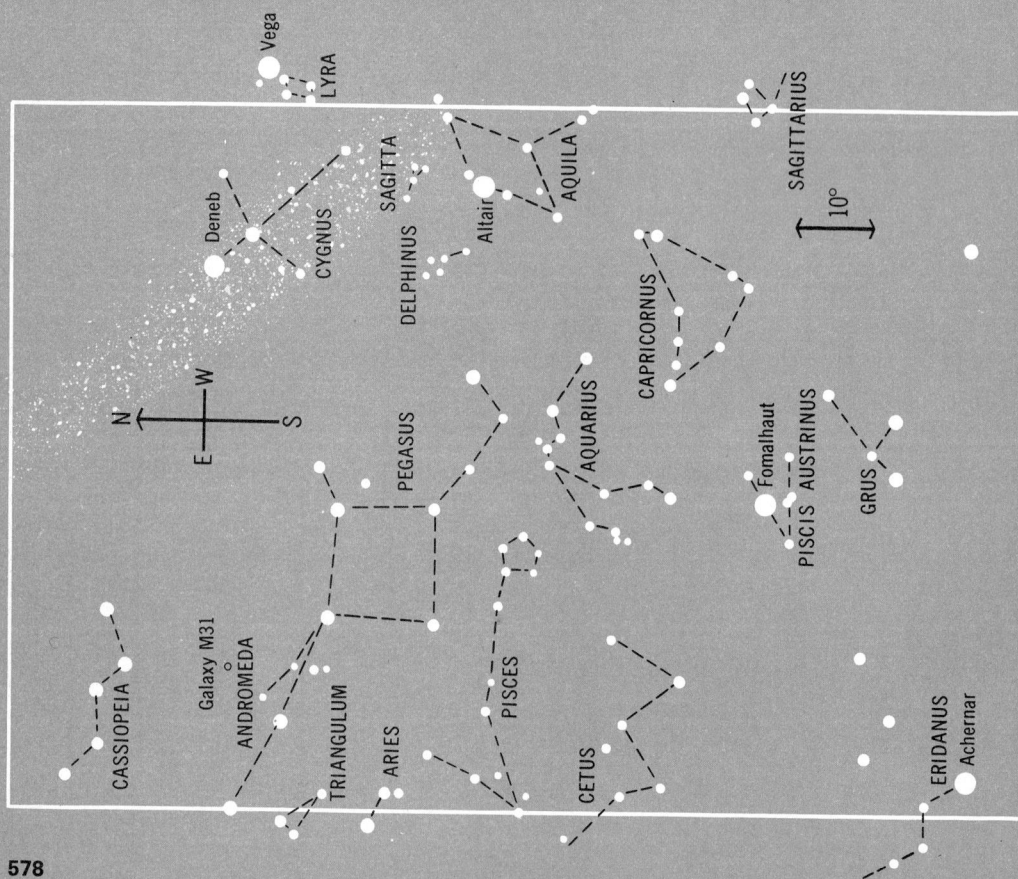

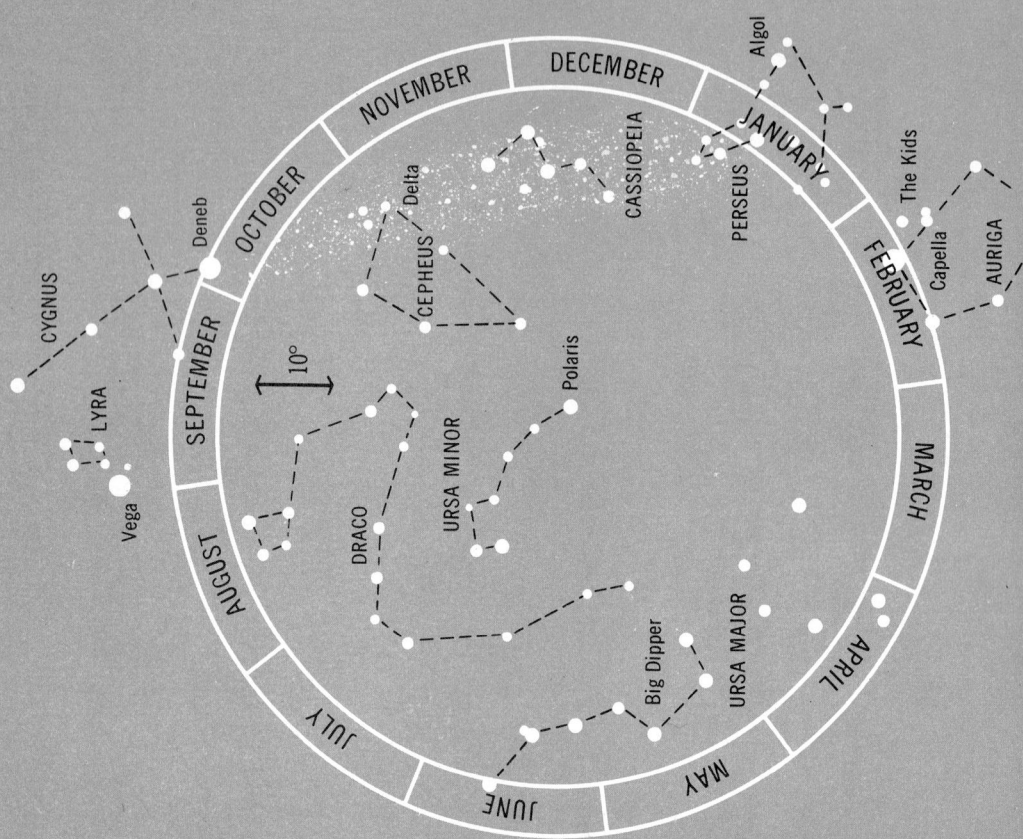

NORTHERN HEMISPHERE

578

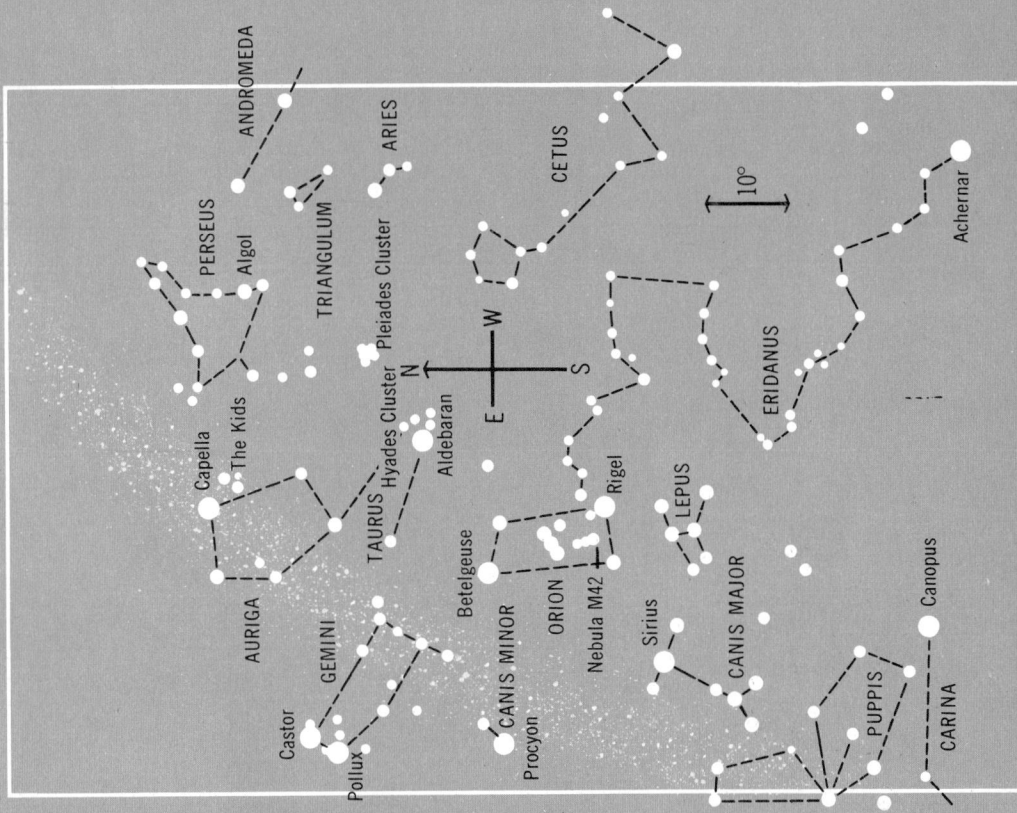

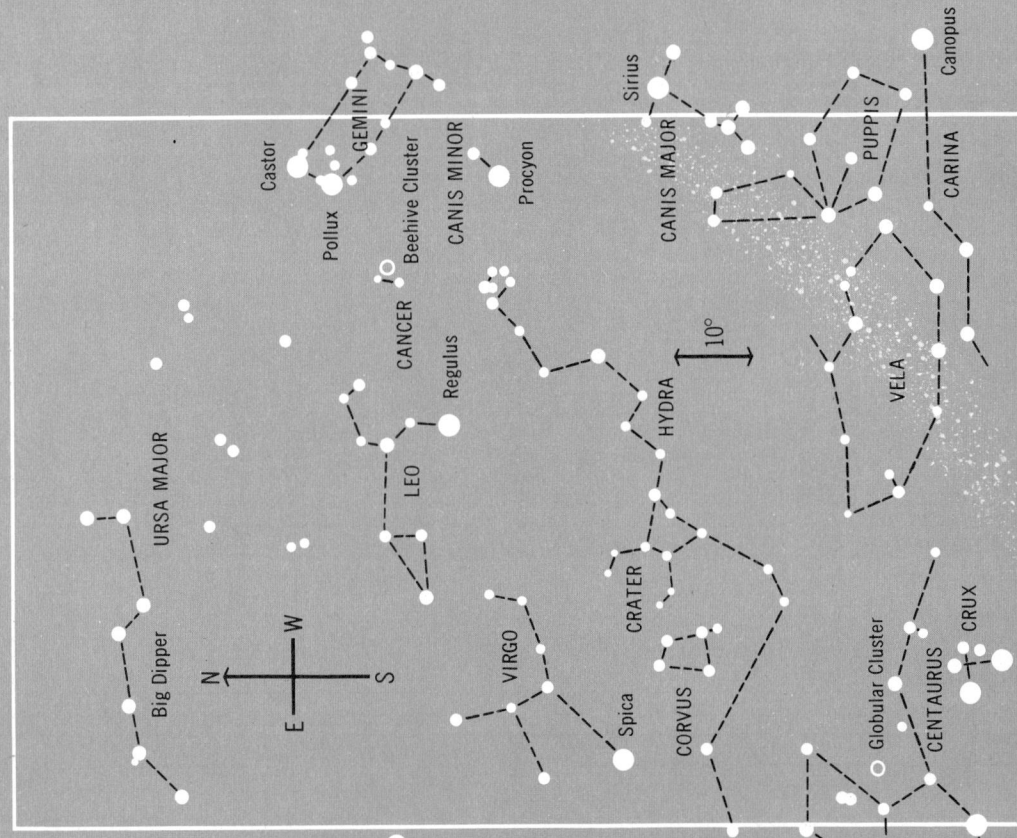

579

E-PART 2   DATA FOR DETERMINATION OF THE LUNAR PHASES (INVESTIGATION 22-4)

DATE	CELESTIAL LONGITUDE	ANGULAR DIAMETER	DISTANCE FROM ANGULAR DIAMETER	CELESTIAL LONGITUDE OF SUN
MAY 1	185°	33.1′	629	40°
3	215	33.2	628	42
5	244	32.6	638	44
7	273	31.7	657	46
9	299	30.7	678	48
11	324	30.0	695	50
13	348	29.5	705	52
15	12	29.5	707	54
17	36	29.7	702	56
19	60	30.0	693	57
21	85	30.5	682	59
23	111	31.1	670	61
25	138	31.7	657	63
27	166	32.3	645	65
29	195	32.7	637	67
31	224	32.8	636	69

E-PART 3   PHYSICAL PROPERTIES OF THE PLANETS

CHARACTERISTICS	MEMBERS OF THE SYSTEM									
	MERCURY	VENUS	EARTH	MOON	MARS	JUPITER	SATURN	URANUS	NEPTUNE	PLUTO
DIAMETER (EARTH=1)	0.38	0.96	1.0	0.27	0.53	11.2	9.5	3.7	3.5	1.0
VOLUME "	0.06	0.88	1.0	0.02	0.15	1318	769	50	42	1.0
MASS "	0.05	0.81	1.0	0.01	0.1	318	95	1.5	17	?
SURFACE GRAVITY "	0.4	0.9	1.0	0.16	0.4	2.6	1.1	1.0	1.5	?
ORBITAL PERIOD "	0.24	0.62	1.0	—	1.9	11.9	29.5	94	164.8	0.248
SPIN PERIOD "	58	247*	1.0	27.3	1.0	0.41	0.43	0.45	0.65	?
MEAN DISTANCE FROM SUN "	39	0.72	1.0	1.0	1.52	5.2	9.54	19.18	30.07	39.44
MEAN DENSITY	5.4	5.1	5.5	3.3	4.0	1.3	0.7	1.6	2.25	?
NUMBER OF SATELLITES	0	0	1	—	2	12	10	5	2	0
MAXIMUM MAGNITUDE	−0.2	−4.2	—	−12.7	−2	−2.5	−0.7	5.5	7.9	14.9
AVERAGE °K	960	600	287	300	285†	135	120	90	?	?
OBSERVED COMPONENTS OF ATMOSPHERE		CO_2	$N_2, O_2,$ H_2O, CO_2		$N_2, CO_2,$ HO	$H_2, NH_3,$ CH_4	$NH_3, H_2,$ CH_4	CH_4, H_2	CH_4, H_2	

*RETROGRADE   †WARMEST PORTION

E-PART 4   THE 20 BRIGHTEST AND THE 20 NEAREST STARS (Investigation 24-9)

THE 20 BRIGHTEST STARS

STAR	TEMPERATURE °K	(NUMBER OF TIMES THE SUN'S LUMINOSITY)
SIRIUS	10,400	2×10^1
CANOPUS	7,400	1.2×10^3
ALPHA CENTAURI A	5,800	1
ARCTURUS	4,500	9×10^1
VEGA	10,700	4×10^1
CAPELLA	5,900	1.3×10^2
RIGEL	11,800	4×10^4
PROCYON A	6,500	6
BETELGEUSE	3,200	1.1×10^4
ACHERNAR	14,000	1.7×10^2
BETA CENTAURI	21,000	3.3×10^3
ALTAIR	8,000	10
ALPHA CRUCIS	21,000	2.7×10^3
ALDEBARAN	4,200	8×10^1
SPICA	21,000	1.9×10^3
ANTARES	3,400	4.4×10^3
POLLUX	4,900	3.3×10^3
FOMALHAUT	9,500	1.1×10^1
DENEB	9,900	4×10^4
BETA CRUCIS	22,000	4.8×10^3
(SUN	5,600	1)

THE 20 NEAREST STARS

STAR	TEMPERATURE °K	(NUMBER OF TIMES THE SUN'S LUMINOSITY)
ALPHA CENTAURI A	5,800	1
ALPHA CENTAURI B	4,200	3.3×10^1
ALPHA CENTAURI C	2,800	1×10^{-4}
BARNARD'S STAR	2,800	4×10^{-4}
WOLF 359	2,700	1.3×10^{-4}
LALANDE 21185	3,200	4×10^{-2}
SIRIUS A	10,400	2.5×10^{-1}
SIRIUS B	10,700	1.7×10^{-3}
LUYTEN 726-8A	2,700	5×10^{-3}
LUYTEN 726-8B	2,700	3.3×10^{-5}
ROSS 154	2,800	4×10^{-4}
ROSS 248	2,700	1×10^{-4}
EPSILON ERIDANI	4,500	2.5×10^{-5}
ROSS 128	2,800	2.5×10^{-4}
LUYTEN 789-6	2,700	7.7×10^{-5}
61 CYGNI A	4,200	6.7×10^{-2}
61 CYGNI B	3,900	3.3×10^{-2}
PROCYON A	6,500	1.7×10^{-1}
PROCYON B	7,400	4×10^{-4}
EPSILON INDI	4,200	1×10^{-1}
(SUN	5,600	1)

ACKNOWLEDGMENTS

Acknowledgments are made with great appreciation for those illustrations contributed by individuals and organizations from all over the world. The source of each picture or other credited element is listed alphabetically, followed by the page number, a word or phrase describing the picture, and, where distinct from the source, the photographer's name in parentheses.

Myles J. Adler: 109 Hot rod. Aero Service Corp., a Division of Litton Industries: 124 Airplane, 229 Mississippi R., 309 Delta. AGI-EBF film *Why Do We Still Have Mountains?*: 23 Bench mark. Alpha Magnetics Corp.: 127 Electro-magnet. American Forest Products Industries: 28 Forests (2), 29 Tree stump. American Iron and Steel Institute: 26 Hotel, 356 Collapsed mosque. The American Museum of Natural History: 19 Canyon, 20 Lunar eclipse, 94 Palm trees, 301 Foraminifera, 357 Meteorites (2), 377 Clam shell, 410 Brontosaurus, 420 Archaeopteryx, 496 Ancient instruments (3), 505 Meteorite. Arizona Photographic Associates, Inc.: 208, 222, 246 Desert (Herb & Dorothy McLaughlin), 248 Shepherd (Mel Pifer). Ray Atkeson: 19, 36 Waves, 158 Glacier (left), 270 Devil's Tower, 398 Checkerboard Mesa, 480 Crater Lake. Australian News & Information Bureau: 264 Desert.

E. S. Barghoorn and J. W. Schopf, "Microorganisms Three Billion Years Old," *Science*. May 6, 1966: 424 Electron Micrographs of chert (4). Bell Helicopter Company: 57 Helicopter. Bell Telephone Laboratories, Inc.: 49 Synthetic crystals. James B. Benedict: 281 Soil creep. Bethlehem Steel Corporation: 49 Blast furnace. R. E. Bisque: 342 Dike. Black Star: 197 Tornadoes (Mike Fletcher), 238 Map (Werner Wolff). Boeing Company: 61 Lunar eclipse (Richard Shorthill). William C. Bradley: 281 Landslide. Brookhaven National Laboratory: 43 Particle accelerator, 132 Particle tracks. Bureau of Mines: 369 Mine timbers. Bureau of Reclamation: 132 Landslide, 225 Dam, Orchard, Aqueduct, 319 Fault (left).

© 1959 by California Institute of Technology: 540 Pleiades, 543 Trifid and Dumb-bell Nebulas, 544 Sculptor. © 1959 by California Institute of Technology and Carnegie Institution of Washington: 62, 531 Nebulas, 534 Andromeda, 538 Nebula. © 1965 by California Institute of Technology and Carnegie Institution of Washington: 533 Jupiter, Saturn, 543 Horsehead Nebula, Serpens, 544 Pegasus (All Caltech photographs from the Mount Wilson and Palomar Observatories.) C. W. Chesterman: 335 Contact metamorphism. Chevrolet Motor Division: 117 Soapbox derby. Chicago Natural History Museum: 428 Woolly mammoth. Colorado School of Mines: 367 Strain meter (3). Walter P. Cottam: 262 Mountain slopes. Farrington Daniels, University of Wisconsin: 148 Solar cooker. John A. Day: 189 Clouds B,C,F,G, 192 Contrail. R. L. DeLuise: 361 X-ray. *The Denver Post:* 536 Crowd (Bill Johnson). Department of Fisheries of Canada: 243 Ship. Department of Mines and Technical Surveys, Ottawa: 122 North magnetic pole, #T423R–115. Dominion Observatory, Ottawa: 481 Deep Bay Crater. R. H. Dott, Jr.: 359 Quartzite. DPI: 360 Moon (B. Pierno). Joseph Dudziak: 46 Ice, 286 Dungeon Canyon (2), 289 Drainage (center). Ted Dutton: 117 Ski jumper, 190 Snow scene. Eleanor A. Dye: 194 Air mass C, 278 Forest, 461 Canadian Rockies.

ESCP: 4 Two lab scenes, 6 Beakers, 37 Rock, Model molecule, 38 Three rocks, 40 Six rocks, 46 Crystal, Quartz, 48 Four rocks, 51 Four rocks, 72 Ball bearing, 76 Ground view, 90 Girl holding globe, 117 Scale, 121 Lodestone, 139 Lab equipment, 184 Bell jar, Water glass, 194 Air mass B, 273 Weathering (5), 274 Rock, 313 Field trip (13), 336 Five rocks, 338 Four rocks, 344 Field trip (3 left), 379 Key, 392 Rocks (2 right), 414 Outcrop. Earth Sciences, Inc.: 37 Photomicrograph. Harold Edgerton: 389 Bullet, Milk drop. ESSA, Atmospheric Physics and Chemistry Laboratory: 191 Hailstones (2). Coast and Geodetic Survey: 5 Nansen bottle. Institutes for Environmental Research: 124 Storm tracing (Wallace H. Campbell). National Hurricane Research Laboratory: 197 Hurricane. Weather Bureau: 79 Weather map, 164, 165 Cyclone, Eddy patterns, 166–7 World weather map, 173 Barograph, 267 Cloud-seeding (Joanne Simpson). Richard Erdoes: 202 Fog, 278 Grassland, Cliff dwelling, Petroglyphs, 280 Balanced rock, 281 Bryce Canyon, 285 Cross-bedded sandstone, 288 Stream ripples, 301 Kelp. M. C. Escher: 18 Woodcut *Sky and Earth*. Jack V. Everett: 54 Gold vein.

Dan Feray: 359 Salt. Charles Finance, Chem Study: 42 Bromine, Sodium. Elaine Fisher: 98 Clocks. Florida State News Bureau: 159 Beach. Harrison Forman: 259 North India in dry season. Fort Hays Kansas State College Museum: 431 Fossils. H. D. Foth: 270 Limestone jointing, 271 Tree roots, 274 Soil from granite. FPG: ii Bridge (Phil Palmer). Freeport Sulphur Co.: 42 Sulfur. Tony Gauba: 49 Gold mine, 180 Stream, 202 Rainbow, 268 Mountain scene, 280 Red rocks, 317 Folded rock. General Electric: 49 Synthetic diamonds. © Geodetic Institute, Denmark: 447 Glacier. Geophysical Institute, University of Alaska: 125 Aurora (Vic Hessler). 194 Air mass A (Carl Benson). German Hydrographic Institute: 293 RV *Meteor*. © Dr. Georg Gerster: 288 Sand dunes, 330, 390 Antarctica. M. F. Glaessner, University of Adelaide, Australia: 416 Fossil jellyfish, 437 Fossil worm. H. G. Goodell, Florida State University: 302 Manganese nodules. Jim Greenwood: 105 Sky diver. Carola Gregor: 228 Sea. Homer Groening: 46 Wave. Charles E. Grover for Colorado State University Air Pollution Study: 162 Smog (2).

Hagans Clock Manor Museum, Bergen Park, Colorado: 376 Water clock, 378 Rope. Jan Hahn: 27 Village, 235 Wave, 246 Ships. James Hall, *Geological Survey of the State of New York. Paleontology*, 1847–94: 312 Fossil shells (2). Johnny Hart and Publishers Newspaper Syndicate: 81, 137, 191 *B.C.* 112, 375 *Wizard of Id*. The Harvard College Library: 466 Drawing by William Morris Davis (vignette). Grant Heilman: 28 Contour farming, 177 Snow fence, 358 Hot spring, 398 Shells, 430 Beach. Karen Higgins: 512 Lichen. High Altitude Observatory: 143 Corona. Mary Hill, California Division of Mines and Geology: 317 Deformed Rock. Humble Oil & Refining Company: ii Water spouts, 301 Diatoms. Gerald G. Hunt, Jr.: 279 Mountain stream. George Hunter: 264 Canadian landscape.

IBM Corporation: 2–3 Computer. The University of Illinois Committee on Aerial Photography: 480 Meteor Crater. H. A. Ireland: 285 Sand dunes, 317 Faulted rock, 456 Mountains in Iraq.

Jamaica Tourist Board: 248 River. Don James: 226 Surfers (6). Japan National Tourist Organization: 264 Japanese landscape. *Japan Times,* The Harvard-Yenching Library, Harvard University: 31 "'Mountain' Still Grows". James Jeans: 567 Quotation, *The Universe Around Us,* 4th edition, Cambridge University Press. Jordan Tourist Information Office: 381 Dead Sea Scrolls.

Marshall Kay: 435 Unconformity. Kennecott Copper Corp.: 49 Open-pit mine. Edwin Kessler: 46 Cloud, 164 Cumulus cloud, 189 Cloud A. E. A. Kirkby, Michigan Geological Survey, Lansing: 440 Pennsylvanian-age rocks. W. M. Krider, Lawrenceburg, Indiana: 132 High tension wires.

Laboratory of Tree Ring Research, University of Arizona: 377 Tree rings. Edward LaChapelle, University of Washington: 117 Gravity meter. E. C. LaFond: 293 Diving saucer. Lamont Geological Observatory of Columbia University: 302 Acorn worm, 380 C^{14} dating equipment. Lawrence Radiation Laboratory: 145 Explosion crater. Leeds & Northrup Company: 5 Thermometer. *Le Figaro:* 31 "Volcan sousmarin." By kind permission of the Earl of Leicester: 8 Page from notes of Leonardo daVinci. L. W. LeRoy: 281 Rocks on pinnacles, 314 Ripple marks, 392 Red Rocks (left), 393 Road cut, 416 Worm burrows, 447 Glacial till. Lick Observatory: 84 Stars, 474 Moon (On same photograph: 477 Crater Copernicus, 478 Crater Eratosthenes, 479 Chain craters.), 484 Corona, 503 Mars, 507 Comet, 516 Galaxy, 529 Pleiades, Astronomer, 533 Mars, 552 Stars, 567 Mirror, 569 Mt. Hamilton. Los Angeles Air Pollution Control District: 30 Smog (right). Los Angeles County Museum of Natural History: 418 Bones, 428 Model animals. Laurence R. Lowry: 264 Alaskan landscape, 279 Mississippi River, 284 Glaciers, 292

River mouth, 323 Rift Valley, 461 Salt marshes. Luray Caverns, Virginia: 278 Luray Caverns.

J. Hoover Mackin: 377 Lake varves. Maine Department of Economic Development: 245 Waves. Magnum: 205 Monsoon (Brian Brake). Maser Optics, Inc.: 9 Laser. Arthur W. McCurdy, Courtesy of the Bell Family, © 1965 National Geographic Society: 24 Shipwreck. Steve McCutcheon: 25 Twisted rails, 208 Glaciers, 282 Glacial valley, 447 Glacial outwash. Sol Mednick: 418 Wood cells. Meteorology Research, Inc.: 459 Cloud sequence (3). Metro News, The Chicago Department of Water and Sewers: 209 Filtration plant. *The Minneapolis Star:* iii Solar eclipse (Roy Swan). Montana Highway Commission: 319 Fault (right). Montana Historical Society: 187 *Waiting for a Chinook* painting by Charles M. Russell. Griff Morgan, © E. Bollay Associates: 190 Snowflakes, 196 Cold fronts (2). Morton International, Inc.: 119, 440 Salt mine. Mount Everest Foundation, The American Alpine Club: 71 Mt. Everest, Climbers. Mount Wilson and Palomar Observatories: 2 Telescope, 18 Nebula, 68 Jupiter, 86 Stars, 114 Galaxy, 143 Granular surface, Eruption, (on same photograph: 476 Crater Archimedes, 477 Lunar highlands.), 482 Lunar composite, 494 Moon, Mars, 495 Saturn, Venus, Jupiter, 518 Telescope, 537 Star cluster, 540 Milky Way, 546 Galaxy, 554 Milky Way, 555 Nebula, 561 Galaxies. William R. Muehlberger: 189 Cloud H. Josef Muench: 232 Wave, 246 Monument Valley, 270 Canyon, 286 Grand Canyon, 374 Monument Valley, 398 Rope lava, 407 Twisted tree, 454 Angel Arch. Museum of Science, Boston: 88 Pendulum (bottom).

NASA: Cover and i (All), xiv Earth from moon, 5 Satellite, 18 Curve of earth, 37, 58–59 Earth from space, 75 Satellite, 104 Astronaut, 111 Centrifuge, 124, 149 Satellite, 164 Clouds over Florida, 201 Clouds, Map, Satellite, 250 Nimbus, 289 Earth from space (left), 290 Yangtze River Delta, 293 Nile River Delta, 303 Island, 305 Mississippi River (On same photograph: 469 Lunar landscape, bottom right, 490 Copernicus), 477 Mare Cognitum, 478 Grimaldi, Wrinkle ridges, 479 Rilles, Lunar surface, 486 Lunar crater, Rock shadow, 487 Lunar surface, Lunar material, 488 Lunar close-up, 490 Crater Copernicus, 494 Earth from space, 503 Mars craters. National Bureau of Standards: 5 Weather station. National Center for Atmospheric Research: 171 Balloon, Instruments, Map, 175 Maps (2). National Coal Association: 416 Fossil leaf. National Film Board of Canada: 100 Tides (2), 177 Wind breaks, 206 Lake. The Trustees of the National Maritime Museum: 65 Prime Meridian, 120 Compass. National Museum of Canada: 416 Fossil footprints. National Park Service: 414 Log, 426 Technician. National Radio Astronomy Observatory, Green Bank, West Virginia: 541 Telescope. National Science Foundation: 140 Drilling rig, 156 Penguins. New York Fire Department: 136 Asbestos suit. © 1966 by the New York Times Company: 31 "Computer Study," "Sun is Merciless," "Air from Canada," "Landslides." Tad Nichols: 283 Rainstorm. Walter R. Nickell: 446 Glacial grooves. North American Air Defense Command: 332 Tunnel (2). North American Aviation, Inc.: 9 Remote control manipulators. Novosti Press: 257 Verkhoyansk.

Office of Naval Research: 322 Surtling.

Pan American Union: 264 Brazilian landscape. Pennsylvania Department of Health: 30 Smog (2 left). *The Penrose Annual,* 1964. "The early map printer and his problems" by R. A. Skelton, © 1964 by Percy Lund, Humphries & Co., Ltd.: 400 Detail from map by William Smith. Stephen A. Perrin: 83 Stonehenge. Philco-Ford Corp., Space and Reentry Systems Div.: 511 Automated laboratory. Phoenix Chamber of Commerce: 37 Ground view of mountains. Photo Researchers: iii Volcano (Tom Hollyman), 22 Waterfall (Clark Frank). Pittsburgh Plate Glass Co.: 339 Glass making. Power Authority of the State of New York: 132 Hydro-electric dam. Paul Popper Ltd.: 71 Himalayan Range (Francis Leeson), 148 Car.

Rapho-Guillumette: 17 Bridge (Fred Lyon), 18 Undersea view (Ron Church), 32 Street scene (Louis Goldman), 174 Sailboat (Lynn Pelham), 180 Sunset (J. Allan Cash), 206 Rain (Christian Cambazard), Fog (Fred Lyon), 324 Scuba diver (Ron Church), 360 Pyramids (John Bryson). *Report on the Scientific Results of the Voyage of H.M.S. Challenger During the Years 1873–76:* 8, 231 Table, 300 Map (vignette), 301 Shell remains, Phillipsite, 302 Manganese nodules. Reynolds Metals Company: 2 Aluminaut. Alan W. Richards, Princeton, New Jersey: 564 Einstein's desk. Merrill K. Ridd: 283 Stream bed, 284 U-shaped valley, 323 Fault block mountain. G. R. Roberts: 49 Potassium, 53 Drilling rig, Quarry, 55 Salt lake, 218 Houston area, 222 Savannah area, 229 Salt ponds, 257 Norway, 264 Western plains of U.S., 278 Black soil, 284 V-shaped valley, 285 Loess, 286 Alluvial fan F, 458 Open-pit mine. H. Armstrong Roberts: 180 Street scene. Rocky Mountain Association of Geologists: 79 Geology map. Colin A. Ronan, *Man Probes the Universe.* Aldus Books Limited, London, 1964: 79 Star map. Royal Canadian Air Force: 436 Canadian Shield.

Robert E. Samples: 75 Contrail, 184 Frost, 187 Plains, 189 Cloud E, 194 Air mass D, 202 Frost, Dew, 289 Beach rill (right), 314 Ripple marks. Emil Schulthess, Conzett & Huber, Zürich: 3 Moon time-lapse, 94 Sun time-lapse, 96–7 Midnight sun time-lapse. Scripps Institution of Oceanography, University of California, San Diego: 232 Flip ship, 298 Underwater landslide. Gary Settle: 214 Flood. B.M. Shaub: 270 Weathered granite. Mary Shaub: 259 Farm scene. Shell Oil Company: 60 Bonneville Salt Flats. John S. Shelton: 14, 15 Sand dunes, 23 Cajon Pass, 158 Glacier (right), 285 Dust storm, 286 Alluvial fan E, 323 Dome, 327 Aerial view, 339 Mesa, 341 Lava flow, 344 Field

trip (right), 345 Field trip (3), 394 Lava flow, 434 River, 457 Alluvial fans (2), 458 Moraines, Terraces, Dunes, Karst topography, Mesa, 459 Erosion sequence (3), 460 Santa Elena Canyon, Niagara Gorge, 463 Monadnock, Unconformity, 464 Death Valley, 467 Kettleman Hills, 468 Kettlehole Ponds, Zuni Salt Lake, Sinkhole, Carolina Bays, 469 Meteor Crater, Little Sundance Mountain. John S. Shelton, *Geology Illustrated.* © 1966 by W. H. Freeman and Company: 363 Fault, 396 Ripple marks, 460 Wheeler Ridge. James W. Skehan, S.J.: 313 Outcrops I, J. William G. Smith, Jr.: 388 Geranium (3). Smith Aerial Surveys & Associates: 237 Wave lines. Smithsonian Institution: 88 Pendulum (top), 310 Trilobite, 414 Fossil diatoms, 418 Insect, 424 Trilobites, 437 Fossil algae, 440 Limestone. Soil Science Society of America: 277 Prairie soil, Forest soil, 278 Red swamp soil. Solarfilma Iceland: 16 Geologists, 38 Island. South Dakota Department of Highways: 393 Badlands. Southern Pacific Company: 337 Mt. Shasta. Sovfoto: 257 Reindeer race, 259 Desert, 408 Mammoth. Spence Air Photos: 310 Glacier. Bob & Ira Spring: 159 Glacier, 265 Crevass. Standard Oil of California: 414 Paleontologist. William M. Stephens: 298 Scuba diver, 301 Sea grass, 323 Depth recorder. William Lee Stokes, *Essentials of Earth History.* © 1966, Reproduced by permission of Prentice-Hall Inc., originally from General Biological Supply House, Inc.: 377 Magnified tree rings. Werner Stoy/Camera Hawaii: 235 Surfing. Swissair: 106 Skiers.

Lilli Tanzer: 296, 297, 452, 453 © Maps rendered in INTRINSICOLOR. Tennessee Valley Authority: 33 Gully erosion (2). Texaco, Inc.: 132 Oil storage tanks. Texas Instruments, Inc.: 124 Men using magnetometer. John F. Thompson: 189 Cloud I, 286 Rainstorm. TIMINN-Iceland, Geo-Marine Technology: 12 & 16 Surtsey.

United Air Lines: 159 Clouds. © United Feature Syndicate, Inc.: 515 *Peanuts* © 1962. 551 *Peanuts* © 1961. United States Air Force: 75 X-15, 327 Radar photo. The United States Air Force in cooperation with Ecuadorian Government: 480 Darwin Caldera. United States Army: 318 Anchorage earthquake. United States Coast Guard: 61 Sailor, 136 Iceberg. United States Department of Agriculture: 18 Dust storm, 28 Tractor, 29 Stream pollution, Field, Sediment, 128 Wheat field, 132 Forest fire, 133 Cloud, 159 Wheat field, 178 Dust storm, 212 Burned-over land, 274 Soil from limestone, 277 Desert soil, 278 Desert, 283 Raindrop erosion (close-up), 286 Stream gauging station, 412 Wheat field. United States Department of the Interior, Grand Canyon National Park: 401 Grand Canyon. United States Forest Service: 16 Meanders, 183 Anemometer, 212 Bulldozer, Contour trenches, 215 Measuring evapotranspiration, 220 Measuring rainfall, Measuring snowfall. United States Geological Survey: 76 Aerial view (T. S. Lovering), 77 Stereo view,

78 Map, 141 Geothermal steam field (Roy A. Bailey), 151 Kilauea (2), 220 Stream gauging station, 342 Half Dome (F. E. Matthes), 369 Device to test rock deformation (E. F. Patterson), 398 Sandstone beds (J. B. Hadley), 434 Map model. United States Navy: 75 Balloon, Oxygen mask, 154 Hurricane, 232 Sea smoke, 237 Submarine, 283 Raindrops (2), 324 Atoll, 378 Atomic clock. Univ. of Arizona: 23 Lightning. University of Illinois Elementary School Science Project: 578–579 Star and Constellation Charts. Utah Travel Council: 469 Earth landscape, bottom left (Frank Jensen.)

Vermont Development Department: 464 Mountains (bottom right). Jules Verne, *Journey to the Center of the Earth.* 1874: 369 Engraving. O. D. Von Engeln, Courtesy of A. L. Bloom, Dept. of Geological Sciences, Cornell Univ.: 446 Lake Cayuga.

Ward's Natural Science Establishment, Inc.: 42 Copper, Gold, 183 Hygrothermograph, 189 Cloud D, 200 Clouds, 280 Wave-cut drumlin, 340 Obsidian, Porphyry, 392 Conglomerate, Coquina, 418 Fossil fish. Washington Convention and Visitor's Bureau: 566 Washington Monument. Courtesy of The Welch Scientific Company: 533 Spectra. Western Ways Features: 37 Aerial view of mountains (Bill Mastin), 208 Lake Mead, iii Mud cracks (Tad Nichols), 261 Kilimanjaro, 283 Rocky streambed, 347 Paricutín, 395 Cross-bedded sandstone. Wide World Photos, Inc.: ii Ship, 26 Japanese farmhouse, Greek village, 111 Hammer throw, 259 Monsoon rains. M. Woodbridge Williams: 272 Lichen. Ginny Hill Wood: ii Glaciers.

Yerkes Observatory: 85 Barnard's Star, 493 New moon, 495 Sun, 521 Nova Herculis, 525 Krüger 60.

Donald H. Zenger: 465 Jupiter Serapis.

INDEX

Numerals in boldface (**397**) give the page on which the terms are defined or explained. Numerals in italics (*258*) indicate the page on which an illustration of the subject of the term will be found. "*See . . .*" following a term refers to closely related terms under which the page numbers will be found. "*See also . . .*" refers from a term to related terms under which more information on the subject will be found.

BCDEFGHIJ-KR-76543210/6987